Applied Linear Algebra

PRENTICE-HALL INTERNATIONAL, INC., *London*
PRENTICE-HALL OF AUSTRALIA, PTY. LTD., *Sydney*
PRENTICE-HALL OF CANADA, LTD., *Toronto*
PRENTICE-HALL OF INDIA PRIVATE LTD., *New Delhi*
PRENTICE-HALL OF JAPAN, INC., *Tokyo*

Applied Linear Algebra

BEN NOBLE

Professor of Mathematics
and Computer Sciences
Mathematics Research Center, U.S. Army
The University of Wisconsin

Prentice-Hall, Inc.

Englewood Cliffs, New Jersey

Library of Congress Catalog Card Number 69–10468
Printed in the United States of America
Current Printing (last digit):

10 9 8 7

To the late R. E. Langer,
who profoundly influenced many lives

Preface

Linear algebra is an essential part of the mathematical equipment required in many areas of pure and applied mathematics, computing, the sciences, and engineering. The purpose of this book is to develop the algebra of matrices, the theory of finite-dimensional vector spaces, and the basic results concerning eigenvectors and eigenvalues, with particular attention to topics that arise in applications.

We draw attention to three aspects of the treatment.

The *mathematical theory* is introduced from a concrete point of view, in terms of matrix manipulations in Chapter 1, and elementary row operations on matrices in Chapter 3. An attempt is made to increase gradually the level of abstraction in order to provide a natural introduction to vector spaces in Chapter 4 and rank in Chapter 5. Similarly, eigenvalues and quadratic forms are introduced by means of concrete examples in Chapters 9 and 12, respectively.

A *number of applications* are included. The object of placing the applications in Chapter 2 immediately after Chapter 1 is to emphasize that many of these applications require only the simplest properties of matrices—little more, in fact, than the definition of multiplication and the idea of an inverse matrix. Chapter 6 deals with linear programming. Various other applications are inserted at appropriate points in the text.

Considerable attention is paid to *numerical aspects* of linear algebra. Many of the examples in Chapter 4 on linear independence and vector spaces are computational. Some attention is paid to technical problems connected with solving linear simultaneous equations, including ill-conditioning and choice of pivots. There is a chapter on norms, with applications to error estimation.

The length of this book, and the intertwining of theory and practice, place a special responsibility on the instructor. *Topics taught in class must be chosen very carefully*. Class time is inevitably limited. The instructor must concentrate on essentials, namely the mathematical theory. In order to facilitate this I have tried to keep the theory separate from the applications. This should make the book more acceptable to professional mathematicians (who after all will determine whether the book will be used in teaching), although this is not the main reason for the split. I hope that mathematicians who know nothing about applications or numerical analysis will still find this an acceptable teaching book.

My order of teaching in a one-semester introductory course is to go through matrix algebra in Chapter 1 quite rapidly. I then spend some time on Chapter 3, leading up to the row-echelon form via elementary row operations. The uniqueness of the row-echelon form is fundamental in the treatment in this book, although I usually do not spend much time on the proof (or expect students to be able to reproduce the proof) since it is more important to move on quickly to vector spaces. (Understanding the proof of a theorem and being able to use it in practice are *sometimes* two different things.) Elementary row operations are emphasized partly because they are extremely important in numerical work, but mainly because they are used to prepare the way for the painstaking introduction to linear dependence and vector spaces which now follow in Chapter 4. The ideas of basis and dimension require detailed explanation. The row-echelon form is useful here since it provides a standard method for working examples. At this point, time usually permits only a mention of the properties of rank in Section 5.2, and a brief treatment of determinants. In the remainder of the time available, I introduce ideas connected with eigenvectors, eigenvalues, and inner products, in Sections 9.1–9.5, rather carefully, since these are completely new to most students, and the concepts are of importance in all areas of applied mathematics, not only in linear algebra. In conclusion, it is desirable to deal briefly with the Jordan canonical form and the basic properties of quadratic forms.

An introductory one-semester course of this type cannot get very far because it is necessary to introduce the basic ideas rather slowly. Fortunately there is a growing tendency to introduce elementary linear algebra into the basic calculus sequence. Assuming that this has been done, Chapters 1–4 can be used for review, and there is some chance of a reasonable coverage of topics in a single semester.

I have tried to introduce all the concepts as clearly as possible. Although the treatment is elementary, it is not meant to be superficial. Various sections are deliberately written at different levels. Topics are usually introduced at the beginning of a chapter in a concrete way, and then the treatment becomes more rigorous and abstract as the chapter proceeds. Naturally the level of sophistication increases as the book goes on, partly because the ideas inevitably become deeper, but also because the student should be able to handle more difficult topics as he progresses through the book. However, the book has been written in such a way that it can be used in a wide variety of courses, sophomore to graduate, introductory to advanced, with more or less emphasis on applications, by judicious choice of the sections that are taught.

This book has a long history. My first introduction to linear algebra was a course on abstract vector spaces at Cambridge, England, in 1946, which I found incomprehensible. The necessity of answering questions on linear algebra in the Tripos examination forced me to attend a more traditional course on matrices, upon which the abstract approach immediately became clear. It is this experience that has led me to expound matrix algebra before vector spaces.

I first became seriously interested in matrix algebra at the University of Keele, North Staffordshire, England, in 1952, when I taught part-time courses at the Stafford and Wolverhampton technical colleges, suggested and encouraged by I. N. Sneddon, E. J. Scott, J. Wilcox, and J. Wooldridge. The original courses were taught to English Electric Co. engineers.

In 1963, Dr. R. E. Langer, the first Director of the Mathematics Research Center, U.S. Army, suggested that I prepare a course of orientation lectures on matrices for engineers employed by the U.S. Army. The interest and encouragement of the second Director, Dr. J. B. Rosser, has led directly to the decision to write this book. The experience of giving these lectures at various Army establishments has been most valuable. Several of the sections in this book are taken directly from the original orientation lectures, as acknowledged in detail in the bibliographical notes.

Another major factor that led to the decision to write this book has been contact with the Panel on Physical Sciences and Engineering of CUPM (the Committee on the Undergraduate Program in Mathematics of the Mathematical Association of America). This contact was initiated by Creighton Buck who suggested that I should write and edit, for the Panel, a book on Applications of Undergraduate Mathematics in Engineering (Macmillan, 1967). This contains some fascinating applications of matrices, but unfortunately it has not been possible to include most of these here, owing to lack of space. (Those which have been included are acknowledged in the bibliographical notes.) I must thank Henry Pollak whose enthusiasm for the CUPM project has undoubtedly been one of the influences that led me to write the present book.

I am extremely grateful to George Swan who came from England for three months in 1965 to help me with this project. He kept my nose to the grindstone to such good effect that a major part of the writing of the preliminary edition was accomplished in that time. Without his help this would have been impossible. It is particularly appropriate that I should thank the English Electric Co., Stafford, England, for releasing him, since this means that English Electric has indirectly sponsored both the beginning and the end of the work.

The book has been much improved by the fact that Prentice-Hall printed a preliminary edition and went to a great deal of trouble to obtain criticisms of this. The reviews by H. Allen, R. C. Bollinger, D. A. Foulser, D. Hall, and H. Koller were particularly helpful. At least the idiosyncrasies in the book are now conscious and not subconscious. In this connection perhaps I should mention that phrases like "It is obvious that . . . " are meant to be more than reassuring noises, and the reader should not feel aggrieved if the point in question is not clear. There is a story told of G. H. Hardy (and no doubt of several other eminent mathematicians) that he was lecturing one day when he said "It is obvious that . . . ," stopped, thought hard for ten minutes, said, "Yes, it *is* obvious that . . . " and continued his lecture. Use of the phrase indicates that if the student is thinking along the right lines, he should be able to see the point immediately. However, if he does not see the point, it may be necessary to do some hard thinking.

The graduate assistants who have helped teach the undergraduate applied matrix course at Wisconsin have been most helpful. Perhaps it is invidious to mention S. Slack, K. Hunter, V. Cateforis, N. Locksley. I am now teaching this course using ordinary audio tape recordings, talking the student through the preliminary edition, the student-staff contact being devoted to discussion groups and problem-solving sessions. The student has an individual tape that he starts and stops when he pleases. This is surprisingly effective if the text displays the equations in a suitable way, and the final version has been prepared with this type of use in mind.

I am indebted to C. Y. Cho, T. N. E. Greville, R. W. Hamming, G. Isaacson, H. Karremann, J. B. Rosser, R. M. Thrall, and R. Turner for discussion, comments, and criticism.

My thanks are due to Mrs. G. Krewson for an extremely professional job of typing (correcting the typescript was a pleasure). My wife has encouraged the writing of this book with her usual tolerance. It has been a pleasure to deal with J. Walsh of Prentice-Hall. It was F. Enenbach of Prentice-Hall who first made me think seriously about writing this book.

Madison, Wis. BEN NOBLE

Contents

1 Matrix Algebra 1

2 Some Simple Applications of Matrices 26

3 *Simultaneous Linear Equations and Elementary Operations* 62

4 *Linear Dependence and Vector Spaces* 95

5 *Rank and Inverses* 127

6 Linear Programming 155

7 Determinants and Square Matrices 198

8 The Numerical Solution of Simultaneous Linear Equations 229

9 *Eigenvalues and Eigenvectors* 274

10 *Unitary Transformations* 312

11 *Similarity Transformations* 344

12 Quadratic Forms and Variational Principles 378

13 Norms and Error Estimates 425

14 Abstract Vector Spaces and Linear Transformations 459

Applied Linear Algebra

1 Matrix Algebra

1.1 Introduction

From an elementary point of view, matrices provide a convenient tool for systematizing laborious algebraic and numerical calculations. We define a *matrix* to be simply a set of (real or complex) numbers arranged in a rectangular array. Thus,

$$\begin{bmatrix} 1 \\ 2 \end{bmatrix}, \quad \begin{bmatrix} x-a, & 4+b, & 1 \\ -2, & y, & -4 \end{bmatrix}, \quad [2, b], \tag{1.1}$$

are matrices. The separate numbers in a given array are called the *elements* of the matrix, and these are, in general, completely independent of each other. The commas separating the elements, as in the above examples, will be omitted if there is no risk of confusion.

The general matrix consists of mn numbers arranged in m rows and n columns, giving the following $m \times n$ (or "m by n") array:

$$\mathbf{A} = [a_{ij}] = \begin{bmatrix} a_{11} & a_{12} & \dots & a_{1n} \\ a_{21} & a_{22} & \dots & a_{2n} \\ & & \dots & \\ a_{m1} & a_{m2} & \dots & a_{mn} \end{bmatrix}. \tag{1.2}$$

The symbol a_{ij} denotes the number in the ith row and the jth column of the array:

$$\begin{matrix} & j\text{th col.} \\ i\text{th row} & \begin{bmatrix} & \vdots & \\ \dots & a_{ij} & \dots \\ & \vdots & \end{bmatrix}. \end{matrix}$$

Thus if **A** is the second array in (1.1), then $a_{11} = x - a$, $a_{23} = -4$, etc. We often refer to a_{ij} as the (i, j)th element of **A**. We shall consider matrices whose elements can be real or complex numbers. The notation $[a_{ij}]$ is often convenient since it indicates that the general element of the matrix is a_{ij}. The subscript i runs from 1 to m and j from 1 to n. A comma is used to separate subscripts if there is any risk of confusion, e.g., $a_{p+q,r+s}$.

The utility of matrices in applications arises from the fact that we consider an array of many numbers as a single object, and we denote it by a single symbol. Relationships between large sets of numbers can then be expressed in a clear and concise way. The more complicated the problem, the more useful matrix symbolism proves to be. In addition, however, as has so often happened in the history of mathematics, a device which at first sight may appear to be mainly a notational convenience turns out to have extensive ramifications. The systematic application of matrices provides insights that could not have been obtained as easily (if at all) by other methods.

1.2 Equality, Addition, and Multiplication by a Scalar

In the last section, matrices were defined to be rectangular arrays of numbers. In order to be able to do anything with these arrays we need to specify rules for comparing and combining matrices. In particular, we need to develop, for matrices, rules corresponding to those governing the equality, addition, subtraction, multiplication and division of ordinary numbers. We now quote these rules, without attempting to provide any motivation, apart from stating that they turn out to be precisely the rules required to deal with arrays of numbers which occur in applications and computational problems. This will be amply illustrated later.

DEFINITION **1.1.** The matrices **A** and **B** are said to be *equal* if and only if:

(a) **A** and **B** have the same number of rows and the same number of columns.
(b) All corresponding elements are equal, i.e.,

$$a_{ij} = b_{ij} \qquad \text{(all } i, j\text{)}.$$

We next consider the addition of matrices:

DEFINITION **1.2.** Two matrices can be added if and only if they have the same number of rows and the same number of columns. In this case the *sum* of two $m \times n$ matrices **A** and **B** is a matrix **C** such that any element of **C** is the sum of the corresponding elements in **A** and **B**, i.e., if a_{ij}, b_{ij}, c_{ij} denote the general elements of **A**, **B**, **C**, respectively, then

$$a_{ij} + b_{ij} = c_{ij}, \qquad \text{(all } i, j\text{)},$$

or, in matrix notation,

$$\mathbf{A} + \mathbf{B} = [a_{ij}] + [b_{ij}] = [a_{ij} + b_{ij}] = [c_{ij}] = \mathbf{C}. \tag{1.3}$$

As an example,

$$\begin{bmatrix} x+1 & -1 \\ 2 & y-1 \end{bmatrix} + \begin{bmatrix} -1 & a \\ b & 1 \end{bmatrix} = \begin{bmatrix} x & a-1 \\ 2+b & y \end{bmatrix}.$$

Since the sum of two matrices is formed by simply adding corresponding elements, it should be clear that the rules governing the addition of matrices are precisely the same as those governing the addition of ordinary numbers. Since

$$(a_{ij} + b_{ij}) + c_{ij} = a_{ij} + (b_{ij} + c_{ij}),$$

$$a_{ij} + b_{ij} = b_{ij} + a_{ij},$$

we have:

THEOREM **1.1.** *Matrix addition is associative and commutative:*

(i) $(\mathbf{A} + \mathbf{B}) + \mathbf{C} = \mathbf{A} + (\mathbf{B} + \mathbf{C})$, (*associative law*),

(ii) $\mathbf{A} + \mathbf{B} = \mathbf{B} + \mathbf{A}$, (*commutative law*).

These results state that the order in which matrices are added is not important. One reason for stressing this result is that when we consider the multiplication of matrices we shall see that the commutative law is no longer true for multiplication, although the associative law still holds. The order in which matrices are multiplied is extremely important.

It is natural to define $-\mathbf{A}$ as the matrix whose elements are $-a_{ij}$, since then

$$\mathbf{A} - \mathbf{A} = [a_{ij}] + [-a_{ij}] = [0] = \mathbf{0},$$

where $\mathbf{0}$ is a *null* matrix, i.e., a matrix whose elements are all zero. This enables us to define what we mean by the *subtraction* of matrices:

$$\mathbf{B} - \mathbf{A} = [b_{ij}] + [-a_{ij}] = [b_{ij} - a_{ij}].$$

From the definition of addition we see that $2\mathbf{A} = \mathbf{A} + \mathbf{A} = [2a_{ij}]$, and in general if n is an integer then

$$n\mathbf{A} = [na_{ij}].$$

This comment motivates the following definition of what we mean by multiplying a matrix $\mathbf{A}$ by a scalar k. (Real and complex numbers are called *scalars* to distinguish them from arrays of numbers which are *matrices*.)

DEFINITION **1.3.**

$$k\mathbf{A} = [ka_{ij}]. \tag{1.4}$$

In words, $k\mathbf{A}$ is the matrix whose elements are k times the corresponding elements of $\mathbf{A}$.

As an example,

$$3\begin{bmatrix} 1, & x-1, & 3 \\ -2a, & 4, & -1 \end{bmatrix} = \begin{bmatrix} 3, & 3x-3, & 9 \\ -6a, & 12, & -3 \end{bmatrix}.$$

So far matrices have behaved in much the same way as symbols representing ordinary numbers. The surprises have been reserved for the next section, where we consider the multiplication of two matrices.

Ex. 1.1. Prove that the operation of multiplication by a scalar has the following properties:

(a) $(p + q)\mathbf{A} = p\mathbf{A} + q\mathbf{A}$.
(b) $p(\mathbf{A} + \mathbf{B}) = p\mathbf{A} + p\mathbf{B}$.
(c) $p(q\mathbf{A}) = (pq)\mathbf{A}$.
(d) $\mathbf{A}(p\mathbf{B}) = (p\mathbf{A})\mathbf{B} = p(\mathbf{AB})$.

Ex. 1.2. Prove that

(a) $k\mathbf{0} = \mathbf{0}$.
(b) $0\mathbf{A} = \mathbf{0}$.

1.3 The Multiplication of Matrices

We first of all consider the multiplication of two special types of matrix, namely the product of a $1 \times m$ *row matrix* (or *row vector*) and an $m \times 1$ *column matrix* (or *column vector*), in that order. This is the basic unit operation in terms of which we later define the product of rectangular matrices.

DEFINITION **1.4.** A row matrix can be multiplied by a column matrix, in that order, if and only if they each have the same number of elements. If

$$\mathbf{u} = [u_1, u_2, \ldots, u_m], \qquad \mathbf{v} = \begin{bmatrix} v_1 \\ v_2 \\ \cdot \\ \cdot \\ \cdot \\ v_m \end{bmatrix},$$

then $\mathbf{uv}$ is defined to be the following 1×1 matrix:

$$\mathbf{uv} = [u_1v_1 + u_2v_2 + \ldots + u_mv_m] = \left[\sum_{j=1}^{m} u_jv_j\right]. \tag{1.5}$$

As an example,

$$[4 \quad -1 \quad 3]\begin{bmatrix} 2 \\ 1 \\ -5 \end{bmatrix} = [(4)(2) + (-1)(1) + (3)(-5)] = [-8].$$

We can now state immediately the general rule for the multiplication of two matrices.

DEFINITION 1.5. Two matrices **A** and **B** can be multiplied together in the order **AB** if and only if the number of columns in the first equals the number of rows in the second. The matrices are then said to be *conformable* for the product **AB**. In this case, the (i, k)th element of the product **AB** is the element in the 1×1 matrix obtained by multiplying the ith row of **A** by the kth column of **B**.

Pictorially we have, for example, for the (3, 2) element in the product of a 6×5 times a 5×4 matrix:

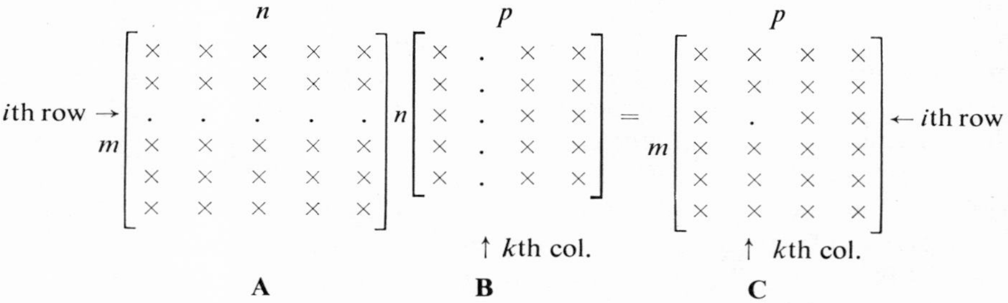

By taking the product of each row of **A** with each column of **B** in turn, we see that **AB** *must* be 6×4.

Algebraically, if $\mathbf{A} = [a_{ij}]$ is $m \times n$ and $\mathbf{B} = [b_{ij}]$ is $n \times p$, then the two matrices can be multiplied together, and if the product is denoted by $\mathbf{AB} = \mathbf{C} = [c_{ik}]$, the matrix **C** is $m \times p$, and

$$c_{ik} = \sum_{j=1}^{n} a_{ij} b_{jk}. \tag{1.6}$$

We give the following examples:

Ex. 1.3. $$\begin{bmatrix} -1 & 5 \\ 2 & 1 \end{bmatrix}\begin{bmatrix} 4 & 3 \\ 0 & -1 \end{bmatrix} = \begin{bmatrix} -4 & -8 \\ 8 & 5 \end{bmatrix}.$$

Ex. 1.4. $$\begin{bmatrix} a_{11} & a_{12} \\ a_{21} & a_{22} \end{bmatrix}\begin{bmatrix} x_1 \\ x_2 \end{bmatrix} = \begin{bmatrix} a_{11}x_1 + a_{12}x_2 \\ a_{21}x_1 + a_{22}x_2 \end{bmatrix}.$$

It is important that the reader should practice the row-column procedure for multiplying matrices until it becomes completely automatic. Also he should be able to pick out immediately the row of **A** and the column of **B** which produce any given element in the product **AB**.

We next compare the products **AB** and **BA** for two specific **A**, **B**. If

$$\mathbf{A} = \begin{bmatrix} a_1 \\ a_2 \end{bmatrix}, \qquad \mathbf{B} = [b_1\, b_2],$$

then

$$\mathbf{AB} = \begin{bmatrix} a_1b_1 & a_1b_2 \\ a_2b_1 & a_2b_2 \end{bmatrix}, \qquad \mathbf{BA} = [a_1b_1 + a_2b_2].$$

The products **AB** and **BA** are quite different. They do not even have the same numbers of rows and columns. Even if **AB** exists, there is no need for **BA** to exist, for the product **AB** can be formed if **A** is $m \times n$ and **B** is $n \times p$, but in this case the product **BA** cannot be formed unless $m = p$.

To distinguish the order of multiplication of matrices, we say that in the product **AB**, the matrix **A** *premultiplies* **B**, or multiplies **B** on the left; similarly **B** *postmultiplies* **A**, or multiplies **A** on the right. Although $\mathbf{AB} \neq \mathbf{BA}$ in general, it may happen that $\mathbf{AB} = \mathbf{BA}$ for special **A** and **B**. In this case, we say that **A** and **B** *commute*.

Since the commutative law of multiplication is not true, in general, when multiplying matrices, it is important to retain the order in which matrices appear in the calculation. As an example, suppose that we wish to multiply both sides of the equation $\mathbf{X} = \mathbf{A}$ by another matrix **P**. We must multiply both sides either on the left to obtain $\mathbf{PX} = \mathbf{PA}$ (premultiplication by **P**), or on the right to obtain $\mathbf{XP} = \mathbf{AP}$ (postmultiplication by **P**), assuming in each case that it is permissible to form the corresponding products. It is not permissible to obtain $\mathbf{PX} = \mathbf{AP}$ or $\mathbf{XP} = \mathbf{PA}$. The truth of these statements is obvious if we think in terms of writing out these equations and operations in longhand. Another way of seeing this is to note that $\mathbf{X} = \mathbf{A}$ implies $\mathbf{X} - \mathbf{A} = \mathbf{0}$. Hence $\mathbf{P}(\mathbf{X} - \mathbf{A}) = \mathbf{0}$, or $\mathbf{PX} - \mathbf{PA} = \mathbf{0}$, or $\mathbf{PX} = \mathbf{PA}$.

Although the commutative law of multiplication is not true for multiplication of matrices, the distributive and associative laws are both valid. We first prove the distributive law,

$$\mathbf{A}(\mathbf{B} + \mathbf{C}) = \mathbf{AB} + \mathbf{AC}. \tag{1.7}$$

The left-hand side is obtained by first forming the sum $\mathbf{B} + \mathbf{C}$, and premultiplying the result by **A**. The right-hand side is obtained by first forming **AB** and **AC**, and adding the results. The distributive law states that the two sequences of operations lead to the same final matrix. The proof follows immediately, on translating these statements into symbols:

$$\mathbf{A}(\mathbf{B} + \mathbf{C}) = [a_{ij}][b_{jk} + c_{jk}] = \left[\sum_{j=1}^{n} a_{ij}(b_{jk} + c_{jk})\right],$$

$$\mathbf{AB} + \mathbf{AC} = \left[\sum_{j=1}^{n} a_{ij}b_{jk}\right] + \left[\sum_{j=1}^{n} a_{ij}c_{jk}\right] = \left[\sum_{j=1}^{n} a_{ij}b_{jk} + \sum_{j=1}^{n} a_{ij}c_{jk}\right]$$

$$= \left[\sum_{j=1}^{n} a_{ij}(b_{jk} + c_{jk})\right].$$

In a similar way, we can prove that

$$(\mathbf{A}+\mathbf{B})\mathbf{C} = \mathbf{AC} + \mathbf{BC}. \tag{1.8}$$

Note that in all cases the order of multiplication must be preserved since the commutative law is not true. As an example of the use of the distributive law, consider

$$(\mathbf{A}+\mathbf{B})(\mathbf{A}-\mathbf{B}) = \mathbf{A}(\mathbf{A}-\mathbf{B}) + \mathbf{B}(\mathbf{A}-\mathbf{B}) = \mathbf{A}^2 - \mathbf{AB} + \mathbf{BA} - \mathbf{B}^2. \tag{1.9}$$

However, we cannot simplify further by cancelling $-\mathbf{AB}$ and $\mathbf{BA}$ in this result.

The associative law states that

$$(\mathbf{AB})\mathbf{C} = \mathbf{A}(\mathbf{BC}), \tag{1.10}$$

i.e., if we first form **AB** and then postmultiply by **C**, we obtain the same result as if we first form **BC** and then premultiply by **A**. The proof consists of expressing this in symbols:

$$\mathbf{AB} = \left[\sum_{j=1}^{n} a_{ij}b_{jk}\right],$$

$$(\mathbf{AB})\mathbf{C} = \left[\sum_{k=1}^{p}\left\{\sum_{j=1}^{n} a_{ij}b_{jk}\right\}c_{kl}\right] \tag{1.11}$$

$$= \left[\sum_{j=1}^{n}\sum_{k=1}^{p} a_{ij}b_{jk}c_{kl}\right]. \tag{1.12}$$

It is left to the reader to show that precisely the same expression for the general element is obtained if we first form **BC** and then **A(BC)**.

[It seems that beginners sometimes have difficulty in seeing that the double sums in (1.11) and (1.12) are the same. If we note first of all that c_{kl} in (1.11) is independent of j, we see that this can be taken inside the inner sum so that we have to prove

$$\sum_{k=1}^{p}\left\{\sum_{j=1}^{n}\alpha_{jk}\right\} = \sum_{k=1}^{p}\sum_{j=1}^{n}\alpha_{jk}, \tag{1.13}$$

where $\alpha_{jk} = a_{ij}b_{jk}c_{kl}$. Consider the array

$$\begin{bmatrix} \alpha_{11} & \alpha_{12} & \cdots & \alpha_{1p} \\ \alpha_{21} & \alpha_{22} & \cdots & \alpha_{2p} \\ & & \cdots & \\ \alpha_{n1} & \alpha_{n2} & \cdots & \alpha_{np} \end{bmatrix}. \tag{1.14}$$

If we sum the elements in each column, and add the results, we obtain the same result as if we simply add together all the elements in (1.14). This is all that (1.13) says.]

The main point which must be remembered when manipulating matrices is that brackets can be removed and powers can be combined, as long as the order of multiplication is preserved. Thus

$$(\mathbf{ABA}^2)\mathbf{A}(\mathbf{AB}^3) = \mathbf{ABA}^4\mathbf{B}^3,$$

but no further simplification is possible. We *cannot* write this as $\mathbf{A}^5\mathbf{B}^4$.

Consider next the example

$$\begin{bmatrix} a & 0 \\ b & 0 \end{bmatrix}\begin{bmatrix} 0 & 0 \\ p & q \end{bmatrix} = \begin{bmatrix} 0 & 0 \\ 0 & 0 \end{bmatrix}.$$

This is of the form $\mathbf{AB} = \mathbf{0}$ where $\mathbf{A}$ and $\mathbf{B}$ can be nonzero. The importance of this example is that if $\mathbf{AB} = \mathbf{0}$ where $\mathbf{0}$ is a null matrix, then we *cannot* conclude that either $\mathbf{A} = \mathbf{0}$ or $\mathbf{B} = \mathbf{0}$. As an application, if $\mathbf{AB} = \mathbf{AC}$ this implies that $\mathbf{A}(\mathbf{B} - \mathbf{C}) = \mathbf{0}$, but we *cannot* conclude that either $\mathbf{A} = \mathbf{0}$ or $\mathbf{B} = \mathbf{C}$. The law of cancellation is not in general true in matrix algebra, though it may be true in special circumstances.

For emphasis and clarity we restate some of the above results in the form of a theorem:

THEOREM **1.2.** *The following statements hold for matrix multiplication:*

(i) *The commutative law is not in general true:*

$$\mathbf{AB} \neq \mathbf{BA}.$$

(ii) *The distributive law is true:*

$$\mathbf{A}(\mathbf{B} + \mathbf{C}) = \mathbf{AB} + \mathbf{AC},$$

$$(\mathbf{A} + \mathbf{B})\mathbf{C} = \mathbf{AC} + \mathbf{BC}.$$

(iii) *The associative law is true:*

$$\mathbf{A}(\mathbf{BC}) = (\mathbf{AB})\mathbf{C}.$$

(iv) *The cancellation law is not true, in general:*

$\mathbf{AB} = \mathbf{0}$ *does not necessarily imply that either* $\mathbf{A} = \mathbf{0}$ *or* $\mathbf{B} = \mathbf{0}$.

Ex. 1.5. Numerical exercises:

$$[4 \quad 1]\begin{bmatrix} 2 \\ 3 \end{bmatrix} = [11], \qquad \begin{bmatrix} 2 \\ 3 \end{bmatrix}[4 \quad 1] = \begin{bmatrix} 8 & 2 \\ 12 & 3 \end{bmatrix},$$

$$\begin{bmatrix} 3 & -2 \\ 1 & -4 \end{bmatrix}\begin{bmatrix} -1 & 6 \\ 4 & 7 \end{bmatrix} = \begin{bmatrix} -11 & 4 \\ -17 & -22 \end{bmatrix},$$

$$\begin{bmatrix} 2 & 1 \\ 4 & 3 \end{bmatrix}\begin{bmatrix} -1 & 6 \\ 3 & 2 \end{bmatrix}\begin{bmatrix} 7 & 4 \\ -1 & -3 \end{bmatrix} = \begin{bmatrix} -7 & -38 \\ 5 & -70 \end{bmatrix}.$$

[In this last example, check by showing that $(\mathbf{AB})\mathbf{C} = \mathbf{A}(\mathbf{BC})$.]

Ex. 1.6. Show that if the third row of **A** is four times the first row, then the third row of **AB** is also four times its first row.

Ex. 1.7. One important case where we can cancel **B** from the equation **AB** = **CB** occurs when this equation is satisfied identically for all **B**. As an example, show that if

$$\begin{bmatrix} a_{11} & a_{12} \\ a_{21} & a_{22} \end{bmatrix}\begin{bmatrix} b_1 \\ b_2 \end{bmatrix} = \begin{bmatrix} c_{11} & c_{12} \\ c_{21} & c_{22} \end{bmatrix}\begin{bmatrix} b_1 \\ b_2 \end{bmatrix}$$

for all b_1, b_2, then $\mathbf{A} = \mathbf{C}$.

In the remainder of this section we consider some special types of matrix.

It is convenient to have a special name and symbol for the matrix obtained by interchanging the rows and columns of a given matrix:

DEFINITION **1.6.** The *transpose* of the $m \times n$ matrix $\mathbf{A} = [a_{ij}]$ is the following $n \times m$ matrix, denoted by $\mathbf{A}^T$, obtained by interchanging the rows and columns of **A**:

$$\mathbf{A}^T = [a_{ji}] = \begin{bmatrix} a_{11} & a_{12} & \dots & a_{m1} \\ a_{12} & a_{22} & \dots & a_{m2} \\ & & \dots & \\ a_{1n} & a_{2n} & \dots & a_{mn} \end{bmatrix}.$$

Note that the (i, j)th element of $\mathbf{A}^T$ is a_{ji}.

The transpose matrix possesses the following properties:

THEOREM **1.3.** (i) *The transpose of the sum of two matrices is the sum of the transposed matrices:*

$$(\mathbf{A} + \mathbf{B})^T = \mathbf{A}^T + \mathbf{B}^T.$$

(ii) *The transpose of the transpose of a given matrix is identical with the given matrix:*

$$(\mathbf{A}^T)^T = \mathbf{A}.$$

(iii) *The transpose of the product of two matrices is the product of the transposes in the reverse order:*

$$(\mathbf{AB})^T = \mathbf{B}^T\mathbf{A}^T.$$

Proof: The truth of (i) and (ii) is obvious from the definition of transpose, and formal proofs are left to the reader. Part (iii) can be proved in the following way, using formula (1.6) for the general element of a product, and the fact that if the

(i, j)th element of a matrix is p_{ij}, then the (i, j)th element of its transpose is p_{ji}. If $\mathbf{A} = [a_{ij}]$, $\mathbf{B} = [b_{ij}]$, then:

the (i, k)th element of **AB** is $\sum_{j=1}^{n} a_{ij}b_{jk}$,

the (i, k)th element of $(\mathbf{AB})^T$ is $\sum_{j=1}^{n} a_{kj}b_{ji}$, (1.15)

the (i, j)th element of $\mathbf{B}^T$ is b_{ji},

the (j, k)th element of $\mathbf{A}^T$ is a_{kj},

the (i, k)th element of $\mathbf{B}^T\mathbf{A}^T$ is $\sum_{j=1}^{n} b_{ji}a_{kj}$. (1.16)

Since (1.15) and (1.16) agree, we have the required result.

We introduce names for some further special matrices.

DEFINITION **1.7.** A matrix for which the number of rows equals the number of columns is known as a *square matrix*. If there are n rows and columns, the matrix is said to be a square matrix of order n. The elements a_{ii} $(i = 1, 2, \ldots, n)$ are said to lie on the *principal diagonal*. A *symmetric matrix* is a square matrix such that $\mathbf{A}^T = \mathbf{A}$, i.e., the elements of the matrix are symmetrically placed about the principal diagonal, $a_{ij} = a_{ji}$. The definition implies that a symmetric matrix is automatically square:

$$\begin{bmatrix} a_{11} & a_{12} & \ldots & a_{1n} \\ a_{12} & a_{11} & \ldots & a_{2n} \\ & & \ldots & \\ a_{1n} & a_{2n} & \ldots & a_{nn} \end{bmatrix}.$$

The product of two symmetric matrices is not in general symmetric for, if $\mathbf{A}^T = \mathbf{A}$, $\mathbf{B}^T = \mathbf{B}$, we have

$$(\mathbf{AB})^T = \mathbf{B}^T\mathbf{A}^T = \mathbf{BA} \neq \mathbf{AB}, \quad \text{in general.} \tag{1.17}$$

However, if **A** is a symmetric matrix of order n, and **B** is a general $n \times m$ matrix, then $\mathbf{B}^T\mathbf{AB}$ is symmetric. For

$$(\mathbf{B}^T\mathbf{AB})^T = \mathbf{B}^T\mathbf{A}^T(\mathbf{B}^T)^T = \mathbf{B}^T\mathbf{AB}, \tag{1.18}$$

which proves the required result.

Ex. 1.8. If

$$\mathbf{A} = \begin{bmatrix} 1 & -2 \\ -2 & 3 \end{bmatrix}, \quad \mathbf{B} = \begin{bmatrix} -2 & 1 \\ 1 & 1 \end{bmatrix},$$

form $(\mathbf{AB})^T$ and $\mathbf{B}^T\mathbf{A}^T$, and verify that these are the same. Note that although **A**, **B** are symmetric, **AB** is not symmetric.

Ex. 1.9. If

$$\mathbf{B} = \begin{bmatrix} 1 & 0 & -2 \\ -1 & 3 & 0 \end{bmatrix}, \quad \mathbf{A} = \begin{bmatrix} 1 & -1 \\ -1 & 1 \end{bmatrix},$$

show that

$$\mathbf{B}^T\mathbf{A}\mathbf{B} = \begin{bmatrix} 4 & -6 & -4 \\ -6 & 9 & 6 \\ -4 & 6 & 4 \end{bmatrix}.$$

Note that $\mathbf{B}^T\mathbf{A}\mathbf{B}$ is symmetric, as it must be [see (1.18)].

Ex. 1.10. A *skew* (or skewsymmetric or antisymmetric) matrix is defined to be a matrix such that $\mathbf{A}^T = -\mathbf{A}$, i.e., $a_{ji} = -a_{ij}$. Show that a skew matrix is square, and the diagonal elements of a skew matrix are zero. Show that if $\mathbf{A}$ is any square matrix, then $\mathbf{A} - \mathbf{A}^T$ is skew. By writing

$$\mathbf{A} = \tfrac{1}{2}(\mathbf{A} + \mathbf{A}^T) + \tfrac{1}{2}(\mathbf{A} - \mathbf{A}^T)$$

show that any square matrix can be decomposed *uniquely* into the sum of a symmetric and a skew matrix.

DEFINITION **1.8.** A *real* matrix is a matrix whose elements are all real. A *complex* matrix has elements that may be complex. An *imaginary* matrix has elements that are all pure imaginary or zero. The symbol $\bar{\mathbf{A}}$ is used to denote the matrix whose (i, j)th element is the complex conjugate $\bar{a}_{ij}$ of the (i, j)th element of $\mathbf{A}$. When dealing with complex matrices, it is often useful to employ the *hermitian transpose* $\mathbf{A}^H = \bar{\mathbf{A}}^T$, which is the complex conjugate of the ordinary transpose. A *hermitian matrix* is a matrix such that $\mathbf{A}^H = \mathbf{A}$.

The reason why hermitian matrices are important will not appear until Chapter 9.

Ex. 1.11. If $\mathbf{x}$ is a complex column vector, show that $\mathbf{x}^H\mathbf{x}$ is real.

Ex. 1.12. Show that a hermitian matrix is the sum of a real symmetric matrix and an imaginary skew symmetric matrix.

Ex. 1.13. Show that the results in Theorem 1.3 are true for hermitian transposes as well as for ordinary transposes. Show that $\overline{(\mathbf{AB})} = \bar{\mathbf{A}}.\bar{\mathbf{B}}$ Show that $(\bar{\mathbf{A}})^T = \overline{(\mathbf{A}^T)}$.

1.4 The Inverse Matrix

Consider the following set of n equations in n unknowns:

$$\begin{aligned} a_{11}x_1 + a_{12}x_2 + \dots + a_{1n}x_n &= b_1 \\ a_{21}x_1 + a_{22}x_2 + \dots + a_{2n}x_n &= b_2 \\ &\dots \\ a_{n1}x_1 + a_{n2}x_2 + \dots + a_{nn}x_n &= b_n. \end{aligned} \tag{1.19}$$

If we introduce the matrices

$$\mathbf{A} = \begin{bmatrix} a_{11} & a_{12} & \dots & a_{1n} \\ a_{21} & a_{22} & \dots & a_{2n} \\ & & \dots & \\ a_{n1} & a_{n2} & \dots & a_{nn} \end{bmatrix}, \quad \mathbf{x} = \begin{bmatrix} x_1 \\ x_2 \\ \cdot \\ \cdot \\ \cdot \\ x_n \end{bmatrix}, \quad \mathbf{b} = \begin{bmatrix} b_1 \\ b_2 \\ \cdot \\ \cdot \\ \cdot \\ b_n \end{bmatrix},$$

then, using the definition of matrix multiplication given in Section 1.3, we see that (1.19) can be written in matrix notation as

$$\mathbf{Ax} = \mathbf{b}. \tag{1.20}$$

This can be regarded as the analogue for matrices of the ordinary equation $ax = b$ for real numbers.

To solve $ax = b$ in real numbers, we divide both sides by a, to obtain $x = b/a$. Since $\mathbf{A}$ is an array of numbers, it is not clear how we should proceed to divide equation (1.20) by $\mathbf{A}$. The clue is to note that the solution of $ax = b$ can be obtained by multiplying both sides of the equation by $1/a$, or a^{-1}, the inverse of a. This is not merely a play on words, since it turns out that the correct method of approach to the solution of (1.20) is to try to find a matrix, say $\mathbf{G}$, such that, when both sides of (1.20) are multiplied by $\mathbf{G}$, to give $\mathbf{GAx} = \mathbf{Gb}$, then the left-hand side of this equation reduces to $\mathbf{x}$, so that we have $\mathbf{x} = \mathbf{Gb}$, and the equation is solved.

DEFINITION **1.9.** A *diagonal* matrix is a square matrix in which all the elements off the principal diagonal are zero, i.e., $a_{ij} = 0$ $(i \neq j)$. The *unit* matrix, denoted by $\mathbf{I}$, is a diagonal matrix whose diagonal elements are all unity:

$$\mathbf{I} = \begin{bmatrix} 1 & 0 & \dots & 0 \\ 0 & 1 & \dots & 0 \\ & & \dots & \\ 0 & 0 & \dots & 1 \end{bmatrix}.$$

If we wish to emphasize that $\mathbf{I}$ has, say, m rows and columns, we write $\mathbf{I}_m$ in place of $\mathbf{I}$.

The important property possessed by the unit matrix (and the reason for its name) is that $\mathbf{IA} = \mathbf{A}$ and $\mathbf{AI} = \mathbf{A}$, for any $\mathbf{A}$ for which the multiplication is possible. The matrix $\mathbf{I}$ behaves like the number "1" in ordinary algebra. If $\mathbf{A}$ is an $m \times n$ matrix, then $\mathbf{I}_m\mathbf{A} = \mathbf{AI}_n = \mathbf{A}$. However, we shall usually write simply $\mathbf{IA} = \mathbf{AI} = \mathbf{A}$, where the orders of the unit matrices are understood to be such that the multiplications are permissible. If $\mathbf{K}$ is a diagonal matrix whose diagonal elements are all equal to k, we have $\mathbf{KA} = k\mathbf{A}$. For this reason $\mathbf{K}$ is called a *scalar matrix*.

We now return to the problem of solving $\mathbf{Ax} = \mathbf{b}$. We suggested that we should find a matrix $\mathbf{G}$ such that $\mathbf{GAx} = \mathbf{x}$. This will be true if $\mathbf{GA} = \mathbf{I}$, where $\mathbf{I}$ is the unit matrix of order n. This leads to the following definition:

DEFINITION **1.10.** A matrix $\mathbf{G}$ such that $\mathbf{GA} = \mathbf{I}$, if such a matrix $\mathbf{G}$ exists, is called a *left-inverse* of $\mathbf{A}$. A matrix $\mathbf{H}$ such that $\mathbf{AH} = \mathbf{I}$, if it exists, is called a *right-inverse of* $\mathbf{A}$.

Inverses (if they exist) can be found by solving sets of simultaneous linear equations. We illustrate by some simple examples.

Ex. 1.14. Find a right-inverse for the matrix

$$\mathbf{A} = \begin{bmatrix} 1 & -1 \\ 1 & 2 \end{bmatrix}.$$

Solution: We have to find a matrix

$$\mathbf{H} = \begin{bmatrix} x & z \\ y & w \end{bmatrix}, \tag{1.21}$$

such that

$$\begin{bmatrix} 1 & -1 \\ 1 & 2 \end{bmatrix} \begin{bmatrix} x & z \\ y & w \end{bmatrix} = \mathbf{I} = \begin{bmatrix} 1 & 0 \\ 0 & 1 \end{bmatrix},$$

i.e., such that

$$\left.\begin{aligned} x - y &= 1 \\ x + 2y &= 0 \end{aligned}\right\} \quad \text{and} \quad \left.\begin{aligned} z - w &= 0 \\ z + 2w &= 1 \end{aligned}\right\}.$$

These equations are easily solved, and we find

$$\mathbf{H} = \tfrac{1}{3}\begin{bmatrix} 2 & 1 \\ -1 & 1 \end{bmatrix}. \tag{1.22}$$

If a matrix $\mathbf{G}$ such that $\mathbf{GA} = \mathbf{I}$ is determined by a similar procedure, it will be found that $\mathbf{G}$ is exactly the same matrix as $\mathbf{H}$ so that $\mathbf{A}$ has a common left- and right-inverse, namely, (1.22).

Ex. 1.15. Does the following matrix have a right-inverse?

$$\mathbf{A} = \begin{bmatrix} 1 & -1 \\ 1 & -1 \end{bmatrix}.$$

Solution: If $\mathbf{H}$ is again the matrix (1.21), we have to solve

$$\left.\begin{aligned} x - y &= 1 \\ x - y &= 0 \end{aligned}\right\} \quad \text{and} \quad \left.\begin{aligned} z - w &= 0 \\ z - w &= 1 \end{aligned}\right\}.$$

These are clearly inconsistent sets of equations which do not possess solutions. Hence the inverse matrix does not exist. The important point that we have illustrated is that a square matrix need not have an inverse.

If we wish to find a right-inverse for an $m \times n$ matrix $\mathbf{A}$, we must try to find $\mathbf{H}$ such that $\mathbf{AH} = \mathbf{I}_m$. In order to form the product $\mathbf{AH}$, the matrix $\mathbf{H}$ must have n rows, and the equality of $\mathbf{AH}$ and $\mathbf{I}_m$ requires that $\mathbf{H}$ have m columns, so that $\mathbf{H}$ must be $n \times m$. Similarly, we see that a left-inverse of $\mathbf{A}$ must also be $n \times m$.

Ex. 1.16. Find a right-inverse of

$$\mathbf{A} = \begin{bmatrix} 1 & -1 & 1 \\ 1 & 1 & 2 \end{bmatrix}.$$

Solution: We try to find a matrix such that

$$\begin{bmatrix} 1 & -1 & 1 \\ 1 & 1 & 2 \end{bmatrix} \begin{bmatrix} x & y \\ z & w \\ u & v \end{bmatrix} = \begin{bmatrix} 1 & 0 \\ 0 & 1 \end{bmatrix}.$$

This requires

$$\left.\begin{aligned} x - z + u &= 1 \\ x + z + 2u &= 0 \end{aligned}\right\}, \qquad \left.\begin{aligned} y - w + v &= 0 \\ y + w + 2v &= 1 \end{aligned}\right\}.$$

It is easy to see that u and v can be given *any* values and then the resulting equations can be solved for x, z, y, w. If we set $u = \alpha$, $v = \beta$, we find that

$$\begin{bmatrix} x & y \\ z & w \\ u & v \end{bmatrix} = \frac{1}{2} \begin{bmatrix} 1 - 3\alpha & 1 - 3\beta \\ -1 - \alpha & 1 - \beta \\ 2\alpha & 2\beta \end{bmatrix}.$$

The matrix on the right is a right-inverse of $\mathbf{A}$ for any values of α and β. $\mathbf{A}$ has an infinite number of right-inverses.

Ex. 1.17. Show that

$$\begin{bmatrix} 1 & -1 & 1 \\ 1 & -1 & 1 \end{bmatrix}$$

does not have either a left- or a right-inverse.

Ex. 1.18. Show that

$$\begin{bmatrix} 1 & -1 & 1 \\ 1 & 1 & 2 \end{bmatrix}$$

does not have a left-inverse.

These exercises on rectangular matrices have again illustrated that inverses may or may not exist. Theoretical questions concerning the existence of inverses for a general $m \times n$ matrix are deferred to Chapter 5 since this needs the technical machinery developed in Chapters 3 and 4. We content ourselves here with the following remarks.

THEOREM **1.4.** *If both a left-inverse and a right-inverse exist, then these are the same, and this common inverse is unique.*

Proof: Suppose that **G**, **H** denote the left- and right-inverses of **A**. Then

$$\mathbf{G} = \mathbf{GI} = \mathbf{G(AH)} = \mathbf{(GA)H} = \mathbf{IH} = \mathbf{H}. \tag{1.23}$$

Suppose that there is another left-inverse $\mathbf{G}_1$. The same argument shows that $\mathbf{G}_1 = \mathbf{H}$ so that $\mathbf{G}_1 = \mathbf{G}$.

DEFINITION **1.11.** If both a left- and right-inverse exist for a matrix, this common inverse is called *the inverse* of **A** and it is denoted by $\mathbf{A}^{-1}$. (Of course $\mathbf{A}^{-1}$ is to be interpreted as a single symbol.)

Important results that will be proved later (Section 5.3) are:

(a) A square matrix *either* possesses an inverse *or* it does not possess either a left- or a right-inverse.

(b) A rectangular (i.e., nonsquare) matrix *never* possesses an inverse. If $m < n$ it will not possess a left-inverse and it may or may not possess a right-inverse. (If $m > n$, interchange "left" and "right.")

There is no need to memorize these facts since they should become intuitively clear later, but they are included to emphasize that matrices with common left- and right-inverses are the exception rather than the rule. The property of having an inverse is so important that such matrices are distinguished by a special name:

DEFINITION **1.12.** A square matrix that possesses an inverse (i.e., a common left- and right-inverse) is said to be *nonsingular*. A square matrix that does *not* possess an inverse is said to be *singular*.

When we are confronted with a square matrix, the very first question we ask is often "Is it singular or nonsingular?"

THEOREM **1.5.** *If* **A** *and* **B** *are nonsingular then*

(i) $(\mathbf{A}^{-1})^{-1} = \mathbf{A}$. (*This includes implicitly the result that* $\mathbf{A}^{-1}$ *is nonsingular.*)

(ii) $(\mathbf{AB})^{-1} = \mathbf{B}^{-1}\mathbf{A}^{-1}$. (*This includes implicitly the result that* **AB** *is nonsingular.*)

Proof: By definition of $\mathbf{A}^{-1}$ we have $\mathbf{A}^{-1}\mathbf{A} = \mathbf{A}\mathbf{A}^{-1} = \mathbf{I}$. Hence $\mathbf{A}^{-1}$ has both left- and right-inverses, namely **A**, and this proves (i). To prove (ii) we show that **AB** has both a left- and right-inverse. If a left-inverse **G** exists,

$$\mathbf{GAB} = \mathbf{I}. \tag{1.24}$$

Postmultiplication by $\mathbf{B}^{-1}$ and $\mathbf{A}^{-1}$ in succession gives

$$\begin{aligned} \mathbf{GA} &= \mathbf{B}^{-1}, \\ \mathbf{G} &= \mathbf{B}^{-1}\mathbf{A}^{-1}. \end{aligned} \tag{1.25}$$

Similarly if $\mathbf{ABH} = \mathbf{I}$ we see that $\mathbf{H} = \mathbf{B}^{-1}\mathbf{A}^{-1}$. Hence, both left- and right-inverses exist, and the required result follows.

The discussion of the inverse was motivated by the suggestion that to solve the equations $\mathbf{Ax} = \mathbf{b}$ we should multiply by $\mathbf{A}^{-1}$ to obtain $\mathbf{x} = \mathbf{A}^{-1}\mathbf{b}$:

Ex. 1.19. Solve the following set of equations by the formula $\mathbf{x} = \mathbf{A}^{-1}\mathbf{b}$:

$$2x - 3y = -13$$
$$x + 4y = 10.$$

Solution: We have

$$\mathbf{A} = \begin{bmatrix} 2 & -3 \\ 1 & 4 \end{bmatrix}, \qquad \mathbf{A}^{-1} = \frac{1}{11}\begin{bmatrix} 4 & 3 \\ -1 & 2 \end{bmatrix},$$

$$\begin{bmatrix} x \\ y \end{bmatrix} = \frac{1}{11}\begin{bmatrix} 4 & 3 \\ -1 & 2 \end{bmatrix}\begin{bmatrix} -13 \\ 10 \end{bmatrix} = \frac{1}{11}\begin{bmatrix} -22 \\ 33 \end{bmatrix} = \begin{bmatrix} -2 \\ 3 \end{bmatrix}.$$

Hence $x = -2$, $y = 3$.

From a strictly practical point of view it is easier to solve the set of equations $\mathbf{Ax} = \mathbf{b}$ directly, rather than to first form $\mathbf{A}^{-1}$ and then $\mathbf{A}^{-1}\mathbf{b}$. However the idea of the inverse matrix has very considerable theoretical advantages from various points of view, for example when considering error analysis, and the inverse is often useful in practice when considering equations having coefficient matrices $\mathbf{A}$ of special forms.

Ex. 1.20. Show that the general 2×2 matrix $\mathbf{A} = [a_{ij}]$ has an inverse if and only if $\Delta = a_{11}a_{22} - a_{12}a_{21}$ is nonzero. (We shall meet Δ later as the determinant of the matrix.) If $\Delta \neq 0$ show that

$$\mathbf{A}^{-1} = \frac{1}{\Delta}\begin{bmatrix} a_{22} & -a_{12} \\ -a_{21} & a_{11} \end{bmatrix}.$$

This result means that the inverse of a 2×2 matrix can be written down immediately by interchanging the diagonal terms a_{11}, a_{22}, changing the signs of the off-diagonal terms a_{12}, a_{21}, and dividing by Δ. Unfortunately, there is no corresponding simple rule for higher order matrices.

Ex. 1.21. Find $\mathbf{A}^{-1}$ if

$$\mathbf{A} = \begin{bmatrix} -1 & 2 & 1 \\ 0 & 1 & -2 \\ 1 & 4 & -1 \end{bmatrix}.$$

Ex. 1.22. Find a left-inverse for the matrix

$$\mathbf{A} = \begin{bmatrix} 1 & -1 \\ 1 & 1 \\ 2 & 3 \end{bmatrix},$$

and show that this left-inverse is not unique. Show that a right-inverse does not exist.

Ex. 1.23. Suppose that

$$2x - 3y + u + 4v - 9w = -13,$$
$$x + 4y - 5u + 2v + w = 10,$$

and we wish to express x, y in terms of u, v, w. Write these equations in matrix notation as

$$\mathbf{Ax} = \mathbf{b} + \mathbf{Eu},$$

where

$$\mathbf{x} = \begin{bmatrix} x \\ y \end{bmatrix}, \qquad \mathbf{u} = \begin{bmatrix} u \\ v \\ w \end{bmatrix}.$$

Hence,

$$\mathbf{x} = \mathbf{A}^{-1}\mathbf{b} + \mathbf{A}^{-1}\mathbf{Eu}.$$

By writing out $\mathbf{A}$, $\mathbf{b}$, $\mathbf{E}$ explicitly and calculating $\mathbf{A}^{-1}\mathbf{b}$ and $\mathbf{A}^{-1}\mathbf{E}$, show that

$$\begin{bmatrix} x \\ y \end{bmatrix} = \begin{bmatrix} -2 \\ 3 \end{bmatrix} + \begin{bmatrix} 1 & -2 & 3 \\ 1 & 0 & -1 \end{bmatrix} \begin{bmatrix} u \\ v \\ w \end{bmatrix}.$$

Ex. 1.24. The inverse of a diagonal matrix with nonzero diagonal elements can be written down immediately:

$$\mathbf{K} = \begin{bmatrix} k_1 & 0 & \dots & 0 \\ 0 & k_2 & \dots & 0 \\ & & \dots & \\ 0 & 0 & \dots & k_n \end{bmatrix}, \qquad \mathbf{K}^{-1} = \begin{bmatrix} \dfrac{1}{k_1} & 0 & \dots & 0 \\ 0 & \dfrac{1}{k_2} & \dots & 0 \\ & & \dots & \\ 0 & 0 & \dots & \dfrac{1}{k_n} \end{bmatrix}.$$

Ex. 1.25. Show that the cancellation law is true if the appropriate inverse exists. For example if $\mathbf{AX} = \mathbf{AB}$, and a left-inverse of $\mathbf{A}$ exists, then $\mathbf{X} = \mathbf{B}$. [Compare Theorem 1.2(iv).]

Ex. 1.26. Find all 2×2 matrices $\mathbf{X}$ such that $\mathbf{X}^2 = \mathbf{I}$, where $\mathbf{I}$ is the 2×2 unit matrix.

[The answer is that $\mathbf{X}$ can be any of:

$$\pm\mathbf{I}, \qquad \pm\begin{bmatrix} 1 & 0 \\ c & -1 \end{bmatrix}, \qquad \pm\begin{bmatrix} 1 & b \\ 0 & -1 \end{bmatrix}, \qquad \begin{bmatrix} a & b \\ \dfrac{(1 - a^2)}{b} & -a \end{bmatrix},$$

where a, b, c are arbitrary numbers. Note that a quadratic matrix equation can have an infinity of solutions, in contrast to the scalar equation $x^2 = 1$ which has only two solutions $x = \pm 1$. Note also that $\mathbf{X}^2 = \mathbf{I}$ implies $(\mathbf{X} - \mathbf{I})(\mathbf{X} + \mathbf{I}) = \mathbf{0}$, so that if $\mathbf{X} \neq \pm\mathbf{I}$ then both $\mathbf{X} - \mathbf{I}$ and $\mathbf{X} + \mathbf{I}$ must be singular, from Ex. 1.25. The reader can verify that the above matrices satisfy this condition.]

Ex. 1.27. Show that if $\mathbf{A}$, $\mathbf{B}$ and $\mathbf{A} + \mathbf{B}$ possess inverses,

$$(\mathbf{A}^{-1} + \mathbf{B}^{-1})^{-1} = \mathbf{A}(\mathbf{A} + \mathbf{B})^{-1}\mathbf{B} = \mathbf{B}(\mathbf{A} + \mathbf{B})^{-1}\mathbf{A}.$$

1.5 The Partitioning of Matrices

In this section, we describe a useful technical device that we shall use frequently to facilitate matrix manipulations.

A *submatrix* is a matrix obtained from an original matrix by deleting certain rows and columns. Suppose that we *partition* a matrix into submatrices by horizontal and vertical lines as illustrated by the following special example:

$$\mathbf{A} = \left[\begin{array}{ccc|c|cc} a_{11} & a_{12} & a_{13} & a_{14} & a_{15} & a_{16} \\ a_{21} & a_{22} & a_{23} & a_{24} & a_{25} & a_{26} \\ \hline a_{31} & a_{32} & a_{33} & a_{34} & a_{35} & a_{36} \end{array}\right]. \tag{1.26}$$

We can write this, using an obvious notation, as

$$\mathbf{A} = \begin{bmatrix} \mathbf{A}_{11} & \mathbf{A}_{12} & \mathbf{A}_{13} \\ \mathbf{A}_{21} & \mathbf{A}_{22} & \mathbf{A}_{23} \end{bmatrix}, \tag{1.27}$$

where

$$\mathbf{A}_{11} = \begin{bmatrix} a_{11} & a_{12} & a_{13} \\ a_{21} & a_{22} & a_{23} \end{bmatrix}, \qquad \mathbf{A}_{22} = [a_{34}], \qquad \text{etc.}$$

Suppose that we partition two $m \times n$ matrices as follows $(a + b + c = m)$:

$$\mathbf{B} = \begin{matrix} & n \\ a & \\ b & \\ c & \end{matrix}\!\!\begin{bmatrix} \mathbf{B}_1 \\ \mathbf{B}_2 \\ \mathbf{B}_3 \end{bmatrix}, \qquad \mathbf{C} = \begin{matrix} & n \\ a & \\ b & \\ c & \end{matrix}\!\!\begin{bmatrix} \mathbf{C}_1 \\ \mathbf{C}_2 \\ \mathbf{C}_3 \end{bmatrix}, \tag{1.28}$$

where the numbers of rows and columns in the submatrices are denoted by a, b, c to the left of, and n above, the matrices. It is readily checked by writing the following equations out in detail that

$$\mathbf{B} + \mathbf{C} = \begin{bmatrix} \mathbf{B}_1 \\ \mathbf{B}_2 \\ \mathbf{B}_3 \end{bmatrix} + \begin{bmatrix} \mathbf{C}_1 \\ \mathbf{C}_2 \\ \mathbf{C}_3 \end{bmatrix} = \begin{bmatrix} \mathbf{B}_1 + \mathbf{C}_1 \\ \mathbf{B}_2 + \mathbf{C}_2 \\ \mathbf{B}_3 + \mathbf{C}_3 \end{bmatrix};$$

the general result is clearly:

THEOREM 1.6. *We can add and subtract partitioned matrices as if the submatrices were ordinary (scalar) elements, provided the matrices are partitioned in the same way, so that it is permissible to form the necessary submatrix additions and subtractions in the final result.*

Proof: Obvious but laborious in the general case.

In a similar way, suppose that a matrix **A** is partitioned as follows:

$$\mathbf{A} = \begin{matrix} & a & b & c \\ p & \mathbf{A}_{11} & \mathbf{A}_{12} & \mathbf{A}_{13} \\ q & \mathbf{A}_{21} & \mathbf{A}_{22} & \mathbf{A}_{23} \end{matrix}. \tag{1.29}$$

It is then possible to form the product **AB**, where **B** is assumed to be partitioned as in (1.28), in the following way:

$$\mathbf{AB} = \begin{matrix} & n \\ p & \mathbf{A}_{11}\mathbf{B}_1 + \mathbf{A}_{12}\mathbf{B}_2 + \mathbf{A}_{13}\mathbf{B}_3 \\ q & \mathbf{A}_{21}\mathbf{B}_1 + \mathbf{A}_{22}\mathbf{B}_2 + \mathbf{A}_{23}\mathbf{B}_3 \end{matrix}. \tag{1.30}$$

To check this result we need only visualize writing out all the matrices and operations involved in full detail. The general result is clearly:

THEOREM 1.7. *We can multiply partitioned matrices as if the submatrices were ordinary (scalar) elements, provided that the matrices are partitioned in such a way that the appropriate products can be formed.*

Proof: A proof can be given by first proving the special cases:

(i) $\begin{bmatrix} \mathbf{A}_1 \\ \mathbf{A}_2 \end{bmatrix}\mathbf{B} = \begin{bmatrix} \mathbf{A}_1\mathbf{B} \\ \mathbf{A}_2\mathbf{B} \end{bmatrix}$.

(ii) $\mathbf{A}[\mathbf{B}_1 \quad \mathbf{B}_2] = [\mathbf{AB}_1 \quad \mathbf{AB}_2]$.

(iii) $[\mathbf{A}_1 \quad \mathbf{A}_2]\begin{bmatrix} \mathbf{B}_1 \\ \mathbf{B}_2 \end{bmatrix} = [\mathbf{A}_1\mathbf{B}_1 + \mathbf{A}_2\mathbf{B}_2]$.

The general case follows by repeated application of these special cases. However the details are laborious and not very important from our point of view.

Partitioned matrices are useful in several ways. If a physical system can be split into subsystems with interconnections, the behavior of the whole system can often be described by a large matrix partitioned in such a way that the submatrices along the diagonal describe the separate parts of the whole system, and the submatrices off the diagonal represent the interconnections of the subsystems. This can clarify the structure of a complicated system.

An important application of partitioned matrices is given by the next theorem. We require the following definition.

DEFINITION 1.13. The *unit column matrix* $\mathbf{e}_j$ is an $n \times 1$ matrix with jth element unity, all other elements zero:

$$\mathbf{e}_1 = \begin{bmatrix} 1 \\ 0 \\ \cdot \\ \cdot \\ \cdot \\ 0 \end{bmatrix}, \quad \mathbf{e}_2 = \begin{bmatrix} 0 \\ 1 \\ \cdot \\ \cdot \\ \cdot \\ 0 \end{bmatrix}, \quad \ldots, \quad \mathbf{e}_n = \begin{bmatrix} 0 \\ 0 \\ \cdot \\ \cdot \\ \cdot \\ 1 \end{bmatrix}. \tag{1.31}$$

In partitioned matrix notation we can write the unit matrix as:

$$\mathbf{I} = [\mathbf{e}_1, \mathbf{e}_2, \ldots, \mathbf{e}_n]. \tag{1.32}$$

The problem of finding an inverse can be reduced to the problem of solving several sets of simultaneous linear equations with the *same coefficient matrix.* It will turn out later that this is extremely important from the point of view of developing efficient methods for inverting matrices in practice (see Sections 3.2, 7.6).

THEOREM 1.8. *If the right-inverse of an $m \times n$ matrix* $\mathbf{A}$ *exists, it is given by*

$$\mathbf{A}^{-1} = [\mathbf{x}_1, \mathbf{x}_2, \ldots, \mathbf{x}_n], \tag{1.33}$$

where the $\mathbf{x}_i$ *are the solutions of the equations*

$$\mathbf{A}\mathbf{x}_j = \mathbf{e}_j, \qquad j = 1, 2, \ldots, n. \tag{1.34}$$

Proof: Suppose that a right-inverse of $\mathbf{A}$ is denoted by $\mathbf{H} = [\mathbf{x}_1, \ldots, \mathbf{x}_n]$ where $\mathbf{x}_j$ is the jth column of $\mathbf{H}$. Then $\mathbf{AH} = \mathbf{I}$ gives

$$\mathbf{A}[\mathbf{x}_1, \mathbf{x}_2, \ldots, \mathbf{x}_n] = [\mathbf{e}_1, \mathbf{e}_2, \ldots, \mathbf{e}_n].$$

On applying Theorems 1.6, 1.7, we see that the $\mathbf{x}_j$ satisfy (1.34) which proves the theorem.

Ex. 1.28. Suppose that the following matrices are partitioned as indicated by the dotted lines:

$$\mathbf{A} = \left[\begin{array}{c:cc:ccc} 2 & 0 & 0 & 4 & -1 & 7 \\ 1 & 0 & 0 & -2 & 0 & 3 \\ \hdashline 1 & 1 & -1 & 0 & 0 & 0 \end{array}\right], \qquad \mathbf{B} = \left[\begin{array}{cc} -1 & 4 \\ \hdashline 2 & 1 \\ -1 & 1 \\ \hdashline 5 & 3 \\ 1 & 2 \\ 0 & -1 \end{array}\right].$$

Write down the matrices $\mathbf{A}_{ij}$, $\mathbf{B}_i$ in the notation of (1.29), (1.28). Show that

$$\mathbf{A}_{11}\mathbf{B}_1 + \mathbf{A}_{12}\mathbf{B}_2 + \mathbf{A}_{13}\mathbf{B}_3 = \begin{bmatrix} 17 & 11 \\ -11 & -5 \end{bmatrix},$$

$$\mathbf{A}_{21}\mathbf{B}_1 + \mathbf{A}_{22}\mathbf{B}_2 + \mathbf{A}_{23}\mathbf{B}_3 = [2 \quad 4].$$

Show that the result given by inserting these in (1.30) is precisely the product obtained by forming **AB** directly.

Ex. 1.29. We show how to use partitioned matrices to solve the following system, taking advantage of the fact that there are two zero elements on the right of the third and fourth equations. (This is included simply as a numerical example of the use of partitioned matrices. We do not imply that the method has any special merit in this example—it has not.)

$$\begin{aligned} 2x_1 - 3x_2 + 2x_3 + 5x_4 &= 3 \\ x_1 - x_2 + x_3 + 2x_4 &= 1 \\ 3x_1 + 2x_2 + 2x_3 + x_4 &= 0 \\ x_1 + x_2 - 3x_3 - x_4 &= 0. \end{aligned}$$

We partition the matrix of coefficients into 2×2 matrices:

$$\begin{bmatrix} \mathbf{A} & \mathbf{B} \\ \mathbf{C} & \mathbf{D} \end{bmatrix} \begin{bmatrix} \mathbf{x} \\ \mathbf{y} \end{bmatrix} = \begin{bmatrix} \mathbf{b} \\ \mathbf{0} \end{bmatrix},$$

where

$$\mathbf{A} = \begin{bmatrix} 2 & -3 \\ 1 & -1 \end{bmatrix}, \quad \text{etc.,} \quad \mathbf{x} = \begin{bmatrix} x_1 \\ x_2 \end{bmatrix}, \quad \mathbf{y} = \begin{bmatrix} x_3 \\ x_4 \end{bmatrix}, \quad \mathbf{b} = \begin{bmatrix} 3 \\ 1 \end{bmatrix}.$$

The above matrix equation gives

$$\mathbf{Ax} + \mathbf{By} = \mathbf{b},$$

$$\mathbf{Cx} + \mathbf{Dy} = \mathbf{0}.$$

Hence,

$$\mathbf{y} = -\mathbf{D}^{-1}\mathbf{Cx},$$

and, on substituting in the first equation,

$$(\mathbf{A} - \mathbf{BD}^{-1}\mathbf{C})\mathbf{x} = \mathbf{b}.$$

Numerically,

$$\mathbf{D}^{-1} = \begin{bmatrix} -1 & -1 \\ 3 & 2 \end{bmatrix}, \quad \mathbf{D}^{-1}\mathbf{C} = \begin{bmatrix} -4 & -3 \\ 11 & 8 \end{bmatrix},$$

$$\mathbf{BD}^{-1}\mathbf{C} = \begin{bmatrix} 47 & 34 \\ 18 & 13 \end{bmatrix}, \quad \mathbf{A} - \mathbf{BD}^{-1}\mathbf{C} = \begin{bmatrix} -45 & -37 \\ -17 & -14 \end{bmatrix}.$$

Hence,

$$\mathbf{x} = \begin{bmatrix} -14 & 37 \\ 17 & -45 \end{bmatrix} \begin{bmatrix} 3 \\ 1 \end{bmatrix} = \begin{bmatrix} -5 \\ 6 \end{bmatrix},$$

$$\mathbf{y} = -\begin{bmatrix} -4 & -3 \\ 11 & 8 \end{bmatrix} \begin{bmatrix} -5 \\ 6 \end{bmatrix} = \begin{bmatrix} -2 \\ 7 \end{bmatrix}.$$

This gives the required solution of the equations.

Miscellaneous Exercises 1

Ex. 1.30. If

$$\mathbf{A} = \begin{bmatrix} 1 & 1 & 1 & -1 \\ 1 & -1 & 1 & 1 \\ 1 & 1 & -1 & 1 \\ 1 & -1 & -1 & -1 \end{bmatrix},$$

show that $\mathbf{A}^T\mathbf{A} = \mathbf{A}\mathbf{A}^T = 4\mathbf{I}$.

Ex. 1.31. Show by induction that if $k \neq 0$ then

$$\begin{bmatrix} \cos\theta & k\sin\theta \\ -\dfrac{1}{k}\sin\theta & \cos\theta \end{bmatrix}^n = \begin{bmatrix} \cos n\theta & k\sin n\theta \\ -\dfrac{1}{k}\sin n\theta & \cos n\theta \end{bmatrix}.$$

["Show by induction" means (a) Verify for $n = 1$; (b) prove that if the result is true for any given n, then it is true for $n + 1$.]

Ex. 1.32. Suppose that **A** is a matrix in which the third column is equal to twice the first column. Show that the same must be true of any product **BA**.

Ex. 1.33. Construct 2×2 matrices **A**, **B** having *no* zero entries for which $\mathbf{AB} = \mathbf{0}$.

Ex. 1.34. Find 2×2 matrices **X**, **Y**, neither of which is null, such that $\mathbf{X}^2 + \mathbf{Y}^2 = \mathbf{0}$.

Ex. 1.35. Construct a 2×2 matrix with no zero entries that does not have an inverse.

Ex. 1.36. Let $\mathbf{A} = \mathbf{B} + \mathbf{C}$ where **B**, **C** are $n \times n$ matrices such that $\mathbf{C}^2 = \mathbf{0}$ and $\mathbf{BC} = \mathbf{CB}$. Show that, for $p > 0$,

$$\mathbf{A}^{p+1} = \mathbf{B}^p\{\mathbf{B} + (p + 1)\mathbf{C}\}.$$

Ex. 1.37. What matrices satisfy $\mathbf{A}^T\mathbf{A} = \mathbf{0}$? Justify your answer.

Ex. 1.38. If **A** is a square matrix of order n and **x** is an $n \times 1$ column vector, show that $\mathbf{k} = \mathbf{x}^T\mathbf{A}\mathbf{x}$ is a 1×1 matrix. If $\mathbf{x} = \mathbf{P}\mathbf{y}$ show that $\mathbf{k} = \mathbf{y}^T(\mathbf{P}^T\mathbf{A}\mathbf{P})\mathbf{y}$.

Ex. 1.39. Show that a product of p nonsingular matrices is nonsingular.

Ex. 1.40. Suppose that **A** is a 2×2 matrix that commutes with *every* 2×2 matrix. Show that **A** must be a multiple of the unit matrix.

Ex. 1.41. Show that if the ith element of a diagonal matrix **D** is d_i, then **DA** is the matrix obtained by multiplying the ith row of **A** by d_i. Similarly, **AD** is the matrix obtained by multiplying the jth column of **A** by d_j.

Ex. 1.42. Detect the flaw in the following argument. Suppose that $\mathbf{AH} = \mathbf{I}$. Premultiply by **H** and postmultiply by **A**. Then $(\mathbf{HA})^2 = \mathbf{HA}$. Multiply this equation on the left by $(\mathbf{HA})^{-1}$. Then $\mathbf{HA} = \mathbf{I}$, so that **H** is a left-inverse of **A**.

Ex. 1.43. Show that

(a) $(\mathbf{A}^T)^{-1} = (\mathbf{A}^{-1})^T$.

(b) If $\mathbf{A}$ is symmetric then $\mathbf{A}^{-1}$ is symmetric.

Ex. 1.44. Prove that the inverse of the matrix obtained by interchanging the pth and qth rows of $\mathbf{A}$ is given by interchanging the pth and qth columns of $\mathbf{A}^{-1}$. Prove that the inverse of the matrix obtained by multiplying the pth column of $\mathbf{A}$ by k ($\neq 0$) is given by dividing the pth row of $\mathbf{A}^{-1}$ by k.

Ex. 1.45. Let $\mathbf{K}$ be a skew-symmetric matrix ($\mathbf{K}^T = -\mathbf{K}$). If

$$\mathbf{B} = (\mathbf{I} + \mathbf{K})(\mathbf{I} - \mathbf{K})^{-1},$$

show that $\mathbf{B}^T\mathbf{B} = \mathbf{B}\mathbf{B}^T = \mathbf{I}$. (This assumes that $\mathbf{I} - \mathbf{K}$ is nonsingular, and the proof of this will be a subject of later exercises, see Exs. 5.51 and 9.11. Prove directly that if $\mathbf{K}$ is 2×2 then $\mathbf{I} - \mathbf{K}$ is nonsingular.)

Ex. 1.46. (a) If a matrix has a row or a column of zeros, then it has no inverse.

(b) If $\mathbf{A}$ is any square matrix in which one row is a multiple of another, then this matrix does not have an inverse.

Ex. 1.47. If

$$\mathbf{A} = \begin{bmatrix} \alpha & \beta & \delta \\ 0 & \alpha & 0 \\ 0 & \gamma & \varepsilon \end{bmatrix},$$

show that, if $\alpha\varepsilon \neq 0$,

$$\mathbf{A}^{-1} = \frac{1}{\alpha^2\varepsilon}\begin{bmatrix} \alpha\varepsilon & \gamma\delta - \beta\varepsilon & -\alpha\delta \\ 0 & \alpha\varepsilon & 0 \\ 0 & -\alpha\gamma & \alpha^2 \end{bmatrix}.$$

Ex. 1.48. Given that

$$\mathbf{a}_1 = \begin{bmatrix} 1 \\ 2 \\ 3 \end{bmatrix}, \quad \mathbf{a}_2 = \begin{bmatrix} 1 \\ 1 \\ -1 \end{bmatrix}, \quad \mathbf{a}_3 = \begin{bmatrix} 5 \\ -4 \\ 1 \end{bmatrix},$$

show that $\mathbf{a}_1^T\mathbf{a}_2 = [0]$, $\mathbf{a}_1^T\mathbf{a}_3 = [0]$, $\mathbf{a}_2^T\mathbf{a}_3 = [0]$. By any method, show that the inverse of $\mathbf{A} = [\mathbf{a}_1\mathbf{a}_2\mathbf{a}_3]$ is given by

$$\mathbf{A}^{-1} = \begin{bmatrix} \mathbf{b}_1 \\ \mathbf{b}_2 \\ \mathbf{b}_3 \end{bmatrix},$$

where, if $\mathbf{a}_i^T\mathbf{a}_i = [k_i]$,

$$\mathbf{b}_i = \frac{1}{k_i}\mathbf{a}_i^T, \qquad i = 1, 2, 3.$$

Ex. 1.49. A real matrix $\mathbf{A}$ that satisfies the relations $\mathbf{A}\mathbf{A}^T = \mathbf{A}^T\mathbf{A} = \mathbf{I}$ is said to be *orthogonal*.

(a) Give an example of a 2×2 orthogonal matrix.
(b) Find the general 2×2 orthogonal matrix.

(c) Show that the product of two orthogonal matrices is an orthogonal matrix.

(d) Show that the inverse of an orthogonal matrix is an orthogonal matrix.

Ex. 1.50. If $\mathbf{A} = [a_{ij}]$, where the a_{ij} are functions of a variable t, then we define $d\mathbf{A}/dt = [da_{ij}/dt]$. Show that

(i) $\dfrac{d}{dt}(\mathbf{AB}) = \dfrac{d\mathbf{A}}{dt}\mathbf{B} + \mathbf{A}\dfrac{d\mathbf{B}}{dt}$.

(ii) By differentiating $\mathbf{Z}^{-1}\mathbf{Z} = \mathbf{I}$,

$$\frac{d\mathbf{Z}^{-1}}{dt} = -\mathbf{Z}^{-1}\frac{d\mathbf{Z}}{dt}\mathbf{Z}^{-1}.$$

Ex. 1.51. Suppose that $\mathbf{B} = \mathbf{P}^{-1}\mathbf{AP}$. Show that $\mathbf{B}^m = \mathbf{P}^{-1}\mathbf{A}^m\mathbf{P}$ if m is integral. Deduce that if

$$a_n\mathbf{A}^n + a_{n-1}\mathbf{A}^{n-1} + \ldots + a_0\mathbf{I} = \mathbf{0},$$

then

$$a_n\mathbf{B}^n + a_{n-1}\mathbf{B}^{n-1} + \ldots + a_0\mathbf{I} = \mathbf{0}.$$

Ex. 1.52. Form **AB** where

$$\mathbf{A} = \left[\begin{array}{cc:ccc} 4 & 3 & -2 & 1 & 4 \\ 2 & -5 & 6 & 3 & -1 \end{array}\right], \qquad \mathbf{B} = \left[\begin{array}{cc:c} 0 & -1 & 3 \\ 2 & -1 & 6 \\ \hdashline 5 & 2 & 1 \\ -3 & 4 & -1 \\ 2 & -1 & 2 \end{array}\right]$$

by (a) straightforward multiplication, (b) block multiplication, partitioning as shown by the dotted lines.

Ex. 1.53. Show that if **B** is the partitioned matrix

$$\mathbf{B} = \begin{bmatrix} \mathbf{A}_{11} & \mathbf{A}_{12} \\ \mathbf{A}_{21} & \mathbf{A}_{22} \end{bmatrix}, \quad \text{then} \quad \mathbf{B}^T = \begin{bmatrix} \mathbf{A}_{11}^T & \mathbf{A}_{21}^T \\ \mathbf{A}_{12}^T & \mathbf{A}_{22}^T \end{bmatrix}.$$

Ex. 1.54. If $\mathbf{A}_1$, $\mathbf{A}_2$, $\mathbf{A}_3$ are nonsingular matrices, then

$$\begin{bmatrix} \mathbf{A}_1 & \mathbf{0} & \mathbf{0} \\ \mathbf{0} & \mathbf{A}_2 & \mathbf{0} \\ \mathbf{0} & \mathbf{0} & \mathbf{A}_3 \end{bmatrix}^{-1} = \begin{bmatrix} \mathbf{A}_1^{-1} & \mathbf{0} & \mathbf{0} \\ \mathbf{0} & \mathbf{A}_2^{-1} & \mathbf{0} \\ \mathbf{0} & \mathbf{0} & \mathbf{A}_3^{-1} \end{bmatrix}.$$

Ex. 1.55. (a) $(\mathbf{ABC})^T = \mathbf{C}^T\mathbf{B}^T\mathbf{A}^T$;

(b) If **A**, **B**, **C** are nonsingular $(\mathbf{ABC})^{-1} = \mathbf{C}^{-1}\mathbf{B}^{-1}\mathbf{A}^{-1}$.

Ex. 1.56. If

$$\mathbf{X} = \begin{bmatrix} 0 & i \\ -i & 0 \end{bmatrix}, \quad \mathbf{Y} = \begin{bmatrix} 0 & 1 \\ 1 & 0 \end{bmatrix}, \quad \mathbf{Z} = \begin{bmatrix} -1 & 0 \\ 0 & 1 \end{bmatrix},$$

verify that

$$\mathbf{XY} = -\mathbf{YX} = -i\mathbf{Z}, \qquad \mathbf{YZ} = -\mathbf{ZY} = -i\mathbf{X},$$

$$\mathbf{ZX} = -\mathbf{XZ} = -i\mathbf{Y}, \qquad \mathbf{X}^2 = \mathbf{Y}^2 = \mathbf{Z}^2 = \mathbf{I}.$$

Show that every 2×2 matrix can be written $\mathbf{A} = a\mathbf{I} + b\mathbf{X} + c\mathbf{Y} + d\mathbf{Z}$.

Ex. 1.57. By the *trace* of a square matrix, written tr $\mathbf{A}$, we mean the sum of its diagonal elements

$$\operatorname{tr} \mathbf{A} = \sum_{i=1}^{n} a_{ii}$$

Show that

(a) if k is a scalar, $\operatorname{tr}(k\mathbf{A}) = k \operatorname{tr} \mathbf{A}$,
(b) $\operatorname{tr}(\mathbf{A} \pm \mathbf{B}) = \operatorname{tr} \mathbf{A} \pm \operatorname{tr} \mathbf{B}$,
(c) $\operatorname{tr} \mathbf{AB} = \operatorname{tr} \mathbf{BA}$,
(d) $\operatorname{tr}(\mathbf{B}^{-1}\mathbf{AB}) = \operatorname{tr} \mathbf{A}$,
(e) $\operatorname{tr}(\mathbf{AA}^T) = \sum_{i=1}^{n} \sum_{j=1}^{n} |a_{ij}|^2$.

Ex. 1.58. Let

$$\begin{bmatrix} \mathbf{A} & \mathbf{u} \\ \mathbf{v}^T & a \end{bmatrix}^{-1} = \begin{bmatrix} \mathbf{B} & \mathbf{p} \\ \mathbf{q}^T & \alpha \end{bmatrix},$$

where $\mathbf{u}$, $\mathbf{v}$, $\mathbf{p}$, $\mathbf{q}$ are column matrices and $\mathbf{A}$ has an inverse. Prove that

$$\mathbf{B} = \mathbf{A}^{-1} + \alpha\mathbf{A}^{-1}\mathbf{u}\mathbf{v}^T\mathbf{A}^{-1}, \qquad \alpha = (a - \mathbf{v}^T\mathbf{A}^{-1}\mathbf{u})^{-1},$$

$$\mathbf{p} = -\alpha\mathbf{A}^{-1}\mathbf{u}, \qquad \mathbf{q}^T = -\alpha\mathbf{v}^T\mathbf{A}^{-1}.$$

Also $\mathbf{A}^{-1} = \mathbf{B} - (1/\alpha)\mathbf{p}\mathbf{q}^T$. (The point of this exercise is that if the inverse of a given matrix is known, it is easy to compute the inverse of the matrix obtained by either adding a row and column, or omitting a row and column. Matrices of the above type are known as *bordered matrices*.)

Ex. 1.59. If, in partitioned form:

$$\mathbf{A} = \begin{bmatrix} \mathbf{P} & \mathbf{Q} \\ \mathbf{R} & \mathbf{S} \end{bmatrix},$$

where $\mathbf{A}$ and $\mathbf{P}$ are nonsingular, prove that

$$\mathbf{A}^{-1} = \begin{bmatrix} \mathbf{X} & -\mathbf{P}^{-1}\mathbf{QW} \\ -\mathbf{WRP}^{-1} & \mathbf{W} \end{bmatrix},$$

where

$$\mathbf{W} = [\mathbf{S} - \mathbf{RP}^{-1}\mathbf{Q}]^{-1}, \qquad \mathbf{X} = \mathbf{P}^{-1} + \mathbf{P}^{-1}\mathbf{QWRP}^{-1}. \tag{1.35}$$

Similarly, if $\mathbf{A}$ and $\mathbf{S}$ are nonsingular, prove that

$$\mathbf{A}^{-1} = \begin{bmatrix} \mathbf{X} & -\mathbf{XQS}^{-1} \\ -\mathbf{S}^{-1}\mathbf{RX} & \mathbf{W} \end{bmatrix},$$

where

$$\mathbf{X} = (\mathbf{P} - \mathbf{QS}^{-1}\mathbf{R})^{-1}, \qquad \mathbf{W} = \mathbf{S}^{-1} + \mathbf{S}^{-1}\mathbf{RXQS}^{-1}. \tag{1.36}$$

If $\mathbf{P}$ and $\mathbf{S}$ are both nonsingular, prove directly that the forms (1.35), (1.36) for $\mathbf{X}$ and $\mathbf{W}$ are equivalent. [The result in Ex. 1.58 is, of course, a special case of (1.35).]

2 Some Simple Applications of Matrices

2.1 Introduction

There exists a superabundance of examples of applications of matrices. The only difficulty in the present context is to choose nontrivial examples that are not too specialized, technical, or detailed, but yet illustrate why matrices are indispensable for dealing with certain types of complicated problems in the applied sciences. In addition, at this stage, we wish to use only concepts and techniques already introduced in Chapter 1, namely the addition, multiplication, and partitioning of matrices, and the idea of an inverse.

There are two main points to be illustrated.

(a) The ease with which matrices can be used to organize and show the structure of complicated sets of relationships.

(b) The utility of matrices in connection with automatic digital computers.

The utility of matrices in many applications arises from the fact that we consider an array of many numbers as a single object, and we denote it by a single symbol. Relationships between variables can then be expressed in a clear and concise way. From one point of view, we do nothing that could not be done by writing out systems of linear simultaneous equations in full detail. On the other hand, we shall see that the introduction of matrices enables us to manipulate the systems of equations, and see the structure of the calculations, much more easily. In the type of problem for which matrices are suitable, the more complicated the problem, the more useful and powerful the idea of a matrix turns out to be.

In Section 2.2 we discuss a simple example of a matrix approach to the calculation of strains and stresses in pin-jointed frameworks. Some remarks on the problem of calculating frameworks by computer are made in Section 2.3. It is illustrated in exercises that the matrix approach to network problems can be applied similarly in other disciplines, for example, electrical engineering and economics.

In Section 2.4 matrices are used to systematize the solution of equations by the method of least squares. As an application, we consider the analysis of photographs of stars.

In Section 2.5 we consider an application of matrix multiplication to a marketing problem in which customers switch from one milk supplier to another. This is a simple example of a Markov chain.

2.2 *A Plane Pin-Jointed Framework*

In this section we show how the calculation of strains and stresses in a simple type of mechanical structure can be facilitated by using matrices. We shall solve a simple problem longhand, first of all, by writing out all the equations in detail. We then introduce matrices to express the manipulations in a compact form.

For the reader who wishes to skip the technical details of the formulation, we note that the basic equations in longhand form are (2.2), (2.3), (2.4), and the corresponding matrix equations are (2.8), (2.9), (2.10). The final equations that have to be solved are (2.6) in longhand, or (2.11) in matrices.

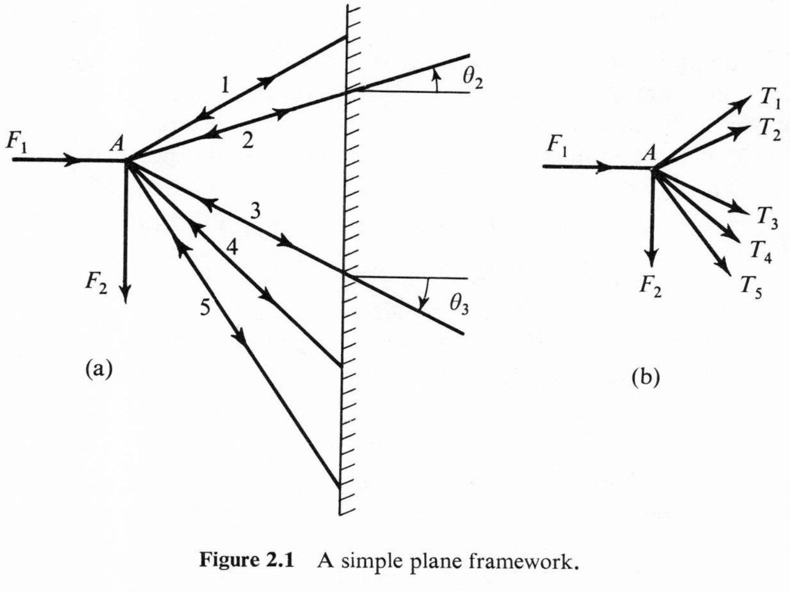

Figure 2.1 A simple plane framework.

Consider the simple plane framework in Figure 2.1. We assume that the framework is *pin-jointed*, which means that the members are connected to the wall, and connected together at A, loosely, by pins. This means that if the five members were not connected to the wall, they could rotate quite freely around the point A. With this kind of joint there is no tendency to bend the members, and the only forces that are present are tensile or compressive forces in the members. (In technical language, no bending moments are transmitted.) It is assumed that the weights of the members are negligible, and that the lengths of the members are such that, if the external forces F_1 and F_2 are zero, there are no stresses in the members.

The only information required about an individual member is knowledge of its extension when a force is applied along its length. We assume Hooke's law, that the extension is linearly proportional to the force, so that

$$e = kT, \tag{2.1}$$

where T is the force (tension), e is the extension, and k is a factor of proportionality, assumed known. In fact $k = l/AE$, where l is the length of the rod, A the area, and E the modulus of elasticity. The constant k is called the *flexibility* of the member, and it is the extension of the member per unit force. (The quantity $1/k$ is known as the *stiffness coefficient* of the member.)

We number the members 1 to 5 as shown in Figure 2.1, and assume that the angle that each member makes with the horizontal is given by θ_i ($i = 1$ to 5). (θ_3, θ_4, θ_5 are negative in the example drawn in Figure 2.1.) The changes in the θ_i produced by the application of forces are considered negligible. Let the flexibilities of the members be denoted by k_i, the tensions by T_i, and the extensions by e_i ($i = 1$ to 5). The externally applied forces are denoted by F_1, F_2, in the directions shown.

The equations of force-equilibrium at the joint A are obtained by resolving all forces horizontally and vertically. The arrows in Figure 2.1(a) indicate that the tension in a rod is positive when the rod is being extended, negative when the rod is being compressed. The force diagram at the point A is therefore given by Figure 2.1(b), which leads to the following equations of equilibrium:

$$\begin{aligned} -T_1 \cos \theta_1 - T_2 \cos \theta_2 - \dots - T_5 \cos \theta_5 &= F_1, \\ +T_1 \sin \theta_1 + T_2 \sin \theta_2 + \dots + T_5 \sin \theta_5 &= F_2. \end{aligned} \tag{2.2}$$

Suppose that, when forces are applied to the framework, the point A moves by a distance d_1 horizontally and d_2 vertically, measured in the same directions as the corresponding forces F_1, F_2. Then the extensions e_i are given in terms of the d_i by the following formulae:

$$e_i = -d_1 \cos \theta_i + d_2 \sin \theta_i, \qquad i = 1, 2, \dots, 5. \tag{2.3}$$

These equations simply state that the extension of the ith member is given by adding the components obtained by resolving d_1, d_2 along the rod, taking account of sign.

Equations (2.2) give relations between internal and external forces. Equations (2.3) give relations between internal and external displacements. To complete the solution we require relations between internal forces and internal displacements. These are given by writing down Hooke's law (2.1) for each member:

$$e_i = k_i T_i, \qquad i = 1, 2, \ldots, 5. \tag{2.4}$$

We have now derived the basic equations for the problem, namely (2.2), (2.3), (2.4). These are twelve equations in the twelve unknowns T_i ($i = 1$ to 5), e_i ($i = 1$ to 5) and d_i ($i = 1, 2$).

One method of solution is to eliminate the unknown forces T_i and strains e_i, and derive simultaneous linear equations for the unknown displacements d_1, d_2. From (2.3), (2.4)

$$T_i = \frac{-d_1 \cos \theta_i + d_2 \sin \theta_i}{k_i}. \tag{2.5}$$

These values for T_i are then substituted in (2.2) to give two simultaneous equations for d_1, d_2. Equations (2.2) are, using summation signs,

$$-\sum_{i=1}^{5} T_i \cos \theta_i = F_1,$$

$$\sum_{i=1}^{5} T_i \sin \theta_i = F_2.$$

Substitution for T_i from (2.5) gives

$$\begin{aligned} a_{11}d_1 + a_{12}d_2 &= F_1, \\ a_{21}d_1 + a_{22}d_2 &= F_2, \end{aligned} \tag{2.6}$$

where

$$a_{11} = \sum_{i=1}^{5} \frac{\cos^2 \theta_i}{k_i}, \qquad a_{22} = \sum_{i=1}^{5} \frac{\sin^2 \theta_i}{k_i},$$

$$a_{12} = a_{21} = -\sum_{i=1}^{5} \frac{\cos \theta_i \sin \theta_i}{k_i}.$$

Equations (2.6) are two equations for the two unknowns d_1, d_2. When d_1, d_2 are found from these equations, the tensions in the members can be found from (2.5).

We now express these manipulations in terms of matrices. Define

$$\mathbf{t} = \begin{bmatrix} T_1 \\ T_2 \\ \vdots \\ T_5 \end{bmatrix}, \qquad \mathbf{e} = \begin{bmatrix} e_1 \\ e_2 \\ \vdots \\ e_5 \end{bmatrix}, \qquad \mathbf{f} = \begin{bmatrix} F_1 \\ F_2 \end{bmatrix}, \qquad \mathbf{d} = \begin{bmatrix} d_1 \\ d_2 \end{bmatrix},$$

$$\mathbf{A} = \begin{bmatrix} -\cos \theta_1, & -\cos \theta_2, & \ldots, & -\cos \theta_5 \\ \sin \theta_1, & \sin \theta_2, & \ldots, & \sin \theta_5 \end{bmatrix}, \tag{2.7}$$

$$\mathbf{K} = \begin{bmatrix} k_1 & 0 & \ldots & 0 \\ 0 & k_2 & \ldots & 0 \\ & & \ldots & \\ 0 & 0 & \ldots & k_5 \end{bmatrix}.$$

Then (2.2), (2.3), (2.4) become, in matrix notation,

$$\mathbf{At} = \mathbf{f}, \tag{2.8}$$

$$\mathbf{e} = \mathbf{A}^T\mathbf{d}, \tag{2.9}$$

$$\mathbf{e} = \mathbf{Kt}. \tag{2.10}$$

The matrix $\mathbf{A}^T$, which occurs in (2.9) is precisely the transpose of the matrix $\mathbf{A}$ in (2.8). This relationship did not spring to our attention when we wrote out the original equations in the longhand form (2.2), (2.3). It is a bonus which we receive merely by writing everything in matrix notation. We can use this relationship as a check that we have written down (2.2), (2.3) correctly from physical reasoning. This is useful since it is easy to confuse signs. Alternatively, if we are sure that (2.2) is correct, we need not write down (2.3) at all.

We wish to set up equations for $\mathbf{d}$. The $\mathbf{e}$ and $\mathbf{t}$ are unknown, so we eliminate these in the following way. From (2.8), (2.10), (2.9), in succession,

$$\mathbf{f} = \mathbf{At} = \mathbf{AK}^{-1}\mathbf{e} = \mathbf{AK}^{-1}\mathbf{A}^T\mathbf{d},$$

i.e.,

$$(\mathbf{AK}^{-1}\mathbf{A}^T)\mathbf{d} = \mathbf{f}. \tag{2.11}$$

These are precisely (2.6). We are of course doing nothing new here since we are merely carrying out in matrix notation the same steps that we previously performed longhand. However, the structure of the calculation is extremely clear.

The reader should appreciate that, although we have confined our attention to a simple specific example, the same procedure can be carried through for more complicated structures. We can generalize the method to deal with three-dimensional structures with many members and many connections (instead of the single connection at A in Figure 2.1). The connections can be rigid as well as pin-jointed, in which case we need to introduce moments and angular displacements. In all cases, we end up with three sets of equations analogous to (2.8)–(2.10). The individual matrices may be very complicated, but the form of the matrix equations (2.8)–(2.10) is always the same, and provides a uniform starting point for the analysis of structures, whatever the method used to actually solve the equations.

The above matrix approach to framework problems can be used in other disciplines. This is illustrated in the following two exercises, where the matrix formulation of problems in electrical networks and economics shows that the underlying mathematical equations are almost identical with those obtained for the structural problem considered above. The reader who is not concerned with this aspect can go on to Section 2.3, where some comments are made concerning the application of computers to the above structural problem.

Ex. 2.1. Consider the electrical network shown in Figure 2.2. A *branch* of the network is a resistor (which may have an electromotive force in series with it) connected to the rest of the network by precisely two terminals, at *nodes*.

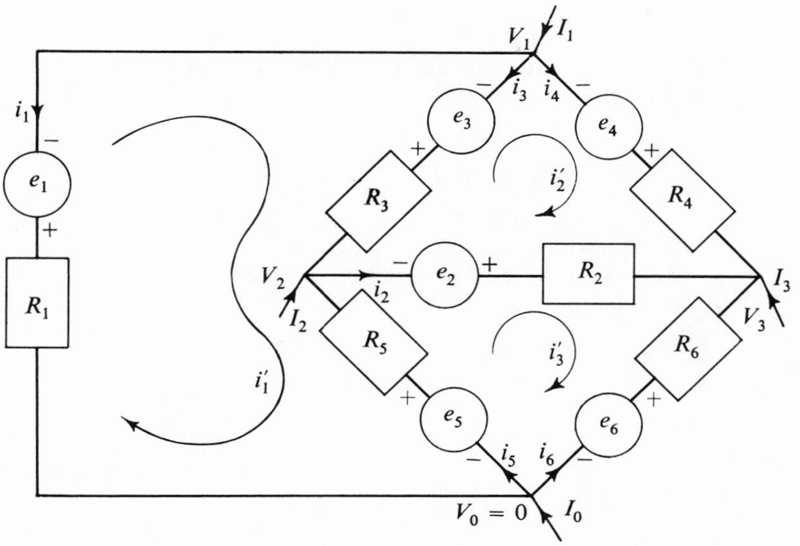

Figure 2.2 An electrical network.

Notation and sign conventions are shown in Figure 2.3. Assuming Ohm's law, we have

$$v_r = R_r i_r, \qquad r = 1, 2, \ldots, 6.$$

In matrix notation

$$\mathbf{v} = \mathbf{Ri}, \tag{2.12}$$

where

$$\mathbf{v} = \begin{bmatrix} v_1 \\ v_2 \\ \vdots \\ v_6 \end{bmatrix}, \qquad \mathbf{i} = \begin{bmatrix} i_1 \\ i_2 \\ \vdots \\ i_6 \end{bmatrix}, \qquad \mathbf{R} = \begin{bmatrix} R_1 & 0 & \ldots & 0 \\ 0 & R_2 & \ldots & 0 \\ & & \ldots & \\ 0 & 0 & \ldots & R_6 \end{bmatrix}.$$

Suppose that the nodes are numbered (arbitrarily) from 0 to 3 as in Figure 2.2, and the voltages and input currents are denoted by V_r, I_r, ($r = 0$ to 3), respectively. From Figure 2.3, the voltage across the rth branch is given by $v_r - e_r$. These voltages can also be expressed in terms of the V_r, so that we can obtain equations relating the V_r, v_r, e_r. For instance,

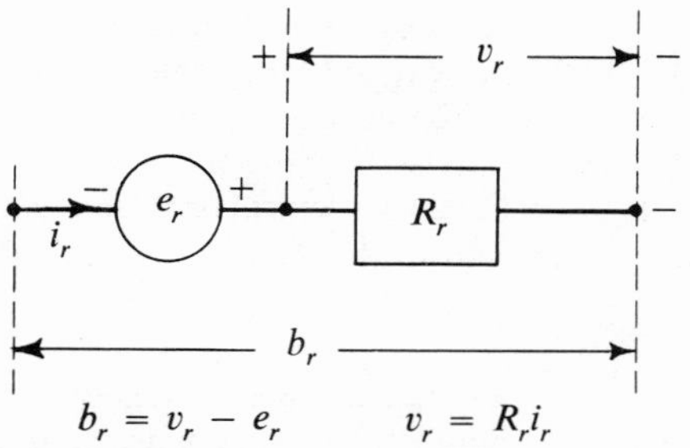

Figure 2.3 Sign conventions.

for the second branch, we obtain

$$V_2 - V_3 = v_2 - e_2.$$

Kirchhoff's current law states that the net current at each node must be zero. Thus for node 2 we see that

$$I_2 = i_2 - i_3 - i_5.$$

Only differences of the V_r are involved, and without loss of generality we can set $V_0 = 0$, and we do not need to write down an equation for I_0 at the node 0. (We say something about this later in Ex. 3.33.) By writing out the equations for all nodes and branches except for the node 0, it is left to the reader to show that

$$\mathbf{J} = \mathbf{A}\mathbf{i} \tag{2.13}$$

$$\mathbf{A}^T\mathbf{V} = \mathbf{v} - \mathbf{e}, \tag{2.14}$$

where

$$\mathbf{V} = \begin{bmatrix} V_1 \\ V_2 \\ V_3 \end{bmatrix}, \quad \mathbf{J} = \begin{bmatrix} I_1 \\ I_2 \\ I_3 \end{bmatrix}, \quad \mathbf{A} = \begin{bmatrix} 1 & 0 & 1 & 1 & 0 & 0 \\ 0 & 1 & -1 & 0 & -1 & 0 \\ 0 & -1 & 0 & -1 & 0 & -1 \end{bmatrix},$$

and $\mathbf{e}$ is a 6×1 matrix whose rth element is e_r.

If we assume that all the I_r are known, and all the V_r unknown, we obtain a set of equations for $\mathbf{V}$ by eliminating $\mathbf{i}$, $\mathbf{v}$ from (2.12)–(2.14). This gives

$$(\mathbf{A}\mathbf{R}^{-1}\mathbf{A}^T)\mathbf{V} = \mathbf{J} - \mathbf{A}\mathbf{R}^{-1}\mathbf{e}. \tag{2.15}$$

For simplicity assume that $\mathbf{J} = \mathbf{0}$ and that all the e_i are zero except e_1. The reader can check that for the network in Figure 2.2, Equation (21.5) gives

$$\begin{bmatrix} Y_1 + Y_3 + Y_4 & -Y_3 & -Y_4 \\ -Y_3 & Y_2 + Y_3 + Y_5 & -Y_2 \\ -Y_4 & -Y_2 & Y_2 + Y_4 + Y_6 \end{bmatrix} \begin{bmatrix} V_1 \\ V_2 \\ V_3 \end{bmatrix} = -\begin{bmatrix} Y_1 e_1 \\ 0 \\ 0 \end{bmatrix} \tag{2.16}$$

where $Y_i = 1/R_i$. These equations could of course be obtained by applying Kirchhoff's current law at each of the nodes 1, 2, 3. The advantages of the present procedure appear only in much more complicated examples.

Because of the matrix formulation, we see that Equations (2.12)–(2.15) for the electrical problem are analogous to (2.10), (2.8), (2.9), (2.11), respectively, for the structural problem. We can, in fact, make the identifications shown in Table 2.1 below.

Ex. 2.2. Suppose that goods are being produced and consumed in four towns, numbered 1 to 4, connected by six roads 1 to 6, as illustrated diagrammatically in Figure 2.4. (Compare Figure 2.2.) We arbitrarily assign directions along each of the roads as shown, for example, by the arrows in Figure 2.4. We assume that goods flow along branch r at a rate f_r per unit time; and that the excess of goods being produced in town s over goods consumed in s, per unit time, is F_s. If no goods are destroyed, F_s must equal the flow of goods leaving along the roads; e.g., for town 2,

$$F_2 = f_2 - f_3 - f_5.$$

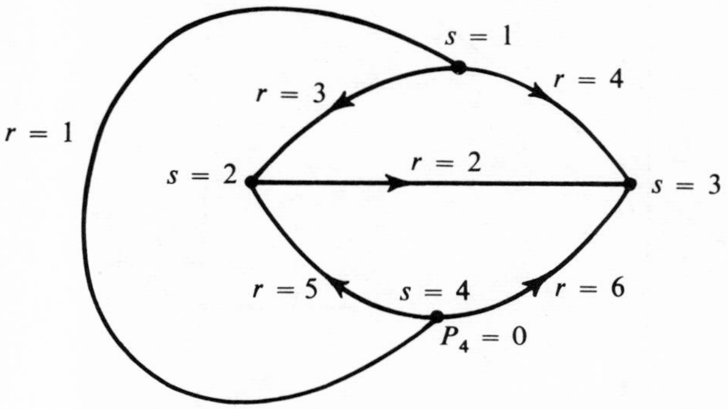

Figure 2.4 A transportation problem.

Suppose that the price of a unit amount of goods at town s is P_s. Since only price differentials will be important, we can choose the price at one of the towns (namely 4 in Figure 2.4) to be zero, and measure all prices relative to this zero level. (Compare the fact that we set $V = 0$ at one of the nodes in Figure 2.2.) Denote the price difference between the two towns at the ends of branch r by p_r. Relations between P_s and p_r can be written down directly. Thus, for branch 2,

$$P_2 - P_3 = p_2.$$

It is left to the reader to show that

$$\mathbf{F} = \mathbf{Af}, \tag{2.17}$$

$$\mathbf{p} = \mathbf{A}^T\mathbf{P}, \tag{2.18}$$

where **A** is precisely the matrix introduced in the previous exercise, and

$$\mathbf{F} = \begin{bmatrix} F_1 \\ F_2 \\ F_3 \end{bmatrix}, \quad \mathbf{f} = \begin{bmatrix} f_1 \\ f_2 \\ \vdots \\ f_6 \end{bmatrix}, \quad \mathbf{P} = \begin{bmatrix} P_1 \\ P_2 \\ P_3 \end{bmatrix}, \quad \mathbf{p} = \begin{bmatrix} p_1 \\ p_2 \\ \vdots \\ p_6 \end{bmatrix}.$$

If the flow in each branch is proportional to the price difference across the branch, we have

$$\mathbf{p} = \mathbf{D}\mathbf{f}, \tag{2.19}$$

where **D** is a diagonal matrix. However, in transportation problems it seldom happens that direct proportionality occurs. One possibility is shown in Figure 2.5(b), namely that flow occurs when the price difference is greater than a

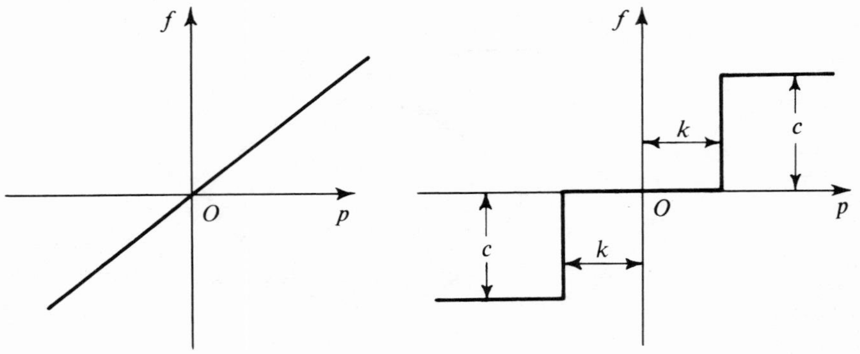

(a) Linear (b) Nonlinear

Figure 2.5 Price-flow relations for transportation problem.

minimum value corresponding to the cost of transporting a unit amount of goods along the route, and when this is true a constant amount of flow occurs. In general, therefore, the relation (2.19) should be replaced by

$$p_r = h_r(f_r), \qquad r = 1 \text{ to } 6,$$

or, symbolically,

$$\mathbf{p} = h(\mathbf{f}). \tag{2.20}$$

Table 2.1

	Electrical network	Economics (transportation)	Mechanical structure
Branch	Voltage difference **v** Current (branch) **i**	Price difference **p** Flow (branch) **f**	Strain **e** Stress (tension) **t**
Node	Voltage **V** Current **J**	Price **P** Net flow **F**	Displacement **d** Force **f**
	$\mathbf{Ai} = \mathbf{J}$ $\mathbf{v} = \mathbf{A}^T\mathbf{V}$	$\mathbf{Af} = \mathbf{F}$ $\mathbf{p} = \mathbf{A}^T\mathbf{P}$	$\mathbf{At} = \mathbf{f}$ $\mathbf{e} = \mathbf{A}^T\mathbf{d}$
	$\mathbf{v} = h(\mathbf{i})$	$\mathbf{p} = h(\mathbf{f})$	$\mathbf{e} = h(\mathbf{t})$
Linear case	Resistance **R** $\mathbf{v} = \mathbf{Ri}$	(Name?) **D** $\mathbf{p} = \mathbf{Df}$	Flexibility **K** $\mathbf{e} = \mathbf{Kt}$

Equations (2.17), (2.18), (2.19) are analogous to (2.8), (2.9), (2.10), respectively. The analogy between the quantities occurring in the electrical, mechanical, and economics problems is summarized in Table 2.1. If the stress-strain or the voltage-current relations are nonlinear, then equations corresponding to (2.20) can be introduced. Note however that the forms of the remaining two basic equations relating branch and node quantities remain unchanged. In particular, they are always linear, and involve a matrix **A** and its transpose.

Although this brief introduction to the matrix treatment of networks is by no means complete (see Ex. 2.14), perhaps enough has been said to give the reader some insight into the convenience and power of the matrix approach.

2.3 The Application of Digital Computers to Framework Calculations

We remind the reader of some elementary facts concerning automatic computers. A digital computer is a machine that can be instructed or *programmed* to carry out a sequence of numerical calculations. For our purposes it will be sufficient to visualize that a computer consists of the following components, interconnected as in Figure 2.6:

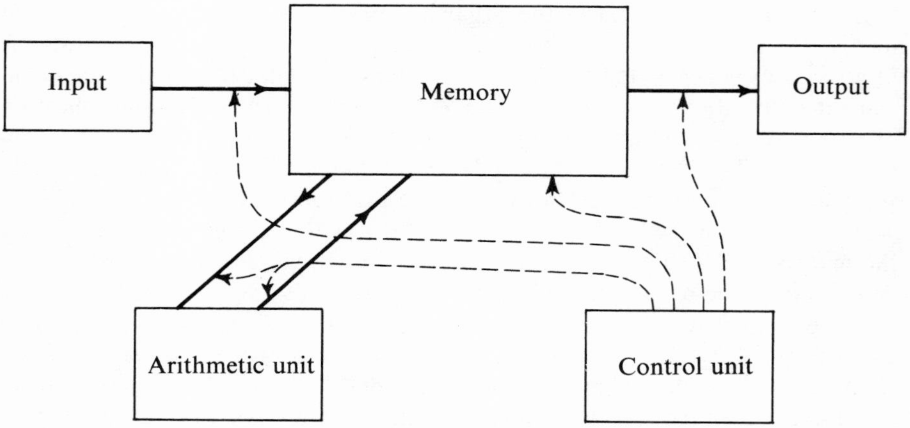

Figure 2.6 The organization of a digital computer.

(a) A *memory* or store in which numbers and instructions can be stored and from which any number can be produced at will.

(b) An *input* mechanism for transferring instructions and initial data for a problem from the outside world into the memory.

(c) An *output* mechanism for transferring information from the memory on to an output sheet.

(d) An *arithmetic unit* for carrying out simple basic arithmetical operations such as addition, subtraction, multiplication, division.

(e) A *control unit* that organizes the calculations, i.e., arranges for the input and output of information and the execution of arithmetic operations in the correct sequence as specified by the instructions.

In order to perform a calculation, the computer must be provided with a sequence of instructions called a *program*. When solving a problem, the computer starts by storing the complete program in its memory. It then proceeds to obey the instructions in a sequence determined by the program. It is clear that if we wish to make the machine form the product

$$ab + cd + ef + gh,$$

it would be laborious to have to tell the machine "Multiply a by b, c by d, e by f, g by h, and add the products." It is much easier to use suffix notation, labelling the numbers as a_i, b_i, ($i = 1$ to 4) in an obvious way, and say "Form the sum of the products a_ib_i ($i = 1$ to 4)." Similarly, if we are dealing with two-dimensional arrays of numbers, it is convenient to arrange that these are rectangular. The machine can manipulate these arrays by systematic operations involving suffixes which run over values lying within fixed limits. This is essentially the reason why matrices are indispensable when programming electronic computers.

In order to show clearly the organization of the sequence of operations involved in a calculation, it is often convenient to draw a *flow-chart*, consisting of a series of boxes connected by directed lines. In order to explain some convenient conventions, consider Figure 2.7, which describes the multiplication of two matrices. The beginning and end are clearly indicated by circles containing the words "start" and "stop." The rectangular assertion boxes contain statements that certain operations are to be performed before leaving the box. The first assertion box, following "start", tells us that the given input data are the matrices **A**, **B**. The final assertion box, preceding "stop", tells us that the end result of the calculation **AB** is **S**. The statement "$i = 1$" means "Set the variable i equal to 1." The statement "$i = i + 1$" means "Set the variable i equal to $i + 1$," i.e., "Replace i by $i + 1$." This use of the "$=$" sign in flow-charts is in some ways equivalent to the use of "$=$" in ordinary mathematical equations, but there are two points to be noted. Only one symbol can appear to the left of an "$=$" sign. Also all symbols to the right of the "$=$" sign must have been defined previously in the flow-chart, either as part of the input data, or on the left of an "$=$" sign. Oval *test-boxes* contain questions to which there are two or more answers. The flow-chart in Figure 2.7 should now be self-explanatory.

We now make some remarks concerning the problem of calculating frameworks by computer. Before automatic computers were available, and all calculations had to be performed by hand, it was natural that emphasis should be placed on methods that minimize the amount of calculation involved. This

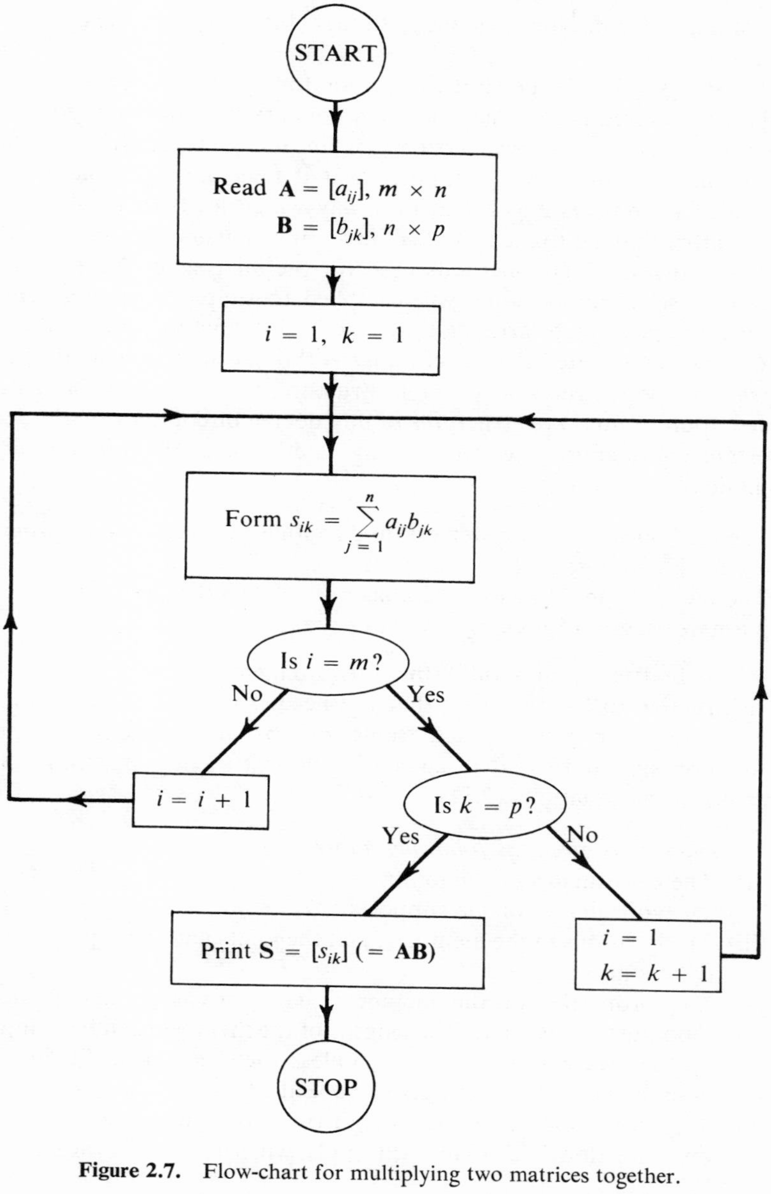

Figure 2.7. Flow-chart for multiplying two matrices together.

inevitably meant that special methods were invented for special types of problems. Many of the older textbooks are little more than collections of tricks for the easy solution of special types of framework. In particular, since the solution of linear simultaneous equations is laborious, many of these special methods were devised specifically to avoid the need for the formulation and solution of sets of equations, as such, though this may not have been the explicit motivation.

If calculations are to be performed by an automatic computer, the amount of calculation required is to some extent a secondary consideration. In particular, computers can easily solve systems of linear equations. In fact, this is such a routine operation on a computer that it may be preferable to use a method which formulates a problem in a way which leads to a set of linear equations, rather than go to the trouble of inventing an ingenious method which avoids these equations. The methods used for the analysis of frameworks by computer may seem cumbersome when applied to simple structures. On the other hand, it is possible to arrange that exactly the same methods will apply, no matter how complicated the structure is. Although the formulae in the last section were developed for a very simple structure, they apply (if the matrices are defined appropriately) to structures of any degree of complexity.

Important considerations when deciding whether a method is suitable for an automatic computer are:

(a) The method should be systematic and routine, so that it can be programmed easily for a computer.

(b) The method should be as general as possible, so that we do not need to make up a new program for each new framework.

Matrix methods admirably fulfill these requirements.

It is instructive to list the steps that are needed in order to calculate the strains and stresses in a pin-jointed framework by an automatic computer, using a method similar to that discussed in the last section, resulting in the simultaneous linear equations (2.11):

(a) *The machine is given the following information:*
- (i) The coordinates of the joints.
- (ii) The coordinates of the supports.
- (iii) The locations of the members, i.e., the joints and the supports which they connect.
- (iv) The properties of the members, e.g., cross-sectional areas and modulus of elasticity. The lengths of the members can be computed by the machine from (i)–(iii), unless there is lack of fit, in which case the lack of fit must also be specified.
- (v) The nature of the supports, e.g., rigid, or constrained to move in one direction, etc. (This will apply when more general structures

are considered, in which case the matrix equations may be of more complicated form.)

(vi) The external forces.

(b) *The machine will then compute:*

(i) The stiffness coefficients of the members and hence the matrix $\mathbf{K}^{-1}$ of stiffness coefficients.

(ii) The matrix $\mathbf{A}$, connecting node and branch quantities.

(c) *The machine then multiplies matrices* to form $\mathbf{AK}^{-1}\mathbf{A}^T$, and hence obtains the simultaneous linear equations (2.11) for the problem.

(d) *The machine solves these equations.*

(e) *The machine evaluates the stresses and deformations of individual members, and any other required information.*

(f) *The end results are printed out.*

In order to find the stresses and strains in a given structure, the engineer need concern himself only with step (a). However two points should be noted:

(a) Since the engineer will not see the details of the computations performed in the computer, checks should be incorporated to ensure that the numerical procedures are as accurate as required, and that, in particular, no numerical errors creep in due to ill-conditioning and other numerical troubles. (Such matters are considered later, for example, in Chapter 8.)

(b) It should be emphasized that the above considerations are only a small part of the overall design problem with which the engineer is faced. There is no reason why the computer should not take over the problem of deciding the best dimensions of the members, and so on, but this is a different problem. The "matrix + computer" approach eliminates the need to spend time and effort on routine calculations, thus giving the designer more time, freedom, and opportunity to concentrate on optimization of the design; this is, after all, the crux of the problem.

2.4 The Method of Least Squares

In the applied sciences, we try to express the relationship between variable quantities by means of mathematical expressions. As an example, if a body is travelling with constant velocity v, the relation between the time t and the position reached by the body, y, is given by the linear equation

$$y = \alpha + vt. \tag{2.21}$$

Suppose that we measure y at various times t and obtain the following figures:

t	0	3	5	8	10
y	2	5	6	9	11

These are plotted in Figure 2.8 where it is seen that the points lie, approximately, on a straight line. There are two reasons why the points may not lie exactly on a straight line:

(a) Errors of measurement.
(b) The velocity may not be constant, so that (2.21) may not be true.

We shall ignore this second possibility, i.e., we shall assume that if y and t could be measured exactly, then the relation between y and t would be given by (2.21). Since measurements are subject to experimental error, equation (2.21) is not satisfied exactly by the measured values of y and t, and it is not possible to deduce exact values of α and v in (2.21) from the data. The problem which we now wish to consider is how to deduce the "best possible" values of α, v or, in other words, how to fit the "best" straight line to the data plotted in Figure 2.8.

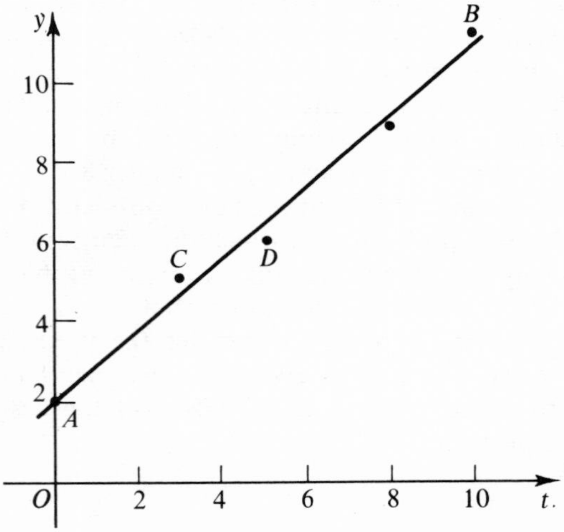

Figure 2.8 Straight-line fitting of data.

If we denote the value of y measured at a time $t = t_i$ by y_i, then the relation between y_i and t_i can be written as [compare (2.21)]

$$y_i = \alpha + vt_i + r_i, \tag{2.22}$$

where r_i is a *residual* resulting from errors in measurement. The criterion we shall use to find the unknown parameters α, v is that we minimize the sum of squares of the residuals (hence the term "least squares"):

$$S = \sum_{i=1}^{m} r_i^2 = \sum_{i=1}^{m} (y_i - \alpha - vt_i)^2, \tag{2.23}$$

where m denotes the total number of observations. The residuals r_i are, geometrically, the distances between the points and the line $y = \alpha + vt$, measured parallel to the y-axis in Figure 2.8. It is intuitively reasonable that we should minimize the sum of squares to find the "best" straight line, since this ensures that the line will pass, in some sense, through the middle of the points.

Minimization of (2.23) with respect to α and v gives, as necessary conditions,

$$\left.\begin{aligned}\frac{\partial S}{\partial \alpha} &= -2\sum_{i=1}^{m}(y_i - \alpha - vt_i) = 0,\\ \frac{\partial S}{\partial v} &= -2\sum_{i=1}^{m} t_i(y_i - \alpha - vt_i) = 0.\end{aligned}\right\} \tag{2.24}$$

On rearranging, these give two equations in the two unknowns α, v,

$$\left.\begin{aligned}p_{11}\alpha + p_{12}v &= q_1,\\ p_{21}\alpha + p_{22}v &= q_2,\end{aligned}\right\} \tag{2.25}$$

where

$$\left.\begin{aligned}&p_{11} = m, \qquad p_{12} = p_{21} = \sum_{i=1}^{m} t_i,\\ &p_{22} = \sum_{i=1}^{m} t_i^2, \qquad q_1 = \sum_{i=1}^{m} y_i, \qquad q_2 = \sum_{i=1}^{m} t_i y_i.\end{aligned}\right\} \tag{2.26}$$

We now express the above analysis in matrix notation. Equation (2.22) can be written

$$\mathbf{y} = \mathbf{A}\mathbf{x} + \mathbf{r}, \tag{2.27}$$

where

$$\mathbf{y} = \begin{bmatrix} y_1 \\ y_2 \\ \vdots \\ y_m \end{bmatrix}, \quad \mathbf{A} = \begin{bmatrix} 1 & t_1 \\ 1 & t_2 \\ \vdots & \vdots \\ 1 & t_m \end{bmatrix}, \quad \mathbf{x} = \begin{bmatrix} \alpha \\ v \end{bmatrix}, \quad \mathbf{r} = \begin{bmatrix} r_1 \\ r_2 \\ \vdots \\ r_m \end{bmatrix}.$$

In this notation, (2.23) is:

$$S = \mathbf{r}^T\mathbf{r} = (\mathbf{y} - \mathbf{A}\mathbf{x})^T(\mathbf{y} - \mathbf{A}\mathbf{x}). \tag{2.28}$$

The definitions (2.26) become

$$\begin{bmatrix} p_{11} & p_{12} \\ p_{21} & p_{22} \end{bmatrix} = \mathbf{A}^T\mathbf{A}, \qquad \begin{bmatrix} q_1 \\ q_2 \end{bmatrix} = \mathbf{A}^T\mathbf{y}. \tag{2.29}$$

Equations (2.25) are then

$$\mathbf{A}^T\mathbf{A}\mathbf{x} = \mathbf{A}^T\mathbf{y}.$$

Summarizing the situation, the original equations (2.27) are usually written as simply

$$\mathbf{A}\mathbf{x} = \mathbf{y}, \qquad (\mathbf{y}\text{ known}). \tag{2.30}$$

where the error term $\mathbf{r}$ is now omitted. These are a set of m equations in two unknowns, and it will not in general be possible to find $\mathbf{x}$ such that all the equations will be satisfied. They are in general an inconsistent set of equations.

The conclusion of the above analysis is that the least squares solution of this set is given by solving

$$\mathbf{A}^T\mathbf{A}\mathbf{x} = \mathbf{A}^T\mathbf{y}, \tag{2.31}$$

which is a set of two equations in two unknowns. Formally, (2.31) is obtained by premultiplying (2.30) by $\mathbf{A}^T$.

For the numbers in the example considered at the beginning of this section, we find that (2.31) becomes

$$\begin{bmatrix} 5 & 26 \\ 26 & 198 \end{bmatrix} \begin{bmatrix} \alpha \\ v \end{bmatrix} = \begin{bmatrix} 33 \\ 227 \end{bmatrix}. \tag{2.32}$$

These give $\alpha = 2.01$, $v = 0.88$. The corresponding line is drawn in Figure 2.8.

Suppose that instead of defining S by (2.23) we set

$$S = \sum_{i=1}^{m} w_i r_i^2, \tag{2.33}$$

where the w_i are given *weighting factors*. (The reason for this terminology will appear presently.) A repetition of the preceding analysis shows that for α and v we obtain linear equations of the same form as before, namely (2.25), where now

$$p_{11} = \sum_{i=1}^{m} w_i, \qquad p_{12} = p_{21} = \sum_{i=1}^{m} w_i t_i, \qquad \text{etc.}$$

Hence, if, for any value of i, say $i = k$, the factor w_k is large, the contribution of the terms $i = k$ in the sums defining the p_{rs} and q_s will also be large, and if w_k is small, the corresponding contributions will be small. One way of looking at this is to say that the kth equation is given more or less weight, depending on whether w_k is large or small, and this is the reason for the term weighting factor. There are various reasons for giving some equations greater weights than others; for example, we may know that the measurements in some equations are more accurate than in others. If the p_{rs}, q_s are written out in detail and the results are expressed in matrix notation, it will be found that the equation analogous to (2.31) for the least squares solution of $\mathbf{A}\mathbf{x} = \mathbf{y}$ is

$$\mathbf{A}^T\mathbf{W}\mathbf{A}\mathbf{x} = \mathbf{A}^T\mathbf{W}\mathbf{y}, \tag{2.34}$$

where $\mathbf{W}$ is a diagonal matrix of weighting factors:

$$\mathbf{W} = \begin{bmatrix} w_1 & 0 & \dots & 0 \\ 0 & w_2 & \dots & 0 \\ & & \dots & \\ 0 & 0 & \dots & w_m \end{bmatrix}.$$

The above analysis is readily generalized to the case where the dependent variable y depends on n independent variables $t^{(1)}, t^{(2)}, \dots, t^{(n)}$, where we use an upper suffix to denote different variables. Equation (2.21) becomes

$$y = x_0 + x_1 t^{(1)} + x_2 t^{(2)} + \dots + x_n t^{(n)},$$

where, instead of α, v in (2.21) we now have $n + 1$ unknown parameters x_0, $x_1, \ldots x_n$. Suppose that we have m different measurements of y, each corresponding to a different set of values of the $t^{(j)}$, so that, instead of (2.22) we have

$$y_i = x_0 + x_1 t_i^{(1)} + x_2 t_i^{(2)} + \ldots + x_n t_i^{(n)} + r_i,$$

for $i = 1, 2, \ldots, m$. For simplicity we introduce the notation $t_i^{(j)} = a_{ij}$, and then this set of equations can be written in exactly the same form as (2.27), namely

$$\mathbf{y} = \mathbf{A}\mathbf{x} + \mathbf{r},$$

where $\mathbf{r}$ is the same as before, but

$$\mathbf{x} = \begin{bmatrix} x_0 \\ x_1 \\ \vdots \\ x_n \end{bmatrix}, \qquad \mathbf{A} = \begin{bmatrix} 1 & a_{11} & \ldots & a_{1n} \\ 1 & a_{21} & \ldots & a_{2n} \\ & & \ldots & \\ 1 & a_{m1} & \ldots & a_{mn} \end{bmatrix}. \tag{2.35}$$

The reader can generalize the previous results, step by step. The sum of squares of residuals S is defined, as before, by

$$S = (\mathbf{y} - \mathbf{A}\mathbf{x})^T(\mathbf{y} - \mathbf{A}\mathbf{x}). \tag{2.36}$$

Instead of (2.24) we have

$$\frac{\partial S}{\partial x_k} = 0, \qquad k = 0, 1, 2, \ldots, n. \tag{2.37}$$

This gives a set of $n + 1$ equations in $n + 1$ unknowns. In matrix notation the final set of equations is identical with (2.31) in form, namely

$$\mathbf{A}^T\mathbf{A}\mathbf{x} = \mathbf{A}^T\mathbf{y}. \tag{2.38}$$

Similarly, on introducing weighting factors, we obtain precisely (2.34) where now of course $\mathbf{A}$ is defined in (2.35). This illustrates one of the virtues of matrix notation, that the appearance of the final expressions does not depend on the numbers of variables involved, i.e., the complexity of the problem.

We now discuss an application of the above results to the problem of deducing the positions of stars from measurements of the relative coordinates of their images on photographic plates. The position of a star is usually specified by giving its angular spherical coordinates, at a certain instant of time, with reference to a given system of coordinates, for instance, a system with its origin at the center of the earth and fixed relative to the distant stars. We need not go into the technical details, but it will be convenient to use the technical terms "right ascension" and "declination" for the coordinates specifying the position of a star in the sky.

Suppose that an arbitrary rectangular coordinate system is fixed on the plate. (This can be done to suit the convenience of the investigator. Again details do not concern us here.) Let the coordinates of a star on the plate, relative to this coordinate system, be denoted by (x, y).

The basic assumption on which the analysis is based is that the relationship between the measured coordinates (x, y) of a star and its right ascension α and declination δ is given to a sufficient degree of accuracy by power series of the form

$$\left.\begin{aligned} \alpha &= u_1 + u_2x + u_3y + u_4x^2 + u_5xy + \dots, \\ \delta &= v_1 + v_2x + v_3y + v_4x^2 + v_5xy + \dots, \end{aligned}\right\} \tag{2.39}$$

where the u_i, v_i are (unknown) constants for any given photograph, known as the *plate constants.* The object of the analysis that follows is to find these plate constants u_i, v_i, using the fact that we can measure the positions x, y on the photograph for certain standard or catalog stars for which we know, independently, estimates of α, δ. We assume that it will be sufficiently accurate to retain only p terms in each of the infinite series given in (2.39). In matrix notation, we introduce

$$\mathbf{u} = \begin{bmatrix} u_1 \\ u_2 \\ \vdots \\ u_p \end{bmatrix}, \qquad \mathbf{v} = \begin{bmatrix} v_1 \\ v_2 \\ \vdots \\ v_p \end{bmatrix},$$

$$\mathbf{x} = [1, x, y, x^2, xy, \dots].$$

Then (2.39) can be written:

$$\begin{bmatrix} \alpha \\ \delta \end{bmatrix} = \begin{bmatrix} \mathbf{x} & \mathbf{0} \\ \mathbf{0} & \mathbf{x} \end{bmatrix} \begin{bmatrix} \mathbf{u} \\ \mathbf{v} \end{bmatrix}. \tag{2.40}$$

Now suppose that there are n stars with right ascensions α_i and declinations δ_i, and that the coordinates of these stars on the photographic plate are given by (x_i, y_i). Introduce the notation

$$\mathbf{y}_i = \begin{bmatrix} \alpha_i \\ \delta_i \end{bmatrix}, \qquad \mathbf{h}_i = \begin{bmatrix} \mathbf{x}_i & \mathbf{0} \\ \mathbf{0} & \mathbf{x}_i \end{bmatrix}, \qquad \mathbf{t} = \begin{bmatrix} \mathbf{u} \\ \mathbf{v} \end{bmatrix},$$

where $\mathbf{x}_i$ denotes $\mathbf{x}$ with (x, y) replaced by (x_i, y_i). Equation (2.40) then gives

$$\mathbf{y}_i = \mathbf{h}_i\mathbf{t}; \qquad i = 1 \text{ to } n. \tag{2.41}$$

Note that $\mathbf{t}$ is independent of i. These equations represent $2n$ relations between $2n + 2p$ unknowns $\mathbf{y}_i$, $\mathbf{t}$ (i.e., α_i, δ_i, u_i, v_i).

Suppose now that the values of α_i, δ_i are known independently, for example, from star catalogs. If these were known exactly, say

$$\begin{bmatrix} \alpha_i \\ \delta_i \end{bmatrix} = \mathbf{k}_i,$$

then we should merely substitute these in (2.41) in place of $\mathbf{y}_i$:

$$\mathbf{h}_i\mathbf{t} = \mathbf{k}_i, \qquad i = 1 \text{ to } n. \tag{2.42}$$

These are a system of $2n$ equations in $2p$ unknowns. If we choose $n = p$, then these can be solved directly. If we choose $n > p$, then we shall in general have a set of inconsistent equations, since the $\mathbf{h}_i$ depend on the (x_i, y_i) which are subject to measurement errors, and in any case the relation (2.40) is approximate. These inconsistent equations must be solved by least squares.

However, the estimates (e.g., catalog values) of $\mathbf{y}_i$ are also subject to error, and we need to consider the system

$$\left.\begin{aligned} \mathbf{y}_i &= \mathbf{h}_i\mathbf{t}, \qquad i = 1 \text{ to } n, \\ \mathbf{y}_i &= \mathbf{k}_i, \qquad i = 1 \text{ to } n. \end{aligned}\right\} \tag{2.43}$$

These are $4n$ equations in $2n + 2p$ unknowns. If we choose $n > p$, there are more equations than unknowns, and the system must be solved by least squares. In partitioned matrix form, (2.43) are

$$\begin{bmatrix} \mathbf{I} & \mathbf{0} \\ \mathbf{I} & -\mathbf{B} \end{bmatrix} \begin{bmatrix} \mathbf{y} \\ \mathbf{t} \end{bmatrix} = \begin{bmatrix} \mathbf{k} \\ \mathbf{0} \end{bmatrix},$$

where we have introduced

$$\mathbf{y} = \begin{bmatrix} \mathbf{y}_1 \\ \mathbf{y}_2 \\ \vdots \\ \mathbf{y}_n \end{bmatrix}, \qquad \mathbf{k} = \begin{bmatrix} \mathbf{k}_1 \\ \mathbf{k}_2 \\ \vdots \\ \mathbf{k}_n \end{bmatrix}, \qquad \mathbf{B} = \begin{bmatrix} \mathbf{h}_1 & \mathbf{0} & \cdots & \mathbf{0} \\ \mathbf{0} & \mathbf{h}_2 & \cdots & \mathbf{0} \\ & & \cdots & \\ \mathbf{0} & \mathbf{0} & \cdots & \mathbf{h}_n \end{bmatrix}.$$

On introducing a weighting matrix

$$\mathbf{W} = \begin{bmatrix} \mathbf{W}_1 & \mathbf{0} \\ \mathbf{0} & \mathbf{W}_2 \end{bmatrix},$$

where $\mathbf{W}_1$ and $\mathbf{W}_2$ are diagonal matrices, the procedure leading from (2.30) to (2.34) gives

$$\begin{bmatrix} \mathbf{I} & \mathbf{I} \\ \mathbf{0} & -\mathbf{B}^T \end{bmatrix} \begin{bmatrix} \mathbf{W}_1 & \mathbf{0} \\ \mathbf{0} & \mathbf{W}_2 \end{bmatrix} \begin{bmatrix} \mathbf{I} & \mathbf{0} \\ \mathbf{I} & -\mathbf{B} \end{bmatrix} \begin{bmatrix} \mathbf{y} \\ \mathbf{t} \end{bmatrix} = \begin{bmatrix} \mathbf{W}_1\mathbf{k} \\ \mathbf{0} \end{bmatrix}.$$

On multiplying out, we find the following system of equations for $\mathbf{y}$, $\mathbf{t}$:

$$(\mathbf{W}_1 + \mathbf{W}_2)\mathbf{y} - \mathbf{W}_2\mathbf{B}\mathbf{t} = \mathbf{W}_1\mathbf{k},$$

$$-\mathbf{B}^T\mathbf{W}_2\mathbf{y} + \mathbf{B}^T\mathbf{W}_2\mathbf{B}\mathbf{t} = \mathbf{0}.$$

The matrix $\mathbf{W}_1 + \mathbf{W}_2$ is diagonal and nonsingular so that it can be inverted. On solving the first equation for $\mathbf{y}$ and substituting in the second, we see that

$$\mathbf{B}^T\mathbf{D}\mathbf{B}\mathbf{t} = \mathbf{B}^T\mathbf{D}\mathbf{k}, \tag{2.44}$$

where $\mathbf{D}$ is a simple diagonal matrix,

$$\mathbf{D} = \mathbf{W}_1\mathbf{W}_2(\mathbf{W}_1 + \mathbf{W}_2)^{-1}.$$

This means that t can be found by solving a set of $2p$ equations in $2p$ unknowns, namely (2.44). We have achieved our objective, which was to find estimates for the unknown plate constants $\mathbf{u}$, $\mathbf{v}$ (i.e., $\mathbf{t}$) from known values of α_i, δ_i for certain standard or catalog stars.

Ex. 2.3. Clarify the implicit assumptions that have been made in the derivation of (2.25) for the straight-line fitting of data y_i measured at times t_i. In particular, discuss the relevance of the following assumptions:

(a) If a measurement were to be made, for a given value of t, a large number of times, the average error would be zero.

(b) Measurements made at various values of t have the same accuracy (in statistical language, they have a *common variance*).

(c) Measurements made at various times are independent.

(d) The measurements are made at exactly the times stated, i.e., the error in the measurement of the time t is negligible.

Ex. 2.4. Verify the numerical results (2.32).

Ex. 2.5. If $\mathbf{x}$ is a $p \times 1$ vector with elements x_i and u is a scalar quantity, we define the following notation:

$$\frac{\partial u}{\partial \mathbf{x}} = \left[\frac{\partial u}{\partial x_i}\right],$$

where this is a $p \times 1$ vector. Show that

(a) If $u = \mathbf{y}^T\mathbf{x}$ where $\mathbf{y}$ is a $p \times 1$ vector, then

$$\frac{\partial u}{\partial \mathbf{x}} = \mathbf{y}.$$

(b) If $\mathbf{A}$ is a $p \times p$ symmetrical matrix and $u = \mathbf{x}^T\mathbf{A}\mathbf{x}$, then

$$\frac{\partial u}{\partial \mathbf{x}} = 2\mathbf{A}\mathbf{x}.$$

The condition (2.37) for minimizing S is, in the present notation, $\partial S/\partial \mathbf{x} = \mathbf{0}$. By using (a) and (b), perform this differentiation directly on the expression (2.36) for S, and hence deduce the basic equation (2.38).

2.5 A Markov Chain Example

We illustrate the idea of a Markov chain by considering the following simple example. Three dairies X, Y, Z supply all the milk consumed in a certain town. Over a given period, some consumers will switch from one supplier to another for various reasons, e.g., advertising, cost, convenience, dissatisfaction, and so on. We wish to analyze the movement of customers from one dairy to another, assuming that constant fractions of consumers switch from any one dairy to any other dairy each month.

Suppose that on, say, December 31, the dairies X, Y, Z have fractions x_0, y_0, z_0 of the total market, and that the corresponding fractions on January 31 are x_1, y_1, z_1. Since X, Y, Z are the only suppliers, we must have

$$\left.\begin{aligned} x_0 + y_0 + z_0 &= 1, \\ x_1 + y_1 + z_1 &= 1. \end{aligned}\right\} \tag{2.45}$$

Suppose that in January dairy X retains a fraction a_{11} of his own customers, and attracts a fraction a_{12} of Y's customers and a_{13} of Z's. On the assumption that the overall number of customers in the town, say N, does not change during the month, the total number that X has on January 31 must equal the number he retains plus the numbers he attracts from Y and Z:

$$(x_1N) = a_{11}(x_0N) + a_{12}(y_0N) + a_{13}(z_0N),$$

or

$$x_1 = a_{11}x_0 + a_{12}y_0 + a_{13}z_0.$$

Similarly,

$$y_1 = a_{21}x_0 + a_{22}y_0 + a_{23}z_0,$$

$$z_1 = a_{31}x_0 + a_{32}y_0 + a_{33}z_0,$$

where, if numbers 1, 2, 3 refer to dairies X, Y, Z, respectively,

$$a_{ii} = \text{fraction of } i\text{'s customers retained by } i,$$

$$a_{ij} = \text{fraction of } j\text{'s customers that switch to } i \ (i \neq j).$$

In matrix notation these are simply

$$\mathbf{x}_1 = \mathbf{A}\mathbf{x}_0, \tag{2.46}$$

where $\mathbf{A} = [a_{ij}]$ and

$$\mathbf{x}_r = \begin{bmatrix} x_r \\ y_r \\ z_r \end{bmatrix}, \qquad r = 0, 1. \tag{2.47}$$

The elements of $\mathbf{A}$ have certain properties that follow directly from their definition:

(a) Obviously the a_{ij} cannot be negative:

$$a_{ij} \geq 0, \qquad (\text{all } i, j). \tag{2.48}$$

(b) Obviously the a_{ij} cannot be greater than unity:

$$a_{ij} \leq 1, \qquad (\text{all } i, j). \tag{2.49}$$

(c) Of the customers that X has on December 31, fractions a_{11} stay with X, a_{21} move to Y, and a_{31} move to Z. Since we have made the basic assumption that all of X's customers are still supplied by X, Y, or Z, this means that the sum of these fractions is unity:

$$a_{11} + a_{21} + a_{31} = 1.$$

Similarly, the sum of the elements in each column of $\mathbf{A}$ is unity:

$$\sum_{i=1}^{3} a_{ij} = 1, \qquad j = 1, 2, 3. \tag{2.50}$$

The matrix $\mathbf{A}$ is known as a *transition matrix*. It should be noted that in much of the literature the transition matrix is defined as the transpose of the matrix $\mathbf{A}$ introduced above.

We now assume that the fractions of customers who change suppliers in the following months are the same as those given by the matrix $\mathbf{A}$. If the months January, Febuary, March, . . . are denoted by numbers 1, 2, 3, . . . respectively, and the column vectors giving the fractions of the total number of customers supplied by X, Y, Z at the ends of each month are denoted by $\mathbf{x}_r$, then in addition to (2.46) we have $\mathbf{x}_2 = \mathbf{A}\mathbf{x}_1$, $\mathbf{x}_3 = \mathbf{A}\mathbf{x}_2$, . . . and in general

$$\mathbf{x}_r = \mathbf{A}\mathbf{x}_{r-1}, \qquad r = 1, 2, 3, \ldots. \tag{2.51}$$

The fractions $\mathbf{x}_r$ at the end of the rth month are easily expressed in terms of those at the end of the first month by substituting for $\mathbf{x}_{r-1}$ in (2.51) in terms of $\mathbf{x}_{r-2}$ and so on:

$$\mathbf{x}_r = \mathbf{A}\mathbf{x}_{r-1} = \mathbf{A}^2\mathbf{x}_{r-2} = \mathbf{A}^3\mathbf{x}_{r-3} = \ldots = \mathbf{A}^r\mathbf{x}_0. \tag{2.52}$$

We now show that if $x_0 + y_0 + z_0 = 1$ then

$$x_r + y_r + z_r = 1, \qquad r = 1, 2, 3, \ldots, \tag{2.53}$$

where the x_r, y_r, z_r are the components of $\mathbf{x}$ as defined in (2.47), and represent fractions of customers supplied by X, Y, Z, respectively, at the end of the rth month. The above equation is simply a consistency check. We know that this relation must be true by virtue of the physical interpretation of x_r, y_r, z_r as fractions of a fixed number of customers. On the other hand, the x_r, y_r, z_r are defined by (2.51) so that (2.53) must be deducible from this definition. From (2.51)

$$x_r = a_{11}x_{r-1} + a_{12}y_{r-1} + a_{13}z_{r-1},$$

with two similar equations for y_r and z_r. On adding these three equations we obtain

$$\begin{aligned} x_r + y_r + z_r &= (a_{11} + a_{21} + a_{31})x_{r-1} + (a_{12} + a_{22} + a_{32})y_{r-1} \\ &\quad + (a_{13} + a_{23} + a_{33})z_{r-1} \\ &= x_{r-1} + y_{r-1} + z_{r-1} \\ &= x_0 + y_0 + z_0 = 1, \end{aligned}$$

where we have used (2.50) and (2.45). This proves (2.53).

At this stage we consider a numerical example. Suppose that

$$\mathbf{x}_0 = \begin{bmatrix} 0.2 \\ 0.3 \\ 0.5 \end{bmatrix}, \qquad \mathbf{A} = \begin{bmatrix} 0.8 & 0.2 & 0.1 \\ 0.1 & 0.7 & 0.3 \\ 0.1 & 0.1 & 0.6 \end{bmatrix}. \tag{2.54}$$

At the beginning, the dairies X, Y, Z have, respectively, 20%, 30%, 50% of the market. In subsequent months, assuming that the transition matrix does not change, the shares are

$$\mathbf{x}_1 = \mathbf{A}\mathbf{x}_0 = \begin{bmatrix} 0.27 \\ 0.38 \\ 0.35 \end{bmatrix}, \qquad \mathbf{x}_2 = \mathbf{A}\mathbf{x}_1 = \begin{bmatrix} 0.327 \\ 0.398 \\ 0.275 \end{bmatrix}.$$

Similarly, we find, rounding to three decimals at each stage,

$$\mathbf{x}_4 = \begin{bmatrix} 0.397 \\ 0.384 \\ 0.219 \end{bmatrix}, \qquad \mathbf{x}_8 = \begin{bmatrix} 0.442 \\ 0.357 \\ 0.201 \end{bmatrix}, \qquad \mathbf{x}_{16} = \begin{bmatrix} 0.450 \\ 0.350 \\ 0.200 \end{bmatrix}. \tag{2.55}$$

On forming $\mathbf{x}_{17} = \mathbf{A}\mathbf{x}_{16}$, we find that $\mathbf{x}_{17}$ is precisely the same as $\mathbf{x}_{16}$, so that $\mathbf{x}_r$ is the same for all values of r greater than 16. This means that the fractions of the market supplied by X, Y, Z become constant after a sufficiently long time.

To investigate this in the case of a general 3×3 matrix $\mathbf{A} = [a_{ij}]$, where the a_{ij} satisfy (2.50), suppose that for large r the vector $\mathbf{x}_r$ tends to a limiting vector $\mathbf{x}$ where $\mathbf{x}^T = [x, y, z]$. The vector $\mathbf{x}$ must satisfy the equation obtained by setting $\mathbf{x}_{r-1} = \mathbf{x}_r = \mathbf{x}$ in (2.51), i.e., $\mathbf{x} = \mathbf{A}\mathbf{x}$. On writing these equations out in detail and rearranging slightly, we obtain

$$\left.\begin{aligned} (1 - a_{11})x - a_{12}y - a_{13}z &= 0, \\ -a_{21}x + (1 - a_{22})y - a_{23}z &= 0, \\ -a_{31}x - a_{32}y + (1 - a_{33})z &= 0. \end{aligned}\right\} \tag{2.56}$$

In addition, since (2.53) is true for all r, it must also be true for the limiting value as r tends to infinity, so that

$$x + y + z = 1. \tag{2.57}$$

At first sight it seems that (2.56), (2.57) are four equations for three unknowns, but it is easily seen, using (2.50), that the sum of the three equations in (2.56) is identically zero, so that one of the equations is redundant. The question of how to choose an independent set of equations under these circumstances is discussed in detail later. In the present situation it is clear that we should take (2.57) with two equations from (2.56). As an example, with $\mathbf{A}$ defined in (2.54), taking (2.57) with the first two equations in (2.56), we obtain

$$\begin{aligned} x + y + z &= 1 \\ -0.2x + 0.2y + 0.1z &= 0 \\ 0.1x - 0.3y + 0.3z &= 0. \end{aligned}$$

The solution of this system is

$$x = 0.45, \qquad y = 0.35, \qquad z = 0.20.$$

This is precisely the result found by finding the limit of $\mathbf{A}^r\mathbf{x}_0$ for large r, above [see (2.55)].

One of the important results of this analysis is that the limiting value $\mathbf{x}$ is completely independent of the initial starting value $\mathbf{x}_0$. This is clear from the way in which $\mathbf{x}$ has been found, since Equations (2.56), (2.57) do not depend on $\mathbf{x}_0$.

We found the limiting value (2.55) by computing $\mathbf{A}^r\mathbf{x}_0$ for increasing values of r. In order to understand the final result from a different point of view we next consider the computed values of $\mathbf{A}^r$ for various r. We find

$$\mathbf{A}^2 = \begin{bmatrix} 0.67 & 0.31 & 0.20 \\ 0.18 & 0.54 & 0.40 \\ 0.15 & 0.15 & 0.40 \end{bmatrix}, \qquad \mathbf{A}^4 = \begin{bmatrix} 0.535 & 0.405 & 0.338 \\ 0.278 & 0.407 & 0.412 \\ 0.188 & 0.188 & 0.250 \end{bmatrix}$$

$$\mathbf{A}^8 = \begin{bmatrix} 0.462 & 0.445 & 0.432 \\ 0.339 & 0.356 & 0.365 \\ 0.199 & 0.199 & 0.203 \end{bmatrix}, \qquad \mathbf{A}^{16} = \begin{bmatrix} 0.450 & 0.450 & 0.450 \\ 0.350 & 0.350 & 0.350 \\ 0.200 & 0.200 & 0.200 \end{bmatrix}.$$

This indicates that, as r increases, $\mathbf{A}^r$ tends to a matrix with constant rows. A proof that this will always happen if the elements a_{ij} of the general 3×3 matrix $\mathbf{A}$ satisfy (a), (b), (c) above, Equations (2.48)–(2.50), and are also strictly positive, is given in Ex. 2.8 below.

The importance of this result is that we can then show that $\mathbf{A}^r\mathbf{x}_0$ tends to a limit as r tends to infinity, where this limit is independent of the initial vector $\mathbf{x}_0$. Suppose that

$$\lim_{r\to\infty} \mathbf{A}^r = \begin{bmatrix} \alpha & \alpha & \alpha \\ \beta & \beta & \beta \\ \gamma & \gamma & \gamma \end{bmatrix}. \tag{2.58}$$

Then for any arbitrary initial vector $\mathbf{x}_0$ we see that

$$\lim_{r\to\infty} \mathbf{A}^r\mathbf{x}_0 = \begin{bmatrix} \alpha(x_0 + y_0 + z_0) \\ \beta(x_0 + y_0 + z_0) \\ \gamma(x_0 + y_0 + z_0) \end{bmatrix} = \begin{bmatrix} \alpha \\ \beta \\ \gamma \end{bmatrix}. \tag{2.59}$$

Hence, the limiting value of $\mathbf{A}^r\mathbf{x}_0$ as r tends to infinity is independent of the initial vector $\mathbf{x}_0$.

We now return to the specific application considered at the beginning of this section. In order to visualize the results more concretely, suppose that there are 1000 customers altogether on December 31. If the distribution of customers on that date is given by $\mathbf{x}_0$ in (2.54) then X has 200, Y has 300, Z has 500. The analysis following (2.54) then gives the information in Table 2.2 for the distribution of customers at the end of January and February, and also the final equilibrium distribution.

Table 2.2

Dairy	Customers (Dec. 31)	Number retained	Gains From X	Gains From Y	Gains From Z	Losses To X	Losses To Y	Losses To Z	Customers (Jan. 31)
X	200	160	0	60	50	0	20	20	270
Y	300	210	20	0	150	60	0	30	380
Z	500	300	20	30	0	50	150	0	350
	Jan. 31								Feb. 28
X	270	216	0	76	35	0	27	27	327
Y	380	266	27	0	105	76	0	38	398
Z	350	210	27	38	0	35	105	0	275
				Equilibrium					
X	450	360	0	70	20	0	45	45	450
Y	350	245	45	0	60	70	0	35	350
Z	200	120	45	35	0	20	60	0	200

It is seen that a fairly complicated interchange of customers between dairies is involved. The basic reason why Z's share of the market is decreasing is that it is losing a large proportion of its customers to Y. In practice this would presumably have a significant application in connection with Z's marketing strategy. Dairy Z should try to find out the reason why it is losing customers to Y, in order to reduce this loss. The mathematics can indicate the effect of reducing the loss by any given amount. Thus if Z's loss to Y is halved, the transition matrix **A** becomes

$$\mathbf{A} = \begin{bmatrix} 0.8 & 0.2 & 0.1 \\ 0.1 & 0.7 & 0.15 \\ 0.1 & 0.1 & 0.75 \end{bmatrix},$$

and the reader can readily show that the equilibrium value of Z's share of the market will increase to $\frac{2}{7} = 0.29$ in place of 0.20. A minor point of interest is that although Y's share of the market increases appreciably during January (see Table 2.2), this is misleading since his share eventually drops back to an equilibrium fraction of 0.35.

To sum up, we see that this type of analysis will predict the share of the market a dairy will have at any future time. The precise details of the way in which the dairy will gain and lose customers is predicted. Also predictions can be made concerning the behavior of the market if any changes are made in the fractions of customers that dairies retain or lose. Note however that it is necessary to have very detailed knowledge of the situation. It is not sufficient to know that dairy X is gaining a net number of 70 customers in January. We need to know that it is retaining 160 out of 200, and gaining 60 from Y, 50 from Z, and so on. Also there are various assumptions built into the analysis:

(a) We have assumed that the numbers in the transition matrix remain constant from month to month. Mathematically it is easy to take account of the situation when the transition matrix changes. If the transition matrix in the rth month is denoted by $\mathbf{A}_r$, then instead of $\mathbf{x}_r = \mathbf{A}^r\mathbf{x}_0$ we have simply

$$\mathbf{x}_r = \mathbf{A}_r\mathbf{A}_{r-1} \cdots \mathbf{A}_1\mathbf{x}_0.$$

The difficulty is of course to know the values of the elements in each of the matrices.

(b) We have assumed that the total number of customers is constant. The effect of customers leaving or entering the market can be built into the mathematical analysis, but this will not be considered here.

We remind the reader that, no matter how elegant the mathematics, the reliability of the conclusions can be no better than the reliability of the initial information and the validity of the assumptions.

The problem we have been considering here is a simple example of a (first-order) Markov chain process. Suppose that a system involves p variables (e.g., the above example involves the $p = 3$ fractions of the market served by dairies X, Y, Z). The state of the system at any instant is described by a *state vector*, say $\mathbf{x}$, which is a $p \times 1$ vector giving the values of the p variables. We are interested in the state vector only at successive instants of time $t_1, t_2, \ldots$. If the corresponding state vectors are denoted by $\mathbf{x}_1, \mathbf{x}_2, \ldots$, the basic assumption is that the state vector $\mathbf{x}_r$ depends only on $\mathbf{x}_{r-1}$ and not on $\mathbf{x}_{r-2}, \mathbf{x}_{r-3}, \ldots$, i.e., if $\mathbf{x}_{r-1}$ is known, then $\mathbf{x}_r$ can be found. As illustrated in the example, the vectors $\mathbf{x}_r$, $\mathbf{x}_{r-1}$ are related by a transition matrix $\mathbf{A}$ by means of which we can write $\mathbf{x}_r = \mathbf{A}\mathbf{x}_{r-1}$. The elements of $\mathbf{A}$ are usually interpreted as transition probabilities, but further discussion lies outside the scope of this section.

Ex. 2.6. Three companies A, B, C introduce new brands of toothpaste simultaneously on the market. At the start, the shares of the market are: A, 0.4; B, 0.2; C, 0.4. During the first year, company A retained 85% of its customers, lost 5% to B, 10% to C. Company B retained 75%, and lost 15% to A, 10% to C. Company C retained 90% and lost 5% to A, 5% to B. Assume that buying habits do not change and that the market does not expand or contract. What share of the market will be held by each company after the end of one and two years? What will the final equilibrium shares be?

Ex. 2.7. Assume that a man's occupation can be classified as professional, skilled, or unskilled. Assume that 70% of the sons of professional men are also professional, 20% are skilled, and 10% are unskilled. Similarly, suppose that 60% of the sons of skilled men are also skilled, 20% are professional, and 20% are unskilled. Also 50% of the sons of unskilled men are unskilled, 30% are skilled, and 20% are professional. Assume that every man has a son. Set up the transition matrix from one generation to the next. Show that the fractions of the grandsons of unskilled men who are professional, skilled, and unskilled are 0.30, 0.37, 0.33, respectively. Show that the equilibrium fractions of professional, skilled, and unskilled men are 0.40, 0.37, 0.23, approximately.

Ex. 2.8. Let $\mathbf{A} = [a_{ij}]$ be a 3×3 matrix whose elements satisfy (2.48)–(2.50), with the additional restriction that its elements are strictly positive, i.e.,

$$a_{ij} \geq d > 0, \qquad (\text{all } i, j).$$

Prove that the following result is true where α, β, γ are constants:

$$\lim_{r \to \infty} \mathbf{A}^r = \begin{bmatrix} \alpha & \alpha & \alpha \\ \beta & \beta & \beta \\ \gamma & \gamma & \gamma \end{bmatrix}. \tag{2.60}$$

Solution: Suppose that $\mathbf{A}^r = [p_{ij}]$. Obviously all the p_{ij}'s are positive. The elements of the first row of $(\mathbf{A}^r)\mathbf{A}$ are given by

$$p_{11}a_{1j} + p_{12}a_{2j} + p_{13}a_{3j}, \qquad j = 1, 2, 3.$$

Suppose that M_{r+1}, m_{r+1} are, respectively, the largest and smallest elements in this row. Suppose also that M_r, m_r are the largest and smallest elements in the first row of $\mathbf{A}^r$. We have

$$\begin{aligned} m_{r+1} &= \min_j \{p_{11}a_{1j} + p_{12}a_{2j} + p_{13}a_{3j}\} \\ &= \min_j \{M_r d + (p_{11}a_{1j} + p_{12}a_{2j} + p_{13}a_{3j} - M_r d)\}. \end{aligned} \tag{2.61}$$

The value of M_r is equal to the value of one of the p's, say p_{1k}. We have

$$p_{1k}a_{kj} - M_r d = M_r(a_{kj} - d) \geq m_r(a_{kj} - d).$$

If the two suffixes other than k are denoted by m, n (i.e., m, n, k are 1, 2, 3 in some order) we have

$$\begin{aligned} p_{11}a_{1j} + p_{12}a_{2j} + p_{13}a_{3j} - M_r d &= (p_{1m}a_{mj} + p_{1n}a_{nj}) + (p_{1k}a_{kj} - M_r d) \\ &\geq m_r(a_{mj} + a_{nj}) + m_r(a_{kj} - d) \\ &= m_r(a_{1j} + a_{2j} + a_{3j} - d) \\ &= m_r(1 - d). \end{aligned}$$

On combining this result with (2.61), we find

$$m_{r+1} \geq M_r d + m_r(1 - d). \tag{2.62}$$

A similar argument can be used to show that

$$M_{r+1} \leq m_r d + M_r(1 - d). \tag{2.63}$$

Multiplying (2.62) by -1 (which reverses the inequality sign) and adding the result to (2.63), we have

$$M_{r+1} - m_{r+1} \leq (1 - 2d)(M_r - m_r). \tag{2.64}$$

Hence,

$$M_r - m_r \leq (1 - 2d)^r(M_0 - m_0). \tag{2.65}$$

Since $a_{1j} + a_{2j} + a_{3j} = 1$, the value of d must be less than one-half. [This can also be seen from (2.64) since, by definition, $M_p - m_p \geq 0$ for all p.] From (2.65) we have, therefore,

$$\lim_{r\to\infty} (M_r - m_r) = 0. \tag{2.66}$$

On using the notation k, m, n for suffixes introduced above,

$$\begin{aligned} M_{r+1} - M_r &= p_{1m}a_{mj} + p_{1n}a_{nj} + p_{1k}a_{kj} - p_{1k} \\ &= (p_{1m} - p_{1k})a_{mj} + (p_{1n} - p_{1k})a_{nj} \leq 0. \end{aligned}$$

Hence,

$$M_0 \geq M_1 \geq M_2 \geq \ldots$$

and similarly,

$$m_0 \leq m_1 \leq m_2 \leq \ldots .$$

Each sequence is monotone and bounded, since $m_0 \leq m_r \leq M_r \leq M_0$. Hence, each of the sequences will have a limit. From (2.66) these limits must be the same. Hence, we have proved that the elements in the first row of $\mathbf{A}^r$ tend to the same constant value as r tends to infinity, as indicated in (2.60). The constancy of the second and third rows in (2.60) is proved similarly.

Ex. 2.9. Generalize the theorem in Ex. 2.8 to the case where $\mathbf{A}$ is $n \times n$, assuming that the elements in $\mathbf{A}$ satisfy the same type of conditions as in Ex. 2.8.

Miscellaneous Exercises 2

Ex. 2.10. In the pin-jointed square framework shown in Figure 2.9 the support at A is fixed (though of course the rods are free to rotate), and the support at B can move parallel to the wall. Let

$$\mathbf{f} = [F_i], \quad \mathbf{t} = [T_i], \quad \mathbf{e} = [e_i], \quad \mathbf{d} = [d_i]$$

denote, respectively, external forces, internal tensions in rods, displacements of joints, and extensions, all in the directions shown. Show that

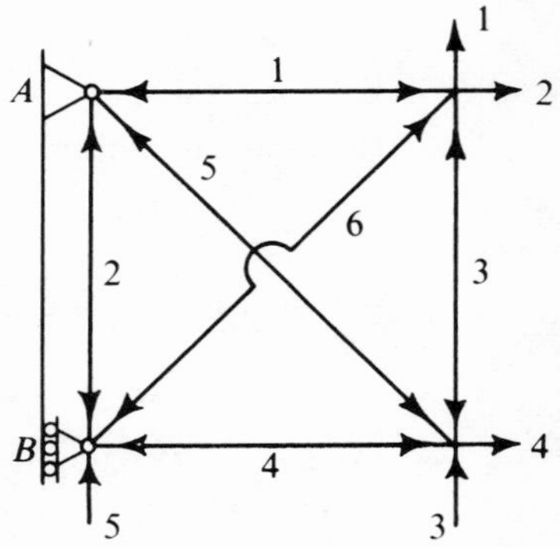

Figure 2.9

$$\mathbf{f} = \mathbf{C}\mathbf{t}, \qquad \mathbf{e} = \mathbf{C}^T\mathbf{d},$$

where

$$\mathbf{C} = \begin{bmatrix} 0 & 0 & 1 & 0 & 0 & 1/\sqrt{2} \\ 1 & 0 & 0 & 0 & 0 & 1/\sqrt{2} \\ 0 & 0 & -1 & 0 & -(1/\sqrt{2}) & 0 \\ 0 & 0 & 0 & 1 & 1/\sqrt{2} & 0 \\ 0 & -1 & 0 & 0 & 0 & -(1/\sqrt{2}) \end{bmatrix}.$$

Ex. 2.11. Any electrical network in which there are two input and two output terminals is called a *two-port* or *fourpole*. Show that for the series impedance in Figure 2.10(b) we have

$$\begin{bmatrix} v_1 \\ i_1 \end{bmatrix} = \begin{bmatrix} 1 & Z \\ 0 & 1 \end{bmatrix} \begin{bmatrix} v_2 \\ i_2 \end{bmatrix}$$

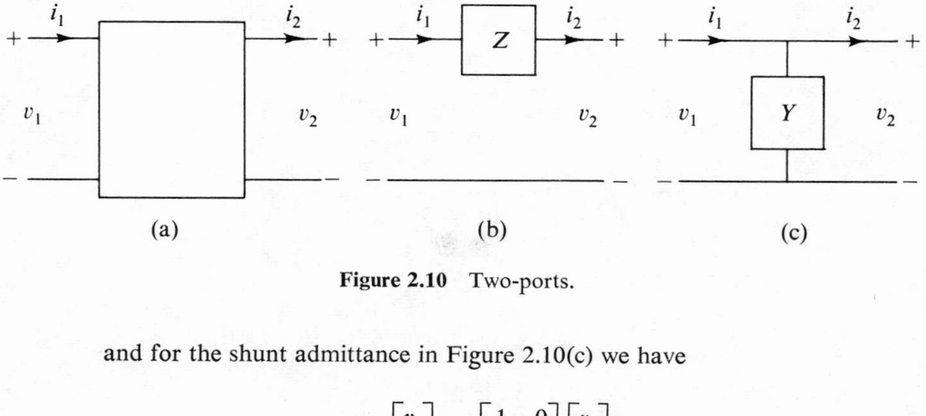

Figure 2.10 Two-ports.

and for the shunt admittance in Figure 2.10(c) we have

$$\begin{bmatrix} v_1 \\ i_1 \end{bmatrix} = \begin{bmatrix} 1 & 0 \\ Y & 1 \end{bmatrix} \begin{bmatrix} v_2 \\ i_2 \end{bmatrix}.$$

If three two-ports are connected in series as in Figure 2.11(a) and the equations relating the input and the output voltages and currents are

$$\mathbf{p}_s = \mathbf{A}_s\mathbf{p}_{s+1}, \qquad s = 1, 2, 3, \quad \text{where} \quad \mathbf{p}_s = \begin{bmatrix} v_s \\ i_s \end{bmatrix},$$

show that $\mathbf{p}_1 = \mathbf{A}_1\mathbf{A}_2\mathbf{A}_3\mathbf{p}_4$. Show that the matrix $\mathbf{A}_1\mathbf{A}_2\mathbf{A}_3$ for the "T" and "Π" networks in Figures 2.11(b), (c) are those given on the right of the corresponding diagrams.

(a)

$$\begin{bmatrix} 1 + Z_1 Y, & Z_1 + Z_2 + Z_1 Z_2 Y \\ Y & , & 1 + Z_2 Y \end{bmatrix}$$

(b)

$$\begin{bmatrix} 1 + Y_2 Z & , & Z \\ Y_1 + Y_2 + Y_1 Y_2 Z, & 1 + Y_1 Z \end{bmatrix}$$

(c)

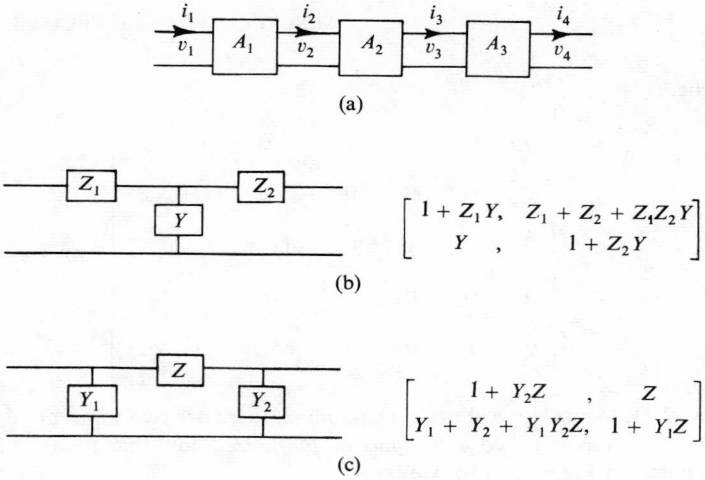

Figure 2.11 Two-ports in series.

(a)   (b)

(c)

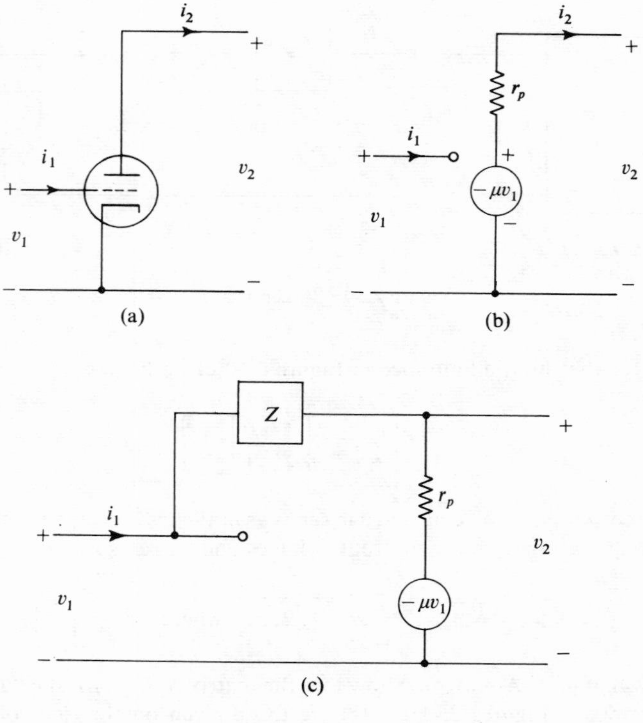

Figure 2.12 Simple vacuum tube.

Ex. 2.12. Show that for the tube in Figure 2.12(a), represented by the equivalent circuit in (b),

$$\begin{bmatrix} v_1 \\ i_1 \end{bmatrix} = \begin{bmatrix} -\dfrac{1}{\mu} & -\dfrac{r_p}{\mu} \\ 0 & 0 \end{bmatrix} \begin{bmatrix} v_2 \\ i_2 \end{bmatrix},$$

where r_p is the plate resistance and μ is the amplification. Note that the square matrix is singular. The physical meaning of this is that the tube does not transmit backwards. Show that for the tube with back-coupling between the anode and grid in Figure 2.12(c) we have

$$\begin{bmatrix} v_1 \\ i_1 \end{bmatrix} = \frac{1}{(\mu Z - r_p)} \begin{bmatrix} -(Z + r_p) & -Zr_p \\ -(1 + \mu) & -r_p \end{bmatrix} \begin{bmatrix} v_2 \\ i_2 \end{bmatrix}.$$

Ex. 2.13. Use the method of Ex. 2.1 to obtain the following equations for the electrical network in Figure 5.5 ($Y_i = 1/R_i$, where R_i is the resistance of resistor i):

$$\begin{bmatrix} Y_1+Y_3+Y_5 & -Y_3 & -Y_5 & 0 & 0 & 0 \\ -Y_3 & Y_2+Y_3+Y_4 & -Y_4 & 0 & 0 & 0 \\ -Y_5 & -Y_4 & Y_4+Y_5+Y_6 & -Y_6 & 0 & 0 \\ 0 & 0 & -Y_6 & Y_6+Y_7+Y_8 & -Y_8 & -Y_7 \\ 0 & 0 & 0 & -Y_8 & Y_8+Y_9+Y_{11} & -Y_9 \\ 0 & 0 & 0 & -Y_7 & -Y_9 & Y_7+Y_9+Y_{10} \end{bmatrix} \begin{bmatrix} V_1 \\ V_2 \\ V_3 \\ V_4 \\ V_5 \\ V_6 \end{bmatrix} = \begin{bmatrix} 0 \\ 0 \\ -Y_6 e \\ Y_6 e \\ 0 \\ 0 \end{bmatrix}.$$

The matrix of coefficients has an interesting structure which reflects the fact that the network in Figure 5.5 separates into two distinct parts if the resistor 6 is removed. Consider a numerical example. Suppose that all the resistors have value unity except for $R_3 = \frac{1}{2}$, $R_{10} = \frac{1}{6}$, $R_{11} = \frac{2}{3}$; also $e = 12$. The equations reduce to:

$$\begin{aligned} 4V_1 - 2V_2 - V_3 \qquad\qquad\qquad\qquad &= 0 \\ -2V_1 + 4V_2 - V_3 \qquad\qquad\qquad\qquad &= 0 \\ -V_1 - V_2 + 3V_3 - V_4 \qquad\qquad\qquad &= -12 \\ -V_3 + 3V_4 - V_5 - V_6 &= 12 \\ -V_4 + 3\tfrac{1}{2}V_5 - V_6 &= 0 \\ -V_4 - V_5 + 8V_6 &= 0. \end{aligned}$$

There are various ingenious ways of obtaining the solution of these equations by solving only systems of three equations. For example, if we solve the first three equations for V_1, V_2, V_3 in terms of V_4, we obtain

$$V_1 = \tfrac{1}{4}V_4 - 3, \qquad V_2 = \tfrac{1}{4}V_4 - 3, \qquad V_3 = \tfrac{1}{2}V_4 - 6. \tag{2.67}$$

Substitution of this value for V_3 in the fourth equation gives:

$$\begin{aligned} 2\tfrac{1}{2}V_4 - V_5 - V_6 &= 6 \\ -V_4 + 3\tfrac{1}{2}V_5 - V_6 &= 0 \\ -V_4 - V_5 + 8V_6 &= 0. \end{aligned}$$

These give $V_4 = 3$, $V_5 = 1$, $V_6 = \frac{1}{2}$, and (2.67) then yields $V_3 = -4\frac{1}{2}$, $V_2 = -2\frac{1}{4}$, $V_1 = -2\frac{1}{4}$. (This example is solved in a different way in Ex. 5.20.)

Ex. 2.14. It is important to realize that the situation summarized in Table 2.1 is only part of a much larger picture. In particular, there are a whole class of "dual" methods that have not been mentioned. The point is perhaps most easily illustrated in connection with electrical networks. The basis of network analysis are Kirchhoff's two laws. Kirchhoff's current law states that the sum of all the currents at any node is zero. Kirchhoff's voltage law states that the sum of the voltages around any loop is zero (a *loop* in a network is a closed circuit). In the method in Ex. 2.1, the node voltages with respect to one fixed node were taken as the unknowns. This meant that Kirchhoff's voltage law is automatically satisfied, and we set up equations to satisfy Kirchhoff's current law. It has already been remarked that the equations in Ex. 2.1 could have been formulated directly in this way. The dual method referred to at the beginning of this exercise is to satisfy Kirchhoff's current law automatically by introducing loop currents, and then set up equations to satisfy Kirchhoff's voltage law. We illustrate how this can be done by considering the circuit in Figure 2.2. A detailed discussion can be found in [90].

Suppose that the network has B branches. (For example, $B = 6$ in Figure 2.2.) We use the sign conventions in Figure 2.3. For simplicity we consider only the case where the impedances are resistors. Define

$$\mathbf{v} = \begin{bmatrix} v_1 \\ v_2 \\ \cdot \\ \cdot \\ \cdot \\ v_B \end{bmatrix}, \quad \mathbf{e} = \begin{bmatrix} e_1 \\ e_2 \\ \cdot \\ \cdot \\ \cdot \\ e_B \end{bmatrix}, \quad \mathbf{i} = \begin{bmatrix} i_1 \\ i_2 \\ \cdot \\ \cdot \\ \cdot \\ i_B \end{bmatrix}, \quad \mathbf{R} = \begin{bmatrix} R_1 & 0 & \cdots & 0 \\ 0 & R_2 & \cdots & 0 \\ & & \cdots & \\ 0 & 0 & \cdots & R_B \end{bmatrix}.$$

Then

$$\mathbf{v} = \mathbf{Ri}.$$

We next choose independent loops in the network. Suppose that we require M loop currents $i'_1, i'_2, \ldots, i'_M$ for analysis of the network, and that when these are arranged as a column matrix, this is denoted by $\mathbf{i}'$. By expressing $\mathbf{i}$ in terms of $\mathbf{i}'$ show that

$$\mathbf{i} = \mathbf{Ci}'$$

where $\mathbf{C}$ is a $B \times M$ interconnection matrix such that

$C_{pq} = +1$ if the branch p is contained in the loop q, and the branch and loop currents are assumed positive in the *same* direction.

$C_{pq} = -1$ if the branch p is contained in the loop q, and the branch and loop currents are assumed positive in *opposite* directions.

$C_{pq} = 0$ if the branch p is *not* contained in the loop q.

Show also that

$$\mathbf{C}^T(\mathbf{v} - \mathbf{e}) = \mathbf{0}.$$

By elimination of $\mathbf{v}$ and $\mathbf{i}$ from the above three matrix equations we obtain

$$\mathbf{C}^T\mathbf{RCi}' = \mathbf{C}^T\mathbf{e}.$$

This is the required formula.

By this method, show that for the network in Figure 2.2

$$\mathbf{C}^T = \begin{bmatrix} -1 & 0 & 1 & 0 & -1 & 0 \\ 0 & -1 & -1 & 1 & 0 & 0 \\ 0 & 1 & 0 & 0 & 1 & -1 \end{bmatrix},$$

$$\mathbf{C}^T\mathbf{R}\mathbf{C} = \begin{bmatrix} R_1 + R_3 + R_5 & -R_3 & -R_5 \\ -R_3 & R_2 + R_3 + R_4 & -R_2 \\ -R_5 & -R_2 & R_2 + R_5 + R_6 \end{bmatrix}.$$

Check by deriving the corresponding mesh equations from first principles. (Of course the real power of these methods will appear only when they are applied to much more complicated problems. One of the main points is that the *interconnection* of the impedances can be considered independently of the *values* of the impedances. Also the effect of mutual inductance can be taken into account in a routine way. This is important, for example, when setting up the equations for rotating electrical machinery. See, for instance, [74].)

Ex. 2.15. H. Bernadelli, in J. Burma Res. Soc. **31** (1941), pp. 1–18, makes the hypothesis that a certain type of beetle lives for exactly three years, and reproduces only in this third year. Suppose that a fraction p of those alive in the first year survive to the second, a fraction q of those alive in the second year survive to the third, and on the average r new beetles are produced for each beetle in its third year. Prove that if α_k, β_k, γ_k beetles of ages 1, 2, 3 are alive in year k,

$$\begin{bmatrix} \alpha_{k+1} \\ \beta_{k+1} \\ \gamma_{k+1} \end{bmatrix} = \begin{bmatrix} 0 & 0 & r \\ p & 0 & 0 \\ 0 & q & 0 \end{bmatrix} \begin{bmatrix} \alpha_k \\ \beta_k \\ \gamma_k \end{bmatrix}.$$

Deduce that

$$\begin{bmatrix} \alpha_{k+3} \\ \beta_{k+3} \\ \gamma_{k+3} \end{bmatrix} = pqr \begin{bmatrix} \alpha_k \\ \beta_k \\ \gamma_k \end{bmatrix},$$

so that there is a three-year cycle in the proportions of beetles of ages 1, 2, 3. If $pqr < 1$, the population will die out, whereas if $pqr > 1$ it will increase in size.

The following essay topics and references to the literature are meant to be suggestive rather than definitive. Projects of this type should take into account the interests of the student and the books available. The essays can be written at various levels of sophistication. The more linear algebra the student knows, the deeper the treatment that can be attempted. The student should not expect to understand everything in the references quoted if he has completed only Chapter 1 of this book. Nevertheless, it is surprising how far matrix algebra alone can take the student.

Ex. 2.16. Write an essay on the analysis of mechanical structures by matrix methods. Distinguish between the "equilibrium" and "compatibility" methods of approach to the calculation of structures. Possible references are Argyris [64], Gennaro [73], Pestel and Leckie [94], Robinson [96], and the following:

(a) S. O. Asplund, *Structural Mechanics, Classical and Matrix Methods*, Prentice-Hall (1966).

(b) H. I. Laursen, *Matrix Analysis of Structures*, McGraw-Hill (1966).

(c) R. K. Livesley, *Matrix Methods of Structural Analysis*. Pergamon (1964).

(d) S. J. McMinn, *Matrices for Structural Analysis*, E. & F. Spon. London (1962).

(e) H. C. Martin, *Introduction to Matrix Methods of Structural Analysis*, McGraw-Hill (1966).

(f) P. B. Morice, *Linear Structural Analysis*, Hudson and Thames (1959).

(g) J. Robinson, *Structural Matrix Analysis for the Engineer*, Wiley (1966).

(h) M. F. Rubinstein, *Matrix Computer Analysis of Structures*, Prentice-Hall (1966).

(i) F. Venancio Filho, *Introduction to Matrix Structural Theory and its Applications to Civil and Aircraft Structures*, Ungar (1960).

(j) C. K. Wang, *Matrix Methods of Structural Analysis*, International Textbook Co., Scranton, Pa. (1966).

(k) P. C. Wang, *Numerical Matrix Methods in Structural Mechanics*, Wiley (1966).

Ex. 2.17. Write an essay on any aspect of the use of matrices in dynamics. Possible references are Frazer, Duncan, and Collar [38], Goldstein [77], Heading [41], and:

(a) R. M. L. Baker, *Astrodynamics*, Academic (1967).

(b) R. Deutsch, *Orbital Dynamics of Space Vehicles*, Prentice-Hall (1963).

(c) W. C. Nelson and E. E. Loft, *Space Mechanics*, Prentice-Hall (1962).

Ex. 2.18. Write an essay on the use of matrix methods in connection with (a) two-port electrical networks, (b) vacuum-tube circuits, (c) transistor circuits. Possible sources of material are Guillemin [79], Nodelman and Smith [92], v. Weiss [48], and:

(a) A. M. Tropper, *Matrix Theory for Electrical Engineers*, Addison-Wesley and Harrap (1962).

(b) G. Zelinger, *Basic Matrix Algebra and Transistor Circuits*, Pergamon (1966).

Ex. 2.19. Write an essay on electrical circuit analysis by matrix methods, with or without special reference to the work of Kron. Possible references are Braae [36], Guillemin [79], Kron [86], [87], [88], Lecorbeiller [90], v. Weiss [48], Zadeh and DeSoer [100].

Ex. 2.20. Write an essay on the analysis of electric motors using matrices. Possible references are Gibbs [74], and

N. N. Hancock, *Matrix Analysis of Electrical Machinery*, Macmillan (1964).

Ex. 2.21. Write a brief essay explaining how the book [66] by Brouwer uses matrices in describing the behavior of optical lenses.

Ex. 2.22. Write an essay on the use of matrices to simplify situations involving polarized light based on:

W. A. Shurcliff, *Polarized Light*, Harvard (1962).

Ex. 2.23. Write an essay on finite Markov chains. Possible references are [44], [84], [85] by Kemeny *et al.*, and

J. C. Mathews and C. E. Langenhop, *Discrete and Continuous Methods in Applied Mathematics*, Wiley (1966).

Ex. 2.24. Write an essay on applications of matrices in the social sciences. Possible references are Johnston, Price, and VanVleck [42], and Kemeny and Snell [85].

Ex. 2.25. Write an essay on the use of matrices in economics. A special topic might be Leontief input-output matrix analysis. Possible references are Chenery and Clark [67], Dorfman, Samuelson, and Solow [69], Gale [70], Johnston, Price, and VanVleck [42], Karlin [43], Schwartz [97], and

O. Morganstern, ed., *Economic Analysis Activity*, Wiley (1964).

Ex. 2.26. Write an essay on the use of matrices in econometrics. Possible references are Goldberger [76], Johnston [83].

Ex. 2.27. Write an essay on applications of matrices in (a) statistics, (b) regression. Possible references are Graybill [78], Rao [95], Searle [47] and

N. R. Draper and H. Smith, *Applied Regression Analysis*, Wiley (1962).

O. Kempthorne, *Design and Analysis of Experiments*, Wiley (1952).

3 Simultaneous Linear Equations and Elementary Operations

3.1 Introduction

In Chapter 1 we did little more than state certain rules for the manipulation of matrix arrays. In Chapter 2 we illustrated some of the ways in which matrices arise in the applied sciences. In this chapter we start to study matrices from a more theoretical point of view in order to obtain a deeper understanding of the potentialities and limitations of matrix methods. As illustrated by the examples considered in the last chapter, the utility of matrices in the applied sciences is, in many cases, connected with the fact that they provide a convenient method for the formulation of physical problems in terms of a set of simultaneous linear algebraic equations. It is therefore of great importance to understand theoretically the various situations that can arise when solving sets of linear equations, and this is the objective of the present chapter.

Each section in this chapter is concerned with ideas that arise naturally from the preceding sections. Sections 3.2–3 are concerned mainly with concrete examples. Sections 3.4–5 provide a transition to a more theoretical treatment. Sections 3.6–8 are concerned with basic tools (equivalence, elementary row operations, row-echelon normal form). Section 3.9 applies these tools to the question of deciding whether a system of linear equations possesses solutions.

Figure 3.1 explains the logical structure of the chapter. It is convenient to distinguish three main threads running through the chapter. The first involves motivation by means of numerical examples. Sections 3.2, 3.3, 3.5 are concerned with this aspect, and these are referred to on the left of Figure 3.1. The second thread is the direct manipulation of the linear equations themselves as in Sections 3.4, 3.6. The third thread concerns operations on the rows of matrices,

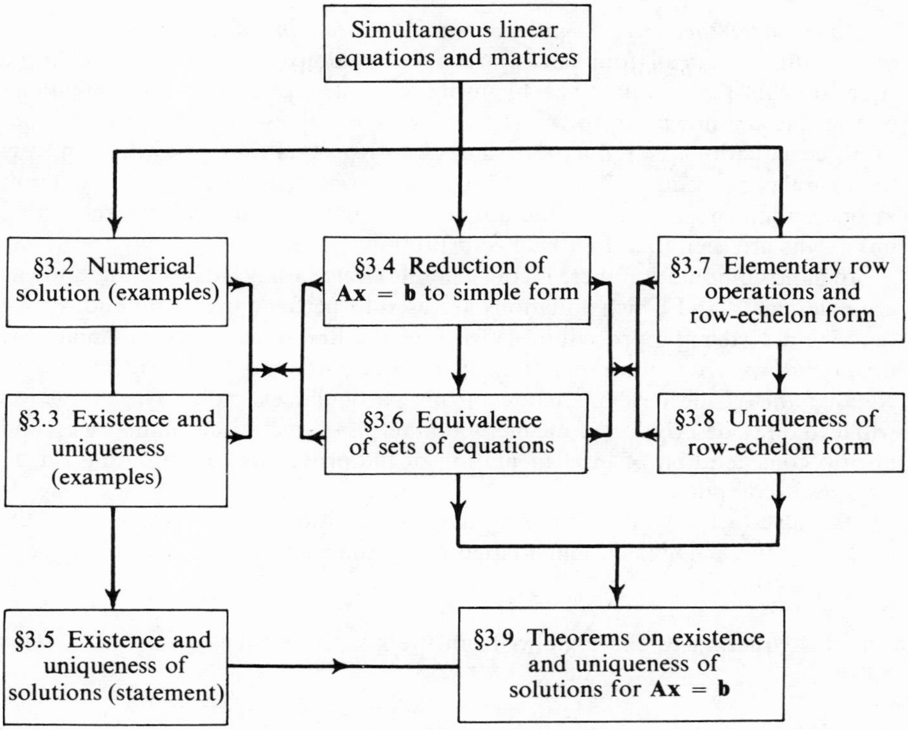

Figure 3.1 The logical structure of Chapter 3.

considered in Sections 3.7, 3.8. These threads come together in the discussion of the existence of solutions of simultaneous equations in Section 3.9.

Different readers and lecturers will prefer to place emphasis on different parts of this chapter. Some readers may feel that we are wasting time by first considering specific examples in great detail in Sections 3.2–3, then making a fresh start, covering essentially similar material, from Section 3.4 onwards. This form of exposition is deliberate. The earlier sections demonstrate that the idea of elementary row operations arises naturally when solving simultaneous linear equations. The reader who has already some acquaintance with the subject matter may prefer to go directly to Section 3.4, and omit Section 3.5.

3.2 *The Method of Successive Elimination*

Consider the following set of equations:

$$\left.\begin{aligned} 2x_1 - 3x_2 + 2x_3 + 5x_4 &= 3 \\ x_1 - x_2 + x_3 + 2x_4 &= 1 \\ 3x_1 + 2x_2 + 2x_3 + x_4 &= 0 \\ x_1 + x_2 - 3x_3 - x_4 &= 0. \end{aligned}\right\} \tag{3.1}$$

The *method of successive elimination* (or *Gaussian elimination*) consists of reducing this system of four equations in four unknowns to a system of three equations in three unknowns by using one of the equations to eliminate one of the unknowns from the remaining three equations. The resulting set of three equations is reduced to a set of two equations in two unknowns by a similar procedure. The set of two equations is reduced to one equation in one unknown, i.e., one of the unknowns is determined, and the remaining unknowns are then found by back-substitution.

In hand computation there is considerable choice as regards which unknowns are eliminated, and which equations are used to perform the eliminations. We describe a systematic procedure which uses the first equation to eliminate the first unknown from the remaining three equations, and so on, regardless of whether this is the best procedure in this particular example. The discussion will lead on to description of the method in terms of operations on matrices, and also to consideration of implementation of the procedure in a program for an automatic computer.

To solve (3.1), we start by using the first equation to eliminate x_1 from the remaining three. Divide the first equation by the coefficient of x_1, obtaining

$$x_1 - 1.5x_2 + x_3 + 2.5x_4 = 1.5. \tag{3.2}$$

Use this equation to eliminate x_1 from the last three equations in (3.1). This gives

$$\left.\begin{aligned} 0.5x_2 \qquad\quad - 0.5x_4 &= -0.5 \\ 6.5x_2 - x_3 - 6.5x_4 &= -4.5 \\ 2.5x_2 - 4x_3 - 3.5x_4 &= -1.5. \end{aligned}\right\} \tag{3.3}$$

Multiply the first of these equations by 2:

$$x_2 - x_4 = -1. \tag{3.4}$$

Use this to eliminate x_2 from the last two equations in (3.3):

$$\begin{aligned} -x_3 \qquad &= 2 \\ -4x_3 - x_4 &= 1. \end{aligned} \tag{3.5}$$

Solution of these equations gives $x_3 = -2$, $x_4 = 7$, and back-substitution in the earlier equations (3.4) and (3.2), in succession, gives $x_2 = 6$, $x_1 = -5$.

In carrying out the elimination procedure described above, there is no need to keep on writing down the unknowns x_1, x_2, x_3, x_4, nor the equality signs. The whole procedure can be systematized by operating directly on the following matrix, known as the *augmented matrix*, formed by writing in matrix form the numbers which occur in the original equations (3.1):

$$\begin{bmatrix} 2 & -3 & 2 & 5 & 3 \\ 1 & -1 & 1 & 2 & 1 \\ 3 & 2 & 2 & 1 & 0 \\ 1 & 1 & -3 & -1 & 0 \end{bmatrix}. \tag{3.6}$$

In the notation of partitioned matrices, the augmented matrix for the system $\mathbf{Ax} = \mathbf{b}$ is $[\mathbf{A}, \mathbf{b}]$. On dividing the first row of (3.6) by 2 and subtracting suitable multiples of the result from the other rows, we obtain [compare (3.2), (3.3)]:

$$\begin{bmatrix} 1 & -1.5 & 1 & 2.5 & 1.5 \\ 0 & 0.5 & 0 & -0.5 & -0.5 \\ 0 & 6.5 & -1 & -6.5 & -4.5 \\ 0 & 2.5 & -4 & -3.5 & -1.5 \end{bmatrix}. \tag{3.7}$$

Similarly, on multiplying the second row by 2 and subtracting suitable multiples of the result from the third and fourth rows, we obtain the matrix

$$\begin{bmatrix} 1 & -1.5 & 1 & 2.5 & 1.5 \\ 0 & 1 & 0 & -1 & -1 \\ 0 & 0 & -1 & 0 & 2 \\ 0 & 0 & -4 & -1 & 1 \end{bmatrix}. \tag{3.8}$$

Finally, multiplying the third row by -1, adding four times the result to the fourth row, and multiplying the result by -1, we obtain

$$\begin{bmatrix} 1 & -1.5 & 1 & 2.5 & 1.5 \\ 0 & 1 & 0 & -1 & -1 \\ 0 & 0 & 1 & 0 & -2 \\ 0 & 0 & 0 & 1 & 7 \end{bmatrix}. \tag{3.9}$$

On interpreting this matrix in terms of simultaneous linear equations, we find that we have reduced the original equations to the following *triangular set*, the first three equations of which are (3.2), (3.4), and (3.5).

$$\begin{aligned} x_1 - 1.5x_2 + x_3 + 2.5x_4 &= 1.5 \\ x_2 + 0 \cdot x_3 - x_4 &= -1 \\ x_3 + 0 \cdot x_4 &= -2 \\ x_4 &= 7. \end{aligned} \tag{3.10}$$

The unknowns x_4, x_3, x_2, x_1 can then be found in that order by *back-substitution*, working from the last equation to the first.

In practice it is sometimes convenient to modify the above procedure in the following way. Instead of leaving the back-substitution to the end, we can do it as we go along (in effect) by the following modification, known as the *Gauss-Jordan* method.

We explain the procedure in terms of simultaneous linear equations and matrices simultaneously by placing the equations and the corresponding matrices side by side below. After eliminating x_1 from the last three equations in (3.1) we have [compare (3.2), (3.3), (3.4), (3.7)]:

$$\begin{aligned} x_1 - 1.5x_2 + x_3 + 2.5x_4 &= 1.5 \\ x_2 \qquad - x_4 &= -1 \\ 6.5x_2 - x_3 - 6.5x_4 &= -4.5 \\ 2.5x_2 - 4x_3 - 3.5x_4 &= -1.5, \end{aligned} \qquad \begin{bmatrix} 1 & -1.5 & 1 & 2.5 & 1.5 \\ 0 & 1 & 0 & -1 & -1 \\ 0 & 6.5 & -1 & 6.5 & -4.5 \\ 0 & 2.5 & -4 & -3.5 & -1.5 \end{bmatrix}. \tag{3.11}$$

We now use the second equation to eliminate x_2 from *all* the remaining equations. (In the matrix, we use the second row to reduce the elements in the second column of the remaining rows to zero.):

$$\begin{aligned} x_1 \qquad + x_3 + x_4 &= 0 \\ x_2 \qquad - x_4 &= -1 \\ - x_3 \qquad &= 2 \\ - 4x_3 - x_4 &= 1, \end{aligned} \qquad \begin{bmatrix} 1 & 0 & 1 & 1 & 0 \\ 0 & 1 & 0 & -1 & -1 \\ 0 & 0 & -1 & 0 & 2 \\ 0 & 0 & -4 & -1 & 1 \end{bmatrix}. \tag{3.12}$$

We similarly use the third equation of this new set to eliminate x_3 from all the remaining equations, and follow the corresponding procedure for the matrix:

$$\begin{aligned} x_1 \qquad + x_4 &= 2 \\ x_2 \qquad - x_4 &= -1 \\ x_3 \qquad &= -2 \\ - x_4 &= -7, \end{aligned} \qquad \begin{bmatrix} 1 & 0 & 0 & 1 & 2 \\ 0 & 1 & 0 & -1 & -1 \\ 0 & 0 & 1 & 0 & -2 \\ 0 & 0 & 0 & -1 & -7 \end{bmatrix}. \tag{3.13}$$

Repetition of the procedure once more gives the final form:

$$\begin{aligned} x_1 \qquad &= -5 \\ x_2 \qquad &= 6 \\ x_3 \qquad &= -2 \\ x_4 &= 7, \end{aligned} \qquad \begin{bmatrix} 1 & 0 & 0 & 0 & -5 \\ 0 & 1 & 0 & 0 & 6 \\ 0 & 0 & 1 & 0 & -2 \\ 0 & 0 & 0 & 1 & 7 \end{bmatrix}. \tag{3.14}$$

This gives the final solution directly.

Summing up, Gaussian elimination consists of a reduction to triangular form, followed by back-substitution. The Gauss-Jordan method in essence does the back-substitution as we go along, so that the final solution is obtained directly. If we enumerate the numbers of additions and multiplications involved (see Section 7.6), it is found that Gaussian elimination is more efficient than the Gauss-Jordan method in the sense that it requires fewer operations. However, the Gauss-Jordan procedure is often more convenient for theoretical discussions, and this is the reason for introducing it here.

In the above example, we have worked systematically, using the first equation to eliminate the first unknown from the other equations, and so on. At the rth stage we use the rth equation to eliminate the rth unknown from the remaining equations. If we wish at any stage to use a given equation to eliminate one unknown from the other equations, the coefficient of this unknown is known as the *pivot*. Thus in (3.3) the pivot is the coefficient of x_2 in the first equation, namely 0.5. We have emphasized that there is an exact correspondence between the elimination method for the solution of linear equations, and row operations on matrices. The pivot that we have just defined in connection with the elimination procedure is also, when considering operations on matrices, the element in the matrix that is used to reduce elements in other rows to zero. Thus the pivot used to reduce (3.7) to (3.8) is the (2, 2) element in (3.7), namely 0.5.

There is no need to proceed systematically by using the first equation to eliminate the first unknown, as in the above description. In fact a very wide choice of pivots is available. Thus we could use the fourth equation in (3.1) to eliminate x_2 from the first three equations:

$$\begin{aligned} 5x_1 - 7x_3 + 2x_4 &= 3 \\ 2x_1 - 2x_3 + x_4 &= 1 \\ x_1 - 8x_3 + 3x_4 &= 0. \end{aligned} \tag{3.15}$$

We can now use the second equation to eliminate x_4 from the first and third:

$$\begin{aligned} x_1 - 3x_3 &= 1 \\ -5x_1 + 14x_3 &= -3. \end{aligned}$$

Hence $x_1 = -5$, $x_3 = -2$, and back-substitution in the pivotal equations gives $x_4 = 7$, $x_2 = 6$. This is the same result as before.

From the discussion in the last paragraph it should be clear that a wide choice of pivots is available. The only restriction that occurs (at least theoretically) can be illustrated by the following example:

$$\begin{aligned} x_2 + x_3 &= 0 \\ x_1 - 5x_2 + 3x_3 &= 0 \\ 2x_1 + x_2 - 4x_3 &= -1. \end{aligned} \tag{3.16}$$

For obvious reasons we cannot use the first equation to eliminate x_1 from the remaining two. From a matrix point of view we wish to reduce the following matrix to a simpler form:

$$\begin{bmatrix} 0 & 1 & 1 & 1 \\ 1 & -5 & 3 & 0 \\ 2 & 1 & -4 & -1 \end{bmatrix}.$$

We cannot use the (1, 1) element as a pivot. We can however use the (1, 2) or (1, 3) elements as pivots. It will turn out later (see Sections 8.5, 8.6) that the way in which pivots are chosen is important if we wish to obtain accurate numerical solutions of linear equations by means of digital computers.

In the remainder of this section we deal with another point that is of considerable practical importance.

Suppose that we have several sets of equations to solve, say $\mathbf{A}\mathbf{x}_1 = \mathbf{b}_1$, $\mathbf{A}\mathbf{x}_2 = \mathbf{b}_2, \ldots$. (The reader must be careful to distinguish the column vectors $\mathbf{x}_1, \mathbf{x}_2, \ldots$ from the notation $x_1, x_2, \ldots$ for the individual unknowns, used previously in this section.) In order to solve several sets of equations $\mathbf{A}\mathbf{x}_i = \mathbf{b}_i$, there is no need to go through the whole of the above procedure separately in each case, since the reduction of **A** to triangular form in the method of successive elimination (or to the unit matrix in the Gauss-Jordan method) is unaffected by the form of **b**. Thus suppose we wish to solve three sets of equations with the same coefficient matrix as above, and

$$\mathbf{b}_1 = \begin{bmatrix} 3 \\ 1 \\ 0 \\ 0 \end{bmatrix}, \quad \mathbf{b}_2 = \begin{bmatrix} -5 \\ -2 \\ 0 \\ 5 \end{bmatrix}, \quad \mathbf{b}_3 = \begin{bmatrix} -6 \\ -2 \\ 5 \\ 3 \end{bmatrix}.$$

Then we perform the row operations on the following matrix:

$$\begin{bmatrix} 2 & -3 & 2 & 5 & 3 & -5 & -6 \\ 1 & -1 & 1 & 2 & 1 & -2 & -2 \\ 3 & 2 & 2 & 1 & 0 & 0 & 5 \\ 1 & 1 & -3 & -1 & 0 & 5 & 3 \end{bmatrix}. \tag{3.17}$$

Using the successive elimination method, reduction to triangular form gives the matrix [compare (3.9)]:

$$\begin{bmatrix} 1 & -1.5 & 1 & 2.5 & 1.5 & -2.5 & -3 \\ 0 & 1 & 0 & -1 & -1 & 1 & 2 \\ 0 & 0 & 1 & 0 & -2 & -1 & -1 \\ 0 & 0 & 0 & 1 & 7 & -1 & 3 \end{bmatrix}. \tag{3.18}$$

Back-substitution in each set separately then gives the solution:

$$\mathbf{x}_1 = \begin{bmatrix} -5 \\ 6 \\ -2 \\ 7 \end{bmatrix}, \qquad \mathbf{x}_2 = \begin{bmatrix} 1 \\ 0 \\ -1 \\ -1 \end{bmatrix}, \qquad \mathbf{x}_3 = \begin{bmatrix} -2 \\ 5 \\ -1 \\ 3 \end{bmatrix}. \tag{3.19}$$

Suppose next that we wish to find the inverse of an $n \times n$ matrix $\mathbf{A}$. Denote the columns of $\mathbf{A}^{-1}$ by $\mathbf{x}_1, \mathbf{x}_2, \ldots, \mathbf{x}_n$, and the columns of the identity matrix by $\mathbf{e}_1, \mathbf{e}_2, \ldots, \mathbf{e}_n$ (i.e., $\mathbf{e}_k$ is a column matrix whose elements are zero except for the kth element which is unity). Using partitioned matrices we see that the problem of finding $\mathbf{A}^{-1}$ such that $\mathbf{A}\mathbf{A}^{-1} = \mathbf{I}$ is equivalent to the problem of solving (see Theorem 1.8)

$$\mathbf{A}[\mathbf{x}_1, \mathbf{x}_2, \ldots, \mathbf{x}_n] = [\mathbf{e}_1, \mathbf{e}_2, \ldots, \mathbf{e}_n],$$

and this is equivalent to solving the n independent sets of equations

$$\mathbf{A}\mathbf{x}_j = \mathbf{e}_j, \qquad j = 1, 2, \ldots, n.$$

These equations all have the same coefficient matrix $\mathbf{A}$ so that they can be solved conveniently by the method described in the last paragraph. We form the augmented matrix

$$[\mathbf{A}, \mathbf{I}],$$

reduce to triangular form, and perform back-substitutions.

As a numerical example, consider the matrix $\mathbf{A}$ consisting of the first four columns of (3.17). This leads to the augmented matrix

$$\begin{bmatrix} 2 & -3 & 2 & 5 & 1 & 0 & 0 & 0 \\ 1 & -1 & 1 & 2 & 0 & 1 & 0 & 0 \\ 3 & 2 & 2 & 1 & 0 & 0 & 1 & 0 \\ 1 & 1 & -3 & -1 & 0 & 0 & 0 & 1 \end{bmatrix}. \tag{3.20}$$

Reduction to triangular form leads to

$$\begin{bmatrix} 1 & -1.5 & 1 & 2.5 & 0.5 & 0 & 0 & 0 \\ 0 & 1 & 0 & -1 & -1 & 2 & 0 & 0 \\ 0 & 0 & 1 & 0 & -5 & 13 & -1 & 0 \\ 0 & 0 & 0 & 1 & 18 & -47 & 4 & -1 \end{bmatrix}. \tag{3.21}$$

The inverse is then obtained by back-substitution,

$$\mathbf{A}^{-1} = [\mathbf{x}_1, \mathbf{x}_2, \mathbf{x}_3, \mathbf{x}_4] = \begin{bmatrix} -14 & 37 & -3 & 1 \\ 17 & -45 & 4 & -1 \\ -5 & 13 & -1 & 0 \\ 18 & -47 & 4 & -1 \end{bmatrix}. \tag{3.22}$$

Various practical aspects of the methods discussed in this section will be considered later. Here we note two results connected with the amount of work involved in solving a set of equations or inverting a matrix. Simple enumeration shows that approximately $\frac{1}{3}n^3$ additions and $\frac{1}{3}n^3$ multiplications are required to solve a set of n equations in n unknowns by the method of successive elimination. This is an important result since it shows that the amount of work involved increases rapidly with the number of equations. Doubling the number of equations increases the work by a factor of 8. The other result that we wish to note here is that the amount of work involved in inverting an $n \times n$ matrix is approximately *three* times the amount of work involved in solving a single set of n equations in n unknowns (not n times, as might be thought at first sight). The reason for this will be examined later, by comparing the work involved in obtaining (3.21) and back-substituting, with the amount of work required to solve a single set of equations (see Section 7.6).

Ex. 3.1. Find the inverses of the matrices given in Exs. 1.21, 1.47, by carrying out row operations on an augmented matrix, as described in connection with (3.20).

Ex. 3.2. Obtain the solutions (3.19) by applying the Gauss-Jordan procedure to (3.17).

Ex. 3.3. Obtain the inverse (3.22) by applying the Gauss-Jordan procedure to (3.20).

Ex. 3.4. Show that when the Gauss-Jordan procedure is applied to the augmented matrix

$$[\mathbf{A}, \mathbf{I}],$$

we obtain the final result

$$[\mathbf{I}, \mathbf{A}^{-1}].$$

3.3 The Existence of Solutions for a Set of Equations

In the last section we considered certain methods for finding the numerical solution of a set of simultaneous linear equations, but we did not pay much attention to the question of whether such a solution existed at all, or whether it was unique. This is the problem which we wish to consider for the remainder of this chapter.

Consider first of all the simple equation $ax = b$, where a, x, b are scalars. We tend to say immediately that the solution of this equation is $x = b/a$, but in fact there are *three* possibilities:

(a) If $a \neq 0$, then $x = b/a$, and this is the unique solution of the equation, whatever the value of b (which may be zero, in which case the solution is simply $x = 0$).

(b) If $a = 0$ there are two possibilities, depending on the value of b:

(i) If $b \neq 0$, then the equation is $0 \cdot x = b \neq 0$, and no finite solution exists. The solution "x equal to infinity" is not considered to be a permissible solution. We say that "no solution exists," or, alternatively, that "the equation is inconsistent" since it implies $0 = b \neq 0$, which is a contradiction.

(ii) If $b = 0$, then *any* number is a solution of the equation, for $0 \cdot x = 0$, whatever value is given to x. Infinity is again excluded, since $0 \cdot \infty$ is meaningless.

The same possibilities exist in the case of two equations in two unknowns. Thus,

$$\left.\begin{aligned} x_1 + x_2 &= 2 \\ x_1 - x_2 &= 0 \end{aligned}\right\}$$

have a unique solution,

$$\left.\begin{aligned} x_1 + x_2 &= 2 \\ x_1 + x_2 &= 1 \end{aligned}\right\}$$

are inconsistent, and

$$\left.\begin{aligned} x_1 + x_2 &= 2 \\ 2x_1 + 2x_2 &= 4 \end{aligned}\right\}$$

have an infinity of solutions, namely $x_1 = k$, $x_2 = 2 - k$, for all k.

Precisely the same possibilities exist in the general case of n equations in n unknowns. For any specific example it is easy to find out what the situation is by direct solution of the equations or, equivalently, by using the triangular reduction of the augmented matrix described in the last section. Thus, consider the equations

$$\begin{aligned} x_1 + 2x_2 - 5x_3 &= 2 \\ 2x_1 - 3x_2 + 4x_3 &= 4 \\ 4x_1 + x_2 - 6x_3 &= 8. \end{aligned} \tag{3.23}$$

The augmented matrix is

$$\begin{bmatrix} 1 & 2 & -5 & 2 \\ 2 & -3 & 4 & 4 \\ 4 & 1 & -6 & 8 \end{bmatrix}.$$

Row operations reduce this to

$$\begin{bmatrix} 1 & 2 & -5 & 2 \\ 0 & 1 & -2 & 0 \\ 0 & 0 & 0 & 0 \end{bmatrix}. \tag{3.24}$$

Note that all the elements in the third row are zero. This means that the third equation has been reduced to $0 \cdot x_3 = 0$, so that a solution of the original equation exists for which $x_3 = k$, where k is any number. Back-substitution then gives $x_2 = 2k$, $x_1 = 2 + k$. This solution can be written in the form

$$\begin{bmatrix} x_1 \\ x_2 \\ x_3 \end{bmatrix} = \begin{bmatrix} 2 \\ 0 \\ 0 \end{bmatrix} + k \begin{bmatrix} 1 \\ 2 \\ 1 \end{bmatrix}. \tag{3.25}$$

If, on the other hand, the third equation in (3.23) is

$$4x_1 + x_2 - 6x_3 = 9,$$

we find, instead of (3.24),

$$\begin{bmatrix} 1 & 2 & -5 & 2 \\ 0 & 1 & -2 & 0 \\ 0 & 0 & 0 & 1 \end{bmatrix}. \tag{3.26}$$

The third equation is now $0 \cdot x_3 = 1$, so that this set of equations is inconsistent.

In the examples considered so far, the number of equations has been exactly equal to the number of unknowns, but the same methods (namely reduction of the augmented matrix to triangular form or, equivalently, direct solutions of the equations) can be used to check whether a given set of m equations in n unknowns, for any m, n, possess no solution, a unique solution, or an infinity of solutions. Thus the reader can verify the following examples by using the method described above:

Ex. 3.5. If the equation

$$x_1 + x_2 + x_3 = 6$$

is added to the set (3.23), the resulting system of four equations in three unknowns has the unique solution $x_1 = 3$, $x_2 = 2$, $x_3 = 1$.

Ex. 3.6. If the equation

$$3x_1 - x_2 - x_3 = 6$$

is added to the set (3.23), the resulting system of four equations in three unknowns has the same set of solutions as (3.23), namely (3.25).

Ex. 3.7. The system of two equations in three unknowns given by the first two equations in (3.23) has the same set of solutions as (3.23), namely (3.25).

The moral of these examples is that it is not, in general, possible to say whether equations have no solution, a unique solution, or an infinity of solutions, merely from knowledge of the number of equations and the number of unknowns, i.e., m and n. Ten equations in two unknowns can have a unique solution, and two equations in ten unknowns may be inconsistent.

We next consider the following example:

$$\begin{aligned} x_1 + 2x_2 - x_3 &= 2 \\ 2x_1 + 4x_2 + x_3 &= 7 \\ 3x_1 + 6x_2 - 2x_3 &= 7. \end{aligned} \tag{3.27}$$

On using the first equation to eliminate x_1 from the remaining two, we obtain (placing the matrix and equation forms alongside each other):

$$\begin{aligned} x_1 + 2x_2 - x_3 &= 2 \\ 3x_3 &= 3 \\ x_3 &= 1, \end{aligned} \qquad \begin{bmatrix} 1 & 2 & -1 & 2 \\ 0 & 0 & 3 & 3 \\ 0 & 0 & 1 & 1 \end{bmatrix}. \tag{3.28}$$

The unknown x_2 does not appear in the second and third equations. We therefore reduce the coefficient of x_3 in the second equation to unity by dividing this equation by 3. We can then omit the third equation because it simply repeats the second. [In terms of the matrix in (3.28), the (2, 2) and (3, 2) elements are zero. We therefore consider the third column, reduce the (2, 3) element to unity by multiplying the second row by 3, and subtract the resulting row from the last row, so that the last row is reduced to a row of zeros.]

$$\begin{aligned} x_1 + 2x_2 - x_3 &= 2 \\ x_3 &= 1, \end{aligned} \qquad \begin{bmatrix} 1 & 2 & -1 & 2 \\ 0 & 0 & 1 & 1 \\ 0 & 0 & 0 & 0 \end{bmatrix}. \tag{3.29}$$

The general solution of the original set of equations is therefore given by

$$x_3 = 1, \qquad x_2 = p, \qquad x_1 = 3 - 2p, \tag{3.30}$$

where p is an arbitrary constant.

Instead of setting x_2 equal to an arbitrary constant, we could have set x_1 equal to an arbitrary constant, and then the general solution is

$$x_3 = 1, \qquad x_1 = q, \qquad x_2 = \tfrac{1}{2}(3 - q). \tag{3.31}$$

It is clear that the solutions (3.30) and (3.31) are essentially the same since if we assign any value to p in (3.30), the same solution will be given by setting $q = 3 - 2p$ in (3.31). However, in more complicated cases, the equivalence of different forms of solutions may not be so obvious. The problem of determining whether solutions are equivalent can be settled by the method discussed in Section 4.6 (see Exs. 4.27, 4.50). It should be noted that in the above example it is not possible to assign an arbitrary value to x_3.

The procedure leading to (3.29) corresponds to what we have previously called "reduction to triangular form," with appropriate modifications for the fact that zero elements in successive matrices mean that we cannot have a strictly triangular form. To see the structure of the solution of (3.29) more clearly, it is convenient to use back-substitution in the equations [in the matrix, use the analog of the Gauss-Jordan procedure to reduce the (1, 3) element to zero]. This gives

$$\begin{aligned} x_1 + 2x_2 \qquad &= 3 \\ x_3 &= 1, \end{aligned} \qquad \begin{bmatrix} 1 & 2 & 0 & 3 \\ 0 & 0 & 1 & 1 \\ 0 & 0 & 0 & 0 \end{bmatrix}.$$

This tells us immediately that either x_1 or x_2 (but not both) can be assigned arbitrary values, but x_3 cannot be given an arbitrary value.

Ex. 3.8. Given

$$\begin{aligned} x - y + z + w &= 1 \\ 2x - 2y - 3z - 3w &= 17 \\ -x + y + 2z + 2w &= -10 \end{aligned}$$

show that it is possible to solve these equations for x, z in terms of y, w, and vice versa, but it is not possible to solve for z, w in terms of x, y, and vice versa. An alternative, more detailed, statement is that the pairs x, w or x, z or y, w or y, z can be given arbitrary values and the equations can then be solved for the remaining pairs of unknowns. However, the pairs x, y or w, z cannot be given arbitrary values.

Ex. 3.9. Find the general solution of the homogeneous system $\mathbf{Ax} = \mathbf{0}$, where

$$\mathbf{A} = \begin{bmatrix} 0 & 1 & -2 & 0 & 0 & 2 & 4 \\ 0 & 0 & 0 & 1 & 0 & 0 & 1 \\ 0 & 0 & 0 & 0 & 1 & -1 & 6 \\ 0 & 0 & 0 & 0 & 0 & 0 & 0 \end{bmatrix}.$$

State precisely the situation concerning which combinations of unknowns can be given arbitrary values. (Note that the fact that the right-hand side of the equations is zero does not affect the procedure.)

Ex. 3.10. Which of the following sets of equations possess zero, one, or an infinity of solutions?

(a)
$$\begin{aligned} x - y + z &= 0 \\ 2x + y - z &= -3 \\ x + 2y - 2z &= -2. \end{aligned}$$

(b)
$$\begin{aligned} x + y + z &= 0 \\ 2x + y - z &= -3 \\ -x - 2y - 4z &= -3 \\ 2x \qquad - 4z &= -6. \end{aligned}$$

(c)
$$\begin{aligned} x - y + z &= 0 \\ 2x + y - z &= -3 \\ x - 3y + 4z &= 5. \end{aligned}$$

3.4 Reduction of a System of Equations to a Simplified Form

We have so far considered the question of the existence of solutions only for particular examples. We now consider the situation theoretically by generalizing the procedure followed for the specific examples. Suppose that we have a system of m equations in n unknowns:

$$\begin{aligned} a_{11}x_1 + a_{12}x_2 + \cdots + a_{1n}x_n &= b_1 \\ a_{21}x_1 + a_{22}x_2 + \cdots + a_{2n}x_n &= b_2 \\ &\cdots \\ a_{m1}x_1 + a_{m2}x_2 + \cdots + a_{mn}x_n &= b_m. \end{aligned} \tag{3.32}$$

It may happen that all the coefficients a_{i1} are zero. If this is the case we can choose x_1 equal to any arbitrary constant. This will not affect the values of $x_2, \ldots, x_n$, and we can move on to consider x_2. If at least one of the a_{i1} is nonzero, we can choose any one such nonzero coefficient, say a_{p1}, interchange the first and pth equations, and divide the new first equation by a_{p1}. The resulting equation is used to eliminate x_1 from the remaining $m - 1$ equations. The final result is a set of equations of the following form:

$$\begin{aligned} x_1 + \alpha_{12}x_2 + \alpha_{13}x_3 + \ldots + \alpha_{1n}x_n &= \beta_1 \\ a'_{22}x_2 + a'_{23}x_3 + \ldots + a'_{2n}x_n &= b'_2 \\ &\cdots \\ a'_{m2}x_2 + a'_{m3}x_3 + \ldots + a'_{mn}x_n &= b'_m. \end{aligned} \tag{3.33}$$

If $a_{11} \neq 0$ in (3.32), and we use the first equation to eliminate x_1 from the other equations, the coefficients in (3.33) are given by:

$$\alpha_{ij} = \frac{a_{1j}}{a_{11}}, \qquad \beta_1 = \frac{b_1}{a_{11}}, \qquad a'_{ij} = a_{ij} - a_{i1}\alpha_{1j}, \qquad b'_i = b - a_{i1}\beta_1.$$

There are now two possibilities:

(a) At least one of the a'_{i2} is nonzero. We can choose any one of these, say a'_{q2}, interchange the second and qth equations in (3.33), divide the new second equation by a'_{q2}. The result is used to eliminate x_2 from the remaining $m - 2$ equations . The final result is of the form

$$\begin{aligned} x_1 + \alpha_{12}x_2 + \alpha_{13}x_3 + \ldots + \alpha_{1n}x_n &= \beta_1 \\ x_2 + \alpha_{23}x_3 + \ldots + \alpha_{2n}x_n &= \beta_2 \\ a''_{33}x_3 + \ldots + a''_{3n}x_n &= b''_3 \\ &\cdots \\ a''_{m3}x_3 + \ldots + a''_{mn}x_n &= b''_m. \end{aligned} \tag{3.34}$$

(b) All the a'_{i2} may be zero ($i = 2$ to m). In this case we simply accept the situation and pass on to consideration of the unknown x_3. Instead of (3.34) we must consider

$$\begin{aligned} x_1 + \alpha_{12}x_2 + \alpha_{13}x_3 + \ldots + \alpha_{1n}x_n &= \beta_1 \\ a'_{23}x_3 + \ldots + a'_{2n}x_n &= b'_2 \\ a'_{33}x_3 + \ldots + a'_{3n}x_n &= b'_3 \\ \ldots \\ a'_{m3}x_3 + \ldots + a'_{mn}x_n &= b'_m. \end{aligned} \tag{3.35}$$

The above procedure can be repeated. If all the a''_{i3} in (3.34) or a'_{i3} in (3.35) are zero, we go on to consider x_4. Otherwise we can choose any equation in which x_3 has a nonzero coefficient, and use this to eliminate x_3 from the remaining equations. Repeating this procedure, we will eventually reach x_n and the process will terminate.

A precise description of the final form of the equations is carried out most easily in terms of matrices, and this is one of the reasons why we consider the "row-echelon normal form" of a matrix in Section 3.7. Here we content ourselves with reminding the reader that the numerical examples considered in Sections 3.2, 3.3 were all illustrations of the above procedure. For example, the system (3.27),

$$\begin{aligned} x_1 + 2x_2 - x_3 &= 2 \\ 2x_1 + 4x_2 + x_3 &= 7 \\ 3x_1 + 6x_2 - 2x_3 &= 7 \end{aligned} \tag{3.36}$$

was reduced to (3.29),

$$\begin{aligned} x_1 + 2x_2 - x_3 &= 2 \\ x_3 &= 1. \end{aligned} \tag{3.37}$$

In this case we obtained an infinity of solutions (3.30). If, instead of (3.36), we consider

$$\begin{aligned} x_1 + 2x_2 - x_3 &= 2 \\ 2x_1 + 4x_2 + x_3 &= 7 \\ 3x_1 + 6x_2 - 2x_3 &= 6, \end{aligned} \tag{3.38}$$

we obtain, instead of (3.37),

$$\begin{aligned} x_1 + 2x_2 - x_3 &= 2 \\ x_3 &= 1 \\ 0 \cdot x_3 &= -1. \end{aligned}$$

The last equation is contradictory so that no solution exists.

There are several important questions that we must now consider. For instance, we have made the implicit assumption that if we solve the simplified system (3.37), then the solutions we obtain [i.e., (3.30)] will also be solutions of (3.36). In order to see what the precise situation is we require a certain amount of mathematical machinery. Since the building up of this machinery may distract some readers from the point of what we are trying to achieve, we interpolate a short section to state some of the main results in a language not couched in theorem-proof form. Some readers (and lecturers) may prefer to omit the next section altogether.

3.5 The Existence of Solutions for a Set of Equations

The procedure described in the last section reduced the general system (3.32), $\mathbf{Ax} = \mathbf{b}$, to a simple form. The first equation in the reduced system has the form

$$x_1 + \alpha_{12}x_2 + \cdots + \alpha_{1n}x_n = \beta_1.$$

The second equation has the form

$$x_p + \alpha_{2,p+1}x_{p+1} + \cdots + \alpha_{2n}x_n = \beta_2,$$

where $p > 1$. The third equation has the form

$$x_q + \alpha_{3,q+1}x_{q+1} + \cdots + \alpha_{3n}x_n = \beta_3,$$

where $q > p$, and so on. The unknowns $x_1, x_p, x_q, \ldots$ play a key role in the procedure. In order to keep the notation simple it is convenient to rename the unknowns by setting

$$z_1 = x_1, \qquad z_2 = x_p, \qquad z_3 = x_q, \qquad \ldots,$$

where, if there are k unknowns $x_1, x_p, x_q, \ldots$, these become $z_1, \ldots, z_k$ and $z_{k+1}, \ldots, z_n$ are the remaining x_i in some order which is not important. The number k is an integer associated with the original equations which is of basic significance in later developments. The question of the existence of solutions depends on the trio of numbers, m, n, k, not on m, n alone.

The resulting set of equations have the following form:

$$\begin{bmatrix} 1 & \gamma_{12} \cdots \gamma_{1,k} & \gamma_{1,k+1} \cdots \gamma_{1n} \\ 0 & 1 \ \ldots \gamma_{2,k} & \gamma_{2,k+1} \cdots \gamma_{2n} \\ & \cdots & \\ 0 & 0 \ \ldots \ 1 & \gamma_{k,k+1} \cdots \gamma_{kn} \\ 0 & 0 \ \ldots \ 0 & 0 \ \ldots \ 0 \\ & \cdots & \\ 0 & 0 \ \ldots \ 0 & 0 \ \ldots \ 0 \end{bmatrix} \begin{bmatrix} z_1 \\ z_2 \\ \cdot \\ \cdot \\ \cdot \\ z_n \end{bmatrix} = \begin{bmatrix} \beta_1 \\ \beta_2 \\ \cdot \\ \beta_k \\ \beta_{k+1} \\ \cdot \\ \beta_m \end{bmatrix} \tag{3.39}$$

where there are precisely k units along the diagonal leading from the top left-hand corner of the matrix of coefficients. All the elements of the $(k + 1)$th and later rows of the $m \times n$ matrix of coefficients are zero. However, the $\beta_{k+1}, \ldots, \beta_m$ need not be all zero.

There are now exactly three possibilities:

(a) *$k < m$ and at least one of the elements $\beta_{k+1}, \ldots, \beta_m$ is nonzero.* Suppose that an element β_p is nonzero ($p > k$). Then the pth equation is of the form

$$0 \cdot z_1 + 0 \cdot z_2 + \cdots + 0 \cdot z_n = \beta_p \neq 0$$

which is a contradiction, and the equations are inconsistent. [This is the case (b)(i) in the simple example considered at the beginning of Section 3.3.]

(b) *$k = n$ and either* (i) *$k < m$ and all the elements $\beta_{k+1}, \ldots, \beta_m$ are zero,* or (ii) *$k = m$.* Then the equations have a definite solution which can be obtained by back-substitution. [This is the case (a) in the example given at the beginning of Section 3.3. We use the word "definite" to avoid use of the word "unique" at this point. We shall prove uniqueness later.]

(c) *$k < n$ and either* (i) *$k < m$ and all the elements $\beta_{k+1}, \ldots, \beta_m$ are zero, or* (ii) *$k = m$.* Then arbitrary values can be assigned to the $n - k$ variables $z_{k+1}, \ldots, z_n$, and the equations can be solved for $z_1, \ldots, z_k$. There is an infinity of solutions. [The nature of the "infinity of solutions" will be examined later. This is the case (b)(ii) in the examples considered at the beginning of Section 3.3.]

An important special case occurs when $\mathbf{b} = \mathbf{0}$ in the original set of equations $\mathbf{Ax} = \mathbf{b}$. In this case we say that the equations are *homogeneous.* Clearly when such equations are reduced to the form (3.39), all the β_i are zero, so that case (a) in the above classification does not arise. There are then only two possibilities:

(b′) *If $k = n$ (which implies $m \geq n$) then equations* (3.39) *have the solution* $\mathbf{z} = \mathbf{0}$ *which leads to the trivial solution* $\mathbf{x} = \mathbf{0}$ *for the original system* $\mathbf{Ax} = \mathbf{0}$. (In fact the solution $\mathbf{x} = \mathbf{0}$ is the *only* solution of $\mathbf{Ax} = \mathbf{0}$ in this case, as we shall see later.)

(c′) *If $k < n$, the equations possess an infinity of solutions given by assigning arbitrary values to $z_{k+1}, \ldots, z_n$.*

These statements contain a great deal of information, and some of the implications will be explored later. However, we have been careful *not* to claim that the above statements are "theorems" because there is one fundamental type of question which we have ignored so far. We are allowed a great deal of flexibility in forming (3.39). We can interchange equations or renumber the unknowns. If we start with a given system of equations and reduce them to forms analogous to (3.39) in two different ways, what guarantee have we that the resulting solutions are the "same," in some sense? In case (b), if we obtain two definite solutions by different sequences of operations, what guarantee have we that these solutions are the same, so that the solution is unique? In case (b′), although we have obtained only the trivial solution $\mathbf{x} = \mathbf{0}$ by one sequence of operations, what guarantee is there that another sequence of operations will not produce a nonzero solution? We begin to answer these questions in the remainder of this chapter, but the final answer will not be obtained until we introduce vector spaces in Chapter 4 (see Section 4.8).

3.6 Equivalence of Sets of Equations

We now resume the systematic development of the theory started in Section 3.4. We wish to state precisely what the relation is between the original set of equations (3.32) and the final reduced form obtained by following the procedure in Section 3.4. In order to do this, we require some preliminary definitions.

DEFINITION 3.1. A system of equations that has a solution is said to be *consistent*. Otherwise the system is said to be *inconsistent*. The collection of all solutions of a consistent system of equations is called its *solution set*. Two systems of equations are said to be *equivalent* if every solution of one system is also a solution of the other, and vice versa, i.e., they have the same solution set.

In order to analyze the reduction procedure in Section 3.4, it is convenient to isolate the three basic kinds of operations that were performed on a system of equations. We are considering the general case of m equations in n unknowns.

DEFINITION 3.2. The following are known as *elementary operations* on a system of equations.

I. Two equations are interchanged.
II. An equation is multiplied by a nonzero scalar.
III. The ith equation is replaced by the sum of the ith and p times the jth equation ($j \neq i$).

The basic result that we require in connection with elementary operations is the following:

THEOREM 3.1. *If one system of equations can be obtained from another system by a sequence of elementary operations, then the two systems are equivalent (i.e., they have the same solution set).*

Proof: It makes no difference whether a given equation in a system is written first, last, or in some intermediate position, so that the theorem is true for elementary operations of Type I. Suppose that the kth equation of the original system is written

$$f_k = a_{k1}x_1 + a_{k2}x_2 + \cdots + a_{kn}x_n - b_k = 0.$$

An elementary operation of Type II replaces one equation, say $f_i = 0$, by $cf_i = 0$ ($c \neq 0$). Clearly any solution of $f_i = 0$ is also a solution of $cf_i = 0$, and since c is nonzero, any solution of $cf_i = 0$ is also a solution of $f_i = 0$. Hence the theorem is proved for elementary operations of Type II. Finally, let the ith equation $f_i = 0$ of the first system be replaced by $f_i + pf_j = 0$. Any solution of the first system satisfies $f_i = 0$ and $f_j = 0$, and hence $f_i + pf_j = 0$. Conversely, any solution of the modified system satisfies $f_i + pf_j = 0$ and $f_j = 0$, and hence $f_i = 0$. This proves the theorem for elementary operations of Type III. If we now perform a sequence of elementary operations, the theorem is true for each step of the sequence, so it is true for the whole sequence.

Note that we have been careful to specify that the elementary operations must be performed in sequence, i.e., one after the other. The theorem is false if we perform simultaneous elementary operations of Type III. Thus suppose we replace $f_i = 0$ by $f_i + pf_j = 0$ and $f_j = 0$ by $f_j + qf_i = 0$. We cannot deduce that a solution satisfying $f_i + pf_j = 0$ and $f_j + qf_i = 0$ is always a solution of $f_i = 0$ and $f_j = 0$ (for example, choose $p = q = 1$).

As an example of the application of Theorem 3.1, we can now say that all the solutions of (3.37) are also solutions of (3.36), and vice versa.

Ex. 3.11. Are the following sets of equations equivalent? Justify your answer.

(a)
$$\begin{aligned} x - 2y + z &= 4 \\ 2x - 3y - z &= 2. \end{aligned} \tag{3.40}$$

(b)
$$\begin{aligned} x + y - 8z &= -14 \\ 3x - 4y - 3z &= 0 \\ 2x - y - 7z &= -10. \end{aligned} \tag{3.41}$$

Solution: We subtract twice the first equation in (a) from the second to obtain the set
$$\begin{aligned} x - 2y + z &= 4 \\ y - 3z &= -6. \end{aligned} \tag{3.42}$$
We see that z can be chosen to be any arbitrary constant, say $z = k$, and then (3.40) gives
$$z = k, \qquad y = 3k - 6, \qquad x = 5k - 8. \tag{3.43}$$
To solve the system (b) we can use the first equation to eliminate x from the second and third. This gives
$$\begin{aligned} x + y - 8z &= -14 \\ -7y - 21z &= 42 \\ -3y + 9z &= 18. \end{aligned} \tag{3.44}$$
Again z can be chosen arbitrary, say $z = k$, as before. The second and third equations in (3.44) are the same and give $y = 3k - 6$. The first equation in (3.44) then gives $x = 5k - 8$, so that we have recovered the general solution (3.43) of the set (a). Hence the two sets of equations are equivalent. (A better method for solving this problem is given in the next section.)

Ex. 3.12. In Section 3.2 it was demonstrated that a wide variety of choice of pivots is available when solving linear equations by the elimination method. Show that the final set of equations is always equivalent to the original system, independent of the way in which the pivots have been chosen.

3.7 Elementary Row Operations and the Row-Echelon Normal Form

We have already emphasized several times that we can solve a set of simultaneous linear equations either by direct manipulation of the equations [as in the discussion of (3.1)–(3.5) above] or by manipulation of the rows of the corresponding augmented matrix [as in the discussion of (3.6)–(3.9)]. The theoretical discussion in Sections 3.4–3.6 was carried out in terms of direct manipulation of the equations. However further developments are most easily carried out in terms of matrices, and this we proceed to consider.

The reduction of a system of equations to a simplified form in Section 3.4 can be carried out in terms of matrices in the following way. We write down the augmented matrix corresponding to (3.32),

$$\begin{bmatrix} a_{11} & a_{12} & \cdots & a_{1n} & b_1 \\ a_{21} & a_{22} & \cdots & a_{2n} & b_2 \\ & & \cdots & & \\ a_{m1} & a_{m2} & \cdots & a_{mn} & b_m \end{bmatrix}. \tag{3.45}$$

If at least one of the elements in the first column is nonzero, we can choose any one of these elements, say a_{p1}, interchange the first and pth rows, and divide the new first row by a_{p1}. Multiples of the resulting first row are subtracted from the remaining $m - 1$ rows, to reduce the last $m - 1$ elements in the first column to zero. The final result is a matrix of the following form [compare (3.33)]:

$$\begin{bmatrix} 1 & \alpha_{12} & \alpha_{13} & \cdots & \alpha_{1n} & \beta_1 \\ 0 & a'_{22} & a'_{23} & \cdots & a'_{2n} & b'_2 \\ & & & \cdots & & \\ 0 & a'_{m2} & a'_{m3} & \cdots & a'_{mn} & b'_m \end{bmatrix}. \tag{3.46}$$

If the matrix has a column of zeros, these will not be altered by the types of operation we are considering (interchanging two rows, multiplying a row by a constant, and adding a multiple of one row to another). Hence, if all the elements in the first column of (3.45) are zero, we simply accept this and move on to consider the second column. If all the elements in this second column are zero, we proceed to consider the third column. Otherwise we apply the procedure that led to (3.46). To simplify (3.46), there are again two possibilities:

(a) If at least one of the elements a'_{i2} is nonzero, we can choose any one of these, say a'_{q2}, interchange the second and qth rows, and divide the new second equation by a'_{q2}. Multiples of the resulting second row are subtracted from the remaining $m - 2$ rows to reduce the last $m - 2$ elements in the second column to zero. We then consider the third column.

(b) If all the elements a'_{i2} ($i = 2$ to m) are zero, we proceed immediately to consider the third column.

This procedure can be repeated until we have dealt with all the columns of the augmented matrix.

We illustrate the procedure by solving Ex. 3.11 by a method different from that used at the end of the last section. It is required to determine whether the sets of equations (3.40) and (3.41) are equivalent. The corresponding matrices are:

$$\begin{bmatrix} 1 & -2 & 1 & 4 \\ 2 & -3 & -1 & 2 \end{bmatrix}, \quad \begin{bmatrix} 1 & 1 & -8 & -14 \\ 3 & -4 & -3 & 0 \\ 2 & -1 & -7 & -10 \end{bmatrix}. \tag{3.47}$$

Following the procedure described above, subtraction of multiples of the first rows from the remaining rows gives

$$\begin{bmatrix} 1 & -2 & 1 & 4 \\ 0 & 1 & -3 & -6 \end{bmatrix}, \quad \begin{bmatrix} 1 & 1 & -8 & -14 \\ 0 & -7 & 21 & 42 \\ 0 & -3 & 9 & 18 \end{bmatrix}.$$

We next divide the second row of the second matrix by -7 and reduce the $(3, 2)$ element to zero, obtaining

$$\begin{bmatrix} 1 & -2 & 1 & 4 \\ 0 & 1 & -3 & -6 \end{bmatrix}, \quad \begin{bmatrix} 1 & 1 & -8 & -14 \\ 0 & 1 & -3 & -6 \\ 0 & 0 & 0 & 0 \end{bmatrix}. \tag{3.48}$$

If we were to proceed as in the last section, we would now write out the systems of equations corresponding to these two matrices and show that they have the same solution set (3.43). However, there is a simpler procedure. We can make the $(1, 2)$ element in each matrix zero by adding a suitable multiple of the appropriate second row to the first. This gives

$$\begin{bmatrix} 1 & 0 & -5 & -8 \\ 0 & 1 & -3 & -6 \end{bmatrix}, \quad \begin{bmatrix} 1 & 0 & -5 & -8 \\ 0 & 1 & -3 & -6 \\ 0 & 0 & 0 & 0 \end{bmatrix}. \tag{3.49}$$

We see immediately that these represent exactly the same set of equations. Hence the original sets (3.40), (3.41) are equivalent.

We now divorce the discussion from consideration of sets of simultaneous linear equations, and consider the procedure from the point of view of operations on the rows of a general $m \times n$ matrix $\mathbf{A} = [a_{ij}]$. As illustrated in the above discussion, these operations are of three types:

DEFINITION **3.3.** *Elementary row operations* on matrices (sometimes shortened to *row operations*) are defined as follows.

I. Interchange of two rows.
II. Multiplication of any row by a nonzero scalar.
III. Replacement of the ith row by the sum of the ith row and p times the jth row ($j \neq i$).

The developments given at the beginning of this section were included in order to lead up to the result that any matrix can be reduced to a unique simple "standard" or "normal" form by using elementary row operations. This we now investigate.

The procedure is described in words in the next paragraph. Some readers may find the corresponding flow-chart in Figure 3.2 easier to follow. The flow-chart and the description in words are entirely equivalent.

A row or column of a matrix is said to be nonzero if at least one element of the row or column is nonzero. Otherwise we talk of a zero row or a zero column, in which all the elements are zero. A zero column cannot be made nonzero by elementary row operations, so that a zero column is already in normal form. We proceed as follows:

(a) Suppose that the first nonzero column is the c_1th, where c_1 may be one. By row interchanges, if necessary, we can arrange that the first element of this column is nonzero. Divide the first row by this element, and subtract multiples of the first row from the other rows (if necessary) so that the 2nd, 3rd, . . ., mth elements of the c_1th column are zero.

(b) If, in the matrix obtained in (a), the 2nd, 3rd, . . . , mth rows are all zero, the matrix has been reduced to the required normal form. Otherwise, suppose that the first column in the matrix obtained in (a) which has a nonzero element in the rows below the first row is the c_2th. By definition of c_1 and c_2 we have $c_1 < c_2$. By interchange of the rows below the first, if necessary, we can arrange that the c_2th element of the second row is nonzero. Divide the second row by this element. Subtract suitable multiples of the resulting second row from the remaining $m - 1$ rows (i.e., the first row as well as the 3rd, . . . , mth) so that all the other elements in the c_2th column are reduced to zero. As an example, if $m = 4$, $n = 7$, $c_1 = 2$, $c_2 = 4$, we would have, at this stage,

$$\begin{bmatrix} 0 & 1 & \times & 0 & \times & \times & \times \\ 0 & 0 & 0 & 1 & \times & \times & \times \\ 0 & 0 & 0 & 0 & \times & \times & \times \\ 0 & 0 & 0 & 0 & \times & \times & \times \end{bmatrix}, \tag{3.50}$$

where the $\times$'s represent numbers that may or may not be zero.

(c) A repetition of the procedure leads to a state at which, say, the c_kth column, for some known $c_k \le n$, has been transformed so that it has a unit in the kth row, for some $k \le m$, all other elements of the c_kth column being zero. Also, either the kth row is the last (i.e., the mth), or all the rows below the kth are zero. In either case, the process terminates. In the above example, for instance, we might obtain

$$\begin{bmatrix} 0 & 1 & \times & 0 & 0 & \times & \times \\ 0 & 0 & 0 & 1 & 0 & \times & \times \\ 0 & 0 & 0 & 0 & 1 & \times & \times \\ 0 & 0 & 0 & 0 & 0 & 0 & 0 \end{bmatrix}. \tag{3.51}$$

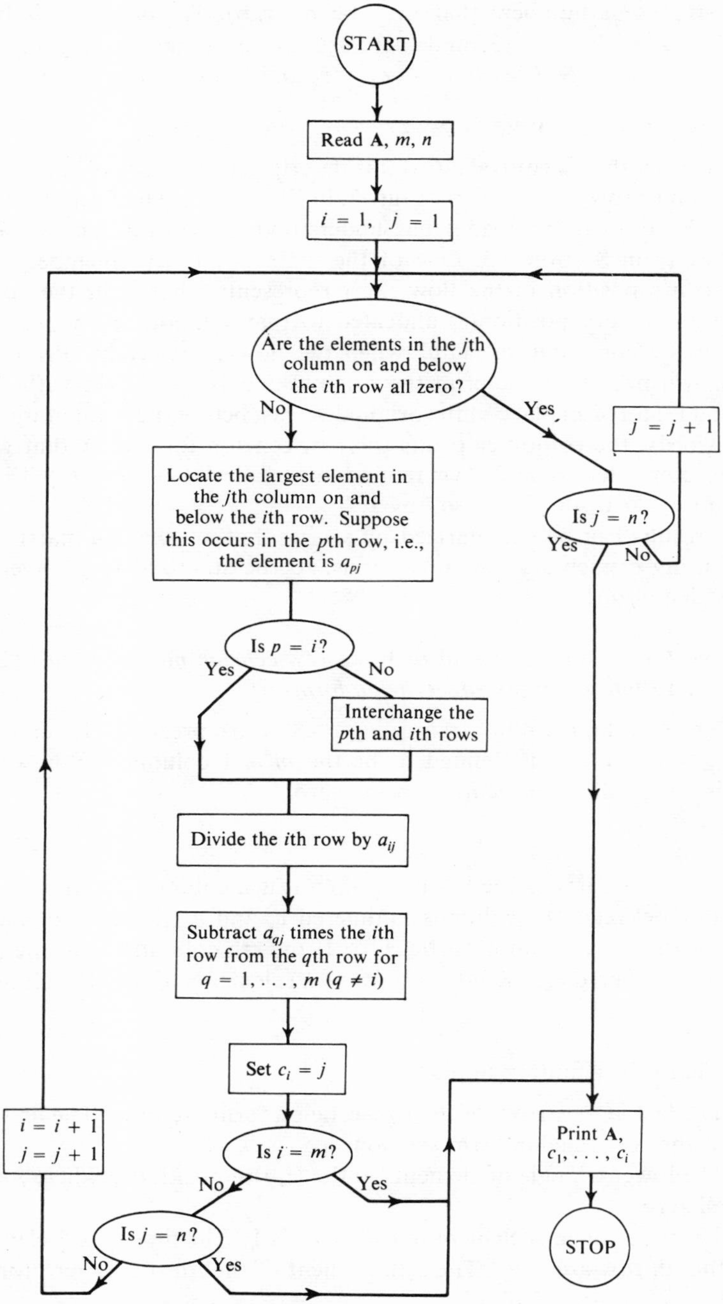

Figure 3.2 Flow-chart for row-echelon form.

The $\times$'s represent numbers that may be nonzero. We have precisely three nonzero rows so that $k = 3$, and there are $k = 3$ numbeıs c_1, c_2, c_3, namely $c_1 = 2$, $c_2 = 4$, $c_3 = 5$. Clearly $c_1 < c_2 < c_3$ and in the general case,

$$c_1 < c_2 < \ldots < c_k.$$

A flow-chart that is equivalent to this description in words of the procedure for reduction to row-echelon form is given in Figure 3.2. The flow-chart should be self-explanatory if the reader has understood the conventions already described briefly in Section 2.3. One of the main points to remember is that a symbol at any position in the flow-chart represents what is in the computer store in the memory position(s) allocated to that symbol, when this point is reached in the computation. Thus when the flow-chart reads "Print **A**" the computer will not of course print the original matrix we started with, but the matrix that is stored in place of the original **A**, just before the computation ends; in other words, the computer prints the row-echelon form of **A** that we have asked the computer to find. We remind the reader that "$i = i + 1$" means "replace i by $i + 1$" or "increase i by 1."

These results can be summarized by saying that any $m \times n$ matrix can be reduced, using elementary row operations, to the standard form given in the following definition:

DEFINITION **3.4.** A matrix is said to be in *row-echelon normal form* (which we sometimes shorten to simply *row-echelon form*) if:

(a) Certain columns numbered $c_1, c_2, \ldots, c_k$ are precisely the unit vectors $\mathbf{e}_1, \mathbf{e}_2, \ldots, \mathbf{e}_k$, where $\mathbf{e}_i$ is defined to be the $m \times 1$ column vector whose ith element is unity, all other elements being zero.

(b) $$c_1 < c_2 < \ldots < c_k.$$

(c) If a column lies to the left of c_1, then it is a column of zeros. If the cth column lies between the columns numbered c_i and c_{i+1}, then the last $m - i$ elements of the cth column must be zero. If the cth column lies to the right of the column numbered c_k, then the last $(m - k)$ elements of the cth column must be zero.

Note that this definition implies:

(i) The last $m - k$ rows of the row-echelon form are zero. The first k rows of the row-echelon form are nonzero.
(ii) The lower triangle of elements in the (i, j)th positions, where $j < i$, are all zero.
(iii) The first nonzero element in each row is 1. The first $c_i - 1$ elements of the ith row are zero. The c_kth element of the ith row is zero for $i \neq k$.

The point of the developments preceding this definition is that we have given a practical procedure by means of which any $m \times n$ matrix can be reduced, by elementary row operations, to the row-echelon form described in the above definition. It is clear that there is a considerable degree of freedom in the detailed sequence of the calculations, when reducing a matrix to row-echelon form, since we are allowed to interchange rows in any way we like. However, it is extremely convenient that, whatever sequence we use, we will always arrive back at the *same* row-echelon form. This is the subject of the next section.

Ex. 3.13. Prove that the question of whether a system of m equations in n unknowns, $\mathbf{Ax} = \mathbf{b}$, has no solution, a unique solution, or an infinity of solutions can be decided by reducing $[\mathbf{A}, \mathbf{b}]$ to row-echelon form and inspecting the set of linear equations corresponding to the reduced form. (*Hint*: Establish a correspondence between the operations on equations and matrices introduced in Definitions 3.1, 3.3. Then use Theorem 3.1. This exercise contains the main point of the proof of Theorem 3.6, but it is convenient to postpone this theorem until some properties of the row-echelon form have been established.)

Ex. 3.14. The following matrices represent the augmented matrix $[\mathbf{A}, \mathbf{b}]$ of a system of linear equations. In each case state whether the equations possess zero, one, or an infinity of solutions. If an infinity of solutions exist, write down an expression for the general solution.

(a) $$\begin{bmatrix} 0 & 1 & 0 & 0 & 4 \\ 0 & 0 & 1 & 2 & 5 \\ 0 & 0 & 0 & 0 & 0 \end{bmatrix}.$$

(b) $$\begin{bmatrix} 0 & 1 & 0 & 0 & 4 \\ 0 & 0 & 1 & 0 & 5 \\ 0 & 0 & 0 & 1 & 6 \end{bmatrix}.$$

(c) $$\begin{bmatrix} 1 & 2 & 3 & 4 & 6 \\ 0 & 0 & 0 & 1 & 5 \\ 0 & 0 & 0 & 0 & 1 \end{bmatrix}.$$

(d) $$\begin{bmatrix} 1 & 0 & 0 & 0 & 4 \\ 0 & 1 & 2 & 0 & 5 \\ 0 & 0 & 0 & 1 & 6 \end{bmatrix}.$$

(e) $$\begin{bmatrix} 1 & 3 & 4 & 9 \\ 0 & 2 & 3 & 7 \\ 0 & 0 & 2 & 6 \\ 0 & 0 & 1 & 4 \end{bmatrix}.$$

(f) $$\begin{bmatrix} 1 & 2 & 3 & 4 & 7 \\ 0 & 5 & 7 & 6 & 8 \\ 0 & 5 & 2 & 4 & 7 \\ 0 & 0 & 2 & 1 & 0 \end{bmatrix}.$$

3.8 Uniqueness of the Row-Echelon Form

In order to prove that the row-echelon form is unique, we require some preliminary results concerning matrices connected by elementary row operations. This relationship is so important that it warrants a special name:

DEFINITION 3.5. If a matrix **A** can be obtained from a matrix **B** by elementary row operations, then **A** is said to be *row-equivalent* to **B**.

THEOREM 3.2. *If* **A** *is row-equivalent to* **B** *then* **B** *is row-equivalent to* **A**. *If* **A** *is row-equivalent to* **B** *and* **B** *is row-equivalent to* **C** *then* **A** *is row-equivalent to* **C**.

Proof: We first note that for each elementary operation there is an "inverse" operation. If **A** is obtained from **B** by interchanging rows i and j, then **B** is obtained from **A** by interchanging rows i and j. If **A** is obtained from **B** by multiplying the ith row of **B** by a nonzero scalar, c, then **B** is obtained from **A** by dividing the ith row of **A** by c. If **A** is obtained from **B** by adding p times the jth row of **B** to the ith row, then **B** is obtained from **A** by subtracting p times the jth row of **A** from the ith row. Hence if **A** is obtained from **B** by a sequence of elementary row operations, **B** can be obtained from **A** by performing a sequence of corresponding inverse row operations in the reverse order. This proves the first part of the theorem. If **A** can be obtained from **B** and **B** from **C** by sequences of elementary row operations, it is obvious that **A** can be obtained from **C** by a sequence of elementary row operations. This proves the last part of the theorem.

The next step is to develop a relationship between elementary row operations and premultiplication by matrices of special forms:

THEOREM 3.3. *The result of performing an elementary row operation on a general* $m \times n$ *matrix* **A** *can also be achieved by forming the product* **EA** *where* **E** *is the matrix obtained by performing the row operation on the unit matrix* **I**.

Proof: Suppose that **A** is an $m \times n$ matrix and that we interchange the pth and qth rows. The matrix obtained by interchanging the pth and qth rows of the $m \times n$ unit matrix is

$$\mathbf{E} = \begin{bmatrix} 1 & \dots & 0 & \dots & 0 & \dots & 0 \\ & & & \dots & & & \\ 0 & \dots & 0 & \dots & 1 & \dots & 0 \\ & & & \dots & & & \\ 0 & \dots & 1 & \dots & 0 & \dots & 0 \\ & & & \dots & & & \\ 0 & \dots & 0 & \dots & 0 & \dots & 1 \end{bmatrix}, \tag{3.52}$$

where we indicate the 1st, pth, qth, and last rows and columns. It is easily seen that the matrix **EA** is in fact precisely the matrix obtained by interchanging the pth and qth rows of **A**. Similarly, the matrix obtained by multiplying the pth row of the unit matrix by c is

$$\mathbf{E} = \begin{bmatrix} 1 & \dots & 0 & \dots & 0 \\ & & \dots & & \\ 0 & \dots & c & \dots & 0 \\ & & \dots & & \\ 0 & \dots & 0 & \dots & 1 \end{bmatrix} \tag{3.53}$$

and the matrix **EA** is precisely the matrix obtained by multiplying the pth row of **A** by c. Finally, if we add c times the qth row of the unit matrix to the pth row, we obtain

$$\mathbf{E} = \begin{bmatrix} 1 & \dots & 0 & \dots & 0 & \dots & 0 \\ & & & \dots & & & \\ 0 & \dots & 1 & \dots & c & \dots & 0 \\ & & & \dots & & & \\ 0 & \dots & 0 & \dots & 1 & \dots & 0 \\ & & & \dots & & & \\ 0 & \dots & 0 & \dots & 0 & \dots & 1 \end{bmatrix}, \tag{3.54}$$

where we indicate the 1st, pth, qth, and last rows and columns. The matrix **EA** is precisely the matrix obtained by adding c times the qth row of **A** to the pth row. This completes the proof of the theorem.

DEFINITION **3.6.** Any matrix **E** obtained by performing a single elementary row operation on the unit matrix **I** is known as an *elementary matrix*. $\mathbf{E}_{pq}$ is the elementary matrix obtained by interchanging the pth and qth rows of **I** [cf. (3.52)]. $\mathbf{E}_p(c)$ is the elementary matrix obtained by multiplying the pth row of **I** by c [cf. (3.53)]. $\mathbf{E}_{pq}(c)$ is the elementary matrix obtained by adding c times the qth row of **I** to the pth [cf. (3.54)].

We also require the following:

DEFINITION **3.7.** A vector **u** is said to be a *linear combination* of vectors $\mathbf{u}_1, \mathbf{u}_2, \dots, \mathbf{u}_s$ if **u** can be expressed in the form

$$\mathbf{u} = \alpha_1\mathbf{u}_1 + \alpha_2\mathbf{u}_2 + \dots + \alpha_s\mathbf{u}_s. \tag{3.55}$$

THEOREM **3.4.** *If a matrix* **C** *with rows* $\mathbf{r}_1, \mathbf{r}_2, \dots, \mathbf{r}_m$ *is row-equivalent to a matrix* $\mathbf{C}'$ *with rows* $\mathbf{r}'_1, \mathbf{r}'_2, \dots, \mathbf{r}'_m$, *then the rows of* $\mathbf{C}'$ *can be expressed as linear combinations of the rows of* **C**.

Proof: The matrix $\mathbf{C}'$ can be formed from $\mathbf{C}$ by means of a sequence of elementary row operations. This means that there exists a sequence of matrices $\mathbf{C}, \mathbf{C}_1, \ldots, \mathbf{C}_{s-1}, \mathbf{C}'$ such that each matrix is obtained by applying a single elementary operation to the preceding matrix in the sequence. From Theorem 3.3 this means that matrices $\mathbf{E}_1, \mathbf{E}_2, \ldots, \mathbf{E}_s$ exist such that

$$\mathbf{C}_1 = \mathbf{E}_1\mathbf{C}, \qquad \mathbf{C}_2 = \mathbf{E}_2\mathbf{C}_1, \ldots, \qquad \mathbf{C}' = \mathbf{E}_s\mathbf{C}_{s-1}. \tag{3.56}$$

Hence,

$$\mathbf{C}' = \mathbf{E}_s\mathbf{E}_{s-1}\ldots\mathbf{E}_1\mathbf{C},$$

i.e., a matrix $\mathbf{E}$ exists such that

$$\mathbf{C}' = \mathbf{E}\mathbf{C}. \tag{3.57}$$

This means that there exist constants β_{ik} such that

$$\mathbf{r}_i' = \sum_{k=1}^{m} \beta_{ik}\mathbf{r}_k, \qquad i = 1 \text{ to } m. \tag{3.58}$$

which is the same thing as saying that the rows of $\mathbf{C}'$ can be expressed as linear combinations of the rows of $\mathbf{C}$.

We are now in a position to prove our main result:

THEOREM 3.5. *The row-echelon form for a matrix is unique. In particular, the number of nonzero rows in the row-echelon form of a matrix is a constant, irrespective of the actual sequence of row operations used to produce the normal form.*

Proof: Suppose that a matrix $\mathbf{A}$ is reduced to two different row-echelon forms $\mathbf{C}$ and $\mathbf{C}'$ by different sequences of row operations. Suppose that the unit column vectors in the row-echelon forms (Definition 3.4) are numbered $c_1, c_2, \ldots, c_p$ for $\mathbf{C}$ and $c_1', c_2', \ldots, c_q'$ for $\mathbf{C}'$. The proof proceeds in two stages:

(a) We first show that $p = q$ and $c_i = c_i'$, $i = 1, \ldots, p$. Since $\mathbf{C}$ and $\mathbf{C}'$ are both row-equivalent to $\mathbf{A}$, they are row-equivalent to each other (Theorem 3.2). If the nonzero rows of $\mathbf{C}$ are denoted by $\mathbf{r}_1, \ldots, \mathbf{r}_p$, and those of $\mathbf{C}'$ by $\mathbf{r}_1', \ldots, \mathbf{r}_q'$, then Theorem 3.4 tells us that $\mathbf{r}_1'$ can be expressed as a linear combination of $\mathbf{r}_1, \ldots, \mathbf{r}_p$ [see (3.58)]:

$$\mathbf{r}_1' = \beta_{11}\mathbf{r}_1 + \beta_{12}\mathbf{r}_2 + \ldots + \beta_{1p}\mathbf{r}_p.$$

By definition of the row-echelon form, the first $c_1 - 1$ elements of the rows $\mathbf{r}_1, \ldots, \mathbf{r}_p$ are zero. Hence, the first $c_1 - 1$ elements of $\mathbf{r}_1'$ are zero. Hence, $c_1' \geq c_1$. By reversing the roles of $\mathbf{C}$ and $\mathbf{C}'$ we see that $c_1 \geq c_1'$. Hence $c_1 = c_1'$. Similarly, consider

$$\mathbf{r}_2' = \beta_{21}\mathbf{r}_1 + \beta_{22}\mathbf{r}_2 + \ldots + \beta_{2p}\mathbf{r}_p. \tag{3.59}$$

It follows immediately from this equation that the c_1th element of $\mathbf{r}_2'$ is β_{21} (since the first c_1 elements of $\mathbf{r}_2, \ldots, \mathbf{r}_p$ are zero). But the first c_2' ($> c_1$) elements of

$\mathbf{r}_2'$ must be zero. Hence, $\beta_{21} = 0$. It follows that the first $c_2 - 1$ elements of $\mathbf{r}_2'$ are zero, and $c_2' \geq c_2$. By reversing the roles of $\mathbf{C}$ and $\mathbf{C}'$ we see that $c_2 \geq c_2'$, so that $c_2 = c_2'$. We can continue the above argument to show that $c_3 = c_3, \ldots$, and so on. Suppose that $p < q$ so that $\mathbf{r}_{p+1}'$ is nonzero. We obtain $c_p = c_p'$ and then

$$\mathbf{r}_{p+1}' = \beta_{p+1,1}\mathbf{r}_1 + \beta_{p+1,2}\mathbf{r}_2 + \ldots + \beta_{p+1,p}\mathbf{r}_p.$$

A repetition of the argument given above shows that $\beta_{p+1,j} = 0$ for $j = 1, \ldots, p$, so that $\mathbf{r}_{p+1}'$ is identically zero, which is a contradiction. Hence $p \geq q$. By reversing the roles of $\mathbf{C}$ and $\mathbf{C}'$ we have $q \geq p$. Hence $p = q$.

(b) To complete the proof we show that $\mathbf{r}_i' = \mathbf{r}_i$ for $i = 1, \ldots, p$. Consider

$$\mathbf{r}_i' = \beta_{i1}\mathbf{r}_1 + \beta_{i2}\mathbf{r}_2 + \ldots + \beta_{ip}\mathbf{r}_p, \tag{3.60}$$

for some i, $1 \leq i \leq p$. By definition of the row-echelon form, the c_1th element of $\mathbf{r}_i'$ is therefore β_{i1}, the c_2th element is β_{i2}, and, in general, the c_kth element is β_{ik}. But the c_kth element of $\mathbf{r}_i'$ is, using part (a) and the definition of the row-echelon form, zero unless $i = k$, in which case the c_ith element is unity. Hence, $\beta_{ik} = 0$ unless $i = k$, in which case $\beta_{ii} = 1$, so that

$$\mathbf{r}_i' = \mathbf{r}_i, \qquad i = 1, \ldots, p.$$

This completes the proof.

The number of nonzero rows in the row-echelon form of a matrix (which Theorem 3.5 tells us is independent of the way in which the row-echelon form is obtained) is so important that we give it a special name:

DEFINITION 3.8. The number of nonzero rows in the row-echelon form of a matrix is known as its *rank*.

The point of what we have been doing can be illuminated by looking at it from a more general point of view. Consider the statements "**A** is equal to **B**" and "**A** is row-equivalent to **B**." These are examples of *relations* that can be represented symbolically by "$\mathbf{A} \sim \mathbf{B}$," where "$\sim$" has the following properties:

DEFINITION 3.9. Consider a set S of mathematical entities $a, b, c, \ldots$ (for example, matrices) and a relation "$\sim$" such that, if a, b are members of S, we can decide whether it is true that $a \sim b$ or not. Then "$\sim$" is said to be an *equivalence relation* if it has the following properties:

(a) It is *reflexive:* $a \sim a$ for all a in S.
(b) It is *symmetric:* if $a \sim b$ then $b \sim a$.
(c) It is *transitive:* if $a \sim b$ and $b \sim c$ then $a \sim c$.

"Equality" of matrices is an equivalence relation, and Theorem 3.2 shows that "row-equivalence" is an equivalence relation (in fact, this is why the word "equivalence" is used in the term "row-equivalence.")

The importance of equivalence is that it divides the set into subsets, all the elements in each subset being equivalent to each other. One of the threads running through this book is that, once we find an equivalence relation, it is necessary to find some *standard* or *canonical* form for equivalent matrices. To find out if $\mathbf{A} \sim \mathbf{B}$, we reduce each to their standard forms, say $\mathbf{A}_1$, $\mathbf{B}_1$. If $\mathbf{A}_1$ and $\mathbf{B}_1$ are the same, then $\mathbf{A} \sim \mathbf{A}_1$ and $\mathbf{B} \sim \mathbf{A}_1$ so that $\mathbf{A} \sim \mathbf{B}$. Otherwise, it is not true that $\mathbf{A} \sim \mathbf{B}$. This is the point of introducing the row-echelon form.

Ex. 3.15. If the rank of a square matrix $\mathbf{A}$ of order m is m, prove that the row-echelon form of $\mathbf{A}$ is the unit matrix. If the rank of $\mathbf{A}$ is less than m, show that the last row of the row-echelon form of $\mathbf{A}$ is zero.

Ex. 3.16. If $\mathbf{A}$ is a general $m \times n$ matrix, show that the rank of $[\mathbf{A}, \mathbf{I}]$ is m.

Ex. 3.17. Show that the sets of linear equations $\mathbf{Ax} = \mathbf{b}$ and $\mathbf{Gx} = \mathbf{h}$ are equivalent if and only if the augmented matrices $[\mathbf{A}, \mathbf{b}]$ and $[\mathbf{G}, \mathbf{h}]$ are row-equivalent.

3.9 Theorems on the Existence of Solution for a Set of Equations

We can use the uniqueness of the row-echelon form to answer two questions concerning the equations $\mathbf{Ax} = \mathbf{b}$:

(i) Do solutions exist?
(ii) If a solution exists, is there a unique solution or an infinity of solutions?

There are three possible cases (which have already been indicated in Sections 3.3–3.5):

(a) The equations are inconsistent, i.e., no solution exists.
(b) The equations are consistent and have a unique solution.
(c) The equations are consistent and have an infinity of solutions.

To decide which case holds for a particular set of equations we can proceed as follows (compare Section 3.5). Write down the augmented matrix $[\mathbf{A}, \mathbf{b}]$ for the system $\mathbf{Ax} = \mathbf{b}$, and reduce to row-echelon form. We arrive at a matrix of the following form

$$\begin{bmatrix} \times & \times & \dots & \times & \delta_1 \\ \times & \times & \dots & \times & \delta_2 \\ & & \dots & & \\ \times & \times & \dots & \times & \delta_k \\ 0 & 0 & \dots & 0 & \delta_{k+1} \\ & & \dots & & \\ 0 & 0 & \dots & 0 & 0 \end{bmatrix} \tag{3.61}$$

where we assume that the row-echelon form of the coefficient matrix $\mathbf{A}$ has precisely k nonzero rows represented by crosses in the above equation, i.e.,

k is the rank of **A**, introduced in Definition 3.8. The number δ_{k+1} may be either 1 or 0. If $\delta_{k+1} = 1$, then the rank of the augmented matrix $[\mathbf{A}, \mathbf{b}]$ is $k + 1$; if $\delta_{k+1} = 0$, the rank of $[\mathbf{A}, \mathbf{b}]$ is k. This leads to the following theorem:

THEOREM 3.6. *Consider the nonhomogeneous equations* $\mathbf{Ax} = \mathbf{b}$ *where* **A** *is* $m \times n$. *One of the following possibilities must hold:*

(a) *If the rank of the augmented matrix* $[\mathbf{A}, \mathbf{b}]$ *is greater than the rank of* **A**, *the system of equations is inconsistent.*

(b) *If the rank of* $[\mathbf{A}, \mathbf{b}]$ *is equal to the rank of* **A**, *this being equal to the number of unknowns, then the equations have a unique solution.*

(c) *If the rank of* $[\mathbf{A}, \mathbf{b}]$ *is equal to the rank of* **A**, *this being less than the number of unknowns, then the equations have an infinity of solutions.*

Proof: The augmented matrix $[\mathbf{A}, \mathbf{b}]$ and the matrix (3.61) are row-equivalent. Hence the set $\mathbf{Ax} = \mathbf{b}$ is equivalent to the set of linear equations corresponding to (3.61). Theorem 3.1 tells us that these two sets of equations have, therefore, the same solution set. If the linear equations corresponding to (3.61) have no solution, a unique solution, or an infinity of solutions, then the same conclusion holds for the original set $\mathbf{Ax} = \mathbf{b}$. The classification into cases (a) or (b) or (c) follows directly from inspection of the linear equations corresponding to (3.61). The details are similar to those in the discussion at the end of Section 3.5. The cases (a), (b), (c) cover all possibilities. This proves the theorem.

We have now cleared up most of the points raised in the last paragraph of Section 3.5, but there is still one thing missing. It is possible to characterize precisely what we mean by an "infinity of solutions." This requires concepts that will be developed in Chapter 4. We supply this missing characterization in Section 4.8.

The case when $\mathbf{b} = \mathbf{0}$ (i.e., we are considering the *homogeneous* equations $\mathbf{Ax} = \mathbf{0}$) is of sufficient importance to merit the statement of a theorem which is simply a special case of that given above:

THEOREM 3.7. *The homogeneous equations* $\mathbf{Ax} = \mathbf{0}$ *can never be inconsistent. If* **A** *is* $m \times n$ *and the rank of* **A** *is* k, *one of the following possibilities must occur:*

(b′) $k = n$. *Then the equations have the unique solution* $\mathbf{x} = \mathbf{0}$.

(c′) $k \leq n$. *Then the equations have an infinity of nonzero solutions.*

In particular, a set of m *homogeneous equations in* n *unknowns with* $m < n$ *always possesses an infinity of nonzero solutions.*

Proof: Applying Theorem 3.6, we reduce $[\mathbf{A}, \mathbf{0}]$ to row-echelon form. The case (a) cannot occur. Case (b) occurs if $k = n$ and case (c) if $k < n$. The last part of the theorem is a special case of (c) since $k \leq m$ and if $m < n$ this implies $k < n$.

One of the reasons for the importance of homogeneous equations is illustrated by the following theorem which is inserted as a tailpiece to this section.

THEOREM 3.8. *Let* $\mathbf{x}_0$ *be a particular solution of the nonhomogeneous system* $\mathbf{Ax} = \mathbf{b}$. *Then a vector* $\mathbf{z}$ *is also a solution if and only if* $\mathbf{z} = \mathbf{x}_0 + \mathbf{u}$, *where* $\mathbf{u}$ *is a solution of the corresponding homogeneous system* $\mathbf{Ax} = \mathbf{0}$.

Proof: If $\mathbf{z} = \mathbf{x}_0 + \mathbf{u}$, then

$$\mathbf{Az} = \mathbf{A}(\mathbf{x}_0 + \mathbf{u}) = \mathbf{Ax}_0 + \mathbf{Au} = \mathbf{b} + \mathbf{0} = \mathbf{b},$$

so that $\mathbf{z}$ is a solution of the nonhomogeneous equations. Conversely, if $\mathbf{z}$ is a solution, then $\mathbf{Az} = \mathbf{b}$. Also $\mathbf{Ax}_0 = \mathbf{b}$. Subtraction gives $\mathbf{A}(\mathbf{z} - \mathbf{x}_0) = \mathbf{0}$ so that $\mathbf{z} - \mathbf{x}_0$ is a solution of the homogeneous system, say $\mathbf{u}$. Hence $\mathbf{z} - \mathbf{x}_0 = \mathbf{u}$, or $\mathbf{z} = \mathbf{x}_0 + \mathbf{u}$. If $\mathbf{z}$ is a solution, it must be of the form $\mathbf{x}_0 + \mathbf{u}$.

Ex. 3.18. If the equations $\mathbf{Ax} = \mathbf{b}$ have a solution, this solution is unique if and only if the homogeneous system $\mathbf{Ax} = \mathbf{0}$ possesses only the trivial solution $\mathbf{x} = \mathbf{0}$.

Ex. 3.19. The trivial solution of the homogeneous equations $\mathbf{Ax} = \mathbf{0}$ is the unique solution if and only if the rank is equal to the number of unknowns.

Ex. 3.20. If the equations $\mathbf{Ax} = \mathbf{b}$ have a solution, this solution is unique, if and only if the rank is equal to the number of unknowns.

Ex. 3.21. Show that the situation concerning the existence and uniqueness of solutions of a set of n equations in n unknowns, $\mathbf{Ax} = \mathbf{b}$, where $\mathbf{A}$ has rank k, can be summarized as follows [δ_{k+1} is defined as in (3.61)]:

(a) If $k = n$, the equations have a unique solution.
(b) If $k < n$ and $\delta_{k+1} = 1$, the equations are inconsistent.
(c) If $k < n$ and $\delta_{k+1} = 0$, the equations have an infinity of solutions.

Miscellaneous Exercises 3

Ex. 3.22. Find the value of α for which the following equations possess solutions.

$$\begin{aligned} x - 3y + 2z &= 4 \\ 2x + y - z &= 1 \\ 3x - 2y + z &= \alpha. \end{aligned}$$

Ex. 3.23. Show that the following equations for x, y, z possess a solution if $\alpha + \beta + \gamma = 0$.

$$\begin{aligned} x + y\cos\gamma + z\cos\beta &= 0 \\ x\cos\gamma + y + z\cos\alpha &= 0 \\ x\cos\beta + y\cos\alpha + z &= 0. \end{aligned}$$

Ex. 3.24. Show that if a, b, c are distinct nonzero numbers, the equations

$$\begin{aligned} ax + by + cz &= 1 \\ a^2x + b^2y + c^2z &= 1 \\ a^3x + b^3y + c^3z &= 1 \end{aligned}$$

possess the solution

$$x = \frac{(b-1)(1-c)}{a(c-a)(a-b)}, \qquad y = \frac{(1-c)(a-1)}{b(a-b)(b-c)}, \qquad z = \frac{(a-1)(1-b)}{c(b-c)(c-a)}.$$

Ex. 3.25. Let $x_0 < x_1 < x_2$ and y_0, y_1, y_2 be given numbers, and let $P(x) = a_0 + a_1x + a_2x^2$. We wish to arrange that $P(x_i) = y_i$, $i = 0, 1, 2$. Show that this gives rise to a set of three linear equations in the three unknowns a_0, a_1, a_2, which always has a unique solution.

Ex. 3.26. Show that if **A** is a square matrix of order m and rank m, it possesses a unique right inverse. Show that if the rank of **A** is less than m, it does not possess a right-inverse.

Ex. 3.27. Show that if **A** is a general $m \times n$ matrix, then:

(a) If $m > n$, **A** has no right-inverse.

(b) If $m < n$ there are exactly two possibilities:

(i) If the rank of **A** is m, there exists an infinite number of right-inverses.

(ii) If the rank of **A** is less than m, there exist no right-inverses.

Ex. 3.28. Let **B** and **C** denote 3×4 matrices and let

$$\mathbf{A} = \begin{bmatrix} 1 & -2 & 3 \\ -2 & 5 & -6 \\ 2 & -3 & 6 \end{bmatrix}.$$

What conclusions can we draw from the equation $\mathbf{AB} = \mathbf{AC}$?

Ex. 3.29. Find all vectors **b** for which the equation $\mathbf{Ax} = \mathbf{b}$ can be solved, and find the corresponding general solution, for

$$\mathbf{A} = \begin{bmatrix} 4 & -1 & 2 & 6 \\ -1 & 5 & -1 & -3 \\ 3 & 4 & 1 & 3 \end{bmatrix}.$$

Ex. 3.30. Reduce the following matrix to row-echelon form.

$$\mathbf{A} = \begin{bmatrix} 1 & -2 & 3 & 1 \\ 2 & k & 6 & 6 \\ -1 & 3 & k-3 & 0 \end{bmatrix}.$$

Suppose that this is the augmented matrix $[\mathbf{A}, \mathbf{b}]$ for a system $\mathbf{Ax} = \mathbf{b}$ of three equations in three unknowns. Deduce from the row-echelon form that for $k = 0$ the system has an infinite number of solutions, for another value of k the system is contradictory, and for all other values of k the system has a unique solution. For the case $k = 0$, what is the general form of the solution?

Ex. 3.31. If a vector $\mathbf{b}_0$ exists such that $\mathbf{Ax} = \mathbf{b}_0$ has a unique solution, where $\mathbf{A}$ is $n \times n$, show that $\mathbf{Ax} = \mathbf{b}$ has a unique solution for any $\mathbf{b}$.

Ex. 3.32. Given any homogeneous system of m equations in $m + 1$ unknowns $x_1, \ldots, x_{m+1}$, show that there is at least one index i such that the system has a solution in which x_i can be given any arbitrary value.

Ex. 3.33. Show that if in the electrical network of Figure 2.2, the voltage V_0 is not set equal to zero, equations (2.16) can be replaced by

$$\begin{bmatrix} Y_1+Y_5+Y_6 & -Y_1 & -Y_5 & -Y_6 \\ -Y_1 & Y_1+Y_3+Y_4 & -Y_3 & -Y_4 \\ -Y_5 & -Y_3 & Y_2+Y_3+Y_5 & -Y_2 \\ -Y_6 & -Y_4 & -Y_2 & Y_2+Y_4+Y_6 \end{bmatrix} \begin{bmatrix} V_0 \\ V_1 \\ V_2 \\ V_3 \end{bmatrix} = \begin{bmatrix} Y_1e_1 \\ -Y_1e_1 \\ 0 \\ 0 \end{bmatrix}.$$

Show that these equations have an infinity of solutions. Show that the solutions for $V_1 - V_0$, $V_2 - V_0$, $V_3 - V_0$ are unique. (The point of this example is that sets of equations with an infinity of solutions often appear quite naturally in applications. In such cases it is often clear physically how these can be replaced by equations with unique solutions. In the present example, we need only introduce a zero voltage reference level.)

4 Linear Dependence and Vector Spaces

4.1 Geometrical Vectors in Three-Dimensional Space

So far, the theoretical development has been concerned with the manipulation of arrays of numbers. Our present situation can be compared with that of a student who has learned the rules for the manipulation of the symbols and equations representing points, lines, and planes in three-dimensional cartesian geometry, without knowing anything about the underlying geometrical picture represented by the symbols. In order to obtain some deeper appreciation of the significance of matrices, it is necessary to understand the idea of a vector space. We introduce this concept by discussing geometrical vectors in three-dimensional space.

To discuss vectors geometrically, we first choose a system of three perpendicular axes, which are labeled x, y, z, (Figure 4.1). The vector is represented by a line OP starting from the origin of coordinates O and pointing in the direction of the vector, the length OP being equal to the magnitude of the vector. Instead of specifying the direction and length of OP we could equally have specified the coordinates (x, y, z) of the point P relative to the given coordinate system. We introduce

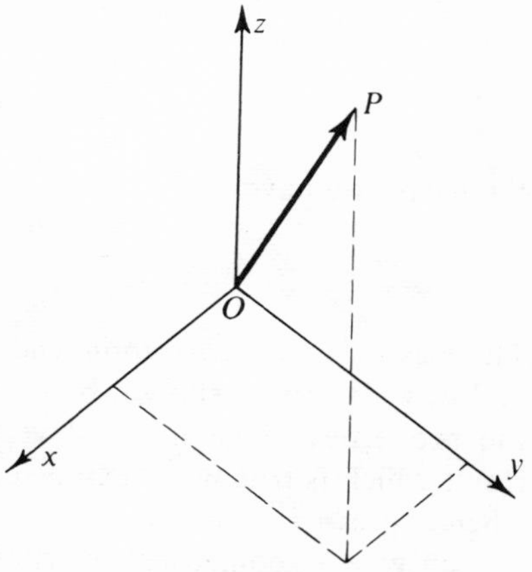

Figure 4.1

the notation $\vec{u}$ (i.e., a symbol with an arrow above it) to represent a geometrical vector. We shall write $\vec{u} = (x_1, y_1, z_1)$ to denote that the components of $\vec{u}$ are given by x_1, y_1, z_1.

Two standard operations on geometrical vectors are:

(a) *Multiplication of a geometrical vector by a scalar, say k.* This leaves the direction of the vector unchanged, but multiplies its length by k. In terms of coordinates, the vector (x_1, y_1, z_1) is changed to (kx_1, ky_1, kz_1):

$$k\vec{u} = (kx_1, ky_1, kz_1).$$

(b) *Addition of two geometrical vectors.* This is performed by the parallelogram law. In terms of coordinates, if we add vectors $\vec{u} = (x_1, y_1, z_1)$ and $\vec{v} = (x_2, y_2, z_2)$ we obtain a vector whose coordinates are the sums of those of $\vec{u}$ and $\vec{v}$:

$$\vec{u} + \vec{v} = (x_1 + x_2, y_1 + y_2, z_1 + z_2).$$

Geometrical vectors obey the commutative and associative laws of addition:

$$\vec{u} + \vec{v} = \vec{v} + \vec{u},$$
$$(\vec{u} + \vec{v}) + \vec{w} = \vec{u} + (\vec{v} + \vec{w}).$$

Instead of thinking in terms of coordinates (x, y, z) we can think in terms of column matrices. Suppose that we define

$$\mathbf{u} = \begin{bmatrix} x_1 \\ y_1 \\ z_1 \end{bmatrix}, \qquad \mathbf{v} = \begin{bmatrix} x_2 \\ y_2 \\ z_2 \end{bmatrix}.$$

Then the definitions of multiplication of a matrix by a scalar, and addition of matrices, give

(a′) $$k\mathbf{u} = \begin{bmatrix} kx_1 \\ ky_1 \\ kz_1 \end{bmatrix}.$$

(b′) $$\mathbf{u} + \mathbf{v} = \begin{bmatrix} x_1 + x_2 \\ y_1 + y_2 \\ z_1 + z_2 \end{bmatrix}.$$

Similarly, we have

$$\mathbf{u} + \mathbf{v} = \mathbf{v} + \mathbf{u},$$
$$(\mathbf{u} + \mathbf{v}) + \mathbf{w} = \mathbf{u} + (\mathbf{v} + \mathbf{w}).$$

There is clearly a correspondence or parallelism between the quantities $\vec{u}$, $\vec{v}$ and $\mathbf{u}$, $\mathbf{v}$. It can be shown, by establishing a strict correspondence between all the properties of geometrical vectors and 3×1 column matrices, that any result which is true when expressed in terms of geometrical vectors is also true when expressed in terms of column matrices, and vice versa. This means that we can give a geometrical interpretation of results involving column matrices.

The reason for developing this correspondence between geometrical vectors and 3×1 column matrices is that we can now give an intuitive background for the more abstract developments discussed later, assuming that the reader has a minimum background in vector analysis and analytic geometry.

The position of a point in a plane can be specified by choosing two perpendicular axes and determining the coordinates (x, y) of the point with reference to the axes. Two numbers are required to specify the point, and we say that we are dealing with a two-dimensional space. Similarly, the position of a point on a line can be specified by giving the distance of the point from a fixed point or origin on the line, and we say that we are dealing with a one-dimensional space. A definition of precisely what is meant by a k-dimensional space will be given later (Section 4.4, Definition 4.5) but the ordinary geometrical interpretation for $k = 1, 2, 3$, as just described, will suffice for our present purposes.

If we consider all possible multiples of a vector $\vec{u}$, i.e., if we consider the set of all vectors of the form $\alpha\vec{u}$ where α is a scalar, we specify a line (or one-dimensional space) in three-dimensional space.

Similarly, vectors of the form $\alpha\vec{u} + \beta\vec{v}$, which are sums of multiples of two vectors $\vec{u}$ and $\vec{v}$ that are not collinear, define a plane (or two-dimensional space) in three-dimensional space. By taking suitable multiples of $\vec{u}$ and $\vec{v}$ we can reach any point in this plane, but we cannot move outside the plane. In order to reach a point outside the plane, we must introduce a third vector $\vec{w}$ which does not lie in the plane defined by $\vec{u}$ and $\vec{v}$. By taking sums of multiples of vectors of the form $\alpha\vec{u} + \beta\vec{v} + \gamma\vec{w}$ we can reach any point in three-dimensional space.

It is convenient to introduce terminology that will be defined precisely in later sections in this chapter. If we are, for instance, dealing with a plane or two-dimensional space, in a three-dimensional space, we say that the plane is a *subspace* of the three-dimensional space. More generally, an m-dimensional space which is contained in an n-dimensional space ($m \leq n$) is said to be an m-dimensional subspace. (We allow the possibility $m = n$ for convenience.) As a further example, a line lying in a plane is a one-dimensional subspace of the plane.

Consider the geometrical object defined by sums of multiples of nonzero vectors $\vec{u}$ and $\vec{v}$,

$$\vec{x} = \alpha\vec{u} + \beta\vec{v}.$$

The vector $\vec{x}$ is said to be a *linear combination* of $\vec{u}$ and $\vec{v}$. If $\vec{u}$ and $\vec{v}$ are not collinear, then the vectors $\vec{u}$ and $\vec{v}$ specify a plane in which $\vec{x}$ lies. If $\vec{u}$ and $\vec{v}$ are collinear, we have $\vec{u} = k\vec{v}$ for some nonzero constant k, and we say that $\vec{u}$ and $\vec{v}$ are *linearly dependent*.

So far we have made the assumption that the vectors involved have nonzero lengths. Although it is convenient to make this assumption in the geometrical discussion, it is a nuisance later, and from now on we allow the possibility that any vector may be the zero vector $\vec{0}$ represented by the point at the origin, with zero length and no direction. A detailed discussion of linear dependence and independence when zero vectors may be present is postponed until later (Ex. 4.3). We now say quite generally that two vectors $\vec{u}$, $\vec{v}$ are *linearly dependent* if constants α, β, not both zero, can be found such that $\alpha\vec{u} + \beta\vec{v} = \vec{0}$. If $\vec{u}$ and $\vec{v}$ are nonzero linearly dependent vectors, both the constants α, β must be nonzero, and $\vec{v} = -(\alpha/\beta)\vec{u}$, i.e., $\vec{u}$, $\vec{v}$ have the same direction. If nonzero vectors $\vec{u}$, $\vec{v}$ do not point in the same direction, then we cannot find constants α, β such that $\alpha\vec{u} + \beta\vec{v} = \vec{0}$ and we say that $\vec{u}$, $\vec{v}$ are *linearly independent*. Similar definitions hold for three or more vectors. Thus vectors $\vec{u}$, $\vec{v}$, $\vec{w}$ are said to be linearly dependent if and only if three constants α, β, γ, at least one of which is nonzero, exist such that $\alpha\vec{u} + \beta\vec{v} + \gamma\vec{w} = \vec{0}$.

If $\vec{u}$, $\vec{v}$ are nonzero vectors that do not have the same direction, the collection of vectors $\alpha\vec{u} + \beta\vec{v}$ forms a plane which is a two-dimensional subspace of three-dimensional space. We say that the subspace is *generated* or *spanned* by $\vec{u}$, $\vec{v}$. Also the vectors $\vec{u}$, $\vec{v}$ are said to form a *basis* (or set of base vectors) for the subspace. Any two vectors lying in the plane can be chosen as a basis, provided that they are linearly independent. The reason why they must be linearly independent is that if they are linearly dependent there are two possibilities: at least one of $\vec{u}$, $\vec{v}$ is zero, or both $\vec{u}$, $\vec{v}$ are nonzero in which case they must have the same direction. In neither case can $\vec{u}$, $\vec{v}$ define a plane. It is intuitively clear that any three coplanar vectors $\vec{p}$, $\vec{q}$, $\vec{r}$ must be related by an equation of the form

$$\alpha\vec{p} + \beta\vec{q} + \gamma\vec{r} = \vec{0},$$

i.e., any three vectors in a two-dimensional space are linearly dependent.

Similar results hold for three-dimensional space. We summarize the results. The definitions of "span," "basis," etc., should be clear from the discussion of the two-dimensional case in the last paragraph.

(a) Three linearly independent vectors in three-dimensional space are non-coplanar.

(b) Any three linearly independent vectors span a three-dimensional space and therefore can be chosen as a basis for the space.

(c) Any basis for a three-dimensional space must consist of three linearly independent vectors.

(d) Any set of four or more vectors in three-dimensional space is linearly dependent.

4.2 *Linear Dependence and Independence of Vectors*

The idea of linear independence has already been introduced by means of geometrical considerations in the last section. We now approach this concept from a purely algebraic point of view.

If we wish to deal with a collection of column vectors with, say, three elements apiece, such as

$$\begin{bmatrix} 1 \\ -1 \\ 0 \end{bmatrix}, \quad \begin{bmatrix} 1 \\ 4 \\ -2 \end{bmatrix}, \quad \begin{bmatrix} 0 \\ 0 \\ 5 \end{bmatrix}, \quad \begin{bmatrix} 2 \\ 3 \\ -4 \end{bmatrix}, \quad \ldots, \tag{4.1}$$

it is often convenient to think of them as consisting of sums of multiples of certain basic column vectors. Thus if we define the "unit vectors"

$$\mathbf{e}_1 = \begin{bmatrix} 1 \\ 0 \\ 0 \end{bmatrix}, \quad \mathbf{e}_2 = \begin{bmatrix} 0 \\ 1 \\ 0 \end{bmatrix}, \quad \mathbf{e}_3 = \begin{bmatrix} 0 \\ 0 \\ 1 \end{bmatrix}, \tag{4.2}$$

then the first vector in (4.1) is $\mathbf{e}_1 - \mathbf{e}_2$, the second is $\mathbf{e}_1 + 4\mathbf{e}_2 - 2\mathbf{e}_3$, and similarly any 3×1 column vector can be expressed as sums of multiples of the three basic vectors $\mathbf{e}_1$, $\mathbf{e}_2$, $\mathbf{e}_3$. It is not necessary to choose the $\mathbf{e}_i$ defined above. We could choose

$$\mathbf{e}_1' = \begin{bmatrix} 1 \\ 2 \\ 1 \end{bmatrix}, \quad \mathbf{e}_2' = \begin{bmatrix} 1 \\ 0 \\ -1 \end{bmatrix}, \quad \mathbf{e}_3' = \begin{bmatrix} 1 \\ -2 \\ 1 \end{bmatrix}. \tag{4.3}$$

In order to express the first vector in (4.1) in terms of these vectors, we have to find numbers α_1, α_2, α_3 such that

$$\begin{bmatrix} 1 \\ -1 \\ 0 \end{bmatrix} = \alpha_1 \begin{bmatrix} 1 \\ 2 \\ 1 \end{bmatrix} + \alpha_2 \begin{bmatrix} 1 \\ 0 \\ -1 \end{bmatrix} + \alpha_3 \begin{bmatrix} 1 \\ -2 \\ 1 \end{bmatrix}.$$

This gives a set of three equations in three unknowns, the solution of which is found to be $\alpha_1 = 0$, $\alpha_2 = \alpha_3 = \frac{1}{2}$. Hence, the first vector in (4.1) is $\frac{1}{2}(\mathbf{e}_2' + \mathbf{e}_3')$.

However, the vectors in (4.1) cannot be expressed in terms of the set

$$\mathbf{e}_1'' = \begin{bmatrix} 1 \\ 1 \\ 1 \end{bmatrix}, \quad \mathbf{e}_2'' = \begin{bmatrix} 1 \\ 0 \\ -1 \end{bmatrix}, \quad \mathbf{e}_3'' = \begin{bmatrix} 1 \\ -1 \\ -3 \end{bmatrix}. \tag{4.4}$$

For instance, suppose that we try to express the first vector in (4.1) in terms of this set, by writing

$$\begin{bmatrix} 1 \\ -1 \\ 0 \end{bmatrix} = \alpha_1 \begin{bmatrix} 1 \\ 1 \\ 1 \end{bmatrix} + \alpha_2 \begin{bmatrix} 1 \\ 0 \\ -1 \end{bmatrix} + \alpha_3 \begin{bmatrix} 1 \\ -1 \\ -3 \end{bmatrix}.$$

This gives a set of three equations in the three unknowns α_1, α_2, α_3. The equation obtained by eliminating α_2 between the first and third of these equations, together with the second equation, gives

$$\alpha_1 - \alpha_3 = \tfrac{1}{2}$$

$$\alpha_1 - \alpha_3 = -1$$

These are contradictory equations, so that it is not possible to express the first vector in (4.1) in terms of the three vectors (4.4). From a more fundamental point of view, the reason for the difficulty can be seen directly from (4.4), because $\mathbf{e}_3'' = 2\mathbf{e}_2'' - \mathbf{e}_1''$. Since we are expressing vectors as sums of multiples of the basic vectors $\mathbf{e}_1''$, $\mathbf{e}_2''$, $\mathbf{e}_3''$, but $\mathbf{e}_3''$ can be expressed in terms of $\mathbf{e}_1''$ and $\mathbf{e}_2''$, there is no point in including $\mathbf{e}_3''$ as one of the basic vectors. We are therefore trying to express the vectors in (4.1) as sums of multiples of only two vectors $\mathbf{e}_1''$ and $\mathbf{e}_2''$. This will not in general be possible, since it will involve finding a solution for a set of three equations in two unknowns.

So far we have discussed only specific examples. The ideas that have been introduced can be formulated in general terms by means of the following definition. The concept that is defined may seem to be so straightforward and even superficial that it may be difficult to appreciate at this stage that it is extremely powerful and fundamental.

DEFINITION **4.1.** A collection of vectors $\mathbf{v}_1, \mathbf{v}_2, \ldots, \mathbf{v}_s$ is said to be *linearly dependent* if there exist numbers $\alpha_1, \alpha_2, \ldots, \alpha_s$, not all zero, such that

$$\alpha_1\mathbf{v}_1 + \alpha_2\mathbf{v}_2 + \ldots + \alpha_s\mathbf{v}_s = \mathbf{0}. \tag{4.5}$$

If the vectors are not linearly dependent, they are said to be *linearly independent.*

As an example, the three vectors in (4.4) are linearly dependent, since we showed that $\mathbf{e}_1'' - 2\mathbf{e}_2'' + \mathbf{e}_3'' = \mathbf{0}$. On the other hand if we wish to find out whether the three vectors in (4.2) are linearly dependent or not, we try to find constants α_i such that

$$\alpha_1\begin{bmatrix}1\\0\\0\end{bmatrix} + \alpha_2\begin{bmatrix}0\\1\\0\end{bmatrix} + \alpha_3\begin{bmatrix}0\\0\\1\end{bmatrix} = \begin{bmatrix}\alpha_1\\\alpha_2\\\alpha_3\end{bmatrix} = \begin{bmatrix}0\\0\\0\end{bmatrix}.$$

This automatically implies that $\alpha_1 = \alpha_2 = \alpha_3 = 0$ so that the vectors are linearly independent. Similarly, to find out whether the three vectors in (4.3) are linearly independent, we set

$$\alpha_1\begin{bmatrix}1\\2\\1\end{bmatrix} + \alpha_2\begin{bmatrix}1\\0\\-1\end{bmatrix} + \alpha_3\begin{bmatrix}1\\-2\\1\end{bmatrix} = \begin{bmatrix}0\\0\\0\end{bmatrix}.$$

This implies

$$\begin{aligned}\alpha_1 + \alpha_2 + \alpha_3 &= 0\\ 2\alpha_1 \qquad - 2\alpha_3 &= 0\\ \alpha_1 - \alpha_2 + \alpha_3 &= 0.\end{aligned}$$

The reader will readily verify that the only solution of these equations is $\alpha_1 = \alpha_2 = \alpha_3 = 0$ so that the three vectors in (4.3) are linearly independent.

(These examples involve column vectors, but the vectors could equally have been row vectors. The idea of linear dependence or independence can be applied to a wide variety of mathematical entities, including general $m \times n$ matrices and functions. See Sections 14.1, 14.2.)

We have investigated the above examples from first principles, reducing the question of whether vectors are linearly dependent to the question of whether a set of homogeneous equations has nonzero solutions. However, as in Chapter 3, it is usually more convenient to work directly in terms of matrices. In particular, the row-echelon normal form is very useful in deciding questions involving linear dependence or independence. In order to exploit this, we require the following result:

THEOREM **4.1.** *Suppose that elementary row operations are performed on a matrix* $\mathbf{A}$ *to produce a matrix* $\mathbf{B}$.

(i) *If a sum of multiples of certain columns of* $\mathbf{B}$ *is zero, then the sum of the same multiples of corresponding columns of* $\mathbf{A}$ *is also zero.*

(ii) *If certain columns of* $\mathbf{B}$ *are linearly dependent (independent), then the corresponding columns of* $\mathbf{A}$ *are linearly dependent (independent).*

Proof: Suppose that a sum of multiples of certain columns $\mathbf{a}_\alpha, \mathbf{a}_\beta, \ldots, \mathbf{a}_\gamma$ of $\mathbf{A}$ is zero:

$$k_\alpha \mathbf{a}_\alpha + k_\beta \mathbf{a}_\beta + \ldots + k_\gamma \mathbf{a}_\gamma = \mathbf{0}. \tag{4.6}$$

This relation can be regarded as a set of homogeneous linear equations for $k_\alpha, \ldots, k_\gamma$. Performing row operations on $\mathbf{A}$ corresponds to interchanging these equations, multiplying them by constants, and adding a multiple of one equation to another. We saw in Theorem 3.1 that a solution of the original set of equations is a solution of the final set, and vice versa. Hence,

$$k_\alpha \mathbf{b}_\alpha + k_\beta \mathbf{b}_\beta + \ldots + k_\gamma \mathbf{b}_\gamma = \mathbf{0},$$

where $\mathbf{b}_\alpha, \ldots$ are the columns of $\mathbf{B}$ corresponding to the columns $\mathbf{a}_\alpha, \ldots$ of $\mathbf{A}$. This proves part (i). Part (ii) follows immediately.

The point of this theorem as regards applications is that it is easy to recognize whether the columns of the row-echelon form of a matrix are linearly dependent or not. Hence to see whether a set of vectors are linearly dependent or not, we write the vectors as columns of a matrix, and reduce the matrix to row-echelon form. We illustrate by an example.

Ex. 4.1. Which of the following vectors are linearly dependent, if any? Explain.

$$\mathbf{u}_1 = \begin{bmatrix} 1 \\ -1 \\ -1 \\ 2 \end{bmatrix}, \quad \mathbf{u}_2 = \begin{bmatrix} -1 \\ 2 \\ 3 \\ 1 \end{bmatrix}, \quad \mathbf{u}_3 = \begin{bmatrix} 2 \\ -3 \\ -3 \\ 2 \end{bmatrix}, \quad \mathbf{u}_4 = \begin{bmatrix} 1 \\ 1 \\ 1 \\ 6 \end{bmatrix}.$$

Solution: Following the procedure sketched in the last paragraph, we reduce

$$\begin{bmatrix} 1 & -1 & 2 & 1 \\ -1 & 2 & -3 & 1 \\ -1 & 3 & -3 & 1 \\ 2 & 1 & 2 & 6 \end{bmatrix},$$

to row-echelon form which leads to

$$\begin{bmatrix} 1 & 0 & 0 & 5 \\ 0 & 1 & 0 & 0 \\ 0 & 0 & 1 & -2 \\ 0 & 0 & 0 & 0 \end{bmatrix}.$$

This tells us immediately that $\mathbf{u}_2$ is independent of the other three vectors, and that $\mathbf{u}_4 = 5\mathbf{u}_1 - 2\mathbf{u}_3$, since these statements are true for the row-echelon form.

We conclude this section by stating some direct consequences of the above definitions.

THEOREM **4.2.** (i) *If among the q vectors* $\mathbf{u}_1, \ldots, \mathbf{u}_q$ *there is a subset of* $p < q$ *vectors that are linearly dependent, then the entire set is linearly dependent.*

(ii) *If the q vectors* $\mathbf{u}_1, \ldots, \mathbf{u}_q$ *are linearly independent, then any subset of* $p < q$ *vectors is linearly independent.*

(iii) *A set of nonzero vectors* $\mathbf{u}_1, \ldots, \mathbf{u}_q$ *is linearly dependent if and only if one of the* $\mathbf{u}_k$, *for some k, is a linear combination of the remaining vectors* $\mathbf{u}_j$, $j \neq k$. *In particular, the set is linearly dependent if and only if one of the* $\mathbf{u}_k$, *for some k, is a linear combination of the preceding* $\mathbf{u}_1, \ldots, \mathbf{u}_{k-1}$.

(iv) *If any vector is a linear combination of a set of vectors* $\mathbf{u}_1, \ldots, \mathbf{u}_q$ *and if* $\mathbf{u}_m$ *is linearly dependent on the remaining* **u**'*s, then the given vector is a linear combination of the set with* $\mathbf{u}_m$ *omitted.*

Proof: To prove (i) we can assume, without loss of generality, that the first p vectors are linearly dependent, so that constants α_i exist, not all zero, such that

$$\alpha_1\mathbf{u}_1 + \alpha_2\mathbf{u}_2 + \ldots + \alpha_p\mathbf{u}_p = \mathbf{0}.$$

If we take $\alpha_{p+1} = \ldots = \alpha_q = 0$, we see that this implies that constants α_i exist, not all zero, such that

$$\alpha_1\mathbf{u}_1 + \alpha_2\mathbf{u}_2 + \ldots + \alpha_q\mathbf{u}_q = \mathbf{0}.$$

This proves part (i). Part (ii) is left as an exercise for the reader. To prove (iii), suppose that the set is linearly dependent. Then an equation of the form

$$\alpha_1\mathbf{u}_1 + \alpha_2\mathbf{u}_\alpha + \ldots + \alpha_k\mathbf{u}_k = \mathbf{0},$$

holds, where some of the α_i are nonzero, and, without loss of generality, we can assume that $\alpha_k \neq 0$. Hence,

$$\mathbf{u}_k = -\frac{\alpha_1}{\alpha_k}\mathbf{u}_1 - \ldots - \frac{\alpha_{k-1}}{\alpha_k}\mathbf{u}_{k-1}$$

and $\mathbf{u}_k$ has been expressed as a linear combination of the preceding vectors. Conversely, if

$$\mathbf{u}_k = \gamma_1\mathbf{u}_1 + \ldots + \gamma_{k-1}\mathbf{u}_{k-1},$$

then

$$\gamma_1\mathbf{u}_1 + \ldots + \gamma_{k-1}\mathbf{u}_{k-1} - \mathbf{u}_k = \mathbf{0},$$

and the set is linearly dependent. To prove (iv), if $\mathbf{u}_m$ is linearly dependent on the remaining **u**'s, then we can write

$$\mathbf{u}_m = \sum_{r=1}^{q}{}' \gamma_r\mathbf{u}_r,$$

where the prime denotes that the term $r = m$ in the sum is omitted. Hence, if

$$\mathbf{u} = \sum_{r=1}^{q} \alpha_r\mathbf{u}_r,$$

we can substitute the above expression for $\mathbf{u}_m$ to obtain

$$\mathbf{u} = \sum_{r=1}^{q}{}'(\alpha_r + \alpha_m\gamma_r)\mathbf{u}_r,$$

and **u** has been expressed as a linear combination of the set with $\mathbf{u}_m$ omitted.

Ex. 4.2. Prove part (ii) of Theorem 4.2.

Ex. 4.3. Note that Definition 4.1 of linear dependence does not specify that the vectors are nonzero. Prove that

(a) If one of the vectors $\mathbf{v}_1, \ldots, \mathbf{v}_p$ is zero, the set is linearly dependent.

(b) If a set of vectors are linearly independent, this implies that all the vectors are nonzero.

(c) A single vector **v** forms a linearly dependent set if $\mathbf{v} = \mathbf{0}$, and a linearly independent set if $\mathbf{v} \neq \mathbf{0}$.

Ex. 4.4. If $\mathbf{u}_1$ and $\mathbf{u}_2$ are linearly independent and $\mathbf{w}_1 = a\mathbf{u}_1 + b\mathbf{u}_2$, $\mathbf{w}_2 = c\mathbf{u}_1 + d\mathbf{u}_2$, show that $\mathbf{w}_1$ and $\mathbf{w}_2$ are linearly independent if and only if $ad \neq bc$.

Ex. 4.5. Show that if **u**, **v**, **w** are linearly independent, then so is the set $\mathbf{u} + \mathbf{v}$, $\mathbf{v} + \mathbf{w}$, $\mathbf{w} + \mathbf{u}$.

Ex. 4.6. If

$$\begin{aligned}\mathbf{v}_1 &= \mathbf{u}_1 + \mathbf{u}_2 + \mathbf{u}_3\\ \mathbf{v}_2 &= \mathbf{u}_1 + \alpha\mathbf{u}_2\\ \mathbf{v}_3 &= \mathbf{u}_2 + \beta\mathbf{u}_3,\end{aligned}$$

where $\mathbf{u}_1$, $\mathbf{u}_2$, $\mathbf{u}_3$ are given linearly independent vectors, find the condition that must be satisfied by α, β in order to ensure that $\mathbf{v}_1$, $\mathbf{v}_2$, $\mathbf{v}_3$ are linearly independent.

Ex. 4.7. Given an upper triangular matrix **A** with nonzero diagonal elements (i.e., $a_{ij} = 0$ if $i > j$ and $a_{ii} \neq 0$), show that the rows of **A** are linearly independent. If any of the diagonal elements is zero, show that the rows are dependent.

Ex. 4.8. If a vector **u** can be expressed in the form

$$\mathbf{u} = \alpha_1\mathbf{u}_1 + \ldots + \alpha_p\mathbf{u}_p,$$

where $\mathbf{u}_1, \ldots, \mathbf{u}_p$ are linearly independent, show that the coefficients α_i are uniquely determined. Conversely, if the expression for **u** in this form is unique, show that the $\mathbf{u}_i$ are linearly independent.

Ex. 4.9. Express a general vector $[x, y, z]$ as a linear combination of $[1, 2, 1]$, $[1, 0, -1]$, $[1, -2, 1]$.

Ex. 4.10. Which one of the following matrices is linearly independent of the others:

$$\begin{bmatrix} 1 & -1 \\ -1 & 2 \end{bmatrix}, \quad \begin{bmatrix} -1 & 2 \\ 3 & 1 \end{bmatrix}, \quad \begin{bmatrix} 2 & -3 \\ -3 & 2 \end{bmatrix}, \quad \begin{bmatrix} 1 & 1 \\ 1 & 6 \end{bmatrix}.$$

4.3 Vector Spaces

In Section 4.1 we illustrated how 2×1 and 3×1 column matrices could be interpreted as vectors in three-dimensional space. We now wish to consider general $m \times 1$ column matrices. Since we live in three-dimensional space, we cannot visualize geometrically, for example, 4×1 column matrices as vectors in four-dimensional space. We shall therefore have to base our development of the theory of m-component vectors on a sequence of strictly algebraic definitions and theorems, obtained by extending and generalizing the properties possessed by three-component vectors. To a large extent we are forced to divorce the idea of an m-component vector from either physical or geometrical considerations. Nevertheless, it will be useful to keep in mind the intuitive ideas connected with the linear dependence of vectors, subspaces, and so on, that were discussed in Section 4.1.

We now define what is meant by a "vector space." As already indicated, the implication of using the word "space" is simply that, in the case of 3×1 column vectors, we can interpret the properties of the corresponding vector space in terms of properties of ordinary three-dimensional space. It will be seen later (Chapter 14) that "vector spaces" can be defined which are much more general than those considered here, in the sense that the word "vector" can be used to apply to mathematical entities or objects that are quite different from matrices. However, in this chapter, when we use the phrase "a set of vectors" we shall mean a collection of $m \times n$ matrices—in particular, a set of column vectors, or a set of row vectors. (It perhaps should be mentioned that Definition 4.2 given below corresponds to the definition of a "subspace" in Section 14.2 rather than Definition 14.1 of an "abstract vector space." However, it is unnecessary, and it would be confusing, to go into this distinction here, although it will be clear later.)

DEFINITION **4.2.** A set of vectors is said to form a *vector space* if, given any two members $\mathbf{u}$, $\mathbf{v}$ of the set, then $\mathbf{u} + \mathbf{v}$ and $\alpha\mathbf{u}$ are also members of the set, where α is any scalar.

This is obviously a very general definition, but if we are given a set of vectors, it is often easy to check whether we are dealing with a vector space or not.

Ex. 4.11. The set of all 3×1 column vectors forms a vector space.

Solution: To show this, we set

$$\mathbf{u} = \begin{bmatrix} u_1 \\ u_2 \\ u_3 \end{bmatrix}, \qquad \mathbf{v} = \begin{bmatrix} v_1 \\ v_2 \\ v_3 \end{bmatrix}; \tag{4.7}$$

then

$$\mathbf{u} + \mathbf{v} = \begin{bmatrix} u_1 + v_1 \\ u_2 + v_2 \\ u_3 + v_3 \end{bmatrix}, \qquad \alpha\mathbf{u} = \begin{bmatrix} \alpha u_1 \\ \alpha u_2 \\ \alpha u_3 \end{bmatrix}$$

are also 3×1 column vectors, and therefore members of the set we started with.

Ex. 4.12. Show that the set of all 3×1 column vectors with first elements zero forms a vector space.

Solution: Two members of the set are given by taking $u_1 = v_1 = 0$ in (4.7), and then

$$\mathbf{u} + \mathbf{v} = \begin{bmatrix} 0 \\ u_2 + v_2 \\ u_3 + v_3 \end{bmatrix}, \qquad \alpha\mathbf{u} = \begin{bmatrix} 0 \\ \alpha u_2 \\ \alpha u_3 \end{bmatrix}. \tag{4.8}$$

These also have zero first elements, and are therefore members of the set, so that the set forms a vector space.

Ex 4.13. Show that the set of vectors whose first elements are unity does *not* form a vector space.

Solution: In this case,

$$\mathbf{u} + \mathbf{v} = \begin{bmatrix} 2 \\ u_2 + v_2 \\ u_3 + v_3 \end{bmatrix}, \qquad \alpha\mathbf{u} = \begin{bmatrix} \alpha \\ \alpha u_2 \\ \alpha u_3 \end{bmatrix}.$$

The first elements of these vectors are not unity, so that they do not belong to the set, and the set does not form a vector space.

Ex. 4.14. As a slightly less obvious example, we show that *the set of all solutions of the homogeneous linear equations* $\mathbf{Ax} = \mathbf{0}$ *forms a vector space.*

Solution: If $\mathbf{u}$ and $\mathbf{v}$ are solutions, i.e., $\mathbf{Au} = \mathbf{0}$, $\mathbf{Av} = \mathbf{0}$, then

$$\mathbf{A}(\mathbf{u} + \mathbf{v}) = \mathbf{Au} + \mathbf{Av} = \mathbf{0}, \qquad \mathbf{A}(\alpha\mathbf{u}) = \alpha\mathbf{Au} = \mathbf{0}.$$

Hence, $\mathbf{u} + \mathbf{v}$ and $\alpha\mathbf{u}$ are solutions, so that the set of solutions is a vector space.

Ex. 4.15. On the other hand, *the set of solutions of the nonhomogeneous equations* $\mathbf{Ax} = \mathbf{b}$, $\mathbf{b} \neq \mathbf{0}$, *does not form a vector space*, since if $\mathbf{u}$ is a solution, then $\mathbf{A}(\alpha\mathbf{u}) = \alpha\mathbf{Au} = \alpha\mathbf{b}$, so that $\alpha\mathbf{u}$, $\alpha \neq 1$, is not a solution.

Ex. 4.16. Show that the following statements are all special cases of Exs. 4.14, 4.15. (*Hint:* Write out $\mathbf{A}$ explicitly.) The vectors are all 1×4 vectors $[x_1\ x_2\ x_3\ x_4]$.

(a) The set with $x_2 = 0$ forms a vector space.

(b) The set with $x_1 - x_2 + x_3 = 1$ does *not* form a vector space.

(c) The set with $x_1 - x_2 = x_2 - x_3 = x_1 + x_2 + x_3 = 0$ forms a vector space.

Ex. 4.17. Show that the set of all $m \times n$ matrices constitutes a vector space.

Ex. 4.18. Sets of vectors are formed by imposing the following conditions in turn on the set of all $1 \times n$ row vectors, $\mathbf{x} = [x_1, \ldots, x_n]$. In each case, state, with explanation, whether the resulting set of vectors constitutes a vector space:

(a) $x_1 = 0$.

(b) $x_1 + x_n = 0$.

(c) $x_1 + x_n = 1$.

(d) $x_1 + x_n \geq 0$.

(e) $x_1 = x_2 = x_{n-1} = x_n$.

(f) $x_1x_2 = 0$.

(g) $x_1x_2 \neq 0$.

(h) $x_1 = x_2 + x_3$.

4.4 Basis and Dimension

Vector spaces arise frequently in practice when we consider the set of all linear combinations of a given set of vectors:

THEOREM **4.3.** *Let* $\mathbf{u}_1, \ldots, \mathbf{u}_s$ *be a set of m-component vectors. Then the set of all linear combinations of these vectors forms a vector space.*

Proof: Let

$$\mathbf{u} = \alpha_1\mathbf{u}_1 + \alpha_2\mathbf{u}_2 + \ldots + \alpha_s\mathbf{u}_s,$$

$$\mathbf{v} = \beta_1\mathbf{u}_1 + \beta_2\mathbf{u}_2 + \ldots + \beta_s\mathbf{u}_s.$$

Then

$$\mathbf{u} + \mathbf{v} = (\alpha_1 + \beta_1)\mathbf{u}_1 + (\alpha_2 + \beta_2)\mathbf{u}_2 + \ldots + (\alpha_s + \beta_s)\mathbf{u}_s,$$

$$\alpha\mathbf{u} = (\alpha\alpha_1)\mathbf{u}_1 + (\alpha\alpha_2)\mathbf{u}_2 + \ldots + (\alpha\alpha_s)\mathbf{u}_s.$$

Each of these is a linear combination of $\mathbf{u}_1, \ldots, \mathbf{u}_s$, so that the set of linear combinations is a vector space.

This theorem leads to the following definition.

DEFINITION 4.3. If a vector space consists of the set of all linear combinations of a finite set of vectors $\mathbf{u}_1, \ldots, \mathbf{u}_s$, then the vectors are said to *span* the space. We also say that the vectors *generate* the space.

As an example, the vectors

$$\begin{bmatrix}1\\0\\0\end{bmatrix}, \quad \begin{bmatrix}0\\1\\0\end{bmatrix}, \quad \begin{bmatrix}0\\0\\1\end{bmatrix}, \tag{4.9}$$

span the vector space consisting of all 3×1 column vectors. This space is also generated by the vectors

$$\begin{bmatrix}1\\0\\0\end{bmatrix}, \quad \begin{bmatrix}0\\1\\0\end{bmatrix}, \quad \begin{bmatrix}0\\0\\1\end{bmatrix}, \quad \begin{bmatrix}1\\-1\\1\end{bmatrix}, \quad \begin{bmatrix}-2\\0\\3\end{bmatrix}. \tag{4.10}$$

Note that the fact that the last two vectors are linearly dependent on the first three is immaterial since the definition did not say that the vectors which generate a space must be independent. However, we shall be interested in spanning sets containing as few vectors as possible, and we shall see that the question of whether the vectors are linearly independent is then important. The following theorem is useful in this connection.

THEOREM 4.4. (i) *If* $\mathbf{u}_1, \ldots, \mathbf{u}_s$ *span a vector space and one of these vectors, say* $\mathbf{u}_m$, *is linearly dependent on the others, then the vector space is spanned by the set obtained by omitting* $\mathbf{u}_m$ *from the original set.*

(ii) *If* $\mathbf{u}_1, \ldots, \mathbf{u}_s$ *span a vector space, we can always select from these a linearly independent set that spans the same space.*

Proof: If $\mathbf{u}$ is any vector in the space, it can be expressed as a linear combination of $\mathbf{u}_1, \ldots, \mathbf{u}_s$. From Theorem 4.2(iv) it can therefore be expressed as a linear combination of the set with $\mathbf{u}_m$ omitted. Hence, the set with $\mathbf{u}_m$ omitted spans the space. This proves (i). An easy way to prove (ii) is to give a constructive procedure for producing the linearly independent set. Without loss of generality we can assume that all the given vectors are nonzero since zero vectors are linearly dependent (Ex. 4.3). The first step is to select a linearly independent set from $\mathbf{u}_1$, $\mathbf{u}_2$ by checking whether $\mathbf{u}_1$ and $\mathbf{u}_2$ are linearly dependent. If they are, we retain only $\mathbf{u}_1$ and discard $\mathbf{u}_2$; if they are not, we keep $\mathbf{u}_1$ and $\mathbf{u}_2$. The second step is to check whether $\mathbf{u}_3$ is linearly dependent on the linearly independent set obtained from $\mathbf{u}_1$, $\mathbf{u}_2$. If not, retain $\mathbf{u}_3$; otherwise, discard it. At the pth stage we check whether $\mathbf{u}_{p+1}$ is linearly dependent on the linearly independent set selected from $\mathbf{u}_1, \ldots, \mathbf{u}_p$. If not, we retain $\mathbf{u}_p$; otherwise, discard it. Since we start from a finite set of vectors, the procedure will terminate, and this proves the required result. (A practical procedure for selecting a linearly independent set has already been described in Ex. 4.1.)

Linearly independent sets that span a vector space are so important that they are given a special name:

DEFINITION **4.4.** A *basis* for a vector space is a set of linearly independent vectors that spans the space.

As an example, the set of vectors (4.9) forms a basis for the vector space consisting of all 3×1 column vectors, since these vectors are linearly independent, and any 3×1 column vector can be expressed as a sum of multiples of the three vectors in the set. However, the set (4.10) does not form a basis, since the vectors are linearly dependent.

One of the important features of the representation of the vectors in a vector space in terms of the vectors in a basis is the following.

THEOREM **4.5.** *The expression for any vector in a vector space in terms of the vectors in a basis for the space is unique.*

Proof: Suppose that a vector $\mathbf{u}$ can be represented in two ways as a linear combination of vectors $\mathbf{u}_1, \mathbf{u}_2, \ldots, \mathbf{u}_s$ which form a basis for a vector space:

$$\begin{aligned} \mathbf{u} &= \alpha_1\mathbf{u}_1 + \alpha_2\mathbf{u}_2 + \ldots + \alpha_s\mathbf{u}_s \\ &= \beta_1\mathbf{u}_1 + \beta_2\mathbf{u}_2 + \ldots + \beta_s\mathbf{u}_s. \end{aligned}$$

Subtraction gives

$$\mathbf{0} = (\alpha_1 - \beta_1)\mathbf{u}_1 + (\alpha_2 - \beta_2)\mathbf{u}_2 + \ldots + (\alpha_s - \beta_s)\mathbf{u}_s.$$

Since the vectors in a basis are linearly independent, this gives $\alpha_i = \beta_i$ for all i, so that the representations are identical.

It should be clear that the set of vectors constituting a basis is not unique. Thus, in the case of the space consisting of 3×1 column vectors, we could take the following linearly independent vectors as a basis.

$$\begin{bmatrix}1\\2\\1\end{bmatrix}, \quad \begin{bmatrix}1\\0\\-1\end{bmatrix}, \quad \begin{bmatrix}1\\-2\\1\end{bmatrix}.$$

However, it turns out that the number of vectors in a basis for a vector space is unique. Before we can prove this important result, we require the following theorem.

THEOREM **4.6.** *Suppose that a set of nonzero vectors* $\mathbf{u}_1, \mathbf{u}_2, \ldots, \mathbf{u}_n$ *spans a vector space, and* $\mathbf{v}_1, \mathbf{v}_2, \ldots, \mathbf{v}_m$ *are linearly independent vectors in the vector space. Then* $m \leq n$. *In words, the number of vectors in a linearly independent set of vectors belonging to a vector space is less than or equal to the number of vectors in a set that spans the space.*

We give two proofs of this result, one using little more than the definition of linear independence, the other depending on a theorem concerning solutions of a set of homogeneous equations. The first proof uses a method that is often useful in other connections.

First proof: Consider the set of vectors obtained by adding $\mathbf{v}_1$ in front of the $\mathbf{u}$'s:

$$\mathbf{v}_1, \mathbf{u}_1, \mathbf{u}_2, \ldots, \mathbf{u}_n.$$

Since the $\mathbf{u}$'s span the vector space, $\mathbf{v}_1$ can be expressed as a linear combination of the $\mathbf{u}$'s. Hence, the above set is linearly dependent, and from Theorem 4.2(iii), one of the vectors can be expressed as a linear combination of preceding vectors. This means that one of the $\mathbf{u}$'s can be expressed as a linear combination of the preceding vectors. By relabeling the $\mathbf{u}$'s, if necessary, we can arrange that this is $\mathbf{u}_n$. From Theorem 4.4, the vector space is spanned by the set obtained by omitting $\mathbf{u}_n$, i.e., by the set

$$\mathbf{v}_1, \mathbf{u}_1, \ldots, \mathbf{u}_{n-1}. \tag{4.11}$$

We next add the vector $\mathbf{v}_2$ in front of the new set,

$$\mathbf{v}_2, \mathbf{v}_1, \mathbf{u}_1, \ldots, \mathbf{u}_{n-1}.$$

Since the set (4.11) spans the space, $\mathbf{v}_2$ can be expressed as a linear combination of the remaining vectors. As before, this means that one of the vectors can be expressed as a linear combination of the preceding. Since $\mathbf{v}_1$ and $\mathbf{v}_2$ are independent, this means that one of the $\mathbf{u}$'s can be expressed as a linear combination of the preceding vectors. By relabeling, if necessary, we can arrange that this is $\mathbf{u}_{n-1}$, and the vector space is spanned by the set obtained by omitting this vector:

$$\mathbf{v}_2, \mathbf{v}_1, \mathbf{u}_1, \ldots, \mathbf{u}_{n-2}. \tag{4.12}$$

Suppose that $m > n$. By repeating the above procedure we shall arrive at a set

$$\mathbf{v}_n, \mathbf{v}_{n-1}, \ldots, \mathbf{v}_1, \tag{4.13}$$

which spans the space, and we still have the vectors $\mathbf{v}_{n+1}, \ldots, \mathbf{v}_m$ left over. Since the set (4.13) spans the space, the vector $\mathbf{v}_{n+1}$ can be expressed as a linear combination of $\mathbf{v}_1, \mathbf{v}_2, \ldots, \mathbf{v}_n$. This contradicts the original assumption that the $\mathbf{v}$'s are linearly independent. Hence, we cannot have $m > n$. We must have $m \leq n$, as stated in the theorem.

Second proof: Suppose that $m > n$. Since $\mathbf{u}_1, \ldots, \mathbf{u}_n$ span the vector space, there exist scalars a_{ij} such that

$$\mathbf{v}_i = \sum_{j=1}^{n} a_{ij}\mathbf{u}_j, \qquad i = 1, 2, \ldots, m. \tag{4.14}$$

If the vectors $\mathbf{u}$, $\mathbf{v}$ are $p \times 1$, then (4.14), in matrix notation, is

$$\mathbf{V} = \mathbf{UA}, \tag{4.15}$$

where $\mathbf{V}$, $\mathbf{U}$ are $p \times m$ and $p \times n$ matrices with jth columns $\mathbf{v}_j$, $\mathbf{u}_j$, respectively, and $\mathbf{A} = [a_{ij}]$ is $n \times m$. Consider an arbitrary linear combination of the $\mathbf{v}_j$,

$$\mathbf{s} = x_1\mathbf{v}_1 + x_2\mathbf{v}_2 + \ldots + x_m\mathbf{v}_m = \sum_{j=1}^{m} x_j\mathbf{v}_j. \tag{4.16}$$

In matrix notation this is

$$\mathbf{s} = \mathbf{Vx},$$

where $\mathbf{x} = [x_j]$ is $1 \times m$. Substitution of the expression (4.15) for $\mathbf{V}$ gives

$$\mathbf{s} = \mathbf{UAx}. \tag{4.17}$$

The key to this proof is the remark that a nonzero $\mathbf{x}$ always exists such that $\mathbf{Ax} = \mathbf{0}$, since this is a system of n homogeneous equations in m unknowns with $n < m$. For this $\mathbf{x}$ (4.17) tells us that $\mathbf{s}$ is zero, so that, from (4.16), constants x_j exist, not all zero, such that

$$x_1\mathbf{v}_1 + x_2\mathbf{v}_2 + \ldots + x_m\mathbf{v}_m = \mathbf{0},$$

i.e., the $\mathbf{v}_j$ are linearly dependent. This contradicts the assumption that the $\mathbf{v}_j$ are linearly independent, so that we must have $m \leq n$.

We can now prove the following important theorem.

THEOREM **4.7.** *Any two bases of a vector space contain the same number of vectors.*

Proof: Suppose that $\mathbf{u}_1, \mathbf{u}_2, \ldots, \mathbf{u}_n$, and $\mathbf{v}_1, \mathbf{v}_2, \ldots, \mathbf{v}_m$ are two bases for a vector space. The $\mathbf{u}$'s span the space and the $\mathbf{v}$'s are linearly independent, so that, from Theorem 4.6, $m \leq n$. But it is equally true that the $\mathbf{v}$'s span the space and the $\mathbf{u}$'s are linearly independent, so that, from Theorem 4.6, $n \leq m$. Hence $m = n$, and the bases contain the same number of vectors.

The unique number of vectors in a basis is so important that we give it a special name:

DEFINITION **4.5.** The number of vectors in a basis for a vector space is known as the *dimension* of the space. If the dimension of a space is m, then we say that we are dealing with an *m-dimensional space*. If a space has a basis consisting of a finite number of vectors we say that the space is *finite-dimensional.*

The point of introducing the word finite-dimensional is that in more general contexts, vector spaces occur that have bases possessing an infinite number of elements. We restrict our attention to finite-dimensional spaces.

If a vector space consists only of the null vector $\mathbf{x} = \mathbf{0}$, there are no linearly independent vectors in the space, and the dimension of the space is 0.

In order to give the reader some feeling for what we mean by basis and dimension, we illustrate how to find a basis for a vector space in some specific cases. This is the object of the next section.

4.5 Examples on Basis and Dimension

It is important to remember that a basis for a vector space possesses two properties: (a) the vectors are linearly independent, and (b) the vectors span the space.

In order to find a basis when we are given a set of vectors that spans a space, we must select from these a linearly independent set that also spans the space. Theorem 4.4(ii) tells us that this can always be done. We then have a set of linearly independent vectors that span the space. This, by definition, constitutes a basis. In order to select an independent set from a spanning set in practice, it is often convenient to assemble the spanning set as either the columns of a matrix or as the rows of a matrix. We require the following definition and theorem.

DEFINITION **4.6.** The *column space* associated with a matrix $\mathbf{A}$ is the vector space generated or spanned by the columns of $\mathbf{A}$. The dimension of the column space will be denoted by dim $\mathbf{A}$. The *row space* of a matrix $\mathbf{A}$ is the vector space spanned by the rows of $\mathbf{A}$. (We shall prove in Theorem 5.3 that the dimensions of the row and column spaces are the same.)

THEOREM **4.8.** (i) *A basis for the column space of* $\mathbf{A}$ *is given by the columns of* $\mathbf{A}$ *corresponding to the unit columns of the row-echelon form of* $\mathbf{A}$ *(i.e., the columns numbered* $c_1, \ldots, c_k$ *in Definition* 3.4.).

(ii) *The dimension of the column space of* $\mathbf{A}$, dim $\mathbf{A}$, *is equal to the rank of* $\mathbf{A}$, *i.e., the number of nonzero rows in the row-echelon form.*

Proof: The dimension is the number of vectors in a basis, i.e., the number of vectors in a linearly independent set that spans the space. We are given a set that spans the space, namely the columns of the matrix, so what we have to do is to pick out from these a set of linearly independent columns that also spans the space. This can be done by reducing the matrix to row-echelon form and applying Theorem 4.1. The unit column vectors in the row-echelon form described in Definition 3.4 are linearly independent, and the other columns in the row-echelon form can be expressed as linear combinations of these. Hence, the same statements apply for the corresponding columns in the original matrix. This proves (i). The number of unit columns in the row-echelon form is equal to the number of nonzero rows in the row-echelon form, and this proves (ii).

Ex. 4.19. Find the dimension of the vector space spanned by the following vectors, and find a basis for the space.

$$\begin{bmatrix} 1 \\ -1 \\ -1 \\ 2 \end{bmatrix}, \quad \begin{bmatrix} -1 \\ 2 \\ 3 \\ 1 \end{bmatrix}, \quad \begin{bmatrix} 2 \\ -3 \\ -3 \\ 2 \end{bmatrix}, \quad \begin{bmatrix} 1 \\ 1 \\ 1 \\ 6 \end{bmatrix}.$$

Solution: Following Theorem 4.8, we write these as the columns of a matrix and reduce to row-echelon form. This has been done in Ex. 4.1. From the result, we see that there are three linearly independent columns, and the dimension of the vector space is therefore three. Also the second vector, together with any two of the remaining vectors, can be taken as a basis.

If we wish to select a basis when we are given an *infinite* number of vectors, the situation is more difficult. Some helpful theorems will be given in Section 4.7, but meantime it is possible to solve some examples from first principles:

Ex. 4.20. Find a basis for the vector space consisting of all 4×1 vectors for which the third and fourth elements are the same.

Solution: The general vector in the space can be written

$$\begin{bmatrix} x_1 \\ x_2 \\ x_3 \\ x_3 \end{bmatrix} = x_1 \begin{bmatrix} 1 \\ 0 \\ 0 \\ 0 \end{bmatrix} + x_2 \begin{bmatrix} 0 \\ 1 \\ 0 \\ 0 \end{bmatrix} + x_3 \begin{bmatrix} 0 \\ 0 \\ 1 \\ 1 \end{bmatrix}. \tag{4.18}$$

The three vectors on the right are linearly independent and they span the space. Hence, they form a basis for the space. The dimension of the space is three.

At the beginning of this section we said that the vectors in a basis are linearly independent and they span the space. The examples so far have been concerned with sets that span the space but may be linearly dependent. We next consider sets that are linearly independent. The following theorem says that a linearly independent set of vectors in a vector space can always be extended to give a basis for the space.

THEOREM **4.9.** *Let* $\mathbf{u}_1, \ldots, \mathbf{u}_q$ *be a linearly independent set of vectors in a finite-dimensional vector space. Then there exist vectors* $\mathbf{u}_{q+1}, \ldots, \mathbf{u}_p$ *such that* $\mathbf{u}_1, \ldots, \mathbf{u}_p$ *form a basis for the space.*

Proof: Let $\mathbf{v}_1, \ldots, \mathbf{v}_m$ be a set of vectors that span the space (for example, a basis for the space). The set

$$\mathbf{u}_1, \ldots, \mathbf{u}_q, \mathbf{v}_1, \ldots, \mathbf{v}_m$$

spans the set. We select a linearly independent set by the following procedure. Each of the vectors $\mathbf{u}_i$ is linearly independent of the preceding vectors. If $\mathbf{v}_1$ is linearly independent of the preceding vectors in the set we retain it in the set; otherwise we exclude it. Proceeding in this way we obtain a set of say p vectors. The vectors are linearly independent and they span the space (Theorem 4.4(i)). Hence they form a basis for the space.

Ex. 4.21. Extend the vector $\mathbf{u}_1 = [1\ 0\ 1\ 1]^T$ to form a basis for the space of 4×1 column vectors whose third and fourth elements are the same.

Solution: This example is so simple that it can be solved by inspection. We see that if we introduce $\mathbf{u}_2 = [1\ 0\ 0\ 0]^T$ and $\mathbf{u}_3 = [0\ 1\ 0\ 0]^T$, then the vectors $\mathbf{u}_1, \mathbf{u}_2, \mathbf{u}_3$ are linearly independent. Also a general vector $\mathbf{x} = [x_1\ x_2\ x_3\ x_3]^T$ can be written as multiples of these:

$$\mathbf{x} = x_3\mathbf{u}_1 + (x_1 - x_3)\mathbf{u}_2 + x_2\mathbf{u}_3.$$

Hence, $\mathbf{u}_1, \mathbf{u}_2, \mathbf{u}_3$ span the space, and they form a basis.

In more complicated cases, it may be convenient to use Theorem 4.8 in the following way. A basis for the vector space in Ex. 4.21 was found in Ex. 4.20, namely the three vectors on the right of (4.18). We assemble $\mathbf{u}_1$ and these three vectors as a matrix, $\mathbf{u}_1$ being the first column:

$$\begin{bmatrix} 1 & 1 & 0 & 0 \\ 0 & 0 & 1 & 0 \\ 1 & 0 & 0 & 1 \\ 1 & 0 & 0 & 1 \end{bmatrix}. \tag{4.19}$$

The row-echelon form of this matrix is

$$\begin{bmatrix} 1 & 0 & 0 & 1 \\ 0 & 1 & 0 & -1 \\ 0 & 0 & 1 & 0 \\ 0 & 0 & 0 & 0 \end{bmatrix}. \tag{4.20}$$

This tells us that we must include in the basis the third column in the original matrix, and we can take as the third vector either the second or the fourth column in the original matrix.

We shall pursue some further aspects of basis and dimension in the next two sections, but meantime the reader is in a position to do the following exercises.

Ex. 4.22. Find a basis for the vector space consisting of all 4×1 column vectors $[x_i]$ such that $x_1 - x_2 = 0$, $x_2 - x_3 = 0$, and $x_1 - 2x_2 + x_3 = 0$.

Ex. 4.23. Does either of the following sets provide a basis for the set of 4×1 column vectors $[x_i]$ such that $x_1 + x_2 - x_3 - x_4 = 0$?

$$\text{(a)}\quad \begin{bmatrix} 1 \\ -1 \\ -1 \\ 1 \end{bmatrix}, \begin{bmatrix} 1 \\ 0 \\ 1 \\ 0 \end{bmatrix}, \begin{bmatrix} 0 \\ 1 \\ 0 \\ 1 \end{bmatrix}. \qquad \text{(b)}\quad \begin{bmatrix} 1 \\ -1 \\ 1 \\ -1 \end{bmatrix}, \begin{bmatrix} 1 \\ 0 \\ 1 \\ 0 \end{bmatrix}, \begin{bmatrix} 0 \\ 1 \\ 0 \\ 1 \end{bmatrix}.$$

Ex. 4.24. For what values of k will the vectors $[3 - k, -1, 0]$, $[-1, 2 - k, -1]$, $[0, -1, 3 - k]$ span a *two*-dimensional space?

Ex. 4.25. Show that the sets $[1\ 0\ -1]$, $[1\ 1\ 0]$, $[0\ 1\ 1]$ and $[2\ 1\ -1]$, $[1\ 2\ 1]$ span the same vector space. Show that the set $[2\ 1\ -1]$, $[1\ -1\ 0]$ does *not* span this space.

Ex. 4.26. Consider the space of 1×4 vectors $[x_1\, x_2\, x_3\, x_4]$ satisfying $x_1 + x_2 = x_3 + x_4$. Show that $[1\ 0\ 1\ 0]$ and $[0\ 1\ 0\ 1]$ are linearly independent and lie in the space. Extend these two vectors to a basis for the space.

4.6 A Standard Form for a Basis

The basis for a vector space found using the methods developed in the last section is not unique. It is sometimes convenient to use a procedure that yields a *standard form* of basis, for a given vector space, i.e., the same basis is always produced, whatever the spanning set used to describe the vector space. We require the following preliminary theorem:

THEOREM **4.10.** *If a matrix* **C** *is row-equivalent to a matrix* **C**′, *then the rows of* **C**′ *span the same vector space as the rows of* **C**.

Proof: This is an immediate consequence of Theorem 3.4, which states that the rows of **C**′ can be expressed as a linear combination of the rows of **C**. Any vector that can be expressed as a linear combination of the rows of **C**′ can therefore be expressed as a linear combination of the rows of **C**, and this is the result stated in vector space terms in the theorem.

The basic theorem that shows how to produce a unique basis from a given spanning set is:

THEOREM **4.11.** (i) *The nonzero rows of the row-echelon form of a matrix provide a basis for the vector space spanned by the rows of the matrix.*

(ii) *Exactly the same basis will be given by the row-echelon form of any other matrix whose rows span the same space.*

Proof: From Theorem 4.10, the nonzero rows of the row-echelon form span the same vector space as the rows of the original matrix. The nonzero rows of the row-echelon form are linearly independent. Hence, they form a basis for the space. This proves (i). To prove (ii), suppose that the rows of two matrices **A**, **B** span the same vector space. Consider the two matrices

$$\begin{bmatrix} \mathbf{A} \\ \mathbf{B} \end{bmatrix}, \quad \begin{bmatrix} \mathbf{B} \\ \mathbf{A} \end{bmatrix}. \tag{4.21}$$

These two matrices must have the same row-echelon normal form since they can be obtained from each other by interchanging rows. Since the vector space is spanned by the rows of **A**, the rows of **B** are linear combinations of the rows of **A**, so that elementary row operations can be used to reduce the first matrix to

$$\begin{bmatrix} \mathbf{A} \\ \mathbf{0} \end{bmatrix}.$$

Further elementary operations can then be used to reduce this matrix to its row-echelon form, and this will be the row-echelon form of **A**. In a similar way, elementary row operations can be used to reduce the second matrix in (4.21) to its row-echelon normal form, and this will be the row-echelon form of **B**. As we have already said, the two matrices in (4.21) have the same row-echelon form, so that **A** and **B** have the same row-echelon form.

Ex. 4.27. Show that

$$\begin{bmatrix} 1 \\ -1 \\ 2 \end{bmatrix}, \quad \begin{bmatrix} 2 \\ 1 \\ -3 \end{bmatrix}, \quad \begin{bmatrix} 1 \\ -2 \\ -5 \end{bmatrix}$$

and

$$\begin{bmatrix} 1 \\ 3 \\ -7 \end{bmatrix}, \quad \begin{bmatrix} 2 \\ -1 \\ 0 \end{bmatrix}, \quad \begin{bmatrix} 3 \\ -1 \\ -1 \end{bmatrix}, \quad \begin{bmatrix} 4 \\ -3 \\ 2 \end{bmatrix}$$

span the same space.

Solution: Following Theorem 4.11, we simply write the vectors as rows of matrices,

$$\begin{bmatrix} 1 & -1 & 2 \\ 2 & 1 & -3 \\ 1 & -2 & -5 \end{bmatrix}, \quad \begin{bmatrix} 1 & 3 & -7 \\ 2 & -1 & 0 \\ 3 & -1 & -1 \\ 4 & -3 & 2 \end{bmatrix},$$

and reduce them to row-echelon form. This gives

$$\begin{bmatrix} 1 & 0 & -1 \\ 0 & 1 & -2 \\ 0 & 0 & 0 \end{bmatrix}, \quad \begin{bmatrix} 1 & 0 & -1 \\ 0 & 1 & -2 \\ 0 & 0 & 0 \\ 0 & 0 & 0 \end{bmatrix}.$$

Hence, the given vectors span the same two-dimensional space, and the standard form for the basis of this space is

$$\begin{bmatrix} 1 \\ 0 \\ -1 \end{bmatrix}, \quad \begin{bmatrix} 0 \\ 1 \\ -2 \end{bmatrix}.$$

Ex. 4.28. Do the columns of the following matrices span the same vector space? Explain.

$$\begin{bmatrix} 1 & 3 & 1 & -1 \\ 2 & 1 & -2 & -4 \\ 0 & 5 & 4 & 2 \end{bmatrix}, \quad \begin{bmatrix} 1 & -1 & 0 & 2 \\ 1 & 1 & 2 & 1 \\ 1 & -3 & -2 & 3 \end{bmatrix}.$$

4.7 Basis and Dimension (continued)

We give a series of results that clarify some of the implications of the definitions of basis and dimension. Two results that are implicit in Theorem 4.6 can be rephrased in the terminology of m-dimensional space in the following way:

THEOREM **4.12.** *In an m-dimensional space V:*

(i) *Any $m + 1$ vectors are linearly dependent.*
(ii) *No set of less than m vectors can span V.*

Proof: In m-dimensional space, a set of m vectors exists that span the space, so that, by Theorem 4.6, there are at most m linearly independent vectors in the space. This proves (i). If k vectors span V, then, from Theorem 4.6, the maximum number of linearly independent vectors must be less than or equal to k. But if the dimension of the space is m, there are m linearly independent vectors in the space, so that $m \leq k$. This proves (ii).

A set of vectors is a basis of a vector space if (a) the vectors are linearly independent, and (b) the vectors span the space. If we know that a space is m-dimensional, in order to prove that a set of m vectors is a basis, it is sufficient to prove that is satisfies only *one* of these conditions. The other condition will then be automatically satisfied:

THEOREM **4.13.** (i) *If a set of m vectors in an m-dimensional space is linearly independent, then it forms a basis for the space.*

(ii) *If a set of m vectors in an m-dimensional space spans the space, then it forms a basis for the space.*

Proof: To prove (i) we note that if a set of vectors is linearly independent, then from the previous theorem it forms part of a basis. But a basis for an m-dimensional space always consists of precisely m vectors. Hence, the set must be a basis. To prove (ii) we note that if the set $\mathbf{u}_1, \ldots, \mathbf{u}_m$ spans an m-dimensional space, then any vector $\mathbf{u}$ can be written in the form

$$\mathbf{u} = \alpha_1\mathbf{u}_1 + \ldots + \alpha_m\mathbf{u}_m. \tag{4.22}$$

If the $\mathbf{u}_i$ are linearly dependent, then one of the $\mathbf{u}_i$ can be expressed in terms of the others, say $\mathbf{u}_s$. On substituting this expression for $\mathbf{u}_s$ in (4.22), we see that any vector $\mathbf{u}$ can be expressed in terms of only $m - 1$ vectors. This means that we have found a basis with at most $m - 1$ vectors, which contradicts the definition of m-dimensional space. Hence, the $\mathbf{u}_i$ are linearly independent and span the space so that they constitute a basis.

This theorem is useful in examples like Ex. 4.21 where we wish to extend a given set of q linearly independent vectors to form a basis for a vector space. If we know that the dimension of the space is m, we must look for exactly $m - q$ additional linearly independent vectors.

The vector space of all $n \times 1$ column vectors is of fundamental importance:

THEOREM **4.14.** *The set of all $n \times 1$ column vectors forms an n-dimensional space.*

Proof: The fact that the set forms a vector space follows directly from the definition. Consider the set of unit vectors $\mathbf{e}_i$, where all the elements of $\mathbf{e}_i$ are zero except the ith element which is unity. The $\mathbf{e}_i$ are linearly independent and they span the space. Hence, the $\mathbf{e}_i$ form a basis for the space and the dimension of the space is n. This concludes the proof.

The above vector space is so important that it warrants a special symbol:

DEFINITION **4.7.** The n-dimensional space consisting of all $n \times 1$ column vectors is denoted by the symbol V_n.

Of course if we are dealing with an m-dimensional space, we do not imply that the space consists of vectors with m elements. It is advisable to clarify this point.

DEFINITION **4.8.** A *subspace* of a vector space V is a vector space W such that any vector in W is also in V.

An example of a subspace is the set of all 3×1 column vectors with third element zero. This is a subspace of V_3. It follows from the definition that a vector space V is a subspace of itself.

We can now clarify our usage as follows:

(a) If we say simply "m-dimensional space" we are referring to a vector space that may be V_m but equally well could be a subspace of an n-dimensional space ($n > m$).

(b) If we wish to emphasize that the space *is* V_m we shall say "m-dimensional space V_m" or simply "the space V_m."

(c) If we wish to emphasize that the space is contained in another space we shall refer to the "m-dimensional subspace."

THEOREM **4.15.** (i) *If the maximum number of linearly independent vectors in a space is k then k is the dimension of the space, and the space possesses a basis.*

(ii) *Any subspace V of an m-dimensional space W possesses a basis, and the dimension of V is less than or equal to the dimension of W.*

Proof: To prove (i) suppose that $\mathbf{u}_1, \ldots, \mathbf{u}_k$ are linearly independent, and that k is the maximum number of linearly independent vectors. Then any other vector $\mathbf{u}$, together with these k vectors, forms a linearly dependent set. Hence, $\mathbf{u}$ can be expressed as a linear combination of $\mathbf{u}_1, \ldots, \mathbf{u}_k$, i.e., the $\mathbf{u}_1, \ldots, \mathbf{u}_k$ span the space. Therefore, the set of k vectors span the space. Since they are linearly independent they constitute a basis for the space, and the dimension of the space is k. To prove (ii) we note that any $m + 1$ vectors in W are linearly dependent [Theorem 4.12(i)]. Any $m + 1$ vectors in V are in W and hence $m + 1$ vectors in V are linearly dependent. There must be a maximum number of linearly independent vectors, say k, in all possible choices of $m + 1$ vectors from V. From part (i), k is the dimension of V, and V possesses a basis. Obviously $k \leq m$. This concludes the proof.

Ex. 4.29. If $\mathbf{u}_1, \ldots, \mathbf{u}_p$ span a vector space V, but V cannot be spanned by the set of vectors obtained by omitting any vector from this set, show that the set forms a basis for V.

Ex. 4.30. Show that a set of vectors is a basis for a vector space V if and only if each vector in V can be expressed uniquely as a linear combination of vectors in the set.

Ex. 4.31. If the columns of two matrices $\mathbf{U}$, $\mathbf{V}$ are each bases for the same vector space, show that a nonsingular matrix $\mathbf{P}$ exists such that $\mathbf{U} = \mathbf{VP}$, $\mathbf{V} = \mathbf{UP}^{-1}$.

Ex. 4.32. Find the dimension of the vector space consisting of all $m \times n$ matrices $[a_{ij}]$ such that $a_{ij} = 0$ for $i < j - 1$ and $j < i$.

4.8 Linear Equations with an "Infinity of Solutions"

The question of whether a set of simultaneous linear equations has no solution, a unique solution, or an infinity of solutions was considered in Section 3.9. The discussion was incomplete in one important respect, namely we did not state precisely what we meant by an "infinity of solutions." This deficiency can now be remedied. We know from Theorem 3.8 that if a nonhomogeneous set of equations $\mathbf{Az} = \mathbf{b}$ has an infinity of solutions, then the general solution of the set can be written in the form $\mathbf{z} = \mathbf{x}_0 + \mathbf{x}$, where $\mathbf{x}_0$ is a particular solution of the nonhomogeneous equations, and $\mathbf{x}$ is a solution of the homogeneous equations $\mathbf{Ax} = \mathbf{0}$. Hence, it will be sufficient to characterize the solutions of a set of homogeneous equations.

THEOREM **4.16.** *The set of all solutions of* $\mathbf{Ax} = \mathbf{0}$ *is a vector space.*

Proof: If $\mathbf{x}_1$, $\mathbf{x}_2$ are vectors such that $\mathbf{Ax}_1 = \mathbf{0}$, $\mathbf{Ax}_2 = \mathbf{0}$, then

$$\mathbf{A}(\alpha_1\mathbf{x}_1 + \alpha_2\mathbf{x}_2) = \alpha_1\mathbf{Ax}_1 + \alpha_2\mathbf{Ax}_2 = \mathbf{0},$$

so that $\alpha_1\mathbf{x}_1 + \alpha_2\mathbf{x}_2$ belongs to the defining set, namely solutions of $\mathbf{Ax} = \mathbf{0}$. Hence, these solutions constitute a vector space.

DEFINITION **4.9.** The vector space consisting of all solutions of the homogeneous equations $\mathbf{Ax} = \mathbf{0}$ is called the *null space* (or *kernel*) of $\mathbf{A}$. The dimension of the null space of $\mathbf{A}$ will be denoted by $N(\mathbf{A})$.

The next task is to specify the dimension of, and a basis for, the null space.

THEOREM **4.17.** *If* $\mathbf{A}$ *is an* $m \times n$ *matrix, the null space of* $\mathbf{A}$ *(i.e., the set of solutions of the homogeneous equations* $\mathbf{Ax} = \mathbf{0}$*) forms a vector space of dimension* $n - k$ *where* k *is the rank of* $\mathbf{A}$*, i.e., the dimension of the column space of* $\mathbf{A}$*. If* $k = n$*, the only solution is* $\mathbf{x} = \mathbf{0}$*. If* $k < n$*, a basis for the null space can be constructed from the row-echelon form of* $\mathbf{A}$.

Proof: The row-echelon form of $\mathbf{A}$ has k unit column vectors. For simplicity in notation (and without loss of generality) we can assume that the unknowns have been renumbered if necessary so that the unit columns in the row-echelon form are the first k columns. Suppose then that the row-echelon form of $\mathbf{A}$ is

$$\begin{bmatrix} \mathbf{I}_k & \mathbf{B} \\ \mathbf{0} & \mathbf{0} \end{bmatrix}. \tag{4.23}$$

The following set of equations are equivalent to $\mathbf{Ax} = \mathbf{0}$:

$$\begin{bmatrix} \mathbf{I}_k & \mathbf{B} \\ \mathbf{0} & \mathbf{0} \end{bmatrix} \begin{bmatrix} \mathbf{x}_1 \\ \mathbf{x}_2 \end{bmatrix} = \begin{bmatrix} \mathbf{0} \\ \mathbf{0} \end{bmatrix}, \tag{4.24}$$

where $\mathbf{B}$ is $k \times (n - k)$, $\mathbf{x}_1$ is $k \times 1$ and $\mathbf{x}_2$ is $(n - k) \times 1$. This gives

$$\mathbf{x}_1 = -\mathbf{B}\mathbf{x}_2, \tag{4.25}$$

so that we can choose $\mathbf{x}_2$ arbitrarily, and express $\mathbf{x}_1$ in terms of the arbitrary $\mathbf{x}_2$. Suppose that

$$\mathbf{x}_2 = \begin{bmatrix} \alpha_1 \\ \cdot \\ \cdot \\ \cdot \\ \alpha_{n-k} \end{bmatrix}. \tag{4.26}$$

If we denote the columns of $\mathbf{B}$ by $\mathbf{b}_1, \ldots, \mathbf{b}_{n-k}$, Equation (4.25) gives

$$\mathbf{x}_1 = -\alpha_1\mathbf{b}_1 - \alpha_2\mathbf{b}_2 - \ldots - \alpha_{n-k}\mathbf{b}_{n-k}. \tag{4.27}$$

Also,

$$\mathbf{x}_2 = \alpha_1\mathbf{e}_1 + \alpha_2\mathbf{e}_2 + \ldots + \alpha_{n-k}\mathbf{e}_{n-k}, \tag{4.28}$$

where $\mathbf{e}_j$ is the $(n - k) \times 1$ unit vector with jth element equal to unity and other elements zero. Hence every solution of $\mathbf{Ax} = \mathbf{0}$ can be written in the form

$$\mathbf{x} = \alpha_1\mathbf{u}_1 + \alpha_2\mathbf{u}_2 + \ldots + \alpha_{n-k}\mathbf{u}_{n-k} \tag{4.29}$$

where

$$\mathbf{u}_j = \begin{bmatrix} -\mathbf{b}_j \\ \mathbf{e}_j \end{bmatrix}. \tag{4.30}$$

The $\mathbf{u}_j$ are clearly linearly independent and they span the null space. Hence, they form a basis for the space. If $k = n$, then $\mathbf{B}$ is nonexistent, and the only solution is $\mathbf{x} = \mathbf{0}$. This completes the proof.

Ex. 4.33. Find a basis for the null space of the homogeneous equations

$$\begin{aligned} x_1 + 2x_2 + x_3 + 2x_4 - 3x_5 &= 0 \\ 3x_1 + 6x_2 + 4x_3 - x_4 + 2x_5 &= 0 \\ 4x_1 + 8x_2 + 5x_3 + x_4 - x_5 &= 0. \\ -2x_1 - 4x_2 - 3x_3 + 3x_4 - 5x_5 &= 0. \end{aligned} \tag{4.31}$$

Solution: The row-echelon form of the coefficient matrix is

$$\begin{bmatrix} 1 & 2 & 0 & 9 & -14 \\ 0 & 0 & 1 & -7 & 11 \\ 0 & 0 & 0 & 0 & 0 \\ 0 & 0 & 0 & 0 & 0 \end{bmatrix}. \tag{4.32}$$

The rank is 2, so that the dimension of the null space is 3. From (4.30), a basis for the null space is given by

$$\begin{bmatrix} -2 \\ 0 \\ 1 \\ 0 \\ 0 \end{bmatrix}, \quad \begin{bmatrix} -9 \\ 7 \\ 0 \\ 1 \\ 0 \end{bmatrix}, \quad \begin{bmatrix} 14 \\ -11 \\ 0 \\ 0 \\ 1 \end{bmatrix}. \tag{4.33}$$

This result can of course be seen from the row-echelon form, which tells us that a set of equations that is equivalent to the original set is given by

$$\begin{aligned} x_1 + 2x_2 \qquad + 9x_4 - 14x_5 &= 0 \\ x_3 - 7x_4 + 11x_5 &= 0. \end{aligned} \tag{4.34}$$

If we set $x_2 = \alpha_1$, $x_4 = \alpha_2$, $x_5 = \alpha_3$, where α_1, α_2, α_3 are arbitrary, then (4.34) gives

$$\begin{bmatrix} x_1 \\ x_2 \\ x_3 \\ x_4 \\ x_5 \end{bmatrix} = \alpha_1 \begin{bmatrix} -2 \\ 0 \\ 1 \\ 0 \\ 0 \end{bmatrix} + \alpha_2 \begin{bmatrix} -9 \\ 7 \\ 0 \\ 1 \\ 0 \end{bmatrix} + \alpha_3 \begin{bmatrix} 14 \\ -11 \\ 0 \\ 0 \\ 1 \end{bmatrix}, \tag{4.35}$$

which is the same result as before. If we follow this line of reasoning, we do not need to remember (4.30) and in any case we are less likely to forget to change the signs of the columns of **B**.

We discuss a physical application where this theory is relevant. We first describe the physical background of the problem. The reader interested only in the mathematical details can proceed directly to equations (4.38) below.

Consider the heating or cooling of a fluid flowing through a heated or cooled tube. We wish to find out how many independent groups of physical quantities are involved by using what is known as *dimensional analysis*. The word "dimensional" here has nothing to do with the word "dimension" introduced earlier in connection with vector spaces. The heat transfer coefficient h describing the transfer of heat from the tube to the fluid (or vice versa) is defined by

$$Q = hA(\theta_1 - \theta_2), \tag{4.36}$$

where θ_1, θ_2 are the temperatures of the tube and the bulk of the fluid, respectively, Q is the quantity of heat per unit time transferred from temperature

θ_1 to θ_2, and A is the area. Since Q is proportional to A, the quantity h is independent of the area involved, at least to the degree of approximation considered here. We assume that we are considering a situation in which the heat transfer is governed by a thin film of fluid near the surface of the tube. The heat conductivity k of the fluid in this film is obviously involved. The film thickness depends on the mass velocity G of the fluid, the tube diameter D and the viscosity μ. The bulk temperature of the stream θ_2 depends on the specific heat c_p, which, therefore, should also be included.

The dimensions of the various physical quantities that are involved can be expressed in terms of the usual fundamental quantities, mass M, length L, and time T, with, in addition, the independent dimensional quantity temperature Θ. The following results for the dimensions of the various quantities are given in textbooks on physics, apart perhaps for h, for which the dimensions can be deduced from (4.36):

Quantity	h	D	k	G	μ	c_p
Dimension	$MT^{-3}\Theta^{-1}$	L	$MLT^{-3}\Theta^{-1}$	$ML^{-2}T^{-1}$	$ML^{-1}T^{-1}$	$L^2T^{-2}\Theta^{-1}$

The problem is to find as many independent dimensionless products of the following form as possible:

$$h^x D^y k^z G^u \mu^v c_p^w. \tag{4.37}$$

By saying that we have a dimensionless product, we mean that if we substitute the above expressions for the dimensions of $h, D, \ldots$ in terms of M, L, T, Θ, then the powers of each of M, L, T, Θ should be zero. This leads to the following equations that $x, y, \ldots$ must satisfy:

$$\begin{array}{lr} \text{(From powers of } M) & x + z + u + v = 0 \\ \text{(From powers of } L) & y + z - 2u - v + 2w = 0 \\ \text{(From powers of } T) & -3x - 3z - u - v - 2w = 0 \\ \text{(From powers of } \Theta) & -x - z - w = 0. \end{array} \tag{4.38}$$

The corresponding matrix of coefficients is

$$\begin{bmatrix} 1 & 0 & 1 & 1 & 1 & 0 \\ 0 & 1 & 1 & -2 & -1 & 2 \\ -3 & 0 & -3 & -1 & -1 & -2 \\ -1 & 0 & -1 & 0 & 0 & -1 \end{bmatrix}. \tag{4.39}$$

The row-echelon form of this matrix is

$$\begin{bmatrix} 1 & 0 & 1 & 0 & 0 & 1 \\ 0 & 1 & 1 & 0 & 1 & 0 \\ 0 & 0 & 0 & 1 & 1 & -1 \\ 0 & 0 & 0 & 0 & 0 & 0 \end{bmatrix}. \tag{4.40}$$

The rank of this matrix is 3 so that the original equations (4.38) have $6 - 3 = 3$ independent solutions. From (4.40) the unit column vectors in the row-echelon form are the first, second, and fourth, and the following set of equations is equivalent to the original set:

$$\begin{aligned} x &= -z \qquad - w \\ y &= -z - v \\ u &= \qquad - v + w, \end{aligned} \tag{4.41}$$

where z, v, w can be chosen arbitrarily. To obtain three independent solutions we set, in turn [compare (4.28)],

$$\begin{bmatrix} z \\ v \\ w \end{bmatrix} = \begin{bmatrix} 1 \\ 0 \\ 0 \end{bmatrix}, \quad \begin{bmatrix} 0 \\ 1 \\ 0 \end{bmatrix}, \quad \begin{bmatrix} 0 \\ 0 \\ 1 \end{bmatrix}.$$

The corresponding values of x, y, u are, from (4.41),

$$\begin{bmatrix} x \\ y \\ u \end{bmatrix} = \begin{bmatrix} -1 \\ -1 \\ 0 \end{bmatrix}, \quad \begin{bmatrix} 0 \\ -1 \\ -1 \end{bmatrix}, \quad \begin{bmatrix} -1 \\ 0 \\ 1 \end{bmatrix}.$$

Substituting each of these three solutions, in turn, in (4.37), we obtain the following three independent dimensionless quantities.

$$\alpha = \frac{k}{hD}, \qquad \beta = \frac{\mu}{DG}, \qquad \gamma = \frac{Gc_p}{h}.$$

Equivalent sets are obtained by multiplying or dividing these quantities. (This corresponds to assigning different values to z, v, w, above.) In engineering, the quantities usually used are

$$\frac{1}{\beta} = \frac{DG}{\mu}, \qquad \frac{\beta\gamma}{\alpha} = \frac{\mu c_p}{k},$$

and either $1/\alpha$ or $1/\gamma$.

Of course the above results could have been obtained (and usually are obtained) without introducing matrices or the idea of the rank of a matrix, simply by solving the set of equations (4.38) directly. The virtue of the matrix approach is that it gives a clear idea of the structure of the calculation, and a systematic computational procedure. As usual, the more complicated the situation, the more useful the matrix method of approach will be.

To conclude this chapter we state in the language of vector spaces what the position is regarding the solution of the equations $\mathbf{Ax} = \mathbf{b}$, where $\mathbf{A}$ is a general $m \times n$ matrix:

THEOREM 4.18. (i) *If* $\mathbf{b}$ *does not belong to the column space of* $\mathbf{A}$, *then the equations* $\mathbf{Ax} = \mathbf{b}$ *do not have a solution.*

(ii) *If* $\mathbf{b}$ *belongs to the column space of* $\mathbf{A}$ *and the dimension of this column space is equal to* n, *(i.e., the rank of* $\mathbf{A}$ *is* n*), then* $\mathbf{Ax} = \mathbf{b}$ *possesses a unique solution.*

(iii) *If* $\mathbf{b}$ *belongs to the column space of* $\mathbf{A}$ *and the rank of* $\mathbf{A}$ *(i.e., the dimension of the column space of* $\mathbf{A}$*) is less than* n, *then* $\mathbf{Ax} = \mathbf{b}$ *possesses the general solution* $\mathbf{x} = \mathbf{x}_0 + \mathbf{z}$ *where* $\mathbf{x}_0$ *is a particular solution of* $\mathbf{Ax} = \mathbf{b}$, *and* $\mathbf{z}$ *is any solution of the corresponding homogeneous equations* $\mathbf{Ax} = \mathbf{0}$, *i.e.,* $\mathbf{z}$ *belongs to a vector space of dimension* $n - k$ *where* k *is the rank of* $\mathbf{A}$, *i.e.,* $k = \dim \mathbf{A}$, *the dimension of the column space of* $\mathbf{A}$.

Proof: Part (i) is simply a restatement of what we mean by the column space of $\mathbf{A}$. To prove (ii), if $\mathbf{A}$ has n columns and its column space has dimension n, then the n columns of $\mathbf{A}$ form a basis, and any other column vector can be expressed as a linear combination of the columns of $\mathbf{A}$. Hence at least one $\mathbf{x}$ exists such that $\mathbf{Ax} = \mathbf{b}$. Suppose that $\mathbf{x}_1$ and $\mathbf{x}_2$ are two solutions of $\mathbf{Ax} = \mathbf{b}$ so that $\mathbf{Ax}_1 = \mathbf{b}$, $\mathbf{Ax}_2 = \mathbf{b}$, i.e., $\mathbf{A}(\mathbf{x}_1 - \mathbf{x}_2) = \mathbf{0}$. From Theorem 4.17 we can deduce that $\mathbf{x}_1 - \mathbf{x}_2 = \mathbf{0}$, i.e., $\mathbf{x}_1 = \mathbf{x}_2$ and the solution of $\mathbf{Ax} = \mathbf{b}$ is unique. To prove (iii) we note that if $\mathbf{x}_0$ is a particular solution of $\mathbf{Ax} = \mathbf{b}$ and we set $\mathbf{x} = \mathbf{x}_0 + \mathbf{z}$, then $\mathbf{Az} = \mathbf{0}$. From Theorem 4.17 the vector $\mathbf{z}$ belongs to a subspace of dimension $n - k$.

Ex. 4.34. Show that the following equations have an infinity of solutions, and find the general solution [compare Ex. 4.33].

$$\begin{aligned}
x_1 + 2x_2 + x_3 + 2x_4 - 3x_5 &= 2\\
3x_1 + 6x_2 + 4x_3 - x_4 + 2x_5 &= 1\\
4x_1 + 8x_2 + 5x_3 + x_4 - x_5 &= 3\\
-2x_1 - 4x_2 - 3x_3 + 3x_4 - 5x_5 &= 1.
\end{aligned}$$

Miscellaneous Exercises 4

Ex. 4.35. Let p vectors of order n be arranged as the columns of an $n \times p$ matrix $\mathbf{A}$. Prove that a necessary and sufficient condition for these vectors to be linearly dependent is that the rank of $\mathbf{A}$ be less than m.

Ex. 4.36. Prove Theorem 5.11 in the next chapter, without looking at the proof given.

Ex. 4.37. Find a basis for the subspace of V_4 generated by the vectors

$$\begin{bmatrix} 1\\ 2\\ -1\\ 0 \end{bmatrix}, \quad \begin{bmatrix} 4\\ 8\\ -4\\ -3 \end{bmatrix}, \quad \begin{bmatrix} 0\\ 1\\ 3\\ 4 \end{bmatrix}, \quad \begin{bmatrix} 2\\ 5\\ 1\\ 4 \end{bmatrix}.$$

Ex. 4.38. Extend the set

$$\begin{bmatrix} 1 \\ 0 \\ -1 \\ 0 \end{bmatrix}, \quad \begin{bmatrix} 1 \\ 1 \\ 0 \\ 0 \end{bmatrix}, \quad \begin{bmatrix} 1 \\ 2 \\ -1 \\ 4 \end{bmatrix}$$

to form a basis in V_4.

Ex. 4.39. Consider the subspace of V_4 consisting of all 4×1 column vectors $\mathbf{x}$ with $x_1 + x_2 + x_3 = 0$. Extend the following set to form a basis for the space

$$\begin{bmatrix} 1 \\ -2 \\ 1 \\ 0 \end{bmatrix}, \quad \begin{bmatrix} 1 \\ -1 \\ 0 \\ 0 \end{bmatrix}.$$

Ex. 4.40. Show that

$$\begin{bmatrix} 2 \\ -1 \\ 1 \end{bmatrix}, \quad \begin{bmatrix} 1 \\ 2 \\ -3 \end{bmatrix} \quad \text{and} \quad \begin{bmatrix} 3 \\ 1 \\ -2 \end{bmatrix}, \quad \begin{bmatrix} -1 \\ 3 \\ -4 \end{bmatrix}$$

generate the same subspace of V_3.

Ex. 4.41. Find dim $\mathbf{A}$ and a basis for the column space of

$$\mathbf{A} = \begin{bmatrix} 1 & 1 & 2 & -3 & 3 \\ 3 & 4 & -1 & 2 & 15 \\ 4 & 5 & 1 & 1 & 18 \\ -2 & -3 & 3 & -5 & -12 \end{bmatrix}.$$

Ex. 4.42. Given a set of basis vectors $\mathbf{u}_1, \ldots, \mathbf{u}_m$ and any other vector $\mathbf{v}$ such that

$$\mathbf{v} = \alpha_1 \mathbf{u}_1 + \ldots + \alpha_m \mathbf{u}_m,$$

show that a new basis can be obtained by replacing any vector $\mathbf{u}_r$ for which $\alpha_r \neq 0$ by $\mathbf{v}$. If

$$\mathbf{u}_1 = \begin{bmatrix} 1 \\ 2 \\ 1 \end{bmatrix}, \quad \mathbf{u}_2 = \begin{bmatrix} 1 \\ 0 \\ -1 \end{bmatrix}, \quad \mathbf{u}_3 = \begin{bmatrix} 1 \\ -2 \\ 1 \end{bmatrix}, \quad \mathbf{v} = \begin{bmatrix} 1 \\ 2 \\ -3 \end{bmatrix},$$

which of the following sets form a basis for V_3?

(a) $\mathbf{v}, \mathbf{u}_2, \mathbf{u}_3$.

(b) $\mathbf{u}_1, \mathbf{v}, \mathbf{u}_3$.

(c) $\mathbf{v}, \mathbf{u}_2, \mathbf{u}_3$.

Ex. 4.43. If $\mathbf{A}$ has a right-inverse $\mathbf{R}$, prove that all right-inverses of $\mathbf{A}$ are given by $\mathbf{R} + \mathbf{N}$, where $\mathbf{N}$ belongs to the vector space defined by $\mathbf{AN} = \mathbf{0}$.

Ex. 4.44. If $\mathbf{B}$ is a nonsingular matrix, prove that the column spaces of $\mathbf{A}$ and $\mathbf{AB}$ are the same. If $\mathbf{x} = \sum a_j \mathbf{a}_j$, where the a_j are columns of $\mathbf{A}$, express $\mathbf{x}$ as a linear combination of the columns of $\mathbf{AB}$.

Ex. 4.45. If $\mathbf{A}$ is $m \times n$ and $\mathbf{B}$ is $n \times p$, show that the columns of $\mathbf{AB}$ are in the column space of $\mathbf{A}$.

Ex. 4.46. If $\mathbf{x}$ is any $n \times 1$ vector belonging to a vector space V of dimension k, show that the set of vectors $\mathbf{u}$ such that $\mathbf{u}^T\mathbf{x} = \mathbf{0}$ is also a vector space. Find this vector space if V is the space spanned by $\mathbf{x}_1 = [2, 1, 3]^T$, $\mathbf{x}_2 = [-1, 0, 2]^T$.

Ex. 4.47. Construct a system of three homogeneous equations in five unknowns with null space generated by the vectors

$$\mathbf{u}_1 = [1\ 1\ 1\ 1\ 1]^T, \qquad \mathbf{u}_2 = [1\ -1\ 1\ -1\ 1]^T.$$

Describe a general procedure for finding a set of $n - p$ homogeneous equations in n unknowns whose null space is a given p-dimensional subspace of V_n.

Ex. 4.48. Are the vectors $[-3, -1, 15, 6]$, $[1, 0, -1, 0]$, $[1, 1, 1, 0]$ in the subspace of V_4 spanned by the vectors $[-1, 3, 5, 2]$, $[2, -1, 0, 1]$, $[1, -8, 5, 3]$? Explain.

Ex. 4.49. Let V denote the subspace of V_4 spanned by

$$\mathbf{u}_1 = \begin{bmatrix} 1 \\ 2 \\ 2 \\ 1 \end{bmatrix}, \qquad \mathbf{u}_2 = \begin{bmatrix} 1 \\ 0 \\ 2 \\ 0 \end{bmatrix}, \qquad \mathbf{u}_3 = \begin{bmatrix} 2 \\ 0 \\ 4 \\ -3 \end{bmatrix}.$$

(a) Show that these vectors form a basis for V.

(b) If $\mathbf{x} = [x_1, x_2, x_3, x_4]^T$ is an arbitrary vector in V, find $\boldsymbol{\alpha} = [\alpha_i]$ such that $\mathbf{x} = \alpha_1\mathbf{u}_1 + \alpha_2\mathbf{u}_2 + \alpha_3\mathbf{u}_3$.

(c) Show that the following vectors span the same space

$$\mathbf{v}_1 = \begin{bmatrix} 0 \\ 2 \\ 0 \\ 1 \end{bmatrix}, \qquad \mathbf{v}_2 = \begin{bmatrix} 2 \\ 1 \\ 4 \\ -1 \end{bmatrix}, \qquad \mathbf{v}_3 = \begin{bmatrix} 1 \\ 2 \\ 2 \\ 4 \end{bmatrix}.$$

(d) If $\mathbf{x}$ in (b) is written in the form $\mathbf{x} = \beta_1\mathbf{v}_1 + \beta_2\mathbf{v}_2 + \beta_3\mathbf{v}_3$, find a matrix $\mathbf{K}$ such that $\boldsymbol{\alpha} = \mathbf{K}\boldsymbol{\beta}$.

(e) Why does general theory tell us that $\mathbf{K}$ must be nonsingular?

Ex. 4.50. Prove that the following expressions for $\mathbf{x}$ are equivalent (the α_i are arbitrary constants).

$$\mathbf{x} = \begin{bmatrix} 1 \\ 2 \\ -1 \\ 3 \end{bmatrix} + \alpha_1 \begin{bmatrix} 1 \\ -3 \\ 4 \\ 1 \end{bmatrix} + \alpha_2 \begin{bmatrix} 2 \\ 1 \\ 1 \\ -5 \end{bmatrix} + \alpha_3 \begin{bmatrix} 0 \\ 4 \\ -3 \\ -2 \end{bmatrix},$$

$$\mathbf{x} = \begin{bmatrix} 4 \\ 4 \\ 1 \\ -3 \end{bmatrix} + \alpha_3 \begin{bmatrix} 1 \\ 1 \\ 1 \\ -1 \end{bmatrix} + \alpha_5 \begin{bmatrix} -1 \\ 2 \\ -1 \\ 4 \end{bmatrix} + \alpha_6 \begin{bmatrix} 3 \\ -1 \\ 2 \\ -9 \end{bmatrix}.$$

5 Rank and Inverses

5.1 Introduction

This is an appropriate place to draw the reader's attention to Figure 5.1, which illustrates interconnections between concepts developed in the first half of this book. The study of linear simultaneous equations has been fundamental. In Chapter 3 linear systems were studied from the point of view of elementary row operations on matrices. In Chapter 4 we introduced the idea of linear dependence and developed the basic theory of vector spaces. Having established many of the fundamental concepts, we now pursue some of their implications. In this chapter we connect together ideas from elementary row operations (row-echelon form), linear dependence of the rows and columns of a matrix, and the row and column spaces of a matrix. These coalesce in the concept of the rank of a matrix, which allows us to clarify and unify various aspects of matrix theory. In particular, we discuss the question of inverses of matrices in some detail. The one remaining topic in Figure 5.1, namely determinants, will be dealt with in Chapter 7. All of the concepts in Figure 5.1 are important and interrelated.

5.2 Properties of Rank

The rank of a matrix was defined in Definition 3.8 to be the number of nonzero rows in the row-echelon form of the matrix. However, the idea of rank appears in various other contexts that we now attempt to elucidate. The following theorems are immediate consequences or even simply restatements of results in Chapters 3 and 4.

THEOREM 5.1. (i) *The dimension of the column space of a matrix is equal to the rank of the matrix.*

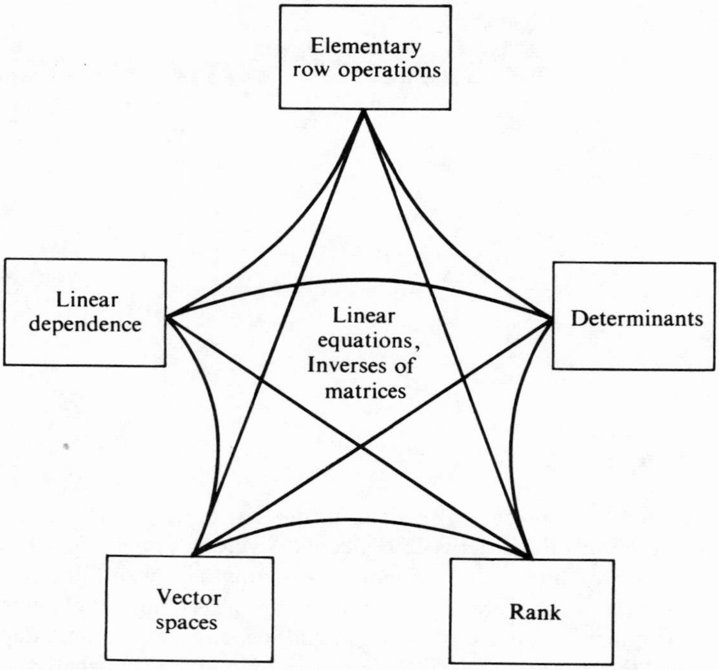

Figure 5.1 Interconnections between concepts.

(ii) *The maximum number of linearly independent columns in a matrix is equal to the rank of the matrix.*

Proof: Part (i) is Theorem 4.8(ii). Part (ii) follows from (i) since the dimension of a vector space is equal to the maximum number of linearly independent vectors in the space [Theorem 4.15(i)]. Alternatively, we can prove (ii) directly from Theorem 4.1. Denote the row-echelon form of a matrix **A** by **B**. The maximum number of linearly independent columns in **B** is equal to the number of unit columns in **B**, which is equal to the number of nonzero rows in **B**, i.e., the rank of **B**, say k. Let α denote the maximum number of linearly independent columns in **A**. From Theorem 4.1, if certain columns of **A** are linearly independent, the same columns of **B** are linearly independent, so that $\alpha \leq k$. The roles of **A** and **B** can be reversed so that $k \leq \alpha$. Hence $\alpha = k$.

THEOREM **5.2.** (i) *The dimension of the row space of a matrix is equal to the rank of the matrix.*

(ii) *The maximum number of linearly independent rows in a matrix is equal to the rank of the matrix.*

Proof: Part (i) is Theorem 4.11(i). Part (ii) follows from (i) since the dimension of a vector space is equal to the maximum number of linearly independent vectors in the space [Theorem 4.15(i)].

The basic theorem that we require is an immediate consequence of the above theorems:

THEOREM 5.3. *For any matrix* **A**,

(i) *The dimension of the column space is equal to the dimension of the row space, each being equal to the rank of the matrix.*

(ii) *The maximum number of linearly independent columns is equal to the maximum number of linearly independent rows, each being equal to the rank of the matrix.*

Proof: Immediate from Theorems 5.1, 5.2.

We now digress in order to illuminate yet another aspect of rank.

In Chapter 3 we considered only elementary operations on the rows of a matrix, but, of course, there is no reason why we should not develop a similar theory for operations on columns. The following definitions for column operations correspond to Definitions 3.3, 3.5 for row operations.

DEFINITION 5.1. *Elementary column operations* of Types I, II, III are defined exactly as in Definition 3.3 except that the word "row" is replaced by "column":

I Interchange of two columns.
II Multiplication of any column by a nonzero scalar.
III Replacement of the ith column by the sum of the ith column and q times the jth column ($j \neq i$).

If a matrix **A** can be obtained from a matrix **B** by elementary column operations, then **A** is said to be *column-equivalent* to **B**. If a matrix **A** can be obtained from a matrix **B** by a combination of elementary row and column operations, then **A** is said to be *equivalent* to **B**.

THEOREM 5.4. *If* **A** *is equivalent to* **B**, *then* **B** *is equivalent to* **A**. *If* **A** *is equivalent to* **B** *and* **B** *is equivalent to* **C**, *then* **A** *is equivalent to* **C**.

Proof: This can be proved by the method used for Theorem 3.2.

DEFINITION 5.2. The *column-echelon normal form* of a matrix is defined by replacing "column" by "row" and "row" by "column" in Definition 3.4 of the row-echelon normal form, i.e., the roles of "row" and "column" are simply interchanged.

The column-echelon form of **A** is the same as the transpose of the row echelon form of $\mathbf{A}^T$. This leads to:

THEOREM 5.5. (i) *The column echelon form of a matrix is unique.*
(ii) *The number of nonzero columns in the column-echelon form is equal to the rank of the matrix.*

Proof: The row-echelon form of $\mathbf{A}^T$ is unique (Theorem 3.5). The number of nonzero rows in the row-echelon form of $\mathbf{A}^T$ is the maximum number of linearly independent rows in $\mathbf{A}^T$, i.e., columns in $\mathbf{A}$, which is the same as the rank of $\mathbf{A}$ (Theorem 5.1). Hence parts (i) and (ii) follow from the remark preceding the theorem.

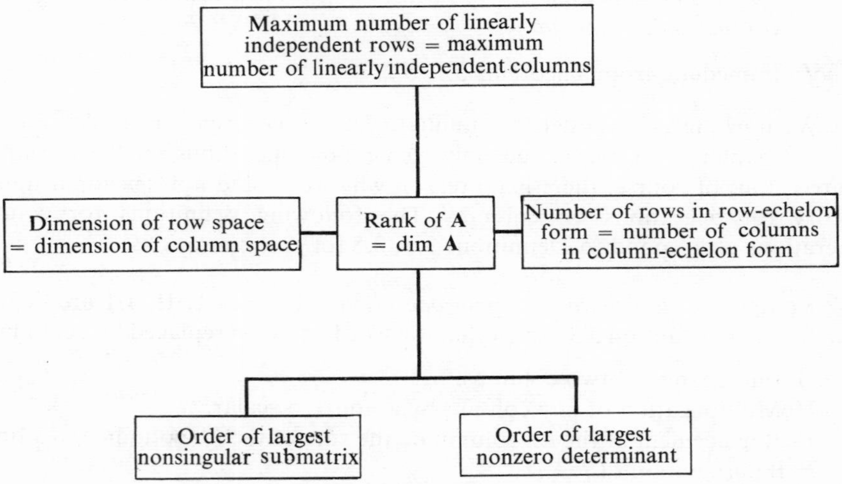

Figure 5.2 Equivalent definitions of rank.

The point of the above developments can now be summarized as follows (see Fig. 5.2). Associated with any matrix $\mathbf{A}$ there is a number called the rank of $\mathbf{A}$, that we defined as the number of nonzero rows in the row-echelon form of $\mathbf{A}$. However we proved in Theorem 5.1(i) that the rank of $\mathbf{A}$ is the same as the dimension of the column space of $\mathbf{A}$, which we denoted by dim $\mathbf{A}$ in Definition 4.6. It turned out (Theorem 5.3) that the rank of $\mathbf{A}$, or dim $\mathbf{A}$, is also the dimension of the row space, the maximum number of linearly independent columns (or rows), and the number of nonzero columns in the column-echelon form of $\mathbf{A}$. Instead of having a sequential structure, starting from one very special definition of rank, and then deducing properties of the rank, we should visualize the situation in Figure 5.2. There is one central number that we call the rank of $\mathbf{A}$ or dim $\mathbf{A}$, and this number can be defined in many equivalent ways, for instance:

(a) The maximum number of linearly independent rows (or the maximum number of linearly independent columns).

(b) The dimension of the row space (or the dimension of the column space).

(c) The number of rows in the row-echelon form (or the number of columns in the column-echelon form).

(d) The order of the largest nonsingular submatrix. (This last property has not yet been discussed. We do this in Section 5.4.)

We have chosen the first property in (c) as fundamental, and we deduce the other properties in (a)–(d). However, we could start from any property as the definition of rank, and deduce all the others. It would take us too far afield to trace through all of these equivalent definitions in detail.

Ex. 5.1. Find the rank of the matrix

$$\mathbf{A} = \begin{bmatrix} -1 & 0 & 1 & 2 \\ -1 & 1 & 0 & -1 \\ 0 & -1 & 1 & 3 \\ 1 & -2 & 1 & 4 \end{bmatrix}.$$

Solution: The row-echelon form is

$$\begin{bmatrix} 1 & 0 & -1 & -2 \\ 0 & 1 & -1 & -3 \\ 0 & 0 & 0 & 0 \\ 0 & 0 & 0 & 0 \end{bmatrix}.$$

The rank is the number of nonzero rows, i.e., 2.

Ex. 5.2. Find the rank of the following matrix by reducing it to row-echelon normal form.

$$\begin{bmatrix} 1 & 3 & -2 & 1 \\ 2 & -1 & 3 & 4 \\ 3 & -5 & 8 & 7 \end{bmatrix}.$$

Verify your result by reducing the matrix to column-echelon form.

Ex. 5.3. Show that for every nonzero scalar k, the rank of $k\mathbf{A}$ is the same as the rank of $\mathbf{A}$. Show that the rank of a matrix remains unchanged if the rows, or the columns, are permuted, or if the matrix is transposed. Show that if $\mathbf{B}$ is a submatrix of $\mathbf{A}$, then the rank of $\mathbf{B}$ is less than or equal to the rank of $\mathbf{A}$.

Ex. 5.4. If $\mathbf{u}$, $\mathbf{v}$ are nonzero $n \times 1$ column vectors, show that the matrix $\mathbf{u}\mathbf{v}^T$ has rank unity.

Ex. 5.5. Prove that by elementary row operations and column interchanges (i.e., elementary column operations of type I only), a general $m \times n$ matrix of rank k can be reduced to the form

$$\begin{bmatrix} \mathbf{I}_k & \mathbf{F} \\ \mathbf{0} & \mathbf{0} \end{bmatrix},$$

where $\mathbf{I}_k$ is a $k \times k$ unit matrix and $\mathbf{F}$ is a $k \times (n - k)$ matrix whose elements may be nonzero. Prove that by elementary row and column operations, $\mathbf{A}$ may be reduced to

$$\begin{bmatrix} \mathbf{I}_k & \mathbf{0} \\ \mathbf{0} & \mathbf{0} \end{bmatrix}.$$

5.3 Inverses of m × n Matrices

We now consider certain questions involving the inverses of $m \times n$ matrices. We remind the reader of some definitions and results from Section 1.4. A *right-inverse* of an $m \times n$ matrix $\mathbf{A}$ (if it exists) is an $n \times m$ matrix $\mathbf{C}$ such that $\mathbf{AC} = \mathbf{I}_m$. A *left-inverse* of $\mathbf{A}$ (if it exists) is an $n \times m$ matrix $\mathbf{B}$ such that $\mathbf{BA} = \mathbf{I}_n$. We proved (Theorem 1.4) that if both left- and right-inverses exist, then they must be the same, and this common inverse must be unique. This common inverse is called *the inverse* and is denoted by $\mathbf{A}^{-1}$.

We first of all elucidate one aspect of the significance of left- and right-inverses. Suppose that the equations $\mathbf{Ax} = \mathbf{b}$ have a solution $\mathbf{x}$ and that a left-inverse $\mathbf{A}_L^{-1}$ of $\mathbf{A}$ exists. Then

$$\mathbf{A}_L^{-1}(\mathbf{Ax}) = \mathbf{x} = \mathbf{A}_L^{-1}\mathbf{b},$$

i.e., *if solutions exist*, $\mathbf{x} = \mathbf{A}_L^{-1}\mathbf{b}$ is a solution. Also, if $\mathbf{x}_1$ and $\mathbf{x}_2$ are solutions of $\mathbf{Ax} = \mathbf{b}$, then $\mathbf{A}(\mathbf{x}_1 - \mathbf{x}_2) = \mathbf{0}$ and premultiplication by $\mathbf{A}_L^{-1}$ gives $\mathbf{x}_1 = \mathbf{x}_2$, i.e., the solution is unique. The existence of the left-inverse tells us about *uniqueness* but *not* about the existence of a solution, which we have to assume. If $\mathbf{A}$ has a right-inverse $\mathbf{A}_R^{-1}$, then

$$\mathbf{A}(\mathbf{A}_R^{-1}\mathbf{b}) = \mathbf{b}.$$

Hence $\mathbf{x} = \mathbf{A}_R^{-1}\mathbf{b}$ is a solution of $\mathbf{Ax} = \mathbf{b}$, but this argument proves nothing about uniqueness. The existence of a right-inverse proves that a solution *exists*, but it tells us nothing about uniqueness.

As an example, consider (compare Ex. 1.16)

$$\begin{aligned} x_1 + x_2 &= b_1 \\ -x_1 + x_2 &= b_2 \\ x_1 + 2x_2 &= b_3, \end{aligned} \qquad \mathbf{A}_L^{-1} = \frac{1}{2}\begin{bmatrix} 1 - 3\alpha, & -1 - \alpha, & 2\alpha \\ 1 - 3\beta, & 1 - \beta, & 2\beta \end{bmatrix},$$

where α, β are arbitrary constants. ($\mathbf{A}$ does not have a right-inverse.)

$$\mathbf{A}_L^{-1}\mathbf{b} = \frac{1}{2}\begin{bmatrix} (b_1 - b_2) - \alpha(3b_1 + b_2 - 2b_3) \\ (b_1 + b_2) - \beta(3b_1 + b_2 - 2b_3) \end{bmatrix}.$$

The equations have no solution unless $b_3 = \frac{1}{2}(3b_1 + b_2)$. If this relation is satisfied, the equations have a solution, given by $\mathbf{A}_L^{-1}\mathbf{b}$, and this solution is then unique, independent of α, β.

As a second example, consider

$$\begin{aligned} x_1 - x_2 + x_3 &= b_1 \\ x_1 + x_2 + 2x_3 &= b_2, \end{aligned} \qquad \mathbf{A}_R^{-1} = \frac{1}{2}\begin{bmatrix} 1 - 3\alpha & 1 - 3\beta \\ -1 - \alpha & 1 - \beta \\ 2\alpha & 2\beta \end{bmatrix},$$

where α, β are arbitrary constants. (Now $\mathbf{A}$ does not have a left-inverse.) This gives

$$\mathbf{A}_R^{-1}\mathbf{b} = \frac{1}{2}\begin{bmatrix} b_1 + b_2 \\ -b_1 + b_2 \\ 0 \end{bmatrix} + \gamma\begin{bmatrix} -3 \\ -1 \\ 2 \end{bmatrix}$$

where $\gamma = \alpha b_1 + \beta b_2$ is an arbitrary constant. A particular right-inverse will give a particular solution of the equations.

The situation can be summarized as follows:

THEOREM 5.6. (i) *If* $\mathbf{A}$ *has a left-inverse* $\mathbf{A}_L^{-1}$, *and* $\mathbf{Ax} = \mathbf{b}$ *has at least one solution, then* $\mathbf{Ax} = \mathbf{b}$ *has precisely one solution, and this is given by* $\mathbf{x} = \mathbf{A}_L^{-1}\mathbf{b}$. (*Uniqueness but not existence.*)

(ii) *If* $\mathbf{A}$ *has a right-inverse* $\mathbf{A}_R^{-1}$, *then* $\mathbf{Ax} = \mathbf{b}$ *has at least one solution* $\mathbf{x} = \mathbf{A}_R^{-1}\mathbf{b}$. (*Existence but not uniqueness.*)

(iii) *If* $\mathbf{A}$ *has both left- and right-inverses, then* $\mathbf{Ax} = \mathbf{b}$ *has a unique solution.*

In order to discuss the existence of left- or right-inverses for a given $m \times n$ matrix, we require some preliminary results on the three types of elementary matrix (Definition 3.6). $\mathbf{E}_{pq}$ is obtained by interchanging the pth and qth rows of the unit matrix $\mathbf{I}$. $\mathbf{E}_p(c)$ is obtained by multiplying the pth row of $\mathbf{I}$ by c. $\mathbf{E}_{pq}(c)$ is obtained by adding c times the qth row to the pth row.

THEOREM 5.7. *Elementary matrices possess inverses, and these are also elementary matrices.*

Proof: We exhibit the explicit forms of the inverses. We have

$$\mathbf{E}_{pq}\mathbf{E}_{pq} = \mathbf{I}$$

since if, starting with $\mathbf{I}$, we interchange rows p and q, and then perform the same interchange on the result, we arrive back at $\mathbf{I}$. Similarly,

$$\mathbf{E}_p(c^{-1})\mathbf{E}_p(c) = \mathbf{E}_p(c)\mathbf{E}_p(c^{-1}) = \mathbf{I},$$

$$\mathbf{E}_{pq}(-c)\mathbf{E}_{pq}(c) = \mathbf{E}_{pq}(c)\mathbf{E}_{pq}(-c) = \mathbf{I}.$$

Hence, the inverse of $\mathbf{E}_{pq}$ is simply $\mathbf{E}_{pq}$, the inverse of $\mathbf{E}_p(c)$ is $\mathbf{E}_p(c^{-1})$, and the inverse of $\mathbf{E}_{pq}(c)$ is $\mathbf{E}_{pq}(-c)$. Thus the inverses exist, and they are also elementary matrices.

THEOREM 5.8. (i) *If* **A** *is an* $m \times n$ *matrix of rank* k *and* **U** *denotes the row-echelon form of* **A**, *then a nonsingular matrix* **E** *exists such that*

$$\mathbf{EA} = \mathbf{U}, \qquad \mathbf{A} = \mathbf{E}^{-1}\mathbf{U}, \tag{5.1}$$

where **E** *and* $\mathbf{E}^{-1}$ *are products of elementary matrices.*

(ii) *A nonsingular matrix can be expressed as a product of elementary matrices.*

(iii) *If* $\mathbf{A} = \mathbf{FU}$, *where* **F** *is nonsingular, then* **A** *has a right-inverse if and only if* **U** *has a right-inverse.*

Proof: The row-echelon form **U** is obtained by performing a sequence of elementary row operations on **A**. From Theorem 3.3 this means that we can find a sequence of elementary matrices $\mathbf{E}_1, \mathbf{E}_2, \ldots, \mathbf{E}_p$ corresponding to the elementary row operations such that

$$\mathbf{E}_p\mathbf{E}_{p-1} \ldots \mathbf{E}_1\mathbf{A} = \mathbf{U}.$$

Theorem 5.6 tells us that elementary matrices are nonsingular. If we multiply through by $\mathbf{E}_p^{-1}, \ldots, \mathbf{E}_1^{-1}$ in succession, we obtain

$$\mathbf{A} = \mathbf{E}_1^{-1} \ldots \mathbf{E}_p^{-1}\mathbf{U}.$$

If we denote $\mathbf{E}_p \ldots \mathbf{E}_1$ by **E**, these results give (5.1). **E** is nonsingular since the product of nonsingular matrices is nonsingular. Part (ii) follows immediately since the row-echelon form of a nonsingular matrix is the unit matrix. To prove part (iii) we note that if **U** has a right-inverse **G** then $\mathbf{I} = \mathbf{UG}$, $\mathbf{AG} = \mathbf{FUG} = \mathbf{F}$, $\mathbf{AGF}^{-1} = \mathbf{I}$, and **A** has a right-inverse. If **A** has a right-inverse, a similar argument shows that **U** has a right-inverse. Hence if **U** is singular, **A** cannot have a right-inverse.

We can now quickly dispose of the question of when matrices have inverses.

THEOREM 5.9 *Figure* 5.3 *summarizes the position concerning the existence of inverses for matrices.*

Proof: From Theorem 5.8, we need consider only whether the row-echelon form **U** of **A** has inverses. To see whether **U** has a right-inverse we have to try to solve the equations $\mathbf{Ux}_i = \mathbf{e}_i$, $i = 1$ to n, where the $\mathbf{e}_i$ are unit column vectors. The possibilities are illustrated diagrammatically in Figure 5.4. The key fact is that **U** has exactly k nonzero rows:

(a) If $k = m < n$, the matrix $[\mathbf{U}, \mathbf{I}]$ will look like Figure 5.4(a). All the rows of **U** are nonzero. Also $k < n$, so that each of the equations $\mathbf{Ux}_i = \mathbf{e}_i$ has an infinity of solutions [Theorem 3.6(c)]. This implies that there are an infinity of right-inverses for both **U** and **A**.

(b) If $k < m < n$, the matrix $[\mathbf{U}, \mathbf{I}]$ will look like Figure 5.4(b). The last row of **U** is a row of zeros, so that the last equation in the system, $\mathbf{Ux}_n = \mathbf{e}_n$, gives $0 = 1$ which is contradictory, and no right-inverse exists for **U** and **A**.

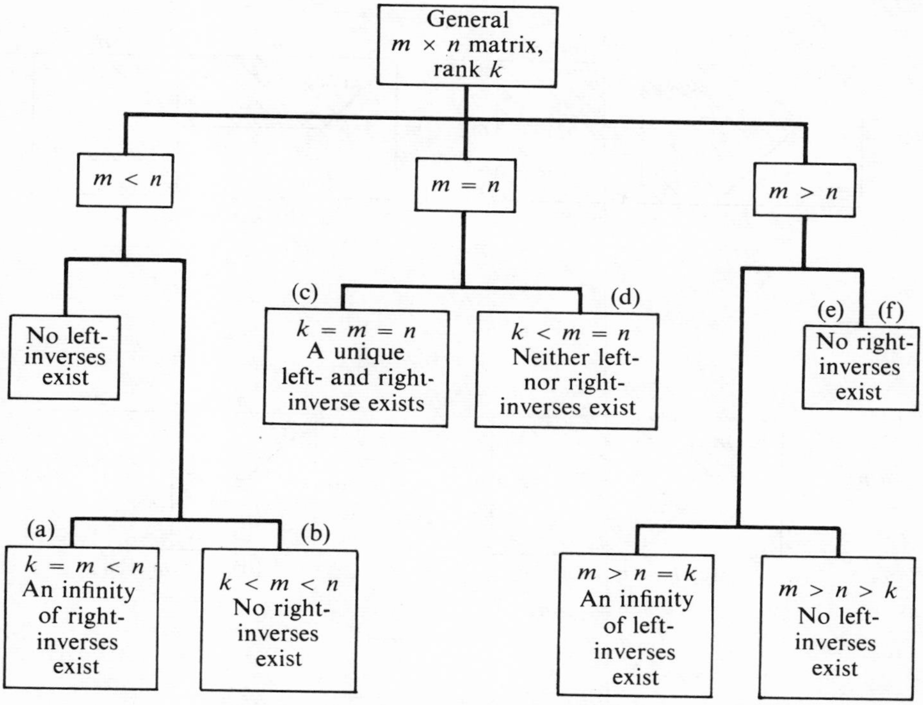

Figure 5.3 The existence of inverses for matrices.

(c) If $k = m = n$, the row-echelon form of $\mathbf{A}$ is simply the unit matrix. Hence a unique right-inverse exists for $\mathbf{A}$.

(d), (e), (f). In each of these cases, represented in Figure 5.4(d), (e), (f), the last row of $\mathbf{U}$ is a row of zeros, and the argument in (b) shows that $\mathbf{U}$, and therefore $\mathbf{A}$, cannot have a right-inverse.

This has proved one-half of the statements in Figure 5.3, namely those referring to right-inverses. The statements about left-inverses can be derived immediately, since a left-inverse of $\mathbf{A}$ is a right-inverse of $\mathbf{A}^T$. (Remember that the ranks of $\mathbf{A}$ and $\mathbf{A}^T$ are the same, so that if a square matrix has a left-inverse, it also has a right-inverse; and if it does not have a right-inverse, it does not have a left-inverse. Also, from Theorem 1.4, if both a left- and a right-inverse exist, these are the same and unique.)

The special case of a square matrix is particularly important. Although we are doing no more than rephrasing part of Theorem 5.9 in a different terminology, it is useful to state criteria for the existence of an inverse for a square matrix in the following way:

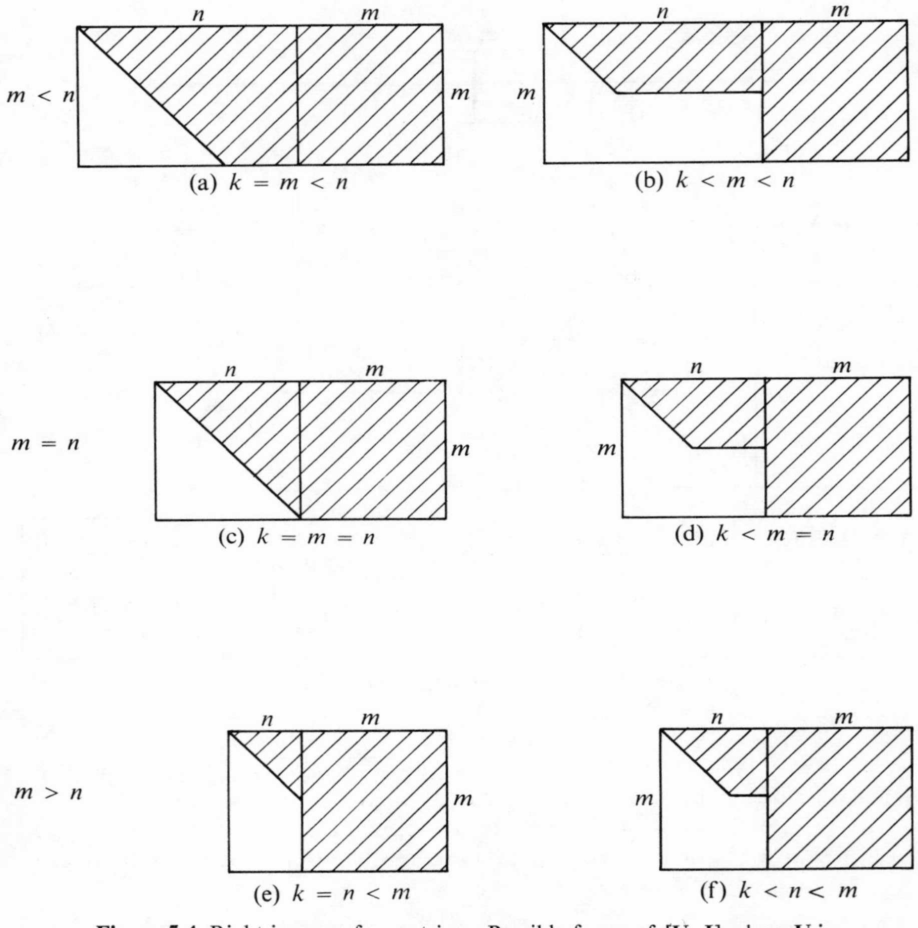

Figure 5.4 Right-inverses for matrices. Possible forms of **[U, I]** where **U** is the row-echelon form of **A**. Unshaded areas denote zeros. k is the rank of **A**.

THEOREM 5.10. *A square matrix is singular (nonsingular) if and only if its rows are linearly dependent (independent). The same statement is true if "rows" is replaced by "columns."*

Proof: If the rows of a square matrix are linearly dependent, its rank is less than its order, case (d) of Theorem 5.9 applies, and the matrix has no inverse. If the rows are linearly independent, the rank is the same as the order, case (c) of Theorem 5.9 applies, and the matrix has an inverse. Similarly for columns.

Ex. 5.6. If **A**, **B** are square and **AB** is nonsingular, prove that **A** and **B** must both be nonsingular. If **A** is nonsingular then **AB** is nonsingular if and only if **B** is nonsingular.

Ex. 5.7. Prove that the result of performing an elementary column operation on a matrix can also be achieved by postmultiplying the matrix by an elementary column matrix, obtained by performing the same elementary column operation on the columns of the unit matrix. Prove that these elementary column matrices are nonsingular.

Ex. 5.8. If an $m \times n$ matrix **A** has rank k, prove that nonsingular matrices **E**, **F**, of orders m, n respectively, exist such that

$$\mathbf{EAF} = \begin{bmatrix} \mathbf{I}_k & \mathbf{0} \\ \mathbf{0} & \mathbf{0} \end{bmatrix}.$$

5.4 *Rank and The Largest Nonsingular Submatrix*

We next explore some connections between rank and nonsingular matrices. We exploit the facts that the rank of a matrix is the maximum number of linearly independent rows (or columns), and that a square matrix is nonsingular if and only if its rows are linearly independent. The following preliminary result is required.

THEOREM **5.11.** *Let* **P** *and* **Q** *be* $m \times p$ *and* $m \times q$ *matrices.*

(i) *If the rows of* **P** *are linearly independent then the rows of* [**P**, **Q**] *are linearly independent.*

(ii) *If the rows of* [**P**, **Q**] *are linearly dependent, then the rows of* **P** *are linearly dependent.*

Proof: Denote the rows of **P** and **Q** by $\mathbf{p}_i$, $\mathbf{q}_i$, $i = 1$ to m. If the rows of **P** are linearly independent, then nonzero α_i cannot exist such that

$$\alpha_1\mathbf{p}_1 + \alpha_2\mathbf{p}_2 + \dots + \alpha_m\mathbf{p}_m = \mathbf{0}. \tag{5.2}$$

Hence, nonzero α_i cannot exist such that

$$\alpha_1[\mathbf{p}_1, \mathbf{q}_1] + \alpha_2[\mathbf{p}_2, \mathbf{q}_2] + \dots + \alpha_m[\mathbf{p}_m, \mathbf{q}_m] = [\mathbf{0}, \mathbf{0}]. \tag{5.3}$$

Therefore, the rows of [**P**, **Q**] must be linearly independent. This proves (i). If the rows of [**P**, **Q**] are linearly dependent, then nonzero α_i exist such that (5.3) is true. Equation (5.2) will be true for the same nonzero α_i. Hence, the rows of **P** are linearly dependent. This proves (ii).

THEOREM **5.12.** *Let the rank of a matrix be k. Then*
(i) *All submatrices of order $k + 1$ are singular.*
(ii) *There is at least one nonsingular submatrix of order k.*

Proof: Consider any square matrix chosen from $k + 1$ rows of **A**. Since **A** has rank k, these $k + 1$ rows must be linearly dependent. Hence, the rows of the square matrix are linearly dependent, from Theorem 5.11(ii), and the matrix is singular. This proves (i). To prove (ii), if **A** is $m \times n$, consider a $k \times n$ submatrix **C** of **A**, whose rows are k linearly independent rows of **A**. The rank of **C** is k so that it must be possible to find k linearly independent columns in **C**. These constitute a nonsingular submatrix of **A** of order k, and this proves (ii).

THEOREM **5.13.** *If the order of the largest nonsingular submatrix in* **A** *is k, then the rank of* **A** *is k.*

Proof: Consider a $k \times n$ submatrix **C** of **A** whose rows contain the k rows of a nonsingular submatrix of order k. The rows of the submatrix are linearly independent, so that from Theorem 5.11(i) the rows of **C** are linearly independent and **A** has at least k linearly independent rows. Let **B** denote any $(k + 1) \times n$ submatrix of **A**. If the rows of **B** are linearly independent, then the rank of **B** is $k + 1$ and **B** has $k + 1$ linearly independent columns. These give a nonsingular matrix of order $k + 1$ which contradicts the assumption that the largest nonsingular submatrix in **A** is of order k. Hence any $k + 1$ rows of **A** are linearly dependent. Since we have already shown that there are k linearly independent rows, the maximum number of linearly independent rows is k, so that the rank of **A** is k.

Ex. 5.9. Give three different proofs that if all submatrices of order k, selected from an $m \times n$ matrix **A**, are singular, then all submatrices of order $k + 1$ are singular. State carefully the results assumed in each proof.

5.5 The Rank of The Product of Matrices

We prove three theorems concerning the rank of a product of matrices, and conclude the section with a physical application.

THEOREM **5.14.** *Multiplication of a matrix by a nonsingular matrix does not change its rank.*

Proof: Consider premultiplication of **A** by a nonsingular matrix **E**. Since any nonsingular matrix can be expressed as a product of elementary matrices [Theorem 5.8(ii)], the matrix **EA** is row-equivalent to **A**. Hence, both have the same (unique) row-echelon form. This means that **A** and **EA** have the same rank. The proof that the same result holds for postmultiplication is left to the reader.

THEOREM 5.15. *The rank of* **AB** *is less than or equal to the rank of either* **A** *or* **B**.

Proof: Suppose that **A** is reduced to its row-echelon form by a series of elementary row operations. From Theorem 5.8 this means that a nonsingular matrix **E** exists such that

$$\mathbf{EA} = \begin{bmatrix} \mathbf{A}_1 \\ \mathbf{0} \end{bmatrix},$$

where, if **A** is an $m \times n$ matrix of rank k, the matrix $\mathbf{A}_1$ is a $k \times n$ matrix of rank k. If the same elementary operations are applied to **AB**, we have

$$\mathbf{EAB} = \begin{bmatrix} \mathbf{A}_1 \\ \mathbf{0} \end{bmatrix} \mathbf{B} = \begin{bmatrix} \mathbf{A}_1\mathbf{B} \\ \mathbf{0} \end{bmatrix}.$$

The matrix $\mathbf{A}_1\mathbf{B}$ has *at most* k nonzero rows so that the number of nonzero rows in the row-echelon form of **AB** (and hence its rank) is at most k. This means that

$$\text{rank}\,(\mathbf{AB}) \leq \text{rank}\,(\mathbf{A}). \tag{5.4}$$

If the same argument is applied to $\mathbf{B}^T\mathbf{A}^T$, we see that

$$\text{rank}\,(\mathbf{B}^T\mathbf{A}^T) \leq \text{rank}\,(\mathbf{B}^T). \tag{5.5}$$

The rank of a matrix and its transpose are the same, so that the proof is complete.

THEOREM 5.16. (i) *If* **A**, **B** *are* $m \times k$ *and* $k \times n$, *and each is of rank* k, *then* **AB** *is of rank* k.

(ii) *If* **A** *is a real matrix then* **A** *and* $\mathbf{A}^T\mathbf{A}$ *have the same rank.*

Proof: The row-echelon form of **A** and the column-echelon form of **B** must be

$$\begin{bmatrix} \mathbf{I}_k \\ \mathbf{0} \end{bmatrix}, \qquad [\mathbf{I}_k\ \mathbf{0}],$$

respectively. From Theorem 5.8(i) this means that nonsingular matrices **E** and **F** exist such that

$$(\mathbf{EA})(\mathbf{BF}) = \begin{bmatrix} \mathbf{I}_k \\ \mathbf{0} \end{bmatrix} [\mathbf{I}_k\ \mathbf{0}] = \begin{bmatrix} \mathbf{I}_k & \mathbf{0} \\ \mathbf{0} & \mathbf{0} \end{bmatrix}. \tag{5.6}$$

From Theorem 5.14, multiplication by nonsingular matrices does not change the rank of a matrix so that the rank of **AB** is k. This proves (i). To prove (ii) we use a different type of argument. Let **x** be a vector such that $\mathbf{A}^T\mathbf{Ax} = \mathbf{0}$. Then $\mathbf{x}^T\mathbf{A}^T\mathbf{Ax} = \mathbf{0}$, and so $(\mathbf{Ax})^T(\mathbf{Ax}) = \mathbf{0}$, or $\mathbf{Ax} = \mathbf{0}$. Conversely, if $\mathbf{Ax} = \mathbf{0}$, then $\mathbf{A}^T\mathbf{Ax} = \mathbf{0}$. It follows that the homogeneous systems $\mathbf{Ax} = \mathbf{0}$ and $\mathbf{A}^T\mathbf{Ax} = \mathbf{0}$ are equivalent. The vector spaces of solutions of these systems must therefore have the same dimension, i.e.,

$$n - \text{rank}\,(\mathbf{A}) = n - \text{rank}\,(\mathbf{A}^T\mathbf{A}) \tag{5.7}$$

Hence, **A** and $\mathbf{A}^T\mathbf{A}$ have the same rank.

We conclude this section by discussing an application of Theorem 5.16(i) in chemistry. This will incidentally make the important point that the definition of rank that we have used so far is not directly applicable in practice since the elements of matrices that occur in applications may not be known exactly.

Suppose that a certain chemical reaction involves m substances, the concentrations of which vary with time and are represented by $c_i(t)$, $i = 1, \ldots, m$. (If the reader wishes a concrete example, he can visualize a mixture of CO, H_2, CH_4 burned with oxygen to form CO, CO_2, H_2O.) Suppose that from the theory of the reaction it can be shown that

$$c_i(t) = c_i(0) + \sum_{j=1}^{r} a_{ij}x_j(t), \qquad i = 1, \ldots, m, \tag{5.8}$$

where the $c_i(0)$ represent the concentrations at time $t = 0$, the a_{ij} are constants of the reaction, independent of the time, and the $x_j(t)$ are variables known as the *extents* of the reaction. [Equations of the form (5.8) arise when a system of simultaneous linear differential equations are solved for the $c_i(t)$ in terms of sums of exponentials. However, we make no assumptions concerning the explicit forms of the $x_j(t)$.] The only quantities that are assumed to be known (since they can be measured) are the $c_i(t)$, including $c_i(0)$. The a_{ij} and $x_j(t)$ are assumed to be unknown. The value of r is not known, and this is in fact the quantity we wish to determine. This will tell us the number of extents that exist, which is assumed to be unknown. The extents are measures of the underlying independent reactions.

Suppose now that the values of $c_i(t)$ are measured at p times $t_1, t_2, \ldots, t_p$, in addition to $t = 0$. We introduce the column matrices:

$$\mathbf{c}_k = \begin{bmatrix} c_1(t_k) - c_1(0) \\ \cdot \\ \cdot \\ \cdot \\ c_m(t_k) - c_m(0) \end{bmatrix}, \qquad \mathbf{x}_k = \begin{bmatrix} x_1(t_k) \\ \cdot \\ \cdot \\ \cdot \\ x_m(t_k) \end{bmatrix}, \qquad k = 1, \ldots, p.$$

In terms of this notation, (5.8) becomes

$$\mathbf{c}_k = \mathbf{A}\mathbf{x}_k, \qquad k = 1, \ldots, p, \tag{5.9}$$

where $\mathbf{A} = [a_{ij}]$. On introducing the further notation

$$\mathbf{C} = [\mathbf{c}_1, \ldots, \mathbf{c}_p], \qquad \mathbf{X} = [\mathbf{x}_1, \ldots, \mathbf{x}_p], \tag{5.10}$$

Equation (5.9) becomes

$$\mathbf{C} = \mathbf{A}\mathbf{X}, \tag{5.11}$$

where $\mathbf{C}$ is $m \times p$, $\mathbf{A}$ is $m \times r$, $\mathbf{X}$ is $r \times p$.

We now wish to discuss the ranks of $\mathbf{C}$, $\mathbf{A}$, $\mathbf{X}$. If the rank of $\mathbf{A}$ is less than r, we can assume, without loss of generality, that the rth column is linearly dependent on the first $r - 1$ columns, i.e., constants α_j exist such that

$$a_{ir} = \sum_{j=1}^{r-1} \alpha_j a_{ij}, \qquad i = 1, \ldots, m.$$

On substituting these in (5.8) we obtain

$$c_i(t) = c_i(0) + \sum_{j=1}^{r-1} a_{ij}\{x_j(t) + \alpha_j x_r(t)\},$$

i.e., on redefining the extents to be the bracketed terms, the concentrations can be expressed in terms of $r - 1$ extents. This means that if we assume that the concentrations in (5.8) are expressed in terms of the smallest possible number of extents, then the rank of **A** is r. Since **A** is $m \times r$, this shows incidentally that $r \leq m$. By a similar argument, the $x_j(t)$ introduced in (5.8) must be linearly independent, i.e., it is not possible to find constants $\beta_1, \ldots, \beta_r$, not all zero, such that

$$\beta_1 x_1(t) + \ldots + \beta_r x_r(t) = 0.$$

For, if this were possible, we could express one of the $x_j(t)$ as a linear combination of the remainder, and use this to express the $c_i(t)$ in (5.8) in terms of $r - 1$ of the $x_j(t)$, which contradicts the assumption that the concentrations are expressed in terms of the smallest possible number of extents. Since the $x_j(t)$ are linearly independent, it is possible to choose the values of the times, t_k, $k = 1, \ldots, p$, introduced earlier, in such a way that the rank of the $r \times p$ matrix **X** introduced in (5.10) is r, provided that $p \leq r$. We assume that this has been done.

We are now in the position that we have shown that the $m \times r$ matrix **A** and the $r \times p$ matrix **X** are both of rank r. Theorem 5.16(i) now tells us that $\mathbf{C} = \mathbf{AX}$ must also be of rank r. This is a useful result since the matrix **C** can be observed experimentally. Even though nothing is known about the matrices **A** and **X**, we can determine the number of independent extents by finding the rank of **C**.

Unfortunately, a difficulty arises in practice because of experimental error. As an example, consider the following matrix **C** obtained from observations made at five instants of time on a reaction involving five concentrations:

$$\mathbf{C} = \begin{bmatrix} 1.02 & 2.03 & 4.20 & 6.63 & 10.21 \\ -1.25 & -2.35 & -4.64 & -7.59 & -12.39 \\ -1.17 & -1.96 & -3.46 & -6.21 & -11.71 \\ 0.45 & 0.62 & 0.91 & 1.93 & 4.50 \\ 0.44 & 0.61 & 0.89 & 1.95 & 4.41 \end{bmatrix}. \qquad (5.12)$$

These are experimental results with errors of at most 0.01. If we take this matrix at its face value, then its rank is found to be 5. However, as we show when we discuss this example in detail in Section 8.4, after the second pivotal operation, the elements in the last three rows of the reduced matrix are very small. Also there is a matrix $\mathbf{C}'$ of rank 2 such that the elements of $\mathbf{C}' - \mathbf{C}$ are all less than the experimental error 0.01. From the detailed examination in Section 8.4, Ex. 8.10, we shall conclude that the chemical reaction has only two independent reactions.

Ex. 5.10. Show that

$$\text{rank}\,(\mathbf{A} + \mathbf{B}) \leq \text{rank}\,\mathbf{A} + \text{rank}\,\mathbf{B}.$$

Ex. 5.11. Prove that if $\mathbf{A}$, $\mathbf{B}$ are $m \times n$, $n \times p$ matrices of ranks r, s, respectively, then the rank of $\mathbf{AB}$ is greater than or equal to $r + s - n$.

5.6 The Generalized Inverse of a Matrix

The solution of least squares equations in Section 2.4 depends on:

THEOREM **5.17.** *If* $\mathbf{A}$ *is an* $m \times n$ *matrix* $(m > n)$ *of rank* n, *then the solution of the equations* $\mathbf{Ax} = \mathbf{b}$ *that minimizes the sum of squares of residuals* $S = \mathbf{r}^T\mathbf{r}$, *where* $\mathbf{r} = \mathbf{b} - \mathbf{Ax}$, *is given by*

$$\mathbf{x} = (\mathbf{A}^T\mathbf{A})^{-1}\mathbf{A}^T\mathbf{b}. \tag{5.13}$$

Proof: We have

$$S = (\mathbf{b} - \mathbf{Ax})^T(\mathbf{b} - \mathbf{Ax}) = \mathbf{b}^T\mathbf{b} - \mathbf{x}^T\mathbf{A}^T\mathbf{b} - \mathbf{b}^T\mathbf{Ax} + \mathbf{x}^T\mathbf{A}^T\mathbf{Ax}.$$

We must minimize S with respect to $\mathbf{x}$, i.e., set $\partial S/\partial x_j = 0, j = 1, \ldots, n$. This gives

$$\mathbf{A}^T\mathbf{Ax} = \mathbf{A}^T\mathbf{b}. \tag{5.14}$$

The matrix $\mathbf{A}^T\mathbf{A}$ is nonsingular from Theorem 5.16(ii). The result (5.13) follows.

One motivation for the introduction of a "generalized inverse" of a matrix can be seen from this theorem. If $\mathbf{A}$ is a nonsingular square matrix, the solution of $\mathbf{Ax} = \mathbf{b}$ is given by $\mathbf{x} = \mathbf{A}^{-1}\mathbf{b}$. If $\mathbf{A}$ is $m \times n$ $(m > n)$, of rank n, and we define

$$\mathbf{A}^+ = (\mathbf{A}^T\mathbf{A})^{-1}\mathbf{A}^T,$$

then the least-squares solution of $\mathbf{Ax} = \mathbf{b}$ is given by $\mathbf{x} = \mathbf{A}^+\mathbf{b}$. We now ask whether it might not be possible to write the "solution" of $\mathbf{Ax} = \mathbf{b}$ in the form $\mathbf{x} = \mathbf{A}^+\mathbf{b}$, where $\mathbf{A}^+$ is a suitably defined matrix, in the general case where $\mathbf{A}$ is $m \times n$ and of rank k.

One difficulty is immediately apparent, namely that even if a solution exists for $\mathbf{Ax} = \mathbf{b}$, this solution may not be unique. In this case we can write $\mathbf{x} = \mathbf{x}_0 + \mathbf{u}$ where $\mathbf{x}_0$ is a particular solution, and $\mathbf{u}$ is a solution of the corresponding homogeneous equations $\mathbf{Ax} = \mathbf{0}$, and we wish to find an "inverse" $\mathbf{A}^+$ such that a particular solution $\mathbf{x}_0$ is given by $\mathbf{A}^+\mathbf{b}$, i.e., $\mathbf{x} = \mathbf{A}^+\mathbf{b} + \mathbf{u}$. In order to specify $\mathbf{A}^+$ uniquely, we shall determine $\mathbf{x} = \mathbf{A}^+\mathbf{b}$ so that $\mathbf{x}^T\mathbf{x}$ is as small as possible.

Suppose that $\mathbf{A}$ is $m \times n$ $(m < n)$, and of rank m. Let $\mathbf{A}$, $\mathbf{x}$ be partitioned in the form

$$\mathbf{A} = [\mathbf{A}_1, \mathbf{A}_2], \qquad \mathbf{x} = \begin{bmatrix} \mathbf{x}_1 \\ \mathbf{x}_2 \end{bmatrix} \tag{5.15}$$

where $\mathbf{A}_1$ is an $m \times m$ nonsingular matrix. This can always be arranged, by renumbering the unknowns if necessary, since the rank of $\mathbf{A}$ is m. Then the equations $\mathbf{Ax} = \mathbf{b}$ can be written

$$\mathbf{A}_1\mathbf{x}_1 = \mathbf{b} - \mathbf{A}_2\mathbf{x}_2, \tag{5.16}$$

with the solution

$$\mathbf{x}_1 = \mathbf{A}_1^{-1}(\mathbf{b} - \mathbf{A}_2\mathbf{x}_2), \tag{5.17}$$

for any $\mathbf{x}_2$. There is an infinity of solutions and, as discussed in the last paragraph, we choose the solution that minimizes $\mathbf{x}^T\mathbf{x}$. This leads to the following theorem:

THEOREM **5.18.** *If* $\mathbf{A}$ *is an* $m \times n$ *matrix* $(m < n)$ *of rank* m, *then the solution of the equation* $\mathbf{Ax} = \mathbf{b}$ *that minimizes* $\mathbf{x}^T\mathbf{x}$ *is given by*

$$\mathbf{x} = \mathbf{A}^T(\mathbf{AA}^T)^{-1}\mathbf{b}. \tag{5.18}$$

Proof: We shall use the method of Lagrange multipliers. The quantity $\mathbf{x}$ that minimizes $\mathbf{x}^T\mathbf{x}$ subject to $\mathbf{Ax} = \mathbf{b}$ can be found by minimizing

$$M = \mathbf{x}^T\mathbf{x} + 2\boldsymbol{\lambda}^T(\mathbf{b} - \mathbf{Ax})$$

where $\boldsymbol{\lambda}$ is an $m \times 1$ column vector of Lagrange multipliers, and the factor of 2 is inserted for convenience. Setting

$$\frac{\partial M}{\partial x_j} = 0, \quad j = 1, \ldots, n, \qquad \frac{\partial M}{\partial \lambda_i} = 0, \quad i = 1, \ldots, m,$$

we find

$$\begin{aligned} \mathbf{x} &= \mathbf{A}^T\boldsymbol{\lambda}, \\ \mathbf{Ax} &= \mathbf{b}. \end{aligned} \tag{5.19}$$

On substituting the first equation in the second, we obtain

$$\mathbf{AA}^T\boldsymbol{\lambda} = \mathbf{b} \quad \text{or} \quad \boldsymbol{\lambda} = (\mathbf{AA}^T)^{-1}\mathbf{b},$$

since $\mathbf{AA}^T$ is nonsingular. Insertion of this expression for $\boldsymbol{\lambda}$ in (5.19) gives (5.18). [A more elementary proof can be obtained by expressing $\mathbf{x}^T\mathbf{x}$ in terms of the independent quantities $\mathbf{x}_2$ by means of (5.17). The resulting expression for $\mathbf{x}^T\mathbf{x}$ is then minimized with respect to $\mathbf{x}_2$. This proof is much more tedious.]

We can now prove our main theorem:

THEOREM **5.19.** *If* $\mathbf{A} = \mathbf{BC}$ *where* $\mathbf{A}$, $\mathbf{B}$, $\mathbf{C}$ *are, respectively,* $m \times n$, $m \times k$, *and* $k \times n$, *and all three matrices are of rank* k, *then the solution of* $\mathbf{Ax} = \mathbf{b}$ *which minimizes*

(a) *the sum of the squares of the residuals* $\mathbf{r}^T\mathbf{r}$, *where* $\mathbf{r} = \mathbf{b} - \mathbf{A}\mathbf{x}$,
(b) *the sum of the squares of the unknowns* $\mathbf{x}^T\mathbf{x}$,
is given by $\mathbf{x} = \mathbf{A}^+\mathbf{b}$, *where*

$$\mathbf{A}^+ = \mathbf{C}^T(\mathbf{C}\mathbf{C}^T)^{-1}(\mathbf{B}^T\mathbf{B})^{-1}\mathbf{B}^T. \tag{5.20}$$

Proof: In order to minimize the sum of the squares of the residuals in the case of general m, n, r, we can proceed as in the proof of Theorem 5.17 up to the result (5.14), namely that $\mathbf{x}$ satisfies

$$\mathbf{A}^T\mathbf{A}\mathbf{x} = \mathbf{A}^T\mathbf{b}.$$

At this point we can no longer invert $\mathbf{A}^T\mathbf{A}$ since this matrix may be singular. On introducing $\mathbf{A} = \mathbf{B}\mathbf{C}$, this equation becomes

$$\mathbf{C}^T(\mathbf{B}^T\mathbf{B})\mathbf{C}\mathbf{x} = \mathbf{C}^T\mathbf{B}^T\mathbf{b}.$$

We multiply this equation by $\mathbf{C}$. Since $\mathbf{C}\mathbf{C}^T$ and $\mathbf{B}^T\mathbf{B}$ are nonsingular matrices, we can then multiply both sides by $(\mathbf{B}^T\mathbf{B})^{-1}(\mathbf{C}\mathbf{C}^T)^{-1}$ to obtain

$$\mathbf{C}\mathbf{x} = (\mathbf{B}^T\mathbf{B})^{-1}\mathbf{B}^T\mathbf{b}. \tag{5.21}$$

The matrix $\mathbf{C}$ is $k \times n$ and of rank k so that we can apply Theorem 5.18. The solution of (5.21) that minimizes $\mathbf{x}$ is given by

$$\mathbf{x} = \mathbf{C}^T(\mathbf{C}\mathbf{C}^T)^{-1}(\mathbf{B}^T\mathbf{B})^{-1}\mathbf{B}^T\mathbf{b},$$

i.e., $\mathbf{x} = \mathbf{A}^+\mathbf{b}$ where $\mathbf{A}^+$ is defined in (5.20).

DEFINITION **5.3.** The matrix $\mathbf{A}^+$ defined in (5.20) is known as the *generalized inverse* of $\mathbf{A}$.

THEOREM **5.20.** *The generalized inverse* $\mathbf{A}^+$ *of* $\mathbf{A}$ *has the following properties:*
(i) $\mathbf{A}^+\mathbf{A}\mathbf{A}^+ = \mathbf{A}^+$.
(ii) $\mathbf{A}\mathbf{A}^+\mathbf{A} = \mathbf{A}$.
(iii) $\mathbf{A}\mathbf{A}^+$ *and* $\mathbf{A}^+\mathbf{A}$ *are symmetrical.*

Proof: These properties follow immediately from the defining formula (5.20).

Generalized inverses can be defined by means of the properties (i)–(iii) above, instead of using the explicit formula (5.20).

In order to evaluate the generalized inverse of $\mathbf{A}$ from (5.20) we must decompose $\mathbf{A}$ in the form $\mathbf{B}\mathbf{C}$. This can be done by means of the following theorem (see also Ex. 5.13).

THEOREM **5.21.** *If* $\mathbf{A}$ *is* $m \times n$ *and of rank* k, *and we can partition* $\mathbf{A}$ *in the form*

$$\mathbf{A} = \begin{bmatrix} \mathbf{A}_{11} & \mathbf{A}_{12} \\ \mathbf{A}_{21} & \mathbf{A}_{22} \end{bmatrix}, \tag{5.22}$$

where $\mathbf{A}_{11}$ *is a nonsingular matrix of rank k, then*

$$\mathbf{A} = \begin{bmatrix}\mathbf{I}\\\mathbf{P}\end{bmatrix}[\mathbf{A}_{11}\ \mathbf{A}_{12}] = \begin{bmatrix}\mathbf{I}\\\mathbf{P}\end{bmatrix}\mathbf{A}_{11}[\mathbf{I}\ \mathbf{Q}] = \begin{bmatrix}\mathbf{A}_{11}\\\mathbf{A}_{21}\end{bmatrix}[\mathbf{I}\ \mathbf{Q}], \tag{5.23}$$

where

$$\mathbf{P} = \mathbf{A}_{21}\mathbf{A}_{11}^{-1}, \qquad \mathbf{Q} = \mathbf{A}_{11}^{-1}\mathbf{A}_{12}. \tag{5.24}$$

Proof: Since the rank of $\mathbf{A}$ is k, the last $m - k$ rows of (5.22) are linear combinations of the first k rows, so that a nonsingular matrix $\mathbf{P}$ exists such that

$$\mathbf{A}_{21} = \mathbf{P}\mathbf{A}_{11}, \qquad \mathbf{A}_{22} = \mathbf{P}\mathbf{A}_{12}. \tag{5.25}$$

Similarly, the last $n - k$ columns of (5.22) are linear combinations of the first k, so that a nonsingular matrix $\mathbf{Q}$ exists such that

$$\mathbf{A}_{12} = \mathbf{A}_{11}\mathbf{Q}, \qquad \mathbf{A}_{22} = \mathbf{A}_{21}\mathbf{Q}. \tag{5.26}$$

Since $\mathbf{A}_{11}$ is nonsingular, the first equations in (5.25), (5.26) give the expressions for $\mathbf{P}$ and $\mathbf{Q}$ in (5.24). From (5.25), (5.26) we see that

$$\mathbf{A}_{22} = \mathbf{P}\mathbf{A}_{11}\mathbf{Q}. \tag{5.27}$$

The expressions in (5.23) follow from (5.25)–(5.27).

Ex. 5.12. Find the generalized inverse of

$$\mathbf{A} = \begin{bmatrix} -1 & 0 & 1 & 2\\ -1 & 1 & 0 & -1\\ 0 & -1 & 1 & 3\\ 0 & 1 & -1 & -3\\ 1 & -1 & 0 & 1\\ 1 & 0 & -1 & -2 \end{bmatrix}. \tag{5.28}$$

Solution: On reducing this matrix to row-echelon form, it is found that its rank is 2. The 2×2 matrix in the upper left of $\mathbf{A}$ is nonsingular so that we can choose

$$\mathbf{A}_{11} = \begin{bmatrix} -1 & 0\\ -1 & 1\end{bmatrix}, \qquad \mathbf{A}_{11}^{-1} = \begin{bmatrix} -1 & 0\\ -1 & 1\end{bmatrix}.$$

Working in terms of the third formula in (5.23), we compute

$$\mathbf{Q} = \mathbf{A}_{11}^{-1}\mathbf{A}_{12} = \begin{bmatrix} -1 & 2\\ -1 & -3\end{bmatrix}. \tag{5.29}$$

In the terminology of Theorem 5.19, we now set

$$\mathbf{B} = \begin{bmatrix}\mathbf{A}_{11}\\\mathbf{A}_{21}\end{bmatrix} = \begin{bmatrix} -1 & 0\\ -1 & 1\\ 0 & -1\\ 0 & 1\\ 1 & -1\\ 1 & 0\end{bmatrix}, \qquad \mathbf{C} = [\mathbf{I}\ \mathbf{Q}] = \begin{bmatrix} 1 & 0 & -1 & 2\\ 0 & 1 & -1 & -3\end{bmatrix}.$$

Substitution in (5.20) yields

$$\mathbf{A}^+ = \frac{1}{102}\begin{bmatrix} -15 & -18 & 3 & -3 & 18 & 15 \\ 8 & 13 & -5 & 5 & -13 & -8 \\ 7 & 5 & 2 & -2 & -5 & -7 \\ 6 & -3 & 9 & -9 & 3 & -6 \end{bmatrix}. \tag{5.30}$$

Ex. 5.13. A *permutation matrix* is a matrix obtained by interchanging rows or columns of the unit matrix. Show that for any matrix $\mathbf{B}$ of rank k, permutation matrices $\mathbf{P}$, $\mathbf{Q}$ can be found so that $\mathbf{PBQ}$ can be partitioned in the form (5.22), where the matrix $\mathbf{A}_{11}$ of order k is nonsingular. Show that $\mathbf{B}^+ = \mathbf{QA}^+\mathbf{P}$. Generalize Theorem 5.21 to show that *any* $m \times n$ matrix of rank k can be written in the form $\mathbf{BC}$ where $\mathbf{B}$ is $m \times k$, $\mathbf{C}$ is $k \times n$, and each is of rank k.

Ex. 5.14. Prove that every matrix has a unique generalized inverse. (*Hint:* Prove that the conditions (i)–(iii) of Theorem 5.20 define $\mathbf{A}^+$ uniquely.)

Ex. 5.15. (a) The generalized inverse of an $m \times n$ matrix is $n \times m$.

(b) The rank of $\mathbf{A}^+$ is the same as the rank of $\mathbf{A}$.

(c) If $\mathbf{A}$ is symmetric, then $\mathbf{A}^+$ is symmetric.

(d) $(c\mathbf{A})^+ = (1/c)\mathbf{A}^+$.

(e) $(\mathbf{A}^+)^T = (\mathbf{A}^T)^+$.

(f) $(\mathbf{A}^+)^+ = \mathbf{A}$.

(g) Show by a counterexample that in general $(\mathbf{AB})^+ \neq \mathbf{B}^+\mathbf{A}^+$.

(h) If $\mathbf{A}$ is $m \times r$, $\mathbf{B}$ is $r \times n$, and both matrices are of rank r, show that $(\mathbf{AB})^+ = \mathbf{B}^+\mathbf{A}^+$.

Ex. 5.16. (a) The generalized inverse of the null matrix is the null matrix.

(b) If $\mathbf{A}$ is diagonal with $a_{ii} \neq 0$, $i = 1, \ldots, k$, and all other elements zero, prove that $\mathbf{A}^+$ is a diagonal matrix with all elements zero except for the first k diagonal elements which are equal to $1/a_{ii}$, $i = 1, \ldots, k$.

(c) If $\mathbf{A}$ is nonsingular, prove that $\mathbf{A}^+ = \mathbf{A}^{-1}$.

(d) If $\mathbf{u}$ is a nonzero column vector, prove that $\mathbf{u}^+ = (\mathbf{u}^T\mathbf{u})^{-1}\mathbf{u}^T$.

(e) Prove that if $\mathbf{A} = \mathbf{uv}^T$ then

$$\mathbf{A}^+ = \frac{\mathbf{A}^T}{(\mathbf{v}^T\mathbf{v})(\mathbf{u}^T\mathbf{u})}.$$

(f) Prove that the generalized inverse of a 2×2 matrix $\mathbf{A}$ of rank one is given by

$$\frac{1}{a_{11}^2 + a_{12}^2 + a_{21}^2 + a_{22}^2}\mathbf{A}^T$$

(g) If all the elements of an $m \times n$ matrix $\mathbf{A}$ are unity, prove that $\mathbf{A}^+ = (1/mn)\mathbf{A}^T$.

5.7 *Inversion of Matrices of a Special Form, and "Tearing"*

THEOREM 5.22. *If a nonsingular matrix* $\mathbf{H}$ *of order* n *can be written in the form*

$$\mathbf{H} = \mathbf{A} + \mathbf{BDC}, \tag{5.31}$$

where $\mathbf{B}$, $\mathbf{D}$, $\mathbf{C}$ *are* $n \times p$, $p \times p$, $p \times n$, *respectively, and* $\mathbf{A}$, $\mathbf{D}$ *are nonsingular then*

$$\mathbf{H}^{-1} = \mathbf{A}^{-1} - \mathbf{A}^{-1}\mathbf{B}(\mathbf{D}^{-1} + \mathbf{CA}^{-1}\mathbf{B})^{-1}\mathbf{CA}^{-1}. \tag{5.32}$$

[The point of this result, as we illustrate later, is that if p is much less than n, it may be comparatively easy to invert $\mathbf{D}^{-1} + \mathbf{CA}^{-1}\mathbf{B}$. If $\mathbf{A}$ and $\mathbf{D}$ are also easy to invert, it may be less work to invert the right-hand side of (5.32) rather than evaluate $\mathbf{H}^{-1}$ directly.]

Proof: Suppose that

$$(\mathbf{A} + \mathbf{BDC})\mathbf{X} = \mathbf{I} \tag{5.33}$$

so that $\mathbf{X}$ is the desired inverse $\mathbf{H}^{-1}$. We first solve this equation for $\mathbf{DCX}$. This can be done by multiplying (5.33) throughout by $\mathbf{CA}^{-1}$ and rearranging; thus,

$$(\mathbf{D}^{-1} + \mathbf{CA}^{-1}\mathbf{B})\mathbf{DCX} = \mathbf{CA}^{-1}. \tag{5.34}$$

We now prove that $\mathbf{D}^{-1} + \mathbf{CA}^{-1}\mathbf{B}$ is nonsingular. Consider

$$(\mathbf{D}^{-1} + \mathbf{CA}^{-1}\mathbf{B})\mathbf{x} = \mathbf{0}. \tag{5.35}$$

On multiplying through by $\mathbf{BD}$ and rearranging,

$$(\mathbf{A} + \mathbf{BDC})\mathbf{A}^{-1}\mathbf{Bx} = \mathbf{0}. \tag{5.36}$$

Since $\mathbf{A} + \mathbf{BDC}$ and $\mathbf{A}$ are nonsingular, this implies that $\mathbf{Bx} = \mathbf{0}$. Substitution of this result in (5.35) gives $\mathbf{D}^{-1}\mathbf{x} = \mathbf{0}$ or $\mathbf{x} = \mathbf{0}$. This proves that $(\mathbf{D}^{-1} + \mathbf{CA}^{-1}\mathbf{B})\mathbf{x} = \mathbf{0}$ implies $\mathbf{x} = \mathbf{0}$. Hence, $\mathbf{D}^{-1} + \mathbf{CA}^{-1}\mathbf{B}$ is nonsingular. From (5.34) we have now

$$\mathbf{DCX} = (\mathbf{D}^{-1} + \mathbf{CA}^{-1}\mathbf{B})^{-1}\mathbf{CA}^{-1} \tag{5.37}$$

and if we substitute this in the second term on the left of (5.33), we can deduce (5.32).

We now give some applications of this theorem.

Ex. 5.17. Find the inverse of the matrix $\mathbf{H}$ formed by adding a quantity λ to the (i, j)th element of a nonsingular matrix $\mathbf{A}$, i.e.,

$$\mathbf{H} = \mathbf{A} + \lambda\mathbf{e}_i\mathbf{e}_j^T,$$

where $\mathbf{e}_i$ is the $n \times 1$ unit column vector having 1 in the ith position and zeros elsewhere.

Solution: This is of the form $\mathbf{H} = \mathbf{A} + \mathbf{BDC}$ with $\mathbf{D}$ equal to a 1×1 unit matrix, and

$$\mathbf{B} = \lambda \mathbf{e}_i, \qquad \mathbf{C} = \mathbf{e}_j^T.$$

The matrix $\mathbf{BDC}$ is of rank unity and

$$\mathbf{D}^{-1} + \mathbf{CA}^{-1}\mathbf{B} = [1 + \lambda \mathbf{e}_j^T \mathbf{A}^{-1} \mathbf{e}_i] = [1 + \lambda \alpha_{ji}]$$

is a 1×1 matrix, where α_{ji} is the (j, i)th element of $\mathbf{A}^{-1}$. Hence, from (5.32),

$$\mathbf{H}^{-1} = \mathbf{A}^{-1} - \frac{\lambda \mathbf{p}_i \mathbf{q}_j^T}{1 + \lambda \alpha_{ji}},$$

where $\mathbf{p}_i = \mathbf{A}^{-1}\mathbf{e}_i$ = the ith column of $\mathbf{A}^{-1}$, and $\mathbf{q}_j^T = \mathbf{e}_j^T \mathbf{A}^{-1}$ = the jth row of $\mathbf{A}^{-1}$.

Ex. 5.18. Invert

$$\mathbf{H} = \begin{bmatrix} \alpha_1 + b_1c_1 & b_1c_2 & \dots & b_1c_n \\ b_2c_1 & \alpha_2 + b_2c_2 & \dots & b_2c_n \\ & \dots & & \\ b_nc_1 & b_nc_2 & \dots & \alpha_n + b_nc_n \end{bmatrix} = \mathbf{A} + \mathbf{bc}^T,$$

where

$$\mathbf{A} = \begin{bmatrix} \alpha_1 & 0 & \dots & 0 \\ 0 & \alpha_2 & \dots & 0 \\ & & \dots & \\ 0 & 0 & \dots & \alpha_n \end{bmatrix}, \qquad \mathbf{b} = \begin{bmatrix} b_1 \\ b_2 \\ \cdot \\ \cdot \\ \cdot \\ b_n \end{bmatrix}, \qquad \mathbf{c} = \begin{bmatrix} c_1 \\ c_2 \\ \cdot \\ \cdot \\ \cdot \\ c_n \end{bmatrix}.$$

Solution: We have, on setting $\mathbf{B} = \mathbf{b}$, $\mathbf{C} = \mathbf{c}^T$ and $\mathbf{D} = [1]$, a 1×1 unit matrix

$$\mathbf{D}^{-1} + \mathbf{CA}^{-1}\mathbf{B} = 1 + \frac{b_1c_1}{\alpha_1} + \dots + \frac{b_nc_n}{\alpha_n} = \alpha,$$

say, and, from (5.32),

$$\mathbf{H}^{-1} = \mathbf{A}^{-1} - \frac{1}{\alpha} \mathbf{A}^{-1}\mathbf{bc}^T\mathbf{A}^{-1}.$$

Ex. 5.19. If we add a column vector $\boldsymbol{\beta}$ to the jth column of $\mathbf{A}$, the resulting matrix being denoted by $\mathbf{H}$, show that

$$\mathbf{H}^{-1} = \mathbf{A}^{-1} - \frac{\mathbf{A}^{-1}\boldsymbol{\beta}\mathbf{q}_j^T}{1 + \mathbf{q}_j^T\boldsymbol{\beta}},$$

where $\mathbf{q}_j^T$ is the jth row of $\mathbf{A}^{-1}$. If we add a row vector $\boldsymbol{\gamma}^T$ to the ith row of $\mathbf{A}$, show that the inverse of the resulting matrix is given by

$$\mathbf{A}^{-1} - \frac{\mathbf{p}_i\boldsymbol{\gamma}^T\mathbf{A}^{-1}}{1 + \boldsymbol{\gamma}^T\mathbf{p}_i},$$

where $\mathbf{p}_i$ is the ith column of $\mathbf{A}^{-1}$.

If we had to rely on inspection of **H** in order to express **H** in the form (5.31), the applications of Theorem 5.22 would be very limited. However there are certain classes of problems in which one can see that the overall system can be broken down into several subsystems, the interconnections between subsystems being small in number compared with the internal connections within the subsystems. (Many of the problems in mechanical structures, electrical networks, economic systems, etc., are of this type.) In this case, we can use our knowledge of the physical structure of the system in order to write **H** in a suitable form (5.31).

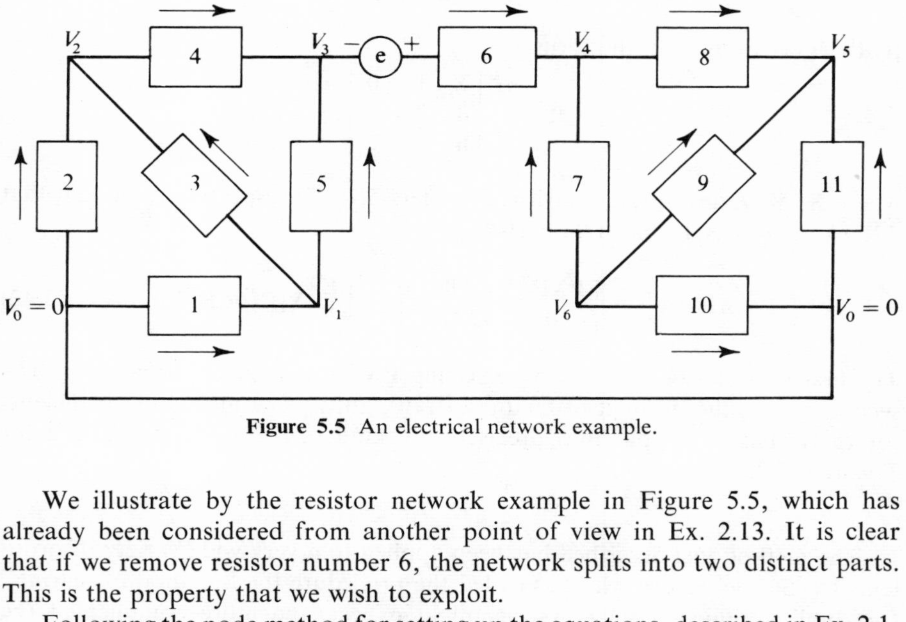

Figure 5.5 An electrical network example.

We illustrate by the resistor network example in Figure 5.5, which has already been considered from another point of view in Ex. 2.13. It is clear that if we remove resistor number 6, the network splits into two distinct parts. This is the property that we wish to exploit.

Following the node method for setting up the equations, described in Ex. 2.1, we find, for Equations (2.12)–(2.14),

$$\mathbf{v} = \mathbf{R}\mathbf{i}, \qquad \mathbf{A}\mathbf{i} = \mathbf{0}, \qquad \mathbf{A}^T\mathbf{V} = \mathbf{v} - \mathbf{e}, \tag{5.38}$$

where $\mathbf{v} = [v_r]$ and $\mathbf{i} = [i_s]$ are 11×1, $\mathbf{V} = [V_i]$ is 6×1, $\mathbf{e}$ is an 11×1 column vector with zero elements except for the sixth which is e, and

$$\mathbf{A} = \left[\begin{array}{ccccc:c:ccccc} -1 & 0 & 1 & 0 & 1 & 0 & 0 & 0 & 0 & 0 & 0 \\ 0 & -1 & -1 & 1 & 0 & 0 & 0 & 0 & 0 & 0 & 0 \\ 0 & 0 & 0 & -1 & -1 & 1 & 0 & 0 & 0 & 0 & 0 \\ \hdashline 0 & 0 & 0 & 0 & 0 & -1 & -1 & 1 & 0 & 0 & 0 \\ 0 & 0 & 0 & 0 & 0 & 0 & 0 & -1 & -1 & 0 & -1 \\ 0 & 0 & 0 & 0 & 0 & 0 & 1 & 0 & 1 & 1 & 0 \end{array}\right]. \tag{5.39}$$

The important thing about the structure of this matrix is that it can be partitioned as shown by the dotted lines:

$$\mathbf{A} = \begin{bmatrix} \mathbf{P} & \mathbf{E} & \mathbf{0} \\ \mathbf{0} & \mathbf{F} & \mathbf{Q} \end{bmatrix}. \tag{5.40}$$

The submatrices **E**, **F** come from resistor 6, the submatrices **P** and **Q** come from the parts of the network to the left and right, respectively, of resistor 6. If we eliminate **v** and **i** from the equations in (5.38), we obtain [see (2.15)]

$$(\mathbf{A}\mathbf{R}^{-1}\mathbf{A}^T)\mathbf{V} = -\mathbf{A}\mathbf{R}^{-1}\mathbf{e}. \tag{5.41}$$

If $\mathbf{R}^{-1}$ is partitioned in the form

$$\mathbf{R}^{-1} = \begin{bmatrix} \mathbf{X} & \mathbf{0} & \mathbf{0} \\ \mathbf{0} & \mathbf{Y} & \mathbf{0} \\ \mathbf{0} & \mathbf{0} & \mathbf{Z} \end{bmatrix},$$

where **X**, **Y**, **Z** are square matrices of orders 5, 1, 5, respectively, we find that $\mathbf{A}\mathbf{R}^{-1}\mathbf{A}^T$ can be split into two parts:

$$\mathbf{A}\mathbf{R}^{-1}\mathbf{A}^T = \begin{bmatrix} \mathbf{P}\mathbf{X}\mathbf{P}^T & \mathbf{0} \\ \mathbf{0} & \mathbf{Q}\mathbf{Z}\mathbf{Q}^T \end{bmatrix} + \begin{bmatrix} \mathbf{E} \\ \mathbf{F} \end{bmatrix} \mathbf{Y}[\mathbf{E}^T \quad \mathbf{F}^T]. \tag{5.42}$$

The first part can be inverted by inverting $\mathbf{P}\mathbf{X}\mathbf{P}^T$ and $\mathbf{Q}\mathbf{Z}\mathbf{Q}^T$ separately. The second part is the product of factors of rank unity. The matrix of coefficients for (5.41) has been split into precisely the kind of form (5.31) required for Theorem 5.22.

The method just described has been applied to a very wide variety of problems by Gabriel Kron, who has called the procedure the "method of tearing" (see bibliographical notes). As we might expect, the more complicated the problem, the more useful the method is.

Ex. 5.20. Solve by the present method the numerical example involving Figure 5.5 that was already solved by a different method in Ex. 2.13.

Ex. 5.21. Show that the electrical network in Figure 5.6 can also be solved by the method of tearing, by removing the resistor 6. (*Note:* In Figure 5.5 the removal of resistor 6 meant that the two distinct subnetworks had no *nodes* in common. This was the reason why we formulated the problem using the node method of Ex. 2.1. This will not apply in Figure 5.6. However, we can choose loop currents in such a way that when resistor 6 is removed, the resulting subnetworks have no loop currents in common. This means that the method of tearing will work if we formulate the problem using the loop method of Ex. 2.14.)

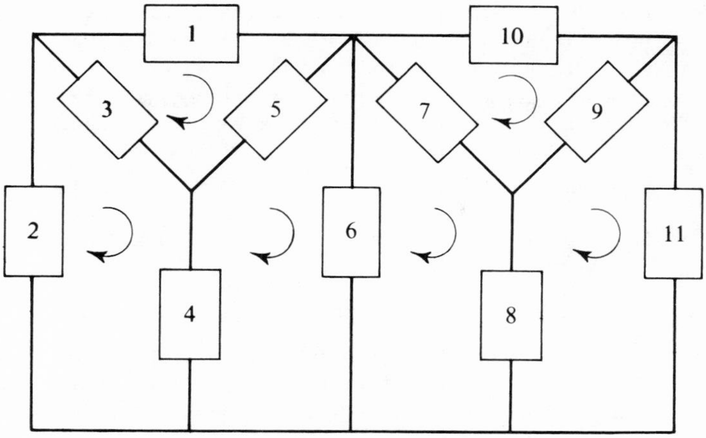

Figure 5.6 A second electrical network.

Miscellaneous Exercises 5

Ex. 5.22. Give three different proofs that if **B** is a submatrix of **A**, then the rank of **B** is not greater than the rank of **A**.

Ex. 5.23. If **A** is any $m \times n$ matrix, the row-echelon form of $[\mathbf{A}, \mathbf{I}]$ has m nonzero rows.

Ex. 5.24. If **B**, **C** are of ranks r, s, respectively, and

$$\mathbf{A} = \begin{bmatrix} \mathbf{B} & \mathbf{0} \\ \mathbf{0} & \mathbf{C} \end{bmatrix},$$

show that **A** is of rank $r + s$.

Ex. 5.25. If **A**, **B** are $m \times n$ matrices with the same rank, show that there exist nonsingular matrices **E**, **F** such that

$$\mathbf{EAF} = \mathbf{B}.$$

Ex. 5.26. Prove that the condition for the n straight lines

$$a_i x + b_i y = c_i, \qquad i = 1, \ldots, n,$$

to pass through one point is that the matrices $[\mathbf{a}, \mathbf{b}]$ and $[\mathbf{a}, \mathbf{b}, \mathbf{c}]$ have the same rank, where $\mathbf{a} = [a_i]$, $\mathbf{b} = [b_i]$, $\mathbf{c} = [c_i]$ are $n \times 1$ column vectors.

Ex. 5.27. Prove that three points (x_i, y_i), $i = 1, 2, 3$, in the plane are colinear if and only if the rank of the following matrix is less than three.

$$\begin{bmatrix} x_1 & y_1 & 1 \\ x_2 & y_2 & 1 \\ x_3 & y_3 & 1 \end{bmatrix}.$$

Ex. 5.28. A matrix $\mathbf{A}$ is said to be *divisor of zero* if $\mathbf{A} \neq \mathbf{0}$ and if there exists a matrix $\mathbf{B} \neq \mathbf{0}$ such that $\mathbf{AB} = \mathbf{0}$, or there exists a matrix $\mathbf{C} \neq \mathbf{0}$ such that $\mathbf{CA} = \mathbf{0}$. Show that an arbitrary matrix $\mathbf{A}$ is a divisor of zero if and only if the rank of $\mathbf{A}$ is less than $\max(m, n)$. (*Hint:* Consider $\mathbf{Ax} = \mathbf{0}$, and $\mathbf{y}^T\mathbf{A} = \mathbf{0}$, where $\mathbf{x}$, $\mathbf{y}$ are column vectors.) Deduce that every rectangular matrix is a divisor of zero, and a square matrix is a divisor of zero only if it is singular.

Ex. 5.29. Prove that every matrix of rank r is a sum of r matrices of rank 1.

Ex. 5.30. If $\mathbf{A}$ is a square matrix of rank 1, prove that $\mathbf{A}^2 = c\mathbf{A}$ for some constant c.

Ex. 5.31. Show that $\mathbf{AB}$ is singular if $\mathbf{A}$ is $m \times n$ and $\mathbf{B}$ is $n \times m$ with $n < m$.

Ex. 5.32. Suppose that $\mathbf{AB} = \mathbf{0}$. If $\mathbf{A}$ is $n \times n$ and $\mathbf{B}$ is $n \times p$, then either $\mathbf{B} = \mathbf{0}$ or $\mathbf{A}$ is singular. If $\mathbf{A}$ is $m \times n$ and $\mathbf{B}$ is $n \times n$, then either $\mathbf{A} = \mathbf{0}$ or $\mathbf{B}$ is singular. If $\mathbf{A}$ and $\mathbf{B}$ are both $n \times n$, then $\mathbf{A} = \mathbf{0}$ or $\mathbf{B} = \mathbf{0}$ or both $\mathbf{A}$ and $\mathbf{B}$ are singular.

Ex. 5.33. A *block diagonal matrix* is a square partitioned matrix in which the diagonal elements are square matrices and all other elements are null matrices. Show that a block diagonal matrix is nonsingular if and only if all the diagonal matrix elements are nonsingular.

Ex. 5.34. Prove that the following statements are equivalent ($\mathbf{A}$ is a square matrix).

(a) $\mathbf{A}$ has a left-inverse.
(b) $\mathbf{A}$ has a right-inverse.
(c) $\mathbf{A}$ has an inverse.
(d) $\mathbf{A}$ is row-equivalent to the unit matrix.
(e) $\mathbf{A}$ can be expressed as a product of elementary matrices.

Ex. 5.35. Show that the only square matrices of order n that commute with all other square matrices are of the form $k\mathbf{I}$, where k is a scalar.

Ex. 5.36. Show that interchanging two rows (columns) of $\mathbf{A}$ interchanges the corrresponding columns (rows) of $\mathbf{A}^{-1}$. Show that if the sth column of $\mathbf{A}$ is the unit vector $\mathbf{e}_i$, then the ith column of $\mathbf{A}^{-1}$ is $\mathbf{e}_s$.

Ex. 5.37. If $\mathbf{A}$ is a square matrix such that the only solution of $\mathbf{Ax} = \mathbf{0}$ is $\mathbf{x} = \mathbf{0}$, show that $\mathbf{A}$ must be nonsingular.

Ex. 5.38. The set of all vectors of the form $\mathbf{Ax}$ where $\mathbf{A}$ is a given $m \times n$ matrix, and $\mathbf{x}$ is an arbitrary $n \times 1$ vector, is a vector space of dimension equal to the rank of $\mathbf{A}$.

Ex. 5.39. Show that $\mathbf{A}$ has a right-inverse if and only if the null space of $\mathbf{A}^T$ is the zero space.

Ex. 5.40. Consider

$$\mathbf{u}_i = \sum_{j=1}^{k} a_{ij}\mathbf{x}_j, \qquad i = 1, \ldots, k,$$

where the $\mathbf{x}_j$ are independent $n \times 1$ vectors. Prove that a necessary and sufficient condition for the $\mathbf{u}_i$ to be linearly independent is that $\mathbf{A} = [a_{ij}]$ be nonsingular.

Ex. 5.41. If $\mathbf{A}$ is a square matrix and the solutions of $\mathbf{Ax} = \mathbf{0}$ form a vector space of dimension p, the same is true of the solutions of $\mathbf{A}^T\mathbf{y} = \mathbf{0}$.

Ex. 5.42. If the last (nonzero) column of an $n \times (n + 1)$ matrix $\mathbf{A}$ is linearly dependent on the first $n - 1$ columns, and also on the $n - 1$ columns numbered $2, \ldots, n$, prove that the rank of $\mathbf{A}$ is less than n.

Ex. 5.43. For any $n \times n$ matrix $\mathbf{A}$ and $n \times 1$ vector $\mathbf{b}$, exactly *one* of the following two systems of equations is consistent:

(a) $\mathbf{Ax} = \mathbf{b}$, (b) $\mathbf{A}^T\mathbf{y} = \mathbf{0}, \quad \mathbf{b}^T\mathbf{y} = 1$.

Another way of stating this is that $\mathbf{Ax} = \mathbf{b}$ will not have a solution if and only if there exists a solution $\mathbf{y}$ of the corresponding homogeneous equation such that $\mathbf{y}^T\mathbf{b} \neq 0$.

Ex. 5.44. Prove Theorem 5.16(ii) by using the decomposition (5.23) and Theorem 5.16(i). (See also the last sentence in Ex. 5.13.)

Ex. 5.45. Consider $\mathbf{Ax} = \mathbf{b}$ where $\mathbf{A}$ can be written in the form (5.22). Let $\mathbf{b}_1$ and $\mathbf{b}_2$ denote column matrices consisting of the first k and last $n - k$ elements of $\mathbf{b}$. Prove that the matrix on the right of (5.43) below is the row-echelon form of the matrix on the left

$$\begin{bmatrix} \mathbf{A}_{11} & \mathbf{A}_{12} & \mathbf{b}_1 & \mathbf{I} \\ \mathbf{A}_{21} & \mathbf{A}_{22} & \mathbf{b}_2 & \mathbf{0} \end{bmatrix}, \qquad \begin{bmatrix} \mathbf{I} & \mathbf{Q} & \mathbf{c}_1 & \mathbf{A}_{11}^{-1} \\ \mathbf{0} & \mathbf{0} & \mathbf{c}_2 & -\mathbf{P} \end{bmatrix}, \tag{5.43}$$

where $\mathbf{c}_1 = \mathbf{A}_{11}^{-1}\mathbf{b}_1$, $\mathbf{c}_2 = \mathbf{b}_2 - \mathbf{Pb}_1$, and $\mathbf{P}$, $\mathbf{Q}$ have been defined in (5.24). Prove that the general least-squares solution of $\mathbf{Ax} = \mathbf{b}$ is given by

$$\mathbf{x} = \begin{bmatrix} \mathbf{c}_1 + \mathbf{y} \\ \mathbf{0} \end{bmatrix} + \begin{bmatrix} -\mathbf{Q} \\ \mathbf{I} \end{bmatrix}\mathbf{z}, \tag{5.44}$$

where $\mathbf{z}$ is an arbitrary $(n - k) \times 1$ vector, and

$$[\mathbf{I} + \mathbf{P}^T\mathbf{P}]\mathbf{A}_{11}\mathbf{y} = \mathbf{P}^T\mathbf{c}_2.$$

Note that

(a) If the equations are consistent, then $\mathbf{c}_2 = \mathbf{0}$, so that $\mathbf{y} = \mathbf{0}$, and it is not necessary to compute $\mathbf{P}$.

(b) To compute $\mathbf{c}_1 + \mathbf{y}$, which gives a particular solution of the equations, it is not necessary to compute $\mathbf{Q}$.

Ex. 5.46. Verify the arithmetic leading to (5.30). Obtain (5.30) independently by using (5.43) to compute $\mathbf{P}$, $\mathbf{Q}$, $\mathbf{A}_{11}^{-1}$, substituting the results in the following formula, derived from (5.20):

$$\mathbf{A}^+ = \begin{bmatrix} \mathbf{I} \\ \mathbf{Q}^T \end{bmatrix} [(\mathbf{I} + \mathbf{P}^T\mathbf{P})\mathbf{A}_{11}(\mathbf{I} + \mathbf{Q}\mathbf{Q}^T)]^{-1}[\mathbf{I} \quad \mathbf{P}^T].$$

Ex. 5.47. A *conditional inverse* of an $m \times n$ matrix $\mathbf{A}$ is a matrix $\mathbf{A}^C$ such that $\mathbf{A}\mathbf{A}^C\mathbf{A} = \mathbf{A}$.

(a) Verify that if $\mathbf{A}$ can be written in the form (5.22) then

$$\begin{bmatrix} \mathbf{A}_{11}^{-1} & \mathbf{0} \\ \mathbf{0} & \mathbf{0} \end{bmatrix}$$

is a conditional inverse of $\mathbf{A}$.

(b) A left-inverse of $\mathbf{A}$ is a conditional inverse.

(c) The ranks of $\mathbf{A}^C\mathbf{A}$ and $\mathbf{I} - \mathbf{A}^C\mathbf{A}$ are k and $n - k$, respectively, where k is the rank of $\mathbf{A}$.

(d) If $\mathbf{A}\mathbf{x} = \mathbf{b}$ is a consistent system then $\mathbf{x} = \mathbf{A}^C\mathbf{b}$ is a particular solution, and the general solution is given by

$$\mathbf{x} = \mathbf{A}^C\mathbf{b} + (\mathbf{I} - \mathbf{A}^C\mathbf{A})\mathbf{w},$$

where $\mathbf{w}$ is an arbitrary vector.

(e) If $\mathbf{x} = \mathbf{B}\mathbf{b}$ is a solution of $\mathbf{A}\mathbf{x} = \mathbf{b}$ for any $\mathbf{b}$ for which the system is consistent, then $\mathbf{B}$ is a conditional inverse of $\mathbf{A}$.

Ex. 5.48. Prove that a right-inverse of a matrix satisfies (i), (ii), and the first part of (iii), in Theorem 5.20. What is the corresponding result for a left-inverse?

Ex. 5.49. Prove that if elementary row operations are used on the matrix on the left below to reduce the nonsingular matrix $\mathbf{A}$ to $\mathbf{I}$, and $\mathbf{C}$ to $\mathbf{0}$, this leads to the matrix on the right.

$$\begin{bmatrix} \mathbf{A} & \mathbf{B} \\ \mathbf{C} & \mathbf{D} \end{bmatrix}, \quad \begin{bmatrix} \mathbf{I} & \mathbf{A}^{-1}\mathbf{B} \\ \mathbf{0} & \mathbf{D} - \mathbf{C}\mathbf{A}^{-1}\mathbf{B} \end{bmatrix}.$$

Ex. 5.50. One of the difficulties in analyzing mechanical structures by computer is to provide an automatic procedure for deciding which members of a framework are redundant, if any. A method for doing this by systematic use of the concept of the rank of a matrix has been described by Robinson [96]. Write a short essay on the method.

Ex. 5.51. If $\mathbf{K}$ is skew-symmetric, prove that $\mathbf{x}^T\mathbf{K}\mathbf{x} = \mathbf{0}$ for all $\mathbf{x}$. Deduce that $\mathbf{I} + \mathbf{K}$ is nonsingular.

6 Linear Programming

6.1 Introduction

In various government, military, and industrial operations there arise situations where we wish to maximize or minimize some quantity which is a measure of the efficiency of the activity. This quantity may be, for example, the total output over a given period of time, or the cost of the operation. Optimization problems of this type are known as (mathematical) *programming problems*. We shall be concerned with a special but important class of programming problem involving only linear equations and inequalities. We shall confine our attention to a method known as the *simplex method* for solving these linear programming problems.

As an example, consider a machine shop with three types of machine 1, 2, 3 that can turn out two different products 1, 2. Each of the products has to be processed on each of the machines. Table 6.1 shows

(a) The hours required on each machine to produce one unit of each of the products.
(b) The total number of hours available on each machine, each week.
(c) The profit made on one unit of each product.

It is assumed that the profit is directly proportional to the number of units sold. It is required to find the weekly output of each product that will maximize profits.

Let x_j denote the numbers of units of product j produced per week ($j = 1, 2$). Restrictions are imposed by the availability of machine time. Thus the amount of time required on machine 1 to produce x_1 items of product 1 and x_2 of 2 is $2x_1 + x_2$ hours, and only 70 hours are available, so that

$$2x_1 + x_2 \leq 70. \qquad (6.1a)$$

Table 6.1

Machine type	Product 1	Product 2	Total hours available
1	2	1	70
2	1	1	40
3	1	3	90
Profit per unit	40	60	

Similarly, from the limited time available on machines 2 and 3,

$$x_1 + x_2 \leq 40, \tag{6.1b}$$

$$x_1 + 3x_2 \leq 90. \tag{6.1c}$$

Also we cannot produce a negative number of articles, so that

$$x_1 \geq 0, \qquad x_2 \geq 0. \tag{6.2}$$

Inequalities like (6.1), (6.2) are known as *constraints*. Since the profit per unit of products 1, 2 is 40, 60 respectively, the total weekly profit is

$$M = 40x_1 + 60x_2. \tag{6.3}$$

The problem is now to maximize the expression (6.3), subject to the inequalities (6.1), (6.2). This is a typical *linear programming problem*, involving the optimization of a certain linear function of unknown variables, subject to linear constraints (equations or inequalities) that restrict the permissible values of the variables. (In a *nonlinear* programming problem the function to be optimized and/or the constraints are nonlinear.)

In order to express the above equations in matrix notation, we require the following definition:

DEFINITION **6.1.** A matrix $\mathbf{P}$ is said to be *greater than* $\mathbf{Q}$, written $\mathbf{P} > \mathbf{Q}$, when $\mathbf{P}$ and $\mathbf{Q}$ have the same numbers of rows and columns, and each element of $\mathbf{P}$ is greater than the corresponding element of $\mathbf{Q}$. Similar definitions hold for $\geq$, $<$, and $\leq$. If $\mathbf{P} > \mathbf{0}$, we say that $\mathbf{P}$ is *positive*. If $\mathbf{P} \geq \mathbf{0}$, we say that $\mathbf{P}$ is *non-negative*.

If we introduce

$$\mathbf{A} = \begin{bmatrix} 2 & 1 \\ 1 & 1 \\ 1 & 3 \end{bmatrix}, \qquad \mathbf{b} = \begin{bmatrix} 70 \\ 40 \\ 90 \end{bmatrix}, \qquad \mathbf{c} = \begin{bmatrix} 40 \\ 60 \end{bmatrix}, \qquad \mathbf{x} = \begin{bmatrix} x_1 \\ x_2 \end{bmatrix}, \tag{6.4}$$

then equations (6.1), (6.2) can be written

$$\mathbf{Ax} \leq \mathbf{b}, \qquad \mathbf{x} \geq \mathbf{0}, \tag{6.5}$$

and the problem is to *maximize*

$$M = \mathbf{c}^T\mathbf{x}. \tag{6.6}$$

(Strictly speaking, $\mathbf{c}^T\mathbf{x}$ is a 1×1 matrix, but we adopt the convention in this chapter that $\mathbf{c}^T\mathbf{x}$ can also be used to denote the element of the matrix.)

The same form of equations will hold if we have m different machines producing n products. Then $\mathbf{A} = [a_{ij}]$ is an $m \times n$ matrix, and a_{ij} represents the number of hours on machine i required to produce one unit of product j. The total hours available will be an $m \times 1$ column matrix, and the profit matrix $\mathbf{c}$ and the matrix $\mathbf{x}$ representing the numbers of units produced will be $n \times 1$ column matrices.

Ex. 6.1. A balanced diet must contain certain minimum quantities of nutrients, such as vitamins, minerals, carbohydrates, and so on. Suppose that we wish to determine, from a given number of foods, the lowest-cost diet that satisfies the minimum requirements for a balanced diet. As a specific example, Table 6.2 gives the numbers of units of nutrients 1, 2 contained in three foods 1, 2, 3, together with the costs of the three foods and the minimum numbers

Table 6.2

Nutrient	Food 1	Food 2	Food 3	Minimum number of units required
1	2	1	1	40
2	1	1	3	60
Cost of food	70	40	90	

of units of the nutrients required in the balanced diet. If we buy amounts y_j ($j = 1, 2, 3$) of the foods, then we must have

$$2y_1 + y_2 + y_3 \geq 40,$$

$$y_1 + y_2 + 3y_3 \geq 60,$$

$$y_1 \geq 0, \qquad y_2 \geq 0, \qquad y_3 \geq 0,$$

and we wish to *minimize*

$$M = 70y_1 + 40y_2 + 90y_3. \tag{6.7}$$

In the general case, let a_{ji} be the number of units of nutrient i in one unit of food j. Suppose that y_j units of food j are to be bought, the cost of one unit of food j being b_j. The diet must supply at least c_i units of nutrient i. In an obvious matrix notation, we must have

$$\mathbf{A}^T\mathbf{y} \geq \mathbf{c}, \qquad \mathbf{y} \geq \mathbf{0}, \tag{6.8}$$

and, subject to these conditions, we wish to minimize

$$M = \mathbf{b}^T\mathbf{y}. \tag{6.9}$$

Note that (6.8), (6.9) are analogous to (6.5), (6.6), but the inequality signs are in opposite senses. Also, we minimize (6.9), compared with maximizing (6.6).

(Note that in a practical problem we should take other factors into account. Thus we should provide variety in the diet, and ensure that it is palatable, and so on. Some of these factors can be built into the above formulation of the linear programming method of approach, but the size and complexity of realistic models means that it is essential to use a digital computer to solve the resulting equations.)

6.2 The Simplex Method

We introduce the simplex method by solving the specific problem formulated in Equations (6.1)–(6.3) in Section 6.1. The first step is to introduce *slack* variables x_3, x_4, x_5 in order to convert the inequalities (6.1a–c) into equalities:

$$\left.\begin{aligned} 2x_1 + x_2 + x_3 &= 70 \\ x_1 + x_2 + x_4 &= 40 \\ x_1 + 3x_2 + x_5 &= 90 \end{aligned}\right\}. \tag{6.10}$$

Because of the signs of the inequalities, the slack variables must be positive so that (6.2) is replaced by

$$x_j \geq 0, \qquad j = 1, 2, \ldots, 5. \tag{6.11}$$

The problem is to find x_j, $j = 1, \ldots, 5$, that also maximize

$$M = 40x_1 + 60x_2. \tag{6.12}$$

Equations (6.10) constitute a system of three equations in five unknowns, with rank 3, so that if the values of two of the variables are assigned arbitrarily, then, in general, we can solve the system for the remaining variables. A particularly simple way of assigning values to two of the variables is simply to set these equal to zero. The resulting solution is called a *basic solution*, and the variables other than those that are set equal to zero are known as *basic variables*. Thus if we set $x_1 = x_2 = 0$ in (6.10) we obtain the basic solution

$$x_3 = 70, \qquad x_4 = 40, \qquad x_5 = 90, \tag{6.13}$$

in terms of the basic variables x_3, x_4, x_5. It is convenient to introduce the following terminology:

Any solution of (6.10) that also satisfies (6.11) is called a *feasible solution.*

A feasible solution that also maximizes (6.12) is called an *optimal feasible solution.*

The fundamental existence theorem (which we prove later) states that *whenever there exists an optimal feasible solution, there exists one which is also basic.* This provides the motivation for the *simplex method*, which we now describe.

We start with the basic solution (6.13) which is also clearly a feasible solution. The nonbasic variables x_1, x_2 are both zero. The value of M corresponding to this basic solution is $M = 0$. We can make either x_1 or x_2 assume a positive value. We choose x_2 for this purpose since $M = 40x_1 + 60x_2$ so that increasing x_2 by one unit increases M by 60, but increasing x_1 by one unit increases M by only 40 units. We therefore increase x_2, *keeping x_1 equal to* 0. This change in the value of x_2 increases M, but it forces us to reduce x_3, x_4, x_5 in order to preserve the equalities in (6.10). Since we are keeping $x_1 = 0$, these equations give

$$\left.\begin{aligned} x_3 &= 70 - x_2 \\ x_4 &= 40 - x_2 \\ x_5 &= 90 - 3x_2 \end{aligned}\right\}. \tag{6.14}$$

Since x_3, x_4, x_5 must be positive, we cannot increase x_2 indefinitely. In fact, the first equation means that x_2 cannot be greater than 70, the second implies $x_2 \leq 40$, and the third $x_2 \leq 30$. We must clearly take the *smallest* of these numbers as the maximum permissible value of x_2. We now have a new basic feasible solution, using (6.14):

$$x_1 = 0, \qquad x_2 = 30, \qquad x_3 = 40, \qquad x_4 = 10, \qquad x_5 = 0, \tag{6.15}$$

and the new basic variables are x_2, x_3, x_4. The value of M is now

$$M = 40x_1 + 60x_2 = 1800, \tag{6.16}$$

which is greater than the previous value of zero.

The next step is to argue that the reason why we were able to write down (6.14) so easily was that only one of the basic variables x_3, x_4, x_5 occurred in each of Equations (6.10). We therefore arrange that each of our new basic variables x_2, x_3, x_4 occurs in only one equation. By inspection of (6.10) it is seen that this can be done by using the third equation in (6.10) to eliminate x_2 from the first and second. This gives

$$\begin{aligned} \tfrac{5}{3}x_1 \qquad + x_3 \qquad\quad - \tfrac{1}{3}x_5 &= 40 \\ \tfrac{2}{3}x_1 \qquad\qquad\quad + x_4 - \tfrac{1}{3}x_5 &= 10 \\ \tfrac{1}{3}x_1 + x_2 \qquad\qquad\quad + \tfrac{1}{3}x_5 &= 30. \end{aligned} \tag{6.17}$$

We also express M in terms of the *nonbasic* variables x_1, x_5. On eliminating x_2 between (6.12) and the third equation in (6.10), we see that

$$M = 1800 + 20x_1 - 20x_5. \tag{6.18}$$

We are still working with the basic feasible solution (6.15) with $x_1 = x_5 = 0$ so that M is still 1800 as it should be, but the advantage of the new form (6.18) over the old form (6.16) is that it shows us what happens if we increase x_1 or x_5. By inspection of (6.18) it is clear that (following a procedure similar to that used previously when we varied x_2) we must now vary x_1, *keeping x_5 equal to* *zero*. Equations (6.17) give [compare (6.14)]

$$\begin{aligned} x_3 &= 40 - \tfrac{5}{3}x_1 \\ x_4 &= 10 - \tfrac{2}{3}x_1 \\ x_2 &= 30 - \tfrac{1}{3}x_1. \end{aligned} \tag{6.19}$$

Since x_3, x_4, x_2 cannot be negative these imply that x_1 cannot be greater than 24, 15, 90, respectively, and we must choose 15 as the maximum permissible value of x_1. This leads to the new basic feasible solution

$$x_1 = 15, \qquad x_2 = 25, \qquad x_3 = 15, \qquad x_4 = 0, \qquad x_5 = 0. \tag{6.20}$$

The new basic variables are x_1, x_2, x_3 and, using the same line of reasoning as before, we arrange that each of these appears in only one equation. This is done by eliminating x_1 from the first and third equations in (6.17) by means of the second equation:

$$\begin{aligned} x_3 - 2.5x_4 + 0.5x_5 &= 15 \\ x_1 \qquad + 1.5x_4 - 0.5x_5 &= 15 \\ x_2 \quad - 0.5x_4 + 0.5x_5 &= 25. \end{aligned} \tag{6.21}$$

On eliminating the new basic variable x_1 between (6.18) and the second equation in (6.21) so as to express M in terms of the nonbasic variables, we see that

$$M = 2100 - 30x_4 - 10x_5. \tag{6.22}$$

The only way we can alter x_4 and x_5 is to make them positive, but this would decrease M. Hence, no further improvement is possible. We have obtained the required optimal feasible solution (6.20). From (6.22), the corresponding value of M is 2100. In the original context of the problem in Section 6.1, we should manufacture 15 items of product 1, and 25 of product 2, for a total profit of 2100 units.

It is important to interpret the above procedure in terms of row operations on matrices. We begin by writing (6.10), (6.12) in the form of an array:

$$\begin{array}{c} M \\ 0 \\ 0 \\ 0 \\ \\ 1 \end{array} \quad \begin{array}{cccccc} x_1 & x_2 & x_3 & x_4 & x_5 & b \end{array} \\ \left[\begin{array}{cccccc} 2 & 1 & 1 & 0 & 0 & 70 \\ 1 & 1 & 0 & 1 & 0 & 40 \\ 1 & 3 & 0 & 0 & 1 & 90 \\ \cdots & \cdots & \cdots & \cdots & \cdots & \cdots \\ -40 & -60 & 0 & 0 & 0 & 0 \end{array}\right], \tag{6.23}$$

where the last line must be interpreted as

$$M - 40x_1 - 60x_2 = 0, \tag{6.24}$$

and we will not carry along the column for M, since it is not changed in subsequent steps.

We started our analysis of (6.10)–(6.12) by deciding to change x_2, because a unit change in x_2 would produce a greater change in M than a unit change in

x_1 [see (6.12)]. In terms of the matrix (6.23) we choose the column with the *most negative* number in the last row. The step following (6.14) consists of dividing the first three elements in the last column of (6.23) by the corresponding elements in the second column, and choosing the row corresponding to the *smallest* of these three positive numbers. This is the third row. The next step in the previous analysis was to eliminate x_2 from the first and second equations in (6.10), and from (6.12). In matrix terms, we pivot on the (3, 2) element in (6.23) and reduce the first, second, and fourth elements in the second column to zero, as in the Gauss-Jordan procedure. This gives

$$\begin{bmatrix} \frac{5}{3} & 0 & 1 & 0 & -\frac{1}{3} & 40 \\ \frac{2}{3} & 0 & 0 & 1 & -\frac{1}{3} & 10 \\ \frac{1}{3} & 1 & 0 & 0 & \frac{1}{3} & 30 \\ \cdots & \cdots & \cdots & \cdots & \cdots & \cdots \\ -20 & 0 & 0 & 0 & 20 & 1800 \end{bmatrix} \tag{6.25}$$

The first three rows, written out longhand as separate equations, are (6.17). The last row of (6.25) must be interpreted as [compare (6.24)]

$$M - 20x_1 + 20x_5 = 1800,$$

which is (6.18).

In exactly the same way, we now find the column that contains the most negative number in the last row of (6.25), in this case the first. We next divide each of the first three elements in the last column of (6.25) by the corresponding element in the first column, and choose the smallest positive number among the results. This is the second. [Compare (6.19) and the statement following.] This leads us to pivot on the (2, 1) element in (6.25), and the standard Gauss-Jordan procedure then yields

$$\begin{bmatrix} 0 & 0 & 1 & -2.5 & 0.5 & 15 \\ 1 & 0 & 0 & 1.5 & -0.5 & 15 \\ 0 & 1 & 0 & -0.5 & 0.5 & 25 \\ \cdots & \cdots & \cdots & \cdots & \cdots & \cdots \\ 0 & 0 & 0 & 30 & 10 & 2100 \end{bmatrix}. \tag{6.26}$$

The first three rows give (6.21), and the last row must be interpreted as

$$M + 30x_4 + 10x_5 = 2100,$$

which is (6.22). The elements in the last row of (6.26) are all positive, and this indicates that M cannot be increased further. We have obtained the same solution as before, by row operations on matrices.

To lead up to a summary of the situation in general, we note first of all that in this section the first step was to convert the inequalities (6.1) into the equalities (6.10). In this discussion we write the original problem (6.1)–(6.3) as

$$\begin{aligned} &\text{maximize} && M = \mathbf{c}_1^T \mathbf{x}_1 \\ &\text{subject to} && \mathbf{A}_1 \mathbf{x}_1 \le \mathbf{b}_1, \qquad \mathbf{x}_1 \ge \mathbf{0}. \end{aligned} \tag{6.27}$$

The modified form of the problem, namely (6.10)–(6.12), is

$$\begin{aligned} &\text{maximize} && M = \mathbf{c}_2^T\mathbf{x}_2 \\ &\text{subject to} && \mathbf{A}_2\mathbf{x}_2 = \mathbf{b}_2, \qquad \mathbf{x}_2 \geq \mathbf{0}. \end{aligned} \tag{6.28}$$

Suppose that in the general case we start with a problem of the form (6.27) where $\mathbf{A}_1$ is $m \times n$, $\mathbf{x}_1$ and $\mathbf{c}_1$ are $n \times 1$, $\mathbf{b}_1$ is $m \times 1$. The simplex method then proceeds as follows:

(a) Introduce slack variables $x_{n+1}, \ldots, x_q$, say, to convert $\mathbf{A}_1\mathbf{x}_1 \leq \mathbf{b}_1$ into a set of linear equations $\mathbf{A}_2\mathbf{x}_2 = \mathbf{b}_2$, where $\mathbf{A}_2$ is now $m \times q$, $\mathbf{x}_2$ is $q \times 1$, and $\mathbf{b}_1 = \mathbf{b}_2$. Add zeros to $\mathbf{c}_1$ to form a $q \times 1$ column vector $\mathbf{c}_2^T = [\mathbf{c}_1^T, \mathbf{0}]$. Arrange $\mathbf{A}_2$, $\mathbf{b}_2$, $\mathbf{c}_2$ in the following array [compare (6.4), (6.5), (6.23)]:

$$\begin{bmatrix} \mathbf{A}_2 & \mathbf{b}_2 \\ -\mathbf{c}_2^T & 0 \end{bmatrix}.$$

(b) Find a basic feasible solution of the equations $\mathbf{A}_2\mathbf{x}_2 = \mathbf{b}_2$. (In the above example it was possible to do this by inspection. A method for finding feasible solutions in more difficult cases will be discussed later, see the discussion of (6.57) in Section 6.5. Note the comment following (6.59).)

(c) Locate the most negative number in the last row. This identifies the variable to be introduced into the basis. (Any negative number may in fact be used, and the negative number which is largest in size is not necessarily the best choice, although it is convenient.)

(d) Divide each element in the column $\mathbf{b}_2$ on the right of the array by the corresponding element in the column corresponding to the variable chosen in (c), if this divisor is *positive*. (If this divisor is negative, then no limitation is imposed on the size of the variable by the corresponding equation.) Locate the divisor that yields the *smallest* quotient.

(e) Pivot, using the Gauss-Jordan procedure, using the pivot located in (d).

(f) Repeat the pivoting, steps (c)–(e), until there are no negative elements in the last row.

This summarizes the situation in the general case.

In this chapter we will be concerned with the form (6.28) in Sections 6.3–6.6, and in these sections we replace $\mathbf{A}_2$, $\mathbf{x}_2$, $\mathbf{b}_2$ by $\mathbf{A}$, $\mathbf{b}$, $\mathbf{c}$. In Section 6.7 we will be concerned with the form (6.27), and in that section $\mathbf{A}$, $\mathbf{b}$, $\mathbf{c}$ will stand for $\mathbf{A}_1$, $\mathbf{b}_1$, $\mathbf{c}_1$. This slight ambiguity in notation should cause no confusion.

6.3 The Theory of the Simplex Method

In the last section we tried to explain the reasoning behind the simplex method from an elementary point of view. We now examine the method from a theoretical point of view in order to determine the conditions under which it will work. This will automatically give us some understanding of exceptional cases.

We shall consider the linear programming problem in the form:

$$\text{maximize} \qquad M = u + \mathbf{c}^T\mathbf{x}, \tag{6.29}$$

$$\text{subject to} \qquad \mathbf{A}\mathbf{x} = \mathbf{b}, \qquad \mathbf{x} \geq \mathbf{0}. \tag{6.30}$$

where $\mathbf{A}$ is $m \times q$. It is convenient to insert the constant u since such constants appear after the first stage in the simplex procedure [see (6.18), (6.22)].

THEOREM **6.1.** *Suppose that elementary row operations are performed on the matrix*

$$\begin{bmatrix} \mathbf{A} & \mathbf{b} \\ -\mathbf{c}^T & u \end{bmatrix} \tag{6.31}$$

in any way, except that the only operation that is allowed on the last row is to add to it sums of multiples of the other rows. Denote the result by

$$\begin{bmatrix} \mathbf{A}' & \mathbf{b}' \\ -(\mathbf{c}')^T & u' \end{bmatrix}.$$

Then the following linear programming problem is completely equivalent to (6.29), (6.30)*:*

$$\text{maximize} \qquad M' = u' + (\mathbf{c}')^T\mathbf{x}, \tag{6.32}$$

$$\text{subject to} \qquad \mathbf{A}'\mathbf{x} = \mathbf{b}', \qquad \mathbf{x} \geq \mathbf{0}. \tag{6.33}$$

Proof: The matrix $[\mathbf{A}', \mathbf{b}']$ is obtained by performing elementary row operations on $[\mathbf{A}, \mathbf{b}]$. Hence, a nonsingular matrix $\mathbf{E}$ exists such that

$$\mathbf{E}[\mathbf{A}, \mathbf{b}] = [\mathbf{A}', \mathbf{b}']$$

which gives

$$\mathbf{E}\mathbf{A} = \mathbf{A}', \qquad \mathbf{E}\mathbf{b} = \mathbf{b}'. \tag{6.34}$$

Also, $[-(\mathbf{c}')^T, u']$ is obtained by adding sums of multiples of $[\mathbf{A}, \mathbf{b}]$ to $[-\mathbf{c}^T, u]$, i.e., a column vector $\mathbf{f}$ exists such that

$$[-(\mathbf{c}')^T, u'] = [-\mathbf{c}^T, u] + \mathbf{f}^T[\mathbf{A}, \mathbf{b}],$$

or

$$(\mathbf{c}')^T = \mathbf{c}^T - \mathbf{f}^T\mathbf{A}, \qquad u' = u + \mathbf{f}^T\mathbf{b}.$$

It is convenient to make the dependence of M and M' on $\mathbf{x}$ explicit by writing $M(\mathbf{x})$ and $M'(\mathbf{x})$. We have the important result that, for any $\mathbf{x}$,

$$\begin{aligned} M'(\mathbf{x}) &= u' + (\mathbf{c}')^T\mathbf{x} = u + \mathbf{f}^T\mathbf{b} + (\mathbf{c}^T - \mathbf{f}^T\mathbf{A})\mathbf{x} \\ &= u + \mathbf{c}^T\mathbf{x} + \mathbf{f}^T(\mathbf{b} - \mathbf{A}\mathbf{x}) = u + \mathbf{c}^T\mathbf{x} = M(\mathbf{x}). \end{aligned} \tag{6.35}$$

Suppose that the vector $\mathbf{x}_0$ maximizes (6.29) subject to (6.30), and $\mathbf{x}_0'$ maximizes (6.32) subject to (6.33). From (6.35), $M'(\mathbf{x}_0) = M(\mathbf{x}_0)$, and by definition of $\mathbf{x}_0'$ we have $M'(\mathbf{x}_0') \geq M'(\mathbf{x}_0)$. Hence, $M'(\mathbf{x}_0') \geq M(\mathbf{x}_0)$. The argument can be reversed, and we find $M(\mathbf{x}_0) \geq M'(\mathbf{x}_0')$. This gives $M(\mathbf{x}_0) = M'(\mathbf{x}_0')$. Hence, the maxima are the same. On multiplying $\mathbf{Ax}_0 = \mathbf{b}$ by $\mathbf{E}$ and using (6.34), we see that $\mathbf{A}'\mathbf{x}_0 = \mathbf{b}'$. Hence, $\mathbf{x}_0$ satisfies the subsidiary conditions (6.33). Similarly, we can show that $\mathbf{x}_0'$ satisfies the subsidiary conditions (6.30). This completes the proof that the two linear programming problems are equivalent.

In the simplex method described in Section 6.2, row operations were performed on the 3×5 matrix in the upper left of (6.23). At each stage, three of the columns of the resulting matrix were the unit vectors [see (6.25), (6.26)]. This implies that the corresponding 3×3 matrices in the original matrix $\mathbf{A}$ in (6.23) were nonsingular. In the general theory it is convenient to assume that *every* $m \times m$ submatrix of the augmented matrix $[\mathbf{A}, \mathbf{b}]$ is nonsingular. This may seem to be a sweeping assumption but it makes the theory much simpler. Special devices have to be employed in both the theory and the practical solution of linear programming problems when this assumption is not true. The assumption is valid in most of the problems encountered in practice.

DEFINITION **6.2.** A linear programming problem is said to be *nondegenerate* if *every* $m \times m$ submatrix selected from the $m \times (q + 1)$ augmented matrix $[\mathbf{A}, \mathbf{b}]$ is nonsingular. Otherwise the problem is said to be *degenerate.*

We next make precise the definition of basic variables already introduced in the last section. A solution of the equation $\mathbf{Ax} = \mathbf{b}$ can be obtained by choosing a nonsingular $m \times m$ submatrix, say $\mathbf{K}$, from $\mathbf{A}$, solving the equations $\mathbf{Kz} = \mathbf{b}$, and setting $x_i = 0$ unless i corresponds to one of the columns of $\mathbf{A}$ selected for $\mathbf{K}$, in which case x_i is given the corresponding value in $\mathbf{z}$. Solutions of this type, in which at least $q - m$ elements are zero, are particularly important in linear programming, and they are given a special name.

DEFINITION **6.3.** The variables associated with the columns of the matrix $\mathbf{K}$ defined in the last paragraph are called the *basic* variables. The other variables are called *nonbasic.* A solution in which the nonbasic variables are zero is called a *basic* solution of the equations.

An important property of basic solutions of nondegenerate problems is the following.

> THEOREM **6.2.** *The basic variables in any basic solution of a nondegenerate problem are nonzero.*

Proof: Consider a set of basic variables obtained by choosing an $m \times m$ submatrix, say $\mathbf{K}$, from $\mathbf{A}$. By definition of a nondegenerate problem, $\mathbf{K}$ is nonsingular. The basic variables are obtained by solving the equation $\mathbf{Kz} = \mathbf{b}$. If $\mathbf{a}_i$ is the ith column of $\mathbf{K}$, then $\mathbf{a}_1, \ldots, \mathbf{a}_m$, $\mathbf{b}$ are linearly dependent, since they are $m \times 1$ column vectors, and there are $m + 1$ of them. Hence, constants $\alpha_1, \ldots, \alpha_{m+1}$ exist such that

$$\alpha_1 \mathbf{a}_1 + \ldots + \alpha_m \mathbf{a}_m + \alpha_{m+1} \mathbf{b} = \mathbf{0}.$$

Since every $m \times m$ submatrix selected from $[\mathbf{A}, \mathbf{b}]$ is nonsingular, all the α_1 are nonzero. Hence, a solution of $\mathbf{Kz} = \mathbf{b}$ is given by

$$z_i = -\frac{\alpha_i}{\alpha_{m+1}} \neq 0.$$

The vector obtained by taking these as the basic variables and setting all other variables equal to zero is a basic solution in which all the basic variables are nonzero.

We now remind the reader of the definition of two terms introduced in the last section:

DEFINITION 6.4. Any solution of $\mathbf{Ax} = \mathbf{b}$ which is nonnegative, i.e., $\mathbf{x} \geq \mathbf{0}$, is called a *feasible* solution.

DEFINITION 6.5. A feasible solution that also maximizes $M = u + \mathbf{c}^T\mathbf{x}$ is called an *optimal feasible solution*.

The reader will remember that in the numerical example in the last section we always worked in terms of basic solutions. The reason for this comes from a theorem that we are just going to prove, namely that if we can find a feasible solution of $\mathbf{Ax} = \mathbf{b}$ with a value M_1 for M, then we can always find a *basic* feasible solution with a value M_2 for M, with $M_2 \geq M_1$. This means that we need only consider basic feasible solutions.

Before proving this result, we illustrate with a numerical example. Suppose that in the problem defined in (6.10)–(6.12) we had found the following feasible solution,

$$x_1 = 20, \quad x_2 = 15, \quad x_3 = 15, \quad x_4 = 5, \quad x_5 = 25, \tag{6.36}$$

for which the corresponding value of M is 1700, from (6.12). We write

$$\mathbf{A} = [\mathbf{a}_1, \mathbf{a}_2, \ldots, \mathbf{a}_n],$$

where $\mathbf{a}_j$ is the jth column of $\mathbf{A}$. The solution (6.36) gives

$$20\mathbf{a}_1 + 15\mathbf{a}_2 + 15\mathbf{a}_3 + 5\mathbf{a}_4 + 25\mathbf{a}_5 = \mathbf{b}. \tag{6.37}$$

Any four columns of $\mathbf{A}$ must be linearly dependent. We choose any four columns of $\mathbf{A}$, and write down the relation between them. (This can be obtained by reducing the corresponding 3×4 matrix to row-echelon form, as discussed in Section 4.2.) As an example, take

$$\mathbf{a}_1 - 2\mathbf{a}_3 - \mathbf{a}_4 - \mathbf{a}_5 = \mathbf{0}.$$

On subtracting λ times this equation from (6.37), we obtain

$$(20 - \lambda)\mathbf{a}_1 + 15\mathbf{a}_2 + (15 + 2\lambda)\mathbf{a}_3 + (5 + \lambda)\mathbf{a}_4 + (25 + \lambda)\mathbf{a}_5 = \mathbf{b}. \quad (6.38)$$

When $\lambda = 0$ we know that we have a feasible solution. Clearly, if we vary λ gradually, making it either positive or negative, we still have a feasible solution as long as λ is not too large. More precisely, λ cannot be made less than -5 or greater than 20, since the coefficients of $\mathbf{a}_4$ and $\mathbf{a}_1$ become negative, respectively. (These coefficients must not be negative because they are going to give the new feasible solution.) If we choose $\lambda = -5$, equation (6.38) gives

$$25\mathbf{a}_1 + 15\mathbf{a}_2 + 5\mathbf{a}_3 + 20\mathbf{a}_5 = \mathbf{b}, \quad (6.39)$$

so that we have found a feasible solution with one less nonzero variable than the solution from which we started. The corresponding value of M is 1900, from (6.12). This is greater than the original value of 1700. [We could have obtained another feasible solution with one less variable by choosing $\lambda = -20$ in (6.38). This gives $x_1 = 0$, $x_2 = 15$, so that $M = 900$ which is less than 1700, so we disregard this possibility.]

The feasible solution in (6.39) contains four nonzero variables. We can reduce this to three by repeating the procedure. We must now write down an equation relating $\mathbf{a}_1$, $\mathbf{a}_2$, $\mathbf{a}_3$, $\mathbf{a}_5$ and this is easily found to be (by reducing the matrix whose columns are these vectors to row-echelon form, if necessary)

$$\mathbf{a}_1 - \mathbf{a}_2 - \mathbf{a}_3 + 2\mathbf{a}_5 = \mathbf{0}.$$

We can obtain a feasible solution involving only three variables by either adding five times this equation to (6.39), or subtracting ten times the equation from (6.39). This latter possibility increases M. In fact, we find the basic feasible solution

$$x_1 = 15, \qquad x_2 = 25, \qquad x_3 = 15, \qquad x_4 = 0, \qquad x_5 = 0.$$

The value of M is 2100, which is greater than 1900.

This example should clarify the proof of the following theorem:

THEOREM 6.3. *If the linear programming problem specified by equations (6.29), (6.30) is nondegenerate and has a feasible solution with a value of say M_1 for M, then either the value of M can be made as large as desired (so that no maximum value of M exists) or there exists a basic feasible solution, with a value M_2 for M such that $M_2 \geq M_1$.*

Proof: Let $\mathbf{A} = [\mathbf{a}_1, \mathbf{a}_2, \ldots, \mathbf{a}_q]$ where the $\mathbf{a}_j$ are the columns of $\mathbf{A}$. Let $\mathbf{x}$ denote a feasible solution with more than m nonzero components. Without loss of generality we can assume that $x_1, x_2, \ldots, x_{m+1}$ are nonzero. We have

$$x_1\mathbf{a}_1 + x_2\mathbf{a}_2 + \ldots + x_q\mathbf{a}_q = \mathbf{b}. \quad (6.40)$$

Assume that the linear dependence of the first $m + 1$ columns of $\mathbf{A}$ is given explicitly by

$$\alpha_1\mathbf{a}_1 + \alpha_2\mathbf{a}_2 + \ldots + \alpha_m\mathbf{a}_m + \alpha_{m+1}\mathbf{a}_{m+1} = \mathbf{0}. \tag{6.41}$$

On subtracting λ times this equation from (6.40), we obtain

$$(x_1 - \lambda\alpha_1)\mathbf{a}_1 + \ldots + (x_{m+1} - \lambda\alpha_{m+1})\mathbf{a}_{m+1} + x_{m+2}\mathbf{a}_{m+2} + \ldots + x_q\mathbf{a}_q = \mathbf{b}. \tag{6.42}$$

Since we have a feasible solution when $\lambda = 0$, the coefficients of $\mathbf{a}_j$ in this equation give a new feasible solution provided that the magnitude of λ is not too large. The old value of M is given by

$$M_1 = c_1x_1 + \ldots + c_qx_q.$$

The value of M corresponding to the new feasible solution is

$$M_2 = c_1(x_1 - \lambda\alpha_1) + \ldots + c_{m+1}(x_{m+1} - \lambda\alpha_{m+1}) + c_{m+2}x_{m+2} + \ldots + c_qx_q.$$

Hence,

$$M_2 - M_1 = -\lambda(c_1\alpha_1 + \ldots + c_{m+1}\alpha_{m+1}) = -\lambda C, \tag{6.43}$$

say. We wish to increase M, i.e., we wish to ensure that the term on the right of this equation is greater than or equal to zero. There are various possibilities, depending on the value of C:

(a) $C = 0$. In this case, $M_1 = M_2$ and (6.43) shows that we can vary λ at will without changing the magnitude of M. By varying λ in (6.42) away from zero we can obtain at least one, and perhaps two values of λ for which one of the coefficients of $\mathbf{a}_1, \ldots, \mathbf{a}_{m+1}$ will vanish, and all the remaining nonzero coefficients of the $\mathbf{a}_j$ will remain positive. (Remember that $x_1, \ldots, x_{m+1}$ are all greater than zero. If all the α_j have the same sign, there is only one value of λ. If there are both positive and negative α_j, then there are two values of λ.) In this way, we obtain a feasible solution with one less nonzero variable than the original solution.

(b) $C < 0$. Then (6.43) shows that we must vary λ in (6.42) in the positive direction. If $\lambda > 0$, then we have the strict inequality $M_2 > M_1$. There are now two possibilities:

(i) If $\alpha_1, \ldots, \alpha_{m+1}$ are all less than or equal to zero then λ can be made as large as we please, the feasible solution given by (6.42) will remain feasible, and M can be increased without limit.

(ii) If at least one of the α_j, $j = 1, \ldots, m + 1$ is positive, then as λ increases from zero, at least one of the bracketed terms in (6.42) will decrease and finally become zero. Corresponding to the first bracketed term that becomes zero, we obtain a feasible solution with one less nonzero variable than the original set.

(c) $C > 0$. This case is not distinct from (b) since the sign of C can be changed at will merely by changing the signs of the α_j throughout the homogeneous equation (6.41).

This concludes the theorem and the section.

6.4 The Simplex Method (continued)

We now examine the way in which Theorems 6.1–6.3 can be utilized when solving a nondegenerate linear programming problem by the simplex method. The simplex method proceeds in stages. We start with the problem:

$$\text{maximize} \qquad M = \mathbf{c}^T\mathbf{x}$$

$$\text{subject to} \qquad \mathbf{Ax} = \mathbf{b}, \qquad \mathbf{x} \geq \mathbf{0}.$$

Elementary row operations (in the form of the Gauss-Jordan procedure) are performed, as in Theorem 6.1, on

$$\begin{bmatrix} \mathbf{A} & \mathbf{b} \\ -\mathbf{c}^T & 0 \end{bmatrix}.$$

At the rth stage, this is replaced by a matrix

$$\begin{bmatrix} \mathbf{A}_r & \mathbf{b}_r \\ -\mathbf{c}_r^T & u_r \end{bmatrix}. \tag{6.44}$$

From Theorem 6.3 we know that it is sufficient to confine our attention to basic feasible solutions. From Theorem 6.2, since the problem is nondegenerate, the basic variables will be nonzero so that there is no difficulty in identifying the basic variables. Suppose that, at the rth stage, a basic feasible solution has been found and that, by renumbering the variables if necessary (which can be done without loss of generality), we have arranged that the basic variables are $x_1, x_2, \ldots, x_m$. We also suppose that, as in the concrete example in Section 6.2, the columns in (6.44) corresponding to the basic variables are unit vectors. Explicitly, (6.44) will have the form

$$\begin{bmatrix} 1 & 0 & \ldots & 0 & a_{1,m+1} & \ldots & a_{1q} & b_1 \\ 0 & 1 & \ldots & 0 & a_{2,m+1} & \ldots & a_{2q} & b_2 \\ & & & & \ldots & & & \\ 0 & 0 & \ldots & 1 & a_{m,m+1} & \ldots & a_{mq} & b_m \\ 0 & 0 & \ldots & 0 & -c_{m+1} & \ldots & -c_q & u_r \end{bmatrix}. \tag{6.45}$$

Also,

$$M = u_r + c_{m+1}x_{m+1} + \ldots + c_q x_q. \tag{6.46}$$

This expression for M is valid whatever the values of $x_1, \ldots, x_q$. For the basic solution available at this stage we have $x_{m+1} = \ldots = x_q = 0$, so that the estimate of M at this stage is $M = u_r$. We wish to find out whether we can modify the values of $x_{m+1}, \ldots, x_q$ so as to increase M. The only way in which we are allowed to change these variables is to make their values positive. If all the c_j, $j = m + 1, \ldots, q$ are negative, then from (6.46) it is clear that any increase in the values of $x_{m+1}, \ldots, x_q$ can only decrease M. In this case, it is not possible to improve the basic feasible solution that we are working with at this stage. If at least one c_j is positive, say c_s, we can increase our value of M by increasing x_s. From Theorem 6.3 we know that we can restrict our attention to basic feasible solutions. We shall maintain all the variables $x_{m+1}, \ldots, x_q$ at the value zero, except x_s, and try to find a basic feasible solution in which $x_s \neq 0$ and one of $x_1, \ldots, x_m$ is zero. The equations $\mathbf{A}_r\mathbf{x}_r = \mathbf{b}_r$ are then simply

$$x_i + a_{is}x_s = b_i, \qquad i = 1, \ldots, m,$$

or

$$x_i = b_i - a_{is}x_s, \qquad i = 1, \ldots, m. \tag{6.47}$$

The b_i are known to be positive since $x_i = b_i$ ($i = 1$ to m), $x_i = 0$ ($i = m + 1$ to n) is assumed to be a feasible solution. If x_s is increased from zero, there are two possibilities:

(a) If $a_{is} \leq 0$ then from (6.47) it is clear that x_i is always positive for $i = 1, \ldots, m$. This means that

$$(x_1, \ldots, x_m, 0, \ldots, 0, x_s, 0, \ldots, 0), \tag{6.48}$$

is a feasible solution for all $x_s > 0$.

(b) If $a_{is} > 0$ then from (6.47), if $x_s > b_i/a_{is}$, the value of x_i is negative, which is not permissible. The value of x_s must lie between 0 and b_i/a_{is} for each i. In order to maximize M, we wish to choose x_s as large as possible, so that the optimum value of x_s is given by the *smallest* of the ratios

$$\frac{b_i}{a_{is}}, \qquad (i = 1, \ldots, m; \quad a_{is} > 0). \tag{6.49}$$

We are now in a position to state and prove the following theorem:

THEOREM 6.4. *Consider a nondegenerate linear programming problem that has been transformed into the form* (6.45), (6.46)*:*

(i) *If $c_j < 0$ for all $j = m + 1, \ldots, q$, then the basic feasible solution $(x_1, \ldots, x_m, 0, \ldots, 0)$ gives a maximum value of M that cannot be improved by making any of the $x_{m+1}, \ldots, x_q$ nonzero.*

(ii) *If one of the c_j is greater than zero, say c_s, then there are two possibilities*

(a) *If $a_{is} \leq 0$ for all $i = 1, \ldots, m$, then feasible solutions exist such that M can be made as large as desired.*

(b) *If $a_{is} > 0$ for at least one i, a new basic solution can be found such that the value of M is increased.*

Proof: Part (i) follows since M is of the form (6.46) and if $c_j < 0$ for all $j = m + 1, \ldots, q$, then any increase in $x_{m+1}, \ldots, x_q$ can only reduce M. In order to prove (ii) (a), we note that the value of M from (6.46) corresponding to the solution (6.48) is $M = u_r + c_sx_s$. Since $c_s > 0$ and x_s can be made as large as desired, this means that M can be made as large as desired. To prove (ii) (b) we note first of all that the b_i are all greater than zero since we are starting from a nondegenerate basic solution. Hence if $a_{is} > 0$ for at least one i, then a positive x_s, defined by the smallest of the ratios (6.49), exists. If this x_s is defined by (6.49) with $i = r$, then from (6.47) we have that the corresponding x_r is zero, i.e.,

$$(x_1, \ldots, x_{r-1}, 0, x_{r+1}, \ldots, x_m, 0, \ldots, 0, x_s, 0, \ldots, 0)$$

is a basic solution. The corresponding value of M is given by

$$M = u_r + c_s x_s$$

which is greater than the old value of M, namely u_r, since both c_s and x_s are greater than zero. This completes the proof.

To summarize, the practical rule for implementing part (ii) (b) of the above theorem (which is the method developed in the concrete example in Section 6.2) is the following:

(a) Choose the most negative element $-c_{m+1}, \ldots, -c_n$ in the last row of the array (6.45). (We could choose any negative element but it is natural to pick the most negative one since unit change in the corresponding variable will cause the largest resulting change in M. The choice of the most negative element is not necessarily the best.)

(b) Calculate the ratios b_i/a_{is} for the positive a_{is}. Choose the smallest of these ratios.

(c) Pivot on the element a_{is} corresponding to the minimum ratio in (b). (This corresponds to an application of Theorem 6.1.)

In order to avoid making Theorem 6.4 too complicated, we have ignored the case $c_j = 0$ and we have said nothing about the uniqueness of the maximum value attained in Theorem 6.4(i). To complete Theorem 6.4, we state the following.

THEOREM **6.5.** *Under the assumptions in Theorem* 6.4*:*

(i) *If, as in Theorem* 6.4(i), $c_j < 0$ *for all* $j = m + 1, \ldots, q$, *then the maximum value of* M *and the corresponding basic feasible solution are unique.*

(ii) *If* $c_j \leq 0$ *where* $c_j = 0$ *for at least one value of* j *corresponding to a nonbasic variable, say* s, *then* M *attains its maximum value for at least two different* $\mathbf{x}$. *If two such optimal solutions are denoted by* $\mathbf{x}^{(1)}$ *and* $\mathbf{x}^{(2)}$, *then*

$$\mathbf{x} = \alpha\mathbf{x}^{(1)} + (1 - \alpha)\mathbf{x}^{(2)}, \qquad 0 \leq \alpha \leq 1,$$

is also an optimal solution.

(iii) *If procedure* (ii) (b) *in Theorem* 6.4 *is repeated, then either the situation in Theorem* 6.4(ii) (a) *is reached, in which case M can be made as large as desired, or a situation is reached, after a finite number of steps, in which* $c_j \leq 0$ *for all* j *and M is finite.*

Proof: To prove (i) we note that the expression (6.46) for M is valid whatever the values of $x_1, \ldots, x_q$. Hence, if $c_j < 0$, $j = m + 1, \ldots, q$, any basic feasible solution in which $x_{m+1}, \ldots, x_q$ are nonzero will give a value of M less than the basic feasible solution in which $x_1, \ldots, x_m$ are all nonzero. But this latter solution is unique since it is obtained by solving a definite nonsingular set of m equations in m unknowns. Hence, the value of M is an absolute maximum and it is given by one single basic feasible solution. To prove (ii) we note that the above argument breaks down if $c_j \leq 0$ and we have $c_j = 0$ for some j, say $j = s$. The position then is that we alter the value of the corresponding variable x_s without altering M. The value of M is still an absolute maximum since all other basic feasible solutions either decrease M or leave M unaltered. If we denote two of the optimal solutions by $\mathbf{x}^{(1)}$ and $\mathbf{x}^{(2)}$ and set

$$\mathbf{x} = \alpha\mathbf{x}^{(1)} + (1 - \alpha)\mathbf{x}^{(2)}, \tag{6.50}$$

then

$$\mathbf{Ax} = \alpha\mathbf{Ax}^{(1)} + (1 - \alpha)\mathbf{Ax}^{(2)} = \alpha\mathbf{b} + (1 - \alpha)\mathbf{b} = \mathbf{b}.$$

Also, if $0 \leq \alpha \leq 1$, then $\mathbf{x} \geq 0$, and

$$M = \mathbf{c}^T\mathbf{x} = \alpha\mathbf{c}^T\mathbf{x}^{(1)} + (1 - \alpha)\mathbf{c}^T\mathbf{x}^{(2)} = \alpha M_0 + (1 - \alpha)M_0 = M_0,$$

say, where M_0 is the optimum M corresponding to each of $\mathbf{x}^{(1)}$, $\mathbf{x}^{(2)}$. Hence $\mathbf{x}$ is an optimal feasible solution. This completes the proof of (ii). The key to the proof of part (iii) lies in the remark that only a finite number of basic solutions exist, this being given by the number of ways in which m columns can be chosen from the columns of $\mathbf{A}$. A repetition of the procedure in Theorem 6.4(ii) (b) may lead to a situation in which this procedure (ii) (b) has to be carried out again. Since the value of M has been increased, this cannot give rise to a basic solution that has already been found. Only a finite number of basic solutions exist, so that procedure (ii) (b) cannot be repeated indefinitely. After a finite number of steps, the procedure must terminate in one of two ways. Either (ii) (a) in Theorem 6.4 holds, or $c_j \leq 0$ for all j. In this latter case, since M has been changed by finite amounts a finite number of times, the resulting value of M must be finite. This concludes the proof.

6.5 Graphical Representations

So far the development has been purely algebraic. The theory and enumeration of cases given in the last two sections arose naturally from our discussion of the numerical procedure given in Section 6.2, but the detailed nature of the analysis may have obscured the simplicity of the overall picture. We now consider the problem from a geometrical point of view. This will clarify the various possibilities that can occur, namely, a problem can have a unique solution, no solution, or an infinite number of solutions, exactly as for a system of simultaneous linear equations.

Consider the concrete example specified by equations (6.1)–(6.3), namely,

$$\text{maximize} \qquad M = 40x_1 + 60x_2, \tag{6.51}$$

$$\text{subject to} \qquad x_1 \geq 0, \qquad x_2 \geq 0,$$

and

$$2x_1 + x_2 \leq 70, \qquad x_1 + x_2 \leq 40, \qquad x_1 + 3x_2 \leq 90. \tag{6.52}$$

To deal with the first inequality, we note that $2x_1 + x_2 = 70$ is the equation of a straight line (see Figure 6.1). The inequality $2x_1 + x_2 \leq 70$ means that the

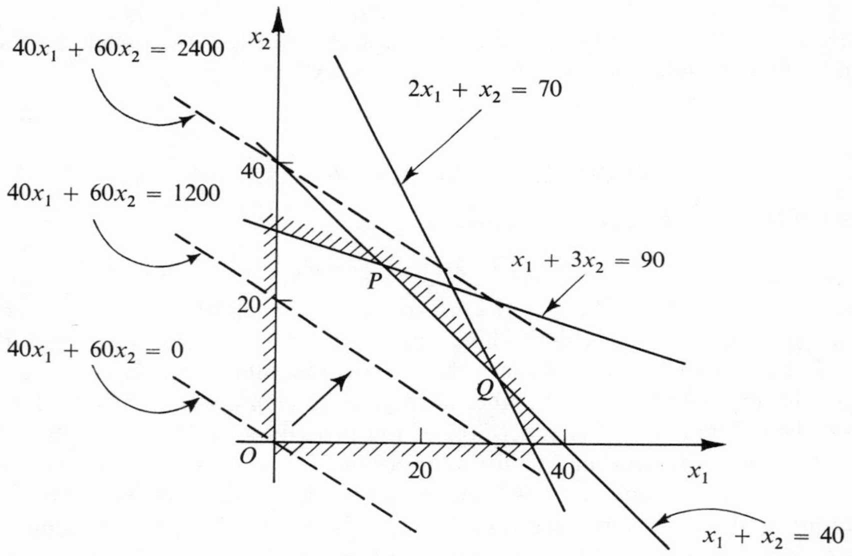

Figure 6.1 The straightforward case.

point (x_1, x_2) must lie *below* the straight line. Similarly, the other two inequalities in (6.52) define half-planes in which the permissible points (x_1, x_2) must lie. The inequalities $x_1 \geq 0$, $x_2 \geq 0$ mean that (x_1, x_2) must lie in the first quadrant. The net result is that the inequalities confine the point (x_1, x_2) to a polygonal region whose boundary is shaded in Figure 6.1. For any given value of M, the equation (6.51), namely $M = 40x_1 + 60x_2$, defines a straight line. The three dashed lines in Figure 6.1 represent this straight line for $M = 0$, 1200, 2400. The value of M corresponding to any point on a given line is a constant, and the lines are parallel. To maximize M we must go as far as possible in a direction perpendicular to these lines in the direction of the arrow in Figure 6.1, without leaving the admissible region. In this way, we reach the point P which is the intersection of

$$x_1 + 3x_2 = 90, \qquad x_1 + x_2 = 40,$$

i.e., $x_1 = 15$, $x_2 = 25$, which is the result obtained by the simplex method in Section 6.2. The corresponding value of M is, of course, 2100, as before. From the geometrical picture it is obvious that two of the equations in (6.52) are now equalities and one is a strict inequality. This means that if slack variables are introduced, two of these will be zero, one nonzero. Thus, the solution is a basic feasible solution with three nonzero variables. The importance of basic feasible solutions from a geometrical point of view is that they correspond to corners of the polygonal figure.

We now examine some special cases which are less straightforward than the above example:

(1) *Non-unique optimal solutions*

Suppose that, instead of maximizing M defined in (6.51), we wish to maximize

$$M = 40x_1 + 40x_2.$$

Graphically, it is clear that the corresponding family of lines, for various M, is parallel to the line $x_1 + x_2 = 40$ in Figure 6.1, which is one of the boundaries of the polygonal region. Any point on the line PQ in the figure will give the maximum value of M. The maximum value itself is unique but an infinity of points (x_1, x_2) will give this maximum value.

We now investigate what happens if we solve this problem by the simplex method. The array corresponding to (6.23) is

2	1	1	0	0	70
1	1	0	1	0	40
1	3	0	0	1	90
−40	−40	0	0	0	0.

Since both nonzero numbers in the last row are −40, we can introduce either x_1 or x_2 into the basic solution. If we choose to introduce x_2, then the rule described previously indicates that we should pivot on the element 3 in the third row, second column. In the resulting array, the standard rule indicates that we should pivot on the element in the second row, first column. This gives the array

0	0	1	−2.5	0.5	15	
1	0	0	1.5	−0.5	15	
0	1	0	−0.5	0.5	25	(6.53)
0	0	0	40	0	1600,	

which yields the basic feasible solution

$$x_1 = 15, \quad x_2 = 25, \quad x_3 = 15, \quad x_4 = 0, \quad x_5 = 0. \tag{6.54}$$

Also,

$$M = 1600 - 40x_4.$$

Since x_5 does not appear in this equation and positive numbers appear in the fifth column in (6.53), we can obtain a second feasible solution from (6.53), without changing the value of M. By pivoting on the fifth element of the first row of (6.53), we obtain

$$\begin{array}{cccccc} 0 & 0 & 2 & -5 & 1 & 30 \\ 1 & 0 & 1 & -1 & 0 & 30 \\ 0 & 1 & 0 & 2 & 0 & 10 \\ 0 & 0 & 0 & 40 & 0 & 1600, \end{array}$$

which gives a second basic feasible solution,

$$x_1 = 30, \quad x_2 = 10, \quad x_3 = 0, \quad x_4 = 0, \quad x_5 = 30. \tag{6.55}$$

But (6.54), (6.55) correspond to $M = 1600$ and it is not possible to find a basic feasible solution which will give a larger M. In terms of the theory in Section 6.4, this is an example of Theorem 6.5(ii) with $c_5 = 0$, as shown in the array (6.53).

(2) *No obvious feasible solution*

If instead of (6.52) we change the direction of the inequality in one of the constraints and consider

$$2x_1 + x_2 \leq 70, \quad x_1 + x_2 \geq 40, \quad x_1 + 3x_2 \leq 90, \tag{6.56}$$

the admissible region in which (x_1, x_2) must lie is now shown in Figure 6.2. The origin of coordinates does not lie in the admissible region, so that the assumption $x_1 = x_2 = 0$ no longer leads directly to a feasible solution. This is, of course, obvious algebraically since introduction of slack variables in (6.56) gives

$$\begin{aligned} 2x_1 + x_2 + x_3 \qquad\qquad &= 70 \\ x_1 + x_2 \qquad - x_4 \qquad &= 40 \\ x_1 + 3x_2 \qquad\qquad + x_5 &= 90, \end{aligned} \tag{6.57}$$

and $x_1 = x_2 = 0$ yields $x_3 = 70$, $x_4 = -40$, $x_5 = 90$, which is not feasible. In order to overcome this difficulty we first of all solve a somewhat different problem, namely we introduce an extra variable, known as an *artificial variable*, into the equation in (6.57) that gave trouble when we set $x_1 = x_2 = 0$, i.e., we replace (6.57) by

$$\begin{aligned} 2x_1 + x_2 + x_3 \qquad\qquad\qquad &= 70 \\ x_1 + x_2 \qquad - x_4 \qquad + x_6 &= 40 \\ x_1 + 3x_2 \qquad\qquad + x_5 \qquad &= 90, \end{aligned} \tag{6.58}$$

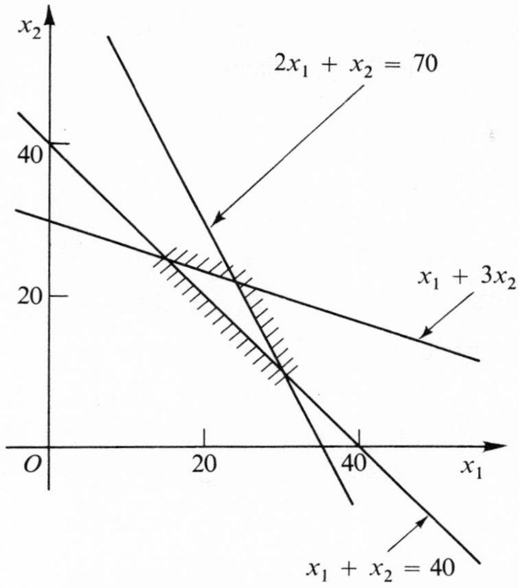

Figure 6.2 No obvious feasible solution.

with $x_i \geq 0$, $i = 1, \ldots, 6$. In this preliminary stage of the problem, when we are trying to find a feasible solution of (6.57), we shall not maximize the M that we ultimately desire to maximize, namely (6.51), but, for reasons explained presently, we maximize

$$M = -x_6.$$

Since $x_6 \geq 0$, the maximum possible value of M is 0. There are two possibilities:

(a) The maximum value is in fact 0. This means that we can find a basic feasible solution of (6.58) in which $x_6 = 0$, i.e., we can find a basic feasible solution of (6.57).

(b) The maximum value of M is less than 0. This means that no basic feasible solution of (6.57) exists because, if such a solution did exist, then we could find a basic feasible solution of (6.58) with $x_6 = 0$, i.e., $M = 0$, and we have just assumed that this is not possible.

We apply this method to (6.58), starting with the array

$$\begin{matrix} 2 & 1 & 1 & 0 & 0 & 0 & 70 \\ 1 & 1 & 0 & -1 & 0 & 1 & 40 \\ 1 & 3 & 0 & 0 & 1 & 0 & 90 \\ 0 & 0 & 0 & 0 & 0 & 1 & 0. \end{matrix} \tag{6.59}$$

There is an obvious basic feasible solution $x_1 = x_2 = x_4 = 0$, $x_3 = 70$, $x_5 = 90$, $x_6 = 40$, but this array is not quite analogous to those considered previously since the elements in the last row of (6.59) corresponding to the basic feasible variables are not all zero. It is necessary to insert an extra step in the standard procedure described at the end of Section 6.2. We reduce the (4, 6) element in (6.59) to zero by pivoting on the (2, 6) element of the array. This gives an array with negative numbers in the last line. If we then perform the simplex method on the resulting array, we finally obtain

$$\begin{array}{ccccccc} 0 & 0 & 1 & 2.5 & 0.5 & -2.5 & 15 \\ 1 & 0 & 0 & -1.5 & -0.5 & 1.5 & 15 \\ 0 & 1 & 0 & 0.5 & 0.5 & 0.5 & 25 \\ 0 & 0 & 0 & 0 & 0 & 0 & 0. \end{array} \tag{6.60}$$

This gives the following basic solution for (6.57):

$$x_1 = 15, \qquad x_2 = 25, \qquad x_3 = 15, \qquad x_4 = 0, \qquad x_5 = 0. \tag{6.61}$$

In order to use this basic feasible solution as a starting point for maximizing the expression (6.51), namely $M = 40x_1 + 60x_2$, we must start with the array

$$\begin{array}{ccccccc} 2 & 1 & 1 & 0 & 0 & 0 & 70 \\ 1 & 1 & 0 & -1 & 0 & 1 & 40 \\ 1 & 3 & 0 & 0 & 1 & 0 & 90 \\ -40 & -60 & 0 & 0 & 0 & 0 & 0. \end{array} \tag{6.62}$$

We wish to use the simplex method to transform this array in such a way that there is an obvious basic feasible solution *not* involving x_6 (i.e., the sixth column is not one of the unit columns). This is exactly what we did in transforming (6.59) to (6.60). Also the first three rows of (6.59) and (6.62) are the same. Hence, we could obtain the required array from (6.62) by using the simplex method to make the first three columns in (6.62) have the same form as the first three columns of (6.60). This would give the form (6.64) below. Rather than do the transformation from scratch, it is convenient to combine this with the reduction of (6.59) to (6.60). This can be achieved by carrying along the last row in (6.59) as an extra row in (6.62); thus,

$$\begin{array}{ccccccc} 2 & 1 & 1 & 0 & 0 & 0 & 70 \\ 1 & 1 & 0 & -1 & 0 & 1 & 40 \\ 1 & 3 & 0 & 0 & 1 & 0 & 90 \\ -40 & -60 & 0 & 0 & 0 & 0 & 0 \\ 0 & 0 & 0 & 0 & 0 & 1 & 0. \end{array}$$

On reducing this, using the same pivots as before, we find

$$\begin{array}{ccccccc} 0 & 0 & 1 & 2.5 & 0.5 & . & 15 \\ 1 & 0 & 0 & -1.5 & -0.5 & . & 15 \\ 0 & 1 & 0 & 0.5 & 0.5 & . & 25 \\ 0 & 0 & 0 & -30 & 10 & . & 2100 \\ 0 & 0 & 0 & 0 & 0 & . & 0, \end{array} \tag{6.63}$$

where we have dropped the sixth column (represented by dots) whenever x_6 is reduced to zero in the basic feasible solution for (6.58), since we do not wish x_6 to reenter the basic solution. From this point onwards we can also, of course, drop the last row in (6.63) and use the simplex method on

$$\begin{matrix} 0 & 0 & 1 & 2.5 & 0.5 & 15 \\ 1 & 0 & 0 & -1.5 & -0.5 & 15 \\ 0 & 1 & 0 & 0.5 & 0.5 & 25 \\ 0 & 0 & 0 & -30 & 10 & 2100. \end{matrix} \tag{6.64}$$

This is the form we should have obtained if we had started with (6.62) and used the same pivot operations as we did on (6.59). It is easy to complete the solution and obtain $M = 2280$, corresponding to

$$x_1 = 24, \qquad x_2 = 22, \qquad x_3 = 0, \qquad x_4 = 6, \qquad x_5 = 0.$$

This solution is confirmed by Figure 6.2.

(3) *Contradictory constraints*

Suppose that instead of the constraints (6.52), we consider

$$2x_1 + x_2 \geq 70, \qquad x_1 + x_2 \leq 40, \qquad x_1 + 3x_2 \geq 90. \tag{6.65}$$

The situation is illustrated in Figure 6.3, from which we see that there is no point (x_1, x_2) that satisfies all three conditions, i.e., the constraints are contradictory. Algebraically, if we insert slack variables to convert (6.65) into

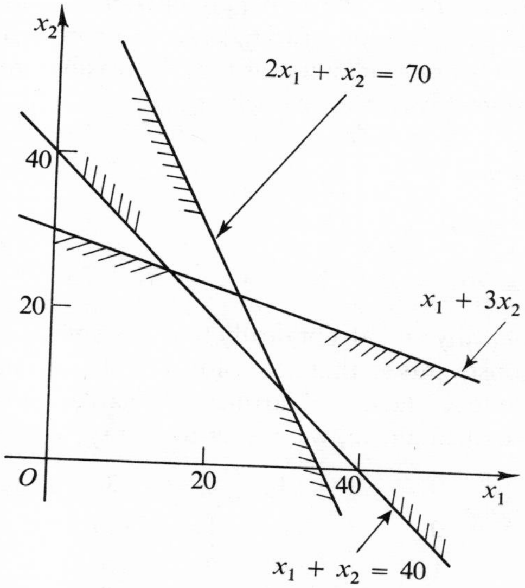

Figure 6.3 Contradictory constraints.

equalities, there is no obvious feasible solution. In order to find a feasible solution, we must introduce two artificial variables [compare (6.58) above] and first maximize

$$M = -x_6 - x_7. \tag{6.66}$$

This means that we start from the array

$$\begin{array}{cccccccc} 2 & 1 & -1 & 0 & 0 & 1 & 0 & 70 \\ 1 & 1 & 0 & 1 & 0 & 0 & 0 & 40 \\ 1 & 3 & 0 & 0 & -1 & 0 & 1 & 90 \\ 0 & 0 & 0 & 0 & 0 & 1 & 1 & 0. \end{array} \tag{6.67}$$

An obvious feasible solution is

$$x_4 = 40, \qquad x_6 = 70, \qquad x_7 = 90, \qquad x_1 = x_2 = x_3 = x_5 = 0.$$

We therefore reduce the elements in the sixth and seventh columns of the last row of (6.67) to zero and then apply the simplex method in the usual way. This gives the array

$$\begin{array}{cccccccc} 0 & 0 & -1 & -2.5 & -0.5 & 1 & 0.5 & 15 \\ 1 & 0 & 0 & 1.5 & 0.5 & 0 & -0.5 & 15 \\ 0 & 1 & 0 & -0.5 & -0.5 & 0 & 0.5 & 25 \\ 0 & 0 & 1 & 2.5 & 0.5 & 0 & 0.5 & -15. \end{array}$$

Hence, the maximum value of M is -15, corresponding to $x_1 = 15$, $x_2 = 25$, $x_6 = 15$, and all the other variables zero. We are now in situation (b) following (6.58), and no basic feasible solution of (6.65) exists. From a slightly different point of view, the reason for our difficulties is that the feasible solution obtained contains one of the artificial variables, namely x_6.

(4) *Unbounded solutions*

Consider the constraints

$$2x_1 + x_2 \geq 70, \qquad x_1 + x_2 \geq 40, \qquad x_1 + 3x_2 \geq 90.$$

It is obvious both graphically and algebraically that any sufficiently large values of x_1, x_2 satisfy these constraints so that $M = 40x_1 + 60x_2$ can be made as large as desired. If we introduce slack and artificial variables, and perform the pivoting operations described above, we obtain the array

$$\begin{array}{cccccc} 1 & 0 & -1 & 1 & 0 & 30 \\ 5 & 0 & -3 & 0 & 1 & 120 \\ 2 & 1 & -1 & 0 & 0 & 70 \\ 80 & 0 & -60 & 0 & 0 & 4200. \end{array}$$

The elements in the third column are all negative, and this is the situation in Theorem 6.4(ii) (a), which shows that M can be made as large as desired.

(5) *Degeneracy*

So far we have always assumed that the linear programming problem was nondegenerate. Consider the constraints

$$2x_1 + x_2 \leq 70, \qquad x_1 + x_2 \leq 40, \qquad x_1 + 3x_2 \leq 120.$$

The corresponding initial array is

$$\begin{array}{rrrrrr} 2 & 1 & 1 & 0 & 0 & 70 \\ 1 & 1 & 0 & 1 & 0 & 40 \\ 1 & 3 & 0 & 0 & 1 & 120 \\ -40 & -60 & 0 & 0 & 0 & 0. \end{array}$$

The -60 in the last row leads us to examine the ratios $70/1 = 70$, $40/1 = 40$, $120/3 = 40$. There is now a choice of pivoting on either the (2, 2) or the (3, 2) element. If we pivot on the (3, 2) element, this gives the array

$$\begin{array}{rrrrrr} \frac{5}{3} & 0 & 1 & 0 & -\frac{1}{3} & 30 \\ \frac{2}{3} & 0 & 0 & 1 & -\frac{1}{3} & 0 \\ \frac{1}{3} & 1 & 0 & 0 & \frac{1}{3} & 40 \\ -20 & 0 & 0 & 0 & 20 & 2400 \end{array}$$

The basic variable x_4 is zero, i.e., the problem is degenerate. If we next pivot on the element $\frac{2}{3}$ in the first column, we obtain

$$\begin{array}{rrrrrr} 0 & 0 & 1 & -2.5 & 0.5 & 30 \\ 1 & 0 & 0 & 1.5 & -0.5 & 0 \\ 0 & 1 & 0 & -0.5 & 0.5 & 40 \\ 0 & 0 & 0 & 30 & 10 & 2400 \end{array}$$

The procedure now terminates and the required maximum is 2400. Two points should be noted:

(a) In going from the first array to the second, a choice of pivots was available.

(b) In going from the second array to the third, the value of M was not changed.

Our previous proof that either the simplex method will terminate or M is unbounded was based on the fact that a change of basic variables in a nondegenerate problem always increases M. This guarantees that the basic solution found at each stage is always different from those found at previous stages. If the problem is degenerate, our proof breaks down, and in fact the result is not true. The basic solution found at one stage may be identical with a basic solution found at a previous stage, in which case the procedure will cycle indefinitely.

Graphically, the situation in the above concrete example is illustrated in Figure 6.4. Two lines *PQ*, *PR* representing inequality constraints go through

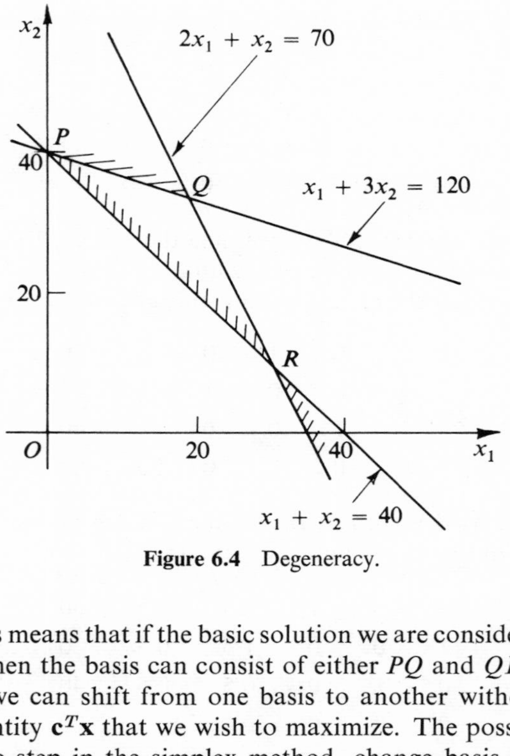

Figure 6.4 Degeneracy.

one point *P*. This means that if the basic solution we are considering corresponds to the point *P*, then the basis can consist of either *PQ* and *QR* or *PR* and *QR*. At the point *P* we can shift from one basis to another without changing the value of the quantity $\mathbf{c}^T\mathbf{x}$ that we wish to maximize. The possibility arises that we might, at one step in the simplex method, change basis from *PR*, *QR* to *PQ*, *QR* and then at the next step change from *PQ*, *QR* to *PR*, *QR*. If this were to happen, the procedure would cycle indefinitely. No difficulty of this type occurred in the above example, but the difficulty might occur in complicated examples. Cycling would be avoided if, when at the point *P*, we ensured that the next step in the simplex method involved a move away from *P* to an adjacent point *R* on the polygon (provided that this increased $\mathbf{c}^T\mathbf{x}$). This idea can be extended to the general case on the basis of ideas developed in the next section. However cycling seems to be rare in practice and will not be discussed further here.

6.6 Convex Sets

In earlier sections we developed the theory of linear programming by describing the simplex method in terms of elementary row operations on matrices. Although this clearly identified various possibilities that could arise, the reader probably obtained a better intuitive picture of the situation from the geometrical discussion of the two-variable case in the last section. We now develop related ideas for the n-variable problem, although, of course, we shall no longer be able to draw graphs for the general case.

The key to the generalization to n variables is to introduce the idea of a *convex set*. We first of all consider this for the two-variable case illustrated graphically in the last section. Points in two dimensions can be represented by 2×1 column vectors $\mathbf{p}$, $\mathbf{q}$, $\mathbf{x}$, etc. A set of points in a plane is called a convex set if all points on the straight line segment joining the two points belong to the set. A rectangle or a circle are examples of convex sets. However, the sets in Figure 6.5 are not convex. If a convex set includes the points on its boundary

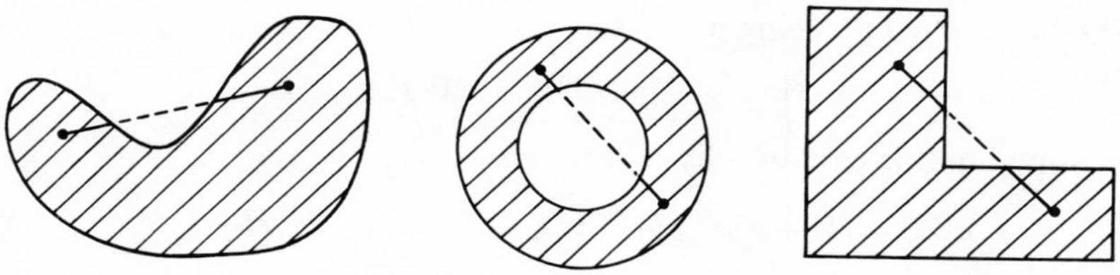

Figure 6.5 Sets that are *not* convex sets.

it is said to be *closed*. If it does not include the points on its boundary it is said to be *open*. It is convenient to include in the class of convex sets, any set consisting of only one point. The set of points common to two or more convex sets in a plane is convex. This is easy to see. Suppose that C_1 and C_2 are two convex sets and S is the set of common points. If $\mathbf{p}$ and $\mathbf{q}$ are two points in S, then all points on the line joining $\mathbf{p}$ and $\mathbf{q}$ are in C_1, and also in C_2. Hence all the points on this line-segment are in S, and S is convex. A linear inequality

$$\alpha_1 x_1 + \alpha_2 x_2 \leq \beta \tag{6.68}$$

defines a convex set. To prove this, suppose that

$$\mathbf{p} = \begin{bmatrix} p_1 \\ p_2 \end{bmatrix}, \quad \mathbf{q} = \begin{bmatrix} q_1 \\ q_2 \end{bmatrix}, \quad \mathbf{x} = \begin{bmatrix} x_1 \\ x_2 \end{bmatrix}, \quad \boldsymbol{\alpha} = \begin{bmatrix} \alpha_1 \\ \alpha_2 \end{bmatrix},$$

where $\mathbf{p}$, $\mathbf{q}$ are any two points in the set defined by (6.68), i.e.,

$$\boldsymbol{\alpha}^T \mathbf{p} \leq \beta, \qquad \boldsymbol{\alpha}^T \mathbf{q} \leq \beta,$$

and $\mathbf{x}$ is a point on the line-segment joining $\mathbf{p}$ and $\mathbf{q}$. The equation of the line joining $\mathbf{p}$ and $\mathbf{q}$ in the x, y-plane is

$$\frac{x - p_1}{q_1 - p_1} = \frac{y - p_2}{q_2 - p_2}.$$

If the point $\mathbf{x}$ with coordinates x_1, x_2 lies on this line, then

$$\frac{x_1 - p_1}{q_1 - p_1} = \frac{x_2 - p_2}{q_2 - p_2} = \lambda,$$

say, where we introduce the parameter λ to denote the common value of the ratios on the left. If the point $\mathbf{x}$ lies in between $\mathbf{p}$ and $\mathbf{q}$, it is easy to see that $0 < \lambda < 1$. When referring to the line-segment joining $\mathbf{p}$ and $\mathbf{q}$ we shall normally include the end-points, and in this case $0 \leq \lambda \leq 1$. Rearrangement of the above equation gives

$$x_1 = (1 - \lambda)p_1 + \lambda q_1,$$

$$x_2 = (1 - \lambda)p_2 + \lambda q_2,$$

i.e., the line-segment joining $\mathbf{p}$ and $\mathbf{q}$ is given by

$$\mathbf{x} = (1 - \lambda)\mathbf{p} + \lambda\mathbf{q}, \qquad 0 \leq \lambda \leq 1.$$

On multiplying this equation by $\boldsymbol{\alpha}^T$, we see that

$$\boldsymbol{\alpha}^T\mathbf{x} = (1 - \lambda)\boldsymbol{\alpha}^T\mathbf{p} + \lambda\boldsymbol{\alpha}^T\mathbf{q} \leq (1 - \lambda)\beta + \lambda\beta = \beta,$$

i.e., the point $\mathbf{x}$ lies in the set defined by (6.68). Hence, the region defined by this inequality is a convex set. It follows that the set of all points satisfying the following constraints,

$$a_{i1}x_1 + a_{i2}x_2 \leq b_i, \qquad (i = 1, \ldots, m), \qquad x_1 \geq 0, \qquad x_2 \geq 0,$$

is a convex set because each constraint defines a convex set, and the points that satisfy all these inequalities lie in a region common to a collection of convex sets which is therefore itself a convex set.

We now develop these ideas for the general n-variable case.

DEFINITION **6.6.** By a *point* in n-dimensional space E_n we mean an $n \times 1$ column vector. The elements of the vector are known as the *coordinates* of the point. The *straight line* passing through two points $\mathbf{x}_1$, $\mathbf{x}_2$ ($\mathbf{x}_1 \neq \mathbf{x}_2$) in E_n is defined to be the set of points

$$\mathbf{x} = (1 - \lambda)\mathbf{x}_1 + \lambda\mathbf{x}_2, \qquad \text{any } \lambda.$$

The *line-segment* joining the two points $\mathbf{x}_1$, $\mathbf{x}_2$ is the set of points

$$\mathbf{x} = (1 - \lambda)\mathbf{x}_1 + \lambda\mathbf{x}_2, \qquad 0 \leq \lambda \leq 1.$$

The set of points whose coordinates satisfy

$$\mathbf{a}^T\mathbf{x} = k,$$

where $\mathbf{a}$ is a fixed vector and k is a constant, is called a *hyperplane*. The set of points satisfying a linear inequality such as

$$\mathbf{a}^T\mathbf{x} \leq k,$$

is called a *half-space*.

DEFINITION 6.7. A set of points in E_n is said to be a *convex set* if, when $\mathbf{x}_1$ and $\mathbf{x}_2$ are in the set, all the points on the line-segment joining $\mathbf{x}_1$ and $\mathbf{x}_2$ are also in the set.

THEOREM 6.6. (i) *The set of points common to two or more convex sets is also convex.*

(ii) *A hyperplane and a half-space are both convex sets.*

(iii) *The set of feasible solutions of a linear programming problem form a convex set.*

Proof: Let C_1 and C_2 be two convex sets and S be the set of points common to C_1 and C_2. Let $\mathbf{p}$, $\mathbf{q}$ be two points in S. Then all points lying on the line-segment joining $\mathbf{p}$ and $\mathbf{q}$ are in C_1 and also in C_2. Hence, they are in S, so that S is convex. The extension to more than two regions is obvious. This proves (i). A hyperplane is a convex set since if $\mathbf{x}_1$ and $\mathbf{x}_2$ are on the hyperplane $\mathbf{a}^T\mathbf{x} = k$, then

$$\mathbf{a}^T\{(1 - \lambda)\mathbf{x}_1 + \lambda\mathbf{x}_2\} = (1 - \lambda)\mathbf{a}^T\mathbf{x}_1 + \lambda\mathbf{a}^T\mathbf{x}_2 = (1 - \lambda)k + \lambda k = k.$$

Hence, the point $(1 - \lambda)\mathbf{x}_1 + \lambda\mathbf{x}_2$ lies on the hyperplane, and the hyperplane is a convex set. Similarly, if $\mathbf{x}_1$ and $\mathbf{x}_2$ lie in the half-space $\mathbf{a}^T\mathbf{x} \leq k$, then

$$\mathbf{a}^T\{(1 - \lambda)\mathbf{x}_1 + \lambda\mathbf{x}_2\} \leq k,$$

i.e., the point $(1 - \lambda)\mathbf{x}_1 + \lambda\mathbf{x}_2$ lies in the half-space, which is therefore convex. This proves (ii). Finally, if the constraints in a linear programming problem are

$$\mathbf{a}_i^T\mathbf{x} \leq b_i, \qquad i = 1, \ldots, m,$$

where $\mathbf{x} \geq \mathbf{0}$, each of the constraints defines a convex set, and the common points form a convex set. An algebraic proof is the following: If $\mathbf{x}_1$ and $\mathbf{x}_2$ satisfy the constraints $\mathbf{x}_j \geq \mathbf{0}$, $\mathbf{a}_i^T\mathbf{x}_j \leq b_i$; $j = 1, 2$; $i = 1, \ldots, m$, then

$$(1 - \lambda)\mathbf{x}_1 + \lambda\mathbf{x}_2 \geq \mathbf{0},$$

$$[(1 - \lambda)\mathbf{x}_1 + \lambda\mathbf{x}_2] \leq \mathbf{b}.$$

Hence all points on the line-segment joining $\mathbf{x}_1$ and $\mathbf{x}_2$ satisfy the constraints, and the set of points satisfying the constraints, therefore, forms a convex set. This concludes the proof.

The examination of the extrema of functions $y = f(x)$ of a single variable x often gives rise to situations in which there are several *local* maxima such as

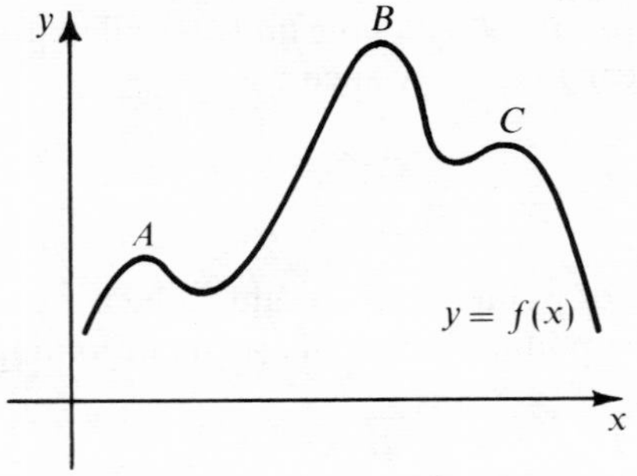

Figure 6.6 Local and global maxima.

A, B, C in Figure 6.6, but only one overall or *global* maximum at B. For our purposes, we say that a function $f(\mathbf{x})$ of a vector $\mathbf{x} = [x_i]$ has a (weak) local maximum at $\mathbf{x}_0 = [\xi_i]$, if

$$f(\mathbf{x}) \le f(\mathbf{x}_0) \quad \text{for all } \mathbf{x} \text{ such that} \quad |x_i - \xi_i| < \varepsilon,$$

where ε is an arbitrary small quantity. (For a strong maximum, we replace $\le$ by $<$, and add the condition $\mathbf{x} \ne \mathbf{x}_0$.) If $f(\mathbf{x}) > f(\mathbf{x}_0)$ for some $\mathbf{x}$ such that $|x_i - \xi_i| < \varepsilon$, for arbitrarily small ε, then $f(\mathbf{x}_0)$ cannot be a maximum of the function.

THEOREM **6.7.** *Let* $\mathbf{x}$ *lie in a convex set. Then:*

(i) *When considering the values of* $M = \mathbf{c}^T\mathbf{x}$, *any value of* $\mathbf{x}$ *that gives a local maximum for* M *also gives a global maximum.*

(ii) *If the same maximum value of* $\mathbf{c}^T\mathbf{x}$ *is given by two points* $\mathbf{x}_1$ *and* $\mathbf{x}_2$, *then it is given by all the points on the line-segment joining* $\mathbf{x}_1$ *and* $\mathbf{x}_2$.

Proof: Let $\mathbf{x}_1$ give a local maximum with $M_1 = \mathbf{c}^T\mathbf{x}_1$, and let $\mathbf{x}_2$ give a global maximum with $M_2 = \mathbf{c}^T\mathbf{x}_2$, and suppose that $M_1 \le M_2$. Any point $(1 - \lambda)\mathbf{x}_1 + \lambda\mathbf{x}_2$, $0 < \lambda < 1$, also lies in the convex set and the corresponding value of M is given by

$$\mathbf{c}^T\{(1 - \lambda)\mathbf{x}_1 + \lambda\mathbf{x}_2\} = (1 - \lambda)M_1 + \lambda M_2, \qquad 0 < \lambda < 1, \qquad (6.69)$$

which lies in between M_1 and M_2. Hence M_1 canot be a local maximum if $M_1 < M_2$. We must have $M_1 = M_2$ and the local maximum at M_1 must also be equal to the global maximum. This proves (i). If $\mathbf{x}_1$ and $\mathbf{x}_2$ are distinct, then (6.69) shows that the same maximum is given by all points on the line-segment joining $\mathbf{x}_1$ and $\mathbf{x}_2$. This proves (ii).

DEFINITION **6.8.** A point $\mathbf{x}$ of a convex set is said to be an *extreme point* if $\mathbf{x}$ does not lie on the line-segment joining two other points in the set.

THEOREM 6.8. (i) *To every basic feasible solution of a linear programming problem there corresponds an extreme point of the convex set of feasible solutions.*

(ii) *To every extreme point there corresponds a basic feasible solution.*

Proof: Suppose that we have a basic feasible solution $\mathbf{x}_0 = [u_i]$ and that, by renumbering variables if necessary,

$$u_i = 0, \qquad i = m + 1, \ldots, n. \tag{6.70}$$

Suppose that $\mathbf{x}_0$ lies on the line-segment joining two points $\mathbf{x}_1 = [v_i]$ and $\mathbf{x}_2 = [w_i]$, both of which correspond to feasible solutions,

$$\mathbf{x}_0 = (1 - \lambda)\mathbf{x}_1 + \lambda\mathbf{x}_2, \qquad 0 < \lambda < 1. \tag{6.71}$$

Since $\lambda > 0$, $1 - \lambda > 0$, $\mathbf{x}_1 \geq \mathbf{0}$, $\mathbf{x}_2 \geq \mathbf{0}$, equations (6.70), (6.71) imply that

$$v_i = w_i = 0, \qquad i = m + 1, \ldots, q.$$

Hence, $\mathbf{x}_1$, $\mathbf{x}_2$ are also basic solutions. But the values of the basic variables are uniquely determined since they correspond to columns in $\mathbf{A}$ that form a nonsingular matrix. This implies that $\mathbf{x}_0 = \mathbf{x}_1 = \mathbf{x}_2$, which contradicts our initial assumption that they were distinct. Hence, $\mathbf{x}_0$ is an extreme point. To prove part (ii), suppose that an extreme point $\mathbf{x}$ corresponds to a solution with more than m nonzero variables. Without loss of generality we can assume that the first $m + 1$ elements of $\mathbf{x} = [x_i]$ are nonzero:

$$x_i > 0, \qquad i = 1, \ldots, m + 1,$$

$$x_i \geq 0, \qquad i = m + 2, \ldots, q.$$

Let $\mathbf{a}_i$ denote the ith column of $\mathbf{A}$. Then

$$\mathbf{Ax} = \sum_{i=1}^{q} x_i\mathbf{a}_i = \mathbf{b}. \tag{6.72}$$

Since the $\mathbf{a}_i$ are $m \times 1$ column vectors, the $m + 1$ vectors $\mathbf{a}_i$ $(i = 1, \ldots, m + 1)$ are linearly dependent, i.e., constants γ_i, not all zero, exist such that

$$\sum_{i=1}^{m+1} \gamma_i\mathbf{a}_i = \mathbf{Ay} = \mathbf{0}, \tag{6.73}$$

where $\mathbf{y} = [y_i]$, with

$$y_i = \gamma_i, \qquad i = 1, \ldots, m + 1,$$

$$y_i = 0, \qquad i = m + 2, \ldots, q.$$

We define

$$\mathbf{x}_1 = \mathbf{x} + \varepsilon\mathbf{y}, \qquad \mathbf{x}_2 = \mathbf{x} - \varepsilon\mathbf{y}, \tag{6.74}$$

where ε is a constant. If ε is sufficiently small, then $\mathbf{x}_1 \geq \mathbf{0}$, $\mathbf{x}_2 \geq \mathbf{0}$. Also on using (6.72), (6.73) we see that $\mathbf{Ax}_1 = \mathbf{b}$, $\mathbf{Ax}_2 = \mathbf{b}$. Hence, $\mathbf{x}_1$, $\mathbf{x}_2$ are feasible solutions. But from the definition of $\mathbf{x}_1$, $\mathbf{x}_2$ in (6.74) we see that $\mathbf{x} = \frac{1}{2}(\mathbf{x}_1 + \mathbf{x}_2)$, so that $\mathbf{x}$ cannot be an extreme point. This is a contradiction that arose from the fact that we assumed $\mathbf{x}$ had more than m nonzero elements. Hence, a solution corresponding to an extreme point must be basic. This concludes the proof.

DEFINITION 6.9. An *edge* of a convex set is a line-segment joining two extreme points, such that no point on this edge lies on the line-segment joining any other two points of the set not on the edge. The two extreme points are said to be *adjacent*.

We now wish to consider a theorem involving extreme points, edges, and basic solutions. From Theorem 6.8(ii), to every extreme point there corresponds a basic feasible solution. Without loss of generality we can assume that the extreme points $\mathbf{p}$ and $\mathbf{q}$ defining an edge have the form

$$\mathbf{p} = \begin{bmatrix} p_1 \\ p_2 \\ \vdots \\ p_m \\ 0 \\ 0 \\ \vdots \\ 0 \end{bmatrix}, \qquad \mathbf{q} = \begin{bmatrix} 0 \\ q_2 \\ \vdots \\ q_m \\ q_{m+1} \\ 0 \\ \vdots \\ 0 \end{bmatrix}, \qquad \mathbf{u} = \begin{bmatrix} u_1 \\ u_2 \\ \vdots \\ u_m \\ u_{m+1} \\ 0 \\ \vdots \\ 0 \end{bmatrix}, \tag{6.75}$$

where we have also introduced notation for a vector $\mathbf{u}$ that has its last $n - m - 1$ components zero. We also introduce partitioned matrix notation

$$\mathbf{p} = \begin{bmatrix} \mathbf{p}_1 \\ \mathbf{p}_2 \end{bmatrix}, \qquad \mathbf{q} = \begin{bmatrix} \mathbf{q}_1 \\ \mathbf{q}_2 \end{bmatrix}, \qquad \mathbf{u} = \begin{bmatrix} \mathbf{u}_1 \\ \mathbf{u}_2 \end{bmatrix}, \tag{6.76}$$

where $\mathbf{p}_1$, $\mathbf{q}_1$, $\mathbf{u}_1$ are $m \times 1$.

THEOREM 6.9. *Consider points corresponding to feasible solutions of a nondegenerate linear programming problem.*

(i) *Any feasible point of the form* $\mathbf{u}$ *defined in* (6.75) *with* $0 < u_{m+1} < q_{m+1}$ *must lie on the line-segment joining* $\mathbf{p}$ *and* $\mathbf{q}$.

(ii) *The line-segment joining* $\mathbf{p}$ *and* $\mathbf{q}$ *is an edge of the convex set of feasible solutions of the programming problem.*

Proof: Since $\mathbf{p}$, $\mathbf{q}$, $\mathbf{u}$ are feasible, we have

$$\mathbf{Ap} = \mathbf{b}, \qquad \mathbf{Aq} = \mathbf{b}, \qquad \mathbf{Au} = \mathbf{b}. \tag{6.77}$$

Denote the matrix formed by the first m columns of $\mathbf{A}$ by $\mathbf{A}_B$ and denote the

$(m+1)$th column of $\mathbf{A}$ by $\mathbf{a}_{m+1}$. Introducing the notation in (6.75), (6.76), equations (6.77) become:

$$\mathbf{A}_B\mathbf{p}_1 = \mathbf{b},$$

$$\mathbf{A}_B\mathbf{q}_1 = \mathbf{b} - q_{m+1}\mathbf{a}_{m+1},$$

$$\mathbf{A}_B\mathbf{u}_1 = \mathbf{b} - u_{m+1}\mathbf{a}_{m+1}.$$

Substitute for $\mathbf{b}$ in the last two of these equations from the first, and multiply through by $\mathbf{A}_B^{-1}$:

$$\mathbf{q}_1 = \mathbf{p}_1 - q_{m+1}\mathbf{A}_B^{-1}\mathbf{a}_{m+1},$$

$$\mathbf{u}_1 = \mathbf{p}_1 - u_{m+1}\mathbf{A}_B^{-1}\mathbf{a}_{m+1}.$$

Eliminate $\mathbf{A}_B^{-1}\mathbf{a}_{m+1}$:

$$u_{m+1}\mathbf{q}_1 - q_{m+1}\mathbf{u}_1 = (u_{m+1} - q_{m+1})\mathbf{p}_1.$$

Since $q_{m+1} \neq 0$, we can divide through by q_{m+1} and introduce

$$\lambda = \frac{u_{m+1}}{q_{m+1}},$$

where $0 < \lambda < 1$, since we are given that $0 < u_{m+1} < q_{m+1}$. This yields

$$\mathbf{u}_1 = (1 - \lambda)\mathbf{p}_1 + \lambda\mathbf{q}_1.$$

Also,

$$u_{m+1} = \qquad \lambda q_{m+1}.$$

Hence,

$$\mathbf{u} = (1 - \lambda)\mathbf{p} + \lambda\mathbf{q}.$$

This proves that $\mathbf{u}$ lies on the line-segment joining $\mathbf{p}$ and $\mathbf{q}$. This is part (i). To prove part (ii), consider any point $\mathbf{u}$ lying on the line-segment joining $\mathbf{p}$ and $\mathbf{q}$. This must have the form given in (6.75), i.e., the last $n - m - 1$ elements are zero. If $\mathbf{u}$ lies on a second line-segment joining points $\mathbf{v}$ and $\mathbf{w}$ in the convex set, where $\mathbf{u} \neq \mathbf{v} \neq \mathbf{w}$, then

$$\mathbf{u} = (1 - \mu)\mathbf{v} + \mu\mathbf{w}, \qquad 0 < \mu < 1,$$

Since $\mathbf{u} \geq \mathbf{0}$, $\mathbf{v} \geq \mathbf{0}$, $\mathbf{w} \geq \mathbf{0}$, $1 - \mu > 0$, $\mu > 0$, this means that the last $n - m - 1$ elements of $\mathbf{v}$ and $\mathbf{w}$ must be zero. Hence, from (i), $\mathbf{v}$ and $\mathbf{w}$ must lie on the line segment joining $\mathbf{p}$ and $\mathbf{q}$. Hence, the set of points $\mathbf{u}$ must lie on the edge joining $\mathbf{p}$ and $\mathbf{q}$. This completes the proof.

It should now be clear to the reader that a geometrical interpretation of the simplex method proceeds as follows. Consider a nondegenerate linear programming problem. *The feasible solutions constitute a convex set of points in n-dimensional space, bounded by hyperplanes. Edges and extreme points of this convex set are given by the intersection of hyperplanes.* The convex set is a generalization of the interior plus boundary of a convex polygon in a plane or a convex polyhedron in three-dimensional space. *We start at an extreme point of the convex set, corresponding to a basic feasible solution. From this extreme point we move to an adjacent extreme point along an edge, in such a way that the quantity* $M = \mathbf{c}^T\mathbf{x}$ *is increased.* This procedure is repeated until we reach an extreme point such that moving along any edge associated with this extreme point does not increase the value of M. We have then reached a relative maximum which, by Theorem 6.7(i), must be a global maximum. It is also possible to interpret other cases, such as multiple solutions and degeneracy, by extending the above ideas. This concludes our discussion of the simplex method from a geometrical point of view. A more detailed treatment of the matters discussed in this paragraph would involve recapitulation of much of the theory given in previous sections.

6.7 Duality

So far in this chapter we have been concerned with the following problem:

$$\text{maximize} \qquad M_1 = \mathbf{c}^T\mathbf{x}, \tag{6.78}$$

$$\text{subject to} \qquad \mathbf{Ax} \le \mathbf{b}, \qquad \mathbf{x} \ge \mathbf{0}. \tag{6.79}$$

(The notation here is slightly different from that used in Sections 6.3–6.6, where $\mathbf{A}$ refers to the situation when slack variables are added. This is explained in the last paragraph of Section 6.2.) It is instructive to compare the solution of the above problem with the solution of the following associated linear programming problem:

$$\text{minimize} \qquad M_2 = \mathbf{b}^T\mathbf{y}, \tag{6.80}$$

$$\text{subject to} \qquad \mathbf{A}^T\mathbf{y} \ge \mathbf{c}, \qquad \mathbf{y} \ge \mathbf{0}. \tag{6.81}$$

The roles of $\mathbf{b}$ and $\mathbf{c}$ are interchanged and the matrix $\mathbf{A}^T$ in the new problem is the transpose of the matrix $\mathbf{A}$ in (6.79). It will appear that there is a close relationship between the above two problems. The problem specified by (6.78), (6.79) is called the *primal*, and the problem specified by (6.80), (6.81) is called the *dual*. Throughout this section we shall assume that these problems are nondegenerate.

Consider the dual of the concrete problem given by (6.1)–(6.3) for which $\mathbf{A}$, $\mathbf{b}$, $\mathbf{c}$ are given in (6.4):

$$\text{minimize} \qquad M_2 = 70y_1 + 40y_2 + 90y_3, \tag{6.82}$$

$$\begin{aligned} \text{subject to} \qquad & 2y_1 + y_2 + y_3 \geqslant 40 \\ & y_1 + y_2 + 3y_3 \geqslant 60, \\ y_1 \ge 0, \qquad & y_2 \ge 0, \qquad y_3 \ge 0. \end{aligned}$$

Proceeding as for the case of no obvious feasible solution in Section 6.5(2), introducing slack and artificial variables, we obtain

$$\begin{matrix} 2 & 1 & 1 & -1 & 0 & 1 & 0 & 40 \\ 1 & 1 & 3 & 0 & -1 & 0 & 1 & 60 \\ 70 & 40 & 90 & 0 & 0 & 0 & 0 & 0 \\ 0 & 0 & 0 & 0 & 0 & 1 & 1 & 0. \end{matrix} \tag{6.83}$$

Note that minimization of (6.82) is equivalent to maximization of

$$M_2' = -70y_1 - 40y_2 - 90y_3,$$

so that we must enter +70, +40, +90 in the third row of (6.83) and the final maximum obtained by the simplex method will be $-M_2$. Omitting rows and columns corresponding to the artificial variables, the simplex method is found to give the following final array:

Initial / *Final*

2	1	1	−1	0	40	2.5	1	0	−1.5	0.5	30
1	1	3	0	−1	60	−0.5	0	1	0.5	−0.5	10
70	40	90	0	0	0	15	0	0	15	25	−2100

(6.84)

This should be compared with the corresponding arrays for the primal, namely (6.23), (6.26):

Initial / *Final*

2	1	1	0	0	70	0	0	1	−2.5	0.5	15
1	1	0	1	0	40	1	0	0	1.5	−0.5	15
1	3	0	0	1	90	0	1	0	−0.5	0.5	25
−40	−60	0	0	0	0	0	0	0	30	10	2100

(6.85)

Inspection shows that the same numbers appear in the two final arrays in (6.84), (6.85). The numbers in the last row (column) of (6.84) appear in the last column (row) of (6.85). The numbers in the other rows and columns are also related, but the correspondence is not completely obvious and will be clarified in Ex. 6.7. The maximum value of M_1 in the primal is exactly the same as the minimum value of M_2 in the dual. We shall show that this is not accidental, but that if both the primal and the dual possess solutions, then $M_1 = M_2$, always.

We first prove:

THEOREM 6.10. (i) *The dual of the dual is the primal.*

(ii) *If* **x**, **y** *are any solutions that satisfy* (6.79), (6.81) *respectively,* *then*

$$\mathbf{c}^T\mathbf{x} \le \mathbf{b}^T\mathbf{y}.$$

(iii) *If* $\hat{\mathbf{x}}$, $\hat{\mathbf{y}}$ *satisfy* (6.79), (6.81) *and also*

$$\mathbf{c}^T\hat{\mathbf{x}} = \mathbf{b}^T\hat{\mathbf{y}},$$

then $\hat{\mathbf{x}}$ *is the solution that maximizes* (6.78) *and* $\hat{\mathbf{y}}$ *minimizes* (6.80).

Proof: To find the dual of the dual, we start with the following primal:

$$\text{maximize} \qquad M_1 = -\mathbf{b}^T\mathbf{y}$$

$$\text{subject to} \qquad -\mathbf{A}^T\mathbf{y} \le -\mathbf{c}, \qquad \mathbf{y} \ge \mathbf{0}.$$

The dual is:

$$\text{minimize} \qquad M_2 = (-\mathbf{c})^T\mathbf{z}$$

$$\text{subject to} \qquad (-\mathbf{A}^T)^T\mathbf{z} \ge -\mathbf{b}, \qquad \mathbf{z} \ge \mathbf{0},$$

that is,

$$\text{maximize} \qquad M_2' = \mathbf{c}^T\mathbf{z},$$

$$\text{subject to} \qquad \mathbf{A}\mathbf{z} \le \mathbf{b}, \qquad \mathbf{z} \ge \mathbf{0},$$

which is the primal. To prove (ii) we note that

$$\mathbf{c}^T\mathbf{x} \le (\mathbf{A}^T\mathbf{y})^T\mathbf{x} = \mathbf{y}^T\mathbf{A}\mathbf{x} \le \mathbf{y}^T\mathbf{b},$$

where we have used the first inequalities in (6.79), (6.81). To prove (iii) we observe that, for any permissible $\mathbf{x}$, from (ii),

$$\mathbf{c}^T\mathbf{x} \le \mathbf{b}^T\hat{\mathbf{y}}.$$

Hence, since $\mathbf{c}^T\hat{\mathbf{x}} = \mathbf{b}^T\hat{\mathbf{y}}$,

$$\mathbf{c}^T\mathbf{x} \le \mathbf{c}^T\hat{\mathbf{x}},$$

so that $\mathbf{c}^T\hat{\mathbf{x}}$ is the maximum value of $\mathbf{c}^T\mathbf{x}$, i.e., $\hat{\mathbf{x}}$ maximizes (6.78). The fact that $\hat{\mathbf{y}}$ minimizes (6.80) follows similarly and this concludes the proof.

The motivation for our next theorem is the following: The initial and final arrays for the primal problem considered earlier in this chapter are given in (6.85). In the general case, we have

$$\begin{matrix} \textit{Initial} & & \textit{Final} \\ \begin{bmatrix} \mathbf{A} & \mathbf{I} & \mathbf{b} \\ -\mathbf{c}^T & \mathbf{0} & 0 \end{bmatrix} & \qquad & \begin{bmatrix} \mathbf{S}_1 & \mathbf{S}_2 & \mathbf{x}_B \\ \mathbf{d}_1^T & \mathbf{d}_2^T & M_0 \end{bmatrix}, \end{matrix} \tag{6.86}$$

where the partitioning of the two matrices are the same. The basic variables will be given by m unit vectors distributed between $\mathbf{S}_1$ and $\mathbf{S}_2$. The column vector $\mathbf{x}_B$ gives the values of these (nonzero) basic variables. Also M_0 is the maximum value of M. When we solved the dual for the specific example considered earlier in this section, we noted that the basic variables for the dual, namely 30, 10 in the last column of the final array in (6.84), also occurred in the last row of the final array in (6.85). If this is a general result, the basic variables for the dual problem are the nonzero variables in $\mathbf{d}_1^T$, $\mathbf{d}_2^T$ in the last row in (6.86). Theorem 6.10(iii) gives us a method for checking whether any given solution is a solution of the dual. Our procedure will therefore be the following: We shall guess the solution of the dual by examination of the explicit form of the last row of (6.86) and then check that our guess is correct by using Theorem 6.10(iii).

In order to go from the initial to the final matrix in (6.86), we perform elementary row operations on the initial matrix, and this can be represented by matrix premultiplication:

$$\begin{bmatrix} \mathbf{P} & \mathbf{0} \\ \mathbf{p}^T & 1 \end{bmatrix} \begin{bmatrix} \mathbf{A} & \mathbf{I} & \mathbf{b} \\ -\mathbf{c}^T & \mathbf{0} & 0 \end{bmatrix} = \begin{bmatrix} \mathbf{S}_1 & \mathbf{S}_2 & \mathbf{x}_B \\ \mathbf{d}_1^T & \mathbf{d}_2^T & M_0 \end{bmatrix}. \tag{6.87}$$

This gives

$$\mathbf{d}_1^T = \mathbf{p}^T\mathbf{A} - \mathbf{c}^T, \tag{6.88}$$

$$\mathbf{d}_2^T = \mathbf{p}^T, \tag{6.89}$$

$$M_0 = \mathbf{p}^T\mathbf{b}. \tag{6.90}$$

We are now in a position to prove the following theorem:

THEOREM **6.11.** (i) *If slack variables* $\mathbf{v}$ *are introduced so that the constraints in the dual problem are*

$$\mathbf{A}^T\mathbf{y} - \mathbf{v} = \mathbf{c}, \qquad \mathbf{y} \geq \mathbf{0}, \qquad \mathbf{v} \geq \mathbf{0},$$

and the primal problem has a solution, then the optimal solution of the dual problem is given by

$$\mathbf{y} = \mathbf{d}_2, \qquad \mathbf{v} = \mathbf{d}_1,$$

where $\mathbf{d}_1$, $\mathbf{d}_2$ *are defined in* (6.87).

(ii) *If* $\hat{\mathbf{x}}$ *is the solution of the primal that maximizes* (6.78) *and* $\hat{\mathbf{y}}$ *is the solution of the dual that minimizes* (6.80), *then*

$$\mathbf{c}^T\hat{\mathbf{x}} = \mathbf{b}^T\hat{\mathbf{y}} \quad or \quad M_1 = M_2. \tag{6.91}$$

Proof: The simplex method produces vectors $\mathbf{d}_1$, $\mathbf{d}_2$ in (6.87) that are greater than or equal to zero. (This is the condition for termination of the simplex method.) Hence, transposing (6.88) and replacing $\mathbf{p}$ by $\mathbf{d}_2$, we see that

$$\mathbf{A}^T\mathbf{d}_2 \geq \mathbf{c}, \qquad \mathbf{d}_2 \geq \mathbf{0}.$$

Hence, $\mathbf{d}_2$ satisfies the constraints of the dual problem. Also the quantity M_0 in (6.90) is the maximum in the primal problem, i.e., the quantity $\mathbf{c}^T\hat{\mathbf{x}}$ where $\hat{\mathbf{x}}$ is the solution of the primal. From (6.90), replacing $\mathbf{p}$ by $\mathbf{d}_2$, this means that

$$\mathbf{d}_2^T\mathbf{b} = \mathbf{c}^T\hat{\mathbf{x}}.$$

Theorem 6.10(iii) then says that $\mathbf{d}_2$ must be the solution of the dual. Also $\mathbf{d}_1 = \mathbf{A}^T\mathbf{d}_2 - \mathbf{c}$ so that $\mathbf{d}_1$ must be the slack variable vector $\mathbf{v}$. This proves part (i). Part (i) shows that if the primal has an optimal solution it is always possible to produce a $\hat{\mathbf{y}}$ such that $\mathbf{c}^T\hat{\mathbf{x}} = \mathbf{b}^T\hat{\mathbf{y}}$. We always have $\mathbf{c}^T\hat{\mathbf{x}} \leq \mathbf{b}^T\mathbf{y}$ [see Theorem 6.10(ii)] so that all solutions of the dual problem must satisfy (6.91). This proves part (ii) of the theorem.

The last theorem stated that if the primal has a solution, then the dual has also a solution. We now show:

THEOREM **6.12.** *If the maximum value of M for the primal is unbounded, then the dual has no feasible solution.*

Proof: Theorem 6.10(ii) states that

$$\mathbf{c}^T\mathbf{x} \leq \mathbf{b}^T\mathbf{y},$$

for all admissible $\mathbf{x}$, $\mathbf{y}$. But admissible $\mathbf{x}$ can be found such that $\mathbf{c}^T\mathbf{x}$ is unbounded. Hence, there is no feasible solution $\mathbf{y}$ for the dual.

The reader should note that the converse is not true, i.e., if the dual has no feasible solution, this does not imply that the maximum value of M for the primal is unbounded. Neither problem may have a solution.

In order to state our concluding theorem we introduce slack variables $\mathbf{u}$, $\mathbf{v}$ so that the constraint equations (6.79), (6.81) become

$$\mathbf{A}\mathbf{x} + \mathbf{u} = \mathbf{b}, \qquad \mathbf{A}^T\mathbf{y} - \mathbf{v} = \mathbf{c}, \tag{6.92}$$

where $\mathbf{x} \geq \mathbf{0}$, $\mathbf{u} \geq \mathbf{0}$, $\mathbf{y} \geq \mathbf{0}$, $\mathbf{v} \geq \mathbf{0}$. We also introduce the following correspondence between these variables:

$$x_1\, x_2 \ldots x_n\, u_1\, u_2 \ldots u_m$$

$$v_1\, v_2 \ldots v_n\, y_1\, y_2 \ldots y_m.$$

THEOREM **6.13.** *If* $\hat{\mathbf{x}}$, $\hat{\mathbf{u}}$, $\hat{\mathbf{y}}$, $\hat{\mathbf{v}}$ *are the optimal solutions of the (nondegenerate) primal and dual, then*

$$\hat{\mathbf{x}}^T\hat{\mathbf{v}} = 0, \qquad \hat{\mathbf{y}}^T\hat{\mathbf{u}} = 0. \tag{6.93}$$

If a variable in the primal is zero (nonzero) then the corresponding variable in the dual is nonzero (zero).

Proof: On replacing $\mathbf{x}$, $\mathbf{y}$, $\mathbf{u}$, $\mathbf{v}$ in (6.92) by $\hat{\mathbf{x}}$, $\hat{\mathbf{y}}$, $\hat{\mathbf{u}}$, $\hat{\mathbf{v}}$, and multiplying the first equation by $\hat{\mathbf{y}}^T$, the second by $\hat{\mathbf{x}}^T$, we obtain

$$\hat{\mathbf{y}}^T\mathbf{A}\hat{\mathbf{x}} + \mathbf{y}^T\hat{\mathbf{u}} = \hat{\mathbf{y}}^T\mathbf{b},$$

$$\hat{\mathbf{x}}^T\mathbf{A}^T\hat{\mathbf{y}} - \hat{\mathbf{x}}^T\hat{\mathbf{v}} = \hat{\mathbf{x}}^T\mathbf{c}.$$

Subtract these equations and use (6.91):

$$\hat{\mathbf{y}}^T\hat{\mathbf{u}} + \hat{\mathbf{x}}^T\hat{\mathbf{v}} = 0.$$

Since $\hat{\mathbf{y}} \geq \mathbf{0}$, $\hat{\mathbf{u}} \geq \mathbf{0}$, $\hat{\mathbf{x}} \geq 0$, $\hat{\mathbf{v}} \geq \mathbf{0}$, each of the terms on the left of this equation must be zero, and this gives (6.93). This implies that

$$\left.\begin{aligned} y_i u_i &= 0, \qquad i = 1, 2, \ldots, m, \\ x_i v_i &= 0, \qquad i = 1, 2, \ldots, n. \end{aligned}\right\} \tag{6.94}$$

Since both the primal and the dual are nondegenerate, there are n nonzero basic variables in the primal and m in the dual. If this statement is combined with (6.94), we see that the result in the last part of the theorem is true.

So far we have been concerned almost entirely with algebraic relations between the primal and dual. As illustrated in Section 6.1, the primal problem arises naturally by considering a situation in which it is required to optimize some quantity like profit. The question arises of whether the dual corresponding to such a primal can be given an interpretation in the same physical context as the primal.

Consider the problem in Section 6.1, which involved the manufacture of two products 1, 2 by means of three machines 1, 2, 3. The interpretation of the elements of **b**, **c**, **x**, **A** are:

b_i = number of hours available of machine i,
c_j = profit from one unit of product j,
x_j = number of units of product j produced,
a_{ij} = number of hours of machine i required to produce one unit of product j.

We now ask the following question: Can we assign an interpretation to the elements of **y**?

From the duality theory, Theorem 6.11(ii), we know that, for the optimal solutions $\hat{\mathbf{x}}$, $\hat{\mathbf{y}}$, we have

$$\mathbf{c}^T\hat{\mathbf{x}} = \mathbf{b}^T\hat{\mathbf{y}}.$$

The quantity on the left is the total profit. The quantity on the right is the sum of products of the total number of hours available on machine i multiplied by y_i. Hence it is natural to think of y_i as the cost per hour associated with machine i. These hypothetical or fictitious costs are usually known as *shadow prices.*

The dual problem is now:

minimize $\quad \mathbf{b}^T\mathbf{y}$ = cost of the available machine time,

subject to $\quad \mathbf{A}^T\mathbf{y} \geq \mathbf{c}, \qquad \mathbf{y} \geq \mathbf{0}.$

The quantity $\mathbf{A}^T\mathbf{y}$ represents the costs of producing one unit of each of the products j, and at first sight it might seem that these should be made *less* than the profits c_j. If the inequality were in this direction, the quantity $\mathbf{b}^T\hat{\mathbf{y}}$ could not be minimized since $\mathbf{b}^T\mathbf{y}$ would be unbounded below. Apart from this, however, the inequality $\mathbf{A}^T\mathbf{y} \geq \mathbf{c}$ can be interpreted as follows. The inequality says that the cost of producing a product is at least as great as the profit on the product. However, if the cost is greater than the profit, we should obviously not produce this product at all, in order to avoid making a loss. If we must manufacture products, then we will choose to make products for which the cost equals the profit so that at least we do not make a loss. This is precisely what the solution of the dual problem gives. If we have an inequality in the dual, this is the same thing as saying that the corresponding slack variable in the dual is nonzero, which, by Theorem 6.13, implies that the corresponding variable in the primal is zero. This means that we have zero production of the corresponding product. Similarly, if we have equality in the dual this means positive production of the corresponding article in the primal. Production is arranged so that the hypothetical machine costs exactly equal the profit.

It would take us too far afield to illustrate in detail why the primal-dual relationship is both important and useful. We remark that it is often easier to solve one problem rather than the other. Thus a basic feasible solution may be obvious in one case but not in the other. (This is in fact true of the concrete example considered in Section 6.2.) Also, if $\mathbf{A}$ is $m \times n$, then basic solutions of the primal and dual have, respectively, m and n nonzero variables. Other things being equal, it will be simpler to solve the problem for which the basic solution has the smaller number of basic variables. Finally, if we have solved a given linear programming problem and wish to add an extra constraint, it would seem to be necessary to start the solution from the beginning, because feasible solutions of the original system do not necessarily satisfy the additional constraint. However, in the dual it is only necessary to add an extra variable. In this case we can start from the previous solution, setting the additional variable in the dual equal to zero, initially.

Miscellaneous Exercises 6

Ex. 6.2. Suppose that m products are produced by n factories. Let a_{ji} be the number of units of product i produced by factory j in one day, where the production pattern of each factory is fixed. We wish to produce at least c_i units of product i. The cost of keeping factory j in production is b_j per day. We wish to determine the numbers of days y_j that each factory should operate in order to produce at least c_i units of product i, at minimum cost. Show that equations (6.8), (6.9) express this problem in matrix notation.

Ex. 6.3. Give an interpretation of the dual of the problem described in Ex. 6.2 by assigning a shadow price or value to each unit of product i produced ($i = 1, 2, 3$). (Consider a manager who is controlling production on the basis of the assigned shadow prices, without knowing anything about operating costs. He will adjust the amounts produced so as to maximize the value of the total production. Of course, the shadow prices need bear no relation to market prices.)

Ex. 6.4. The diet problem of Ex. 6.1 is already in the notation of the dual problem. We can provide an interpretation of the corresponding primal by imputing values x_1, x_2 to the nutrients 1, 2. We must arrange to maximize the total value of the nutrients:

$$M = \mathbf{c}^T\mathbf{x} = 40x_1 + 60x_2,$$

subject to the constraints that the value of the nutrients in the foods 1, 2, 3 is less than the costs of the foods:

$$\mathbf{Ax} \le \mathbf{b}.$$

Ex. 6.5. Show that the inverse of the $m \times m$ matrix $\mathbf{A}_B$ consisting of the columns of $[\mathbf{A}, \mathbf{I}]$ that correspond to the basic variables in the optimal solution is given by $\mathbf{S}_2$ in (6.87).

Solution: Introduce the following notation that indicates the separate columns in the second and third matrices in (6.87),

$$\begin{bmatrix} \mathbf{P} & \mathbf{0} \\ \mathbf{p}^T & 1 \end{bmatrix} \begin{bmatrix} \mathbf{a}_1 & \mathbf{a}_2 & \cdots & \mathbf{a}_{n+m} & \mathbf{b} \\ -c_1 & -c_2 & \cdots & -c_{n+m} & 0 \end{bmatrix} = \begin{bmatrix} \mathbf{s}_1 & \mathbf{s}_2 & \cdots & \mathbf{s}_{n+m} & \mathbf{x}_B \\ d_1 & d_2 & \cdots & d_{n+m} & M_0 \end{bmatrix}, \tag{6.95}$$

where $\mathbf{a}_r$ is the rth column of $\mathbf{A}$ for $r = 1, \ldots, n$ and $\mathbf{a}_r = \mathbf{e}_r$ for $r = n + 1, \ldots, n + m$, where the $\mathbf{e}_r$ are $m \times 1$ unit column vectors. Also, c_r is the rth element of $\mathbf{c}^T$ for $r = 1, \ldots, n$, and $c_r = 0$ for $r = n + 1, \ldots, m + n$. We know that the final matrix in the simplex method is such that m of the vectors $\mathbf{s}_1, \ldots, \mathbf{s}_{m+n}$ are the m unit vectors $\mathbf{e}_i$. Suppose that

$$\mathbf{s}_\alpha = \mathbf{e}_1, \qquad \mathbf{s}_\beta = \mathbf{e}_2, \ldots, \mathbf{s}_\gamma = \mathbf{e}_m$$

where $\alpha, \beta, \ldots, \gamma$ are m of the numbers $1, 2, \ldots, m + n$, and $\alpha, \beta, \ldots, \gamma$ are not necessarily arranged in any particular order. The columns $\mathbf{s}_\alpha, \mathbf{s}_\beta, \ldots, \mathbf{s}_\gamma$ are the columns corresponding to the basic variables, so that the basic variables must be

$$x_\alpha, x_\beta, \ldots, x_\gamma.$$

From (6.95) we see that

$$\mathbf{Pa}_\alpha = \mathbf{e}_1, \qquad \mathbf{Pa}_\beta = \mathbf{e}_2, \ldots, \mathbf{Pa}_\gamma = \mathbf{e}_m$$

that is,

$$\mathbf{PA}_B = \mathbf{I} \quad \text{or} \quad \mathbf{A}_B^{-1} = \mathbf{P},$$

where $\mathbf{A}_B$ is the $m \times m$ matrix consisting of the columns of $\mathbf{A}$ that correspond to the basic variables. Since $\mathbf{a}_{n+r} = \mathbf{e}_r$, $r = 1, \ldots, m$, we see from (6.95) that $\mathbf{Pe}_r = \mathbf{s}_{n+r}$, i.e.,

$$\mathbf{A}_B^{-1} = \mathbf{P} = [\mathbf{s}_{n+1}, \mathbf{s}_{n+2}, \ldots, \mathbf{s}_{n+m}].$$

Hence, the inverse of the matrix $\mathbf{A}_B$ is given by $\mathbf{S}_2$ in (6.87).

Ex. 6.6. Show that if, in the notation of (6.92), the optimal basic solution of the primal contains s nonzero variables $x_1, \ldots, x_s$ from $\mathbf{x}$ and $m - s$ nonzero variables $u_{s+1}, \ldots, u_m$ from $\mathbf{u}$, then the situation in the primal and dual is the following:

	Basic nonzero	*Nonbasic zero*	*Nonbasic zero*	*Basic nonzero*
Primal	s	$n - s$	s	$m - s$
	$x_1, \ldots, x_s$	$x_{s+1}, \ldots, x_n$	$u_1, \ldots, u_s$	$u_{s+1}, \ldots, u_m$
	Basic nonzero	*Nonbasic zero*	*Nonbasic zero*	*Basic nonzero*
Dual	s	$m - s$	s	$n - s$
	$y_1, \ldots, y_s$	$y_{s+1}, \ldots, y_m$	$v_1, \ldots, v_s$	$v_{s+1}, \ldots, v_n$

Ex. 6.7. Using partitioning motivated by Ex. 6.6, show that (6.87) can be written in more detailed form (renumbering variables and reordering equations if necessary) as:

$$\begin{array}{c} s \\ m-s \\ 1 \end{array}\overset{\begin{array}{ccc} s & m-s & 1 \end{array}}{\begin{bmatrix} \mathbf{P}_{11} & \mathbf{0} & 0 \\ \mathbf{P}_{21} & \mathbf{I} & 0 \\ \mathbf{P}_{31} & \mathbf{0} & 1 \end{bmatrix}} \overset{\begin{array}{ccccc} s & n-s & s & m-s & 1 \end{array}}{\begin{bmatrix} \mathbf{A}_{11} & \mathbf{A}_{12} & \mathbf{I}_s & \mathbf{0} & \mathbf{b}_1 \\ \mathbf{A}_{21} & \mathbf{A}_{22} & \mathbf{0} & \mathbf{I}_{m-s} & \mathbf{b}_2 \\ -\mathbf{c}_1^T & -\mathbf{c}_2^T & \mathbf{0} & \mathbf{0} & 0 \end{bmatrix}}$$

$$= \overset{\begin{array}{ccccc} s & n-s & s & m-s & 1 \end{array}}{\begin{bmatrix} \mathbf{I}_s & \mathbf{Y}_{11} & \mathbf{Y}_{12} & \mathbf{0} & \boldsymbol{\beta}_1 \\ \mathbf{0} & \mathbf{Y}_{21} & \mathbf{Y}_{22} & \mathbf{I}_{m-s} & \boldsymbol{\beta}_2 \\ \mathbf{0} & \boldsymbol{\gamma}_2^T & \boldsymbol{\gamma}_1^T & \mathbf{0} & M_0 \end{bmatrix}} \begin{array}{c} s \\ m-s \\ 1 \end{array}$$

Similarly, show that the dual can be written

$$\begin{array}{c} s \\ n-s \\ 1 \end{array}\overset{\begin{array}{ccc} s & n-s & 1 \end{array}}{\begin{bmatrix} \mathbf{Q}_{11} & \mathbf{0} & 0 \\ \mathbf{Q}_{12} & -\mathbf{I} & 0 \\ \mathbf{Q}_{31} & \mathbf{0} & 1 \end{bmatrix}} \overset{\begin{array}{ccccc} s & m-s & s & n-s & 1 \end{array}}{\begin{bmatrix} \mathbf{A}_{11}^T & \mathbf{A}_{21}^T & -\mathbf{I}_s & \mathbf{0} & \mathbf{c}_1 \\ \mathbf{A}_{12}^T & \mathbf{A}_{22}^T & \mathbf{0} & -\mathbf{I}_{n-s} & \mathbf{c}_2 \\ \mathbf{b}_1^T & \mathbf{b}_2^T & \mathbf{0} & \mathbf{0} & 0 \end{bmatrix}}$$

$$= \overset{\begin{array}{ccccc} s & m-s & s & n-s & 1 \end{array}}{\begin{bmatrix} \mathbf{I}_s & \mathbf{Z}_{11} & \mathbf{Z}_{12} & \mathbf{0} & \boldsymbol{\delta}_1 \\ \mathbf{0} & \mathbf{Z}_{21} & \mathbf{Z}_{22} & \mathbf{I}_{n-s} & \boldsymbol{\delta}_2 \\ \mathbf{0} & \boldsymbol{\epsilon}_2^T & \boldsymbol{\epsilon}_1^T & \mathbf{0} & N_0 \end{bmatrix}} \begin{array}{c} s \\ n-s \\ 1 \end{array}$$

Show that the elements in the matrices on the right of these equations can be expressed in terms of the $\mathbf{A}_{ij}$, $\mathbf{b}_i$, $\mathbf{c}_j$. Hence, show that

$$\mathbf{Z}_{11} = -\mathbf{Y}_{22}^T, \qquad \mathbf{Z}_{12} = -\mathbf{Y}_{12}^T, \qquad \mathbf{Z}_{21} = -\mathbf{Y}_{21}^T, \qquad \mathbf{Z}_{22} = -\mathbf{Y}_{11}^T,$$

$$\boldsymbol{\beta}_i = \boldsymbol{\epsilon}_i, \qquad \boldsymbol{\gamma}_i = \boldsymbol{\delta}_i, \qquad i = 1, 2.$$

This identifies precisely the relationship between the primal and dual arrays. In the specific example given in (6.84), (6.85), show that $\mathbf{Y}_{11}$, $\mathbf{Y}_{21}$, $\boldsymbol{\gamma}_2$ are nonexistent, and

$$\boldsymbol{\gamma}_1 = \begin{bmatrix} 30 \\ 10 \end{bmatrix}, \quad \boldsymbol{\beta}_1 = \begin{bmatrix} 15 \\ 25 \end{bmatrix}, \quad \boldsymbol{\beta}_2 = [15],$$

$$\mathbf{Y}_{12} = \begin{bmatrix} 1.5 & -0.5 \\ -0.5 & 0.5 \end{bmatrix}, \qquad \mathbf{Y}_{22} = [-2.5, 0.5].$$

Ex. 6.8. Work out the details of the simplex method for the examples in Section 6.5 for which only the answers are indicated.

Ex. 6.9. Work out the details of the reduction of (6.83) to give the final form in (6.84).

Ex. 6.10. Show that the primal:

$$\begin{array}{ll} \text{maximize} & M_1 = \mathbf{c}^T\mathbf{x}, \\ \text{subject to} & \mathbf{Ax} = \mathbf{b},\ \mathbf{x} \geq \mathbf{0}, \end{array}$$

has the dual:

$$\begin{array}{ll} \text{minimize} & M_2 = \mathbf{b}^T\mathbf{y} \\ \text{subject to} & \mathbf{A}^T\mathbf{y} \geq \mathbf{c},\ \mathbf{y} \text{ unrestricted.} \end{array}$$

Ex. 6.11. Write an essay on connections between linear programming and the theory of games. Possible references are Glicksman [75] and Vajda [98].

Ex. 6.12. Write an essay on applications of linear programming in economics. Possible references are Dorfman, Samuelson, and Solow [69], and Gale [70].

7 Determinants and Square Matrices

7.1 Introduction

Square matrices are so important that we devote a whole chapter to their properties.

In the first part of the chapter we investigate determinants, which are scalars associated with square matrices. It is fashionable in some quarters to decry the use of determinants. Perhaps this is a natural reaction against the overemphasis on determinants and neglect of matrices in older textbooks. From a modern viewpoint we can see that matrices are much more fundamental than determinants—determinants are merely single numbers associated with matrices. Formerly, determinants were the main tool for the discussion of the solution of simultaneous linear equations. However, the use of determinants is a very inefficient method for the numerical solution of equations, and much more effective methods are available. Another reason for the present tendency to neglect determinants is that it is more convenient and illuminating to discuss certain theoretical questions by other more powerful techniques. If all the results that are obtainable by determinants can be derived by other more convenient methods, it can be argued that there is little reason for introducing determinants at all. We do not completely agree with this point of view. Although we devote only a few sections to determinants, we emphasize that the subject is important. We shall see later that determinants often provide a convenient shorthand notation for the discussion of certain questions, even though we do not use much of the machinery associated with determinants. Also, determinants are useful for the practical solution of simultaneous linear equations when the coefficients contain symbols and parameters.

Determinants can be defined in various equivalent ways. We shall use a definition that is closely related to the way in which simultaneous equations are solved by means of determinants. It seems to be an unfortunate fact of life that, whatever the definition used as a starting point, the development of the theory of determinants always involves one theorem that is awkward to prove. In the present development, the awkward theorem is the first one, Theorem 7.1. However, the results of the theorem are more important than the details of the proof, and once the initial theorem is grasped, the remainder of the development is straightforward.

The second half of the chapter is concerned with certain aspects of the numerical solution of systems of n equations in n unknowns. The theory in previous chapters gave a clear-cut answer to the problem of whether a solution exists or not. Unfortunately, there is more to the practical problem than this:

(a) It is desirable to find an *efficient* procedure for solving the equations. We imagine that the calculations are being performed on a digital computer or by a human being. It is then necessary to give a complete specification (i.e., *algorithm*) describing in detail the exact sequence of operations that must be followed in order to obtain the solution of the problem.

(b) It is necessary to find the solution to a given degree of accuracy. The difficulty here is that in computing we are forced to compute with finite precision numbers, specified to only a given number of significant figures.

In Section 7.6 it will be shown that the method of successive elimination requires approximately $\frac{1}{3}n^3$ additions and multiplications to solve a set of n equations in n unknowns. In the 150 years since Gauss published this method, a great deal of effort has been expended in trying to find a more efficient procedure. The end result of all this work is that, unless the matrix has a very special structure (for example, a large number of zero elements), the method of successive elimination is still the best. However, it is necessary to take certain precautions. In particular, the choice of pivots is important. Also, complications can arise because the solution may be very sensitive to small changes in the coefficients of the original system, or to rounding errors introduced in the course of the solution. These matters are discussed in Chapter 8.

7.2 The Definition of a Determinant

We are going to define a single number associated with an $n \times n$ matrix $\mathbf{A} = [a_{ij}]$, called the *determinant* of the matrix, and denoted by $\det \mathbf{A}$ or $|\mathbf{A}|$. (The vertical lines here have nothing to do with the absolute value or modulus of a real or complex number.) The determinant of order n will be defined in terms of determinants of order $n - 1$, together with the statement that, if we are considering a 1×1 matrix consisting of a single element, $\mathbf{A} = [a_{11}]$, then

$$|\mathbf{A}| = \det \mathbf{A} = a_{11}. \tag{7.1}$$

This means that second-order determinants are defined in terms of the first-order determinant just defined. Third-order determinants are defined in terms of second-order determinants, and so on. To be precise, we introduce the following definitions.

DEFINITION 7.1. The determinant of the $(n-1) \times (n-1)$ matrix formed by omitting the ith row and the jth column of the $n \times n$ matrix **A** is called the *minor* of a_{ij}, and is denoted by M_{ij}. The number

$$A_{ij} = (-1)^{i+j} M_{ij}, \tag{7.2}$$

is called the *cofactor* of a_{ij}.

The signs $(-1)^{i+j}$ form a checkerboard pattern:

$$\begin{bmatrix} + & - & + & \cdots \\ - & + & - & \cdots \\ + & - & + & \cdots \\ & \cdots & & \end{bmatrix}.$$

DEFINITION 7.2. The *determinant* of an $n \times n$ matrix **A** is defined by the expression

$$|\mathbf{A}| = \det \mathbf{A} = \sum_{j=1}^{n} a_{1j} A_{1j}, \tag{7.3}$$

in conjunction with the definition of det **A** for $n = 1$ given in (7.1). In words, the determinant of **A** is the sum of the products of the elements in the first row of the matrix times their respective cofactors.

As a simple example, consider

$$\begin{aligned} |\mathbf{A}| = \begin{vmatrix} a_{11} & a_{12} \\ a_{21} & a_{22} \end{vmatrix} &= a_{11}A_{11} + a_{12}A_{12} \\ &= a_{11} \det [a_{22}] - a_{12} \det [a_{21}] = a_{11}a_{22} - a_{12}a_{21}. \end{aligned} \tag{7.4}$$

Similarly,

$$\begin{vmatrix} a_{11} & a_{12} & a_{13} \\ a_{21} & a_{22} & a_{23} \\ a_{31} & a_{32} & a_{33} \end{vmatrix} = a_{11}A_{11} + a_{12}A_{12} + a_{13}A_{13} \tag{7.5}$$

$$\begin{aligned} &= a_{11} \begin{vmatrix} a_{22} & a_{23} \\ a_{32} & a_{33} \end{vmatrix} - a_{12} \begin{vmatrix} a_{21} & a_{23} \\ a_{31} & a_{33} \end{vmatrix} + a_{13} \begin{vmatrix} a_{21} & a_{22} \\ a_{31} & a_{32} \end{vmatrix} \\ &= a_{11}a_{22}a_{33} - a_{11}a_{32}a_{23} - a_{12}a_{21}a_{33} + a_{12}a_{31}a_{23} \\ &\qquad + a_{13}a_{21}a_{32} - a_{13}a_{31}a_{22}. \end{aligned} \tag{7.6}$$

If we choose any term in this expansion, say $a_{12}a_{31}a_{23}$, we see that there is one element from each of the three rows of **A**, and one from each of the three columns. No two elements in the product lie in the same row of **A**, and no two elements lie in the same column.

It is clear from the definition (7.3) that the same rule holds for a determinant of order n. In the general case, the determinant is the sum of all possible products of n elements chosen from the matrix, with appropriate signs, where, in each product, no two elements belong to the same row, and no two elements belong to the same column. A determinant is often defined in this way, with a suitable specification of the signs of the products, but we shall not continue this method of approach. However, this expansion is sometimes needed (e.g., in Ex. 7.29) and we state the situation more precisely in Ex. 7.28.

The first row of the matrix plays a special role in Definition 7.2, Equation (7.3). The first important result which we require is that the value of the determinant can be found by expanding in terms of *any* row or *any* column. Thus, in addition to (7.5) we have the equivalent expansions:

$$\begin{aligned}\det \mathbf{A} &= a_{21}A_{21} + a_{22}A_{22} + a_{23}A_{23} \\ &= a_{11}A_{11} + a_{21}A_{21} + a_{31}A_{31} \\ &= a_{13}A_{13} + a_{23}A_{23} + a_{33}A_{33},\end{aligned}$$

and so on.

THEOREM 7.1. *The sum of the products of the elements in any row (or column) of a square matrix, times their corresponding cofactors, equals the determinant of the matrix. In symbols,*

$$\det \mathbf{A} = \sum_{j=1}^{n} a_{pj}A_{pj} = \sum_{i=1}^{n} a_{iq}A_{iq}, \qquad \text{(all } p, q\text{)}. \tag{7.7}$$

Proof: It is easily checked directly that Equation (7.7) is true for 2×2 determinants:

$$\begin{aligned}\begin{vmatrix} a_{11} & a_{12} \\ a_{21} & a_{22} \end{vmatrix} &= a_{11}A_{11} + a_{12}A_{12} = a_{11}(a_{22}) + a_{12}(-a_{21}) \\ &= a_{21}A_{21} + a_{22}A_{22} = a_{21}(-a_{12}) + a_{22}(a_{11}) \\ &= a_{11}A_{11} + a_{21}A_{21} = a_{11}(a_{22}) + a_{21}(-a_{12}) \\ &= a_{12}A_{12} + a_{22}A_{22} = a_{12}(-a_{21}) + a_{22}(a_{11}).\end{aligned}$$

We shall assume that the result (7.7) is true for determinants of order $n - 1$ and prove that it is then true for determinants of order n. We do this in three stages:

(a) Expansion by first row = expansion by first column.
(b) Expansion by first row = expansion by any row.
(c) Expansion by first column = expansion by any column.

When we have proved these results, since the theorem is true for $n = 2$, the truth of the theorem for all n will follow by induction.

(a) We prove first of all that expansion by the first row is the same as expansion by the first column, i.e.,

$$\sum_{i=1}^{n} a_{i1}A_{i1} = \sum_{j=1}^{n} a_{1j}A_{1j}. \tag{7.8}$$

It is clear from the definition of cofactors that the elements a_{i1} in the first row do not occur in any of the cofactors of the elements in the first row, A_{k1}, and similarly, for the first column, the a_{1l} do not occur in any of the A_{1l}.

The coefficient of a_{11} is the same on both sides of (7.8). Consider the coefficient of $a_{i1}a_{1j}$, $i > 1$, $j > 1$. In the expression on the left of (7.8), this is given by the coefficient of a_{1j} in the expansion of A_{i1}, which is $(-1)^{i+1}$ times the coefficient of a_{1j} in the expansion of M_{i1}. Assuming that the theorem is true for determinants of order $n - 1$, and remembering that a_{1j} is in the $(j - 1)$th column of M_{i1}, we see that the coefficient of $a_{i1}a_{1j}$ is given by

$$(-1)^{i+1}(-1)^{j-1+1}M_{i1,1j} = (-1)^{i+j+1}M_{i1,1j}, \tag{7.9}$$

where we introduce the notation $M_{ip,qj}$ to denote the determinant of the matrix of order $n - 2$ obtained by omitting the ith and pth rows of $\mathbf{A}$ and the qth and jth columns of $\mathbf{A}$. By exactly the same type of argument, the coefficient of $a_{i1}a_{1j}$, $i > 1, j > 1$, in the expression on the right of (7.8) is $(-1)^{j+1}$ times the coefficient of a_{i1} in the expansion of M_{1j}, and this is precisely (7.9). Hence, (7.8) is proved.

(b) We next prove that the expansion in terms of the pth row of $\mathbf{A}$ is the same as the expansion in terms of the first row:

$$\sum_{j=1}^{n} a_{1j}A_{1j} = \sum_{k=1}^{n} a_{pk}A_{pk}, \qquad p = 2, 3, \ldots, n. \tag{7.10}$$

In the expression on the left we single out the term containing $a_{1j}a_{pk}$. The coefficient of a_{1j} is $(-1)^{j+1}M_{1j}$, and the coefficient of $a_{1j}a_{pk}$ ($j \neq k$, of course, since the term $j = k$ does not occur) is therefore $(-1)^{j+1}$ times the coefficient of a_{pk} in the expansion of M_{1j}, or (assuming that the required result is true for determinants of order $n - 1$),

$$\left.\begin{aligned} &(-1)^{j+1}(-1)^{p+k-1}M_{1p,jk}, \qquad (j > k),\\ &(-1)^{j+1}(-1)^{p-1+k-1}M_{1p,jk}, \qquad (j < k),\end{aligned}\right\} \tag{7.11}$$

where $M_{1p,jk}$ is the determinant of the matrix obtained by omitting the 1st and pth rows, and jth and kth columns of $\mathbf{A}$. The reason for the signs in (7.11) can be seen with the help of Figure 7.1. If $j > k$, then a_{pk} is in the pth column and

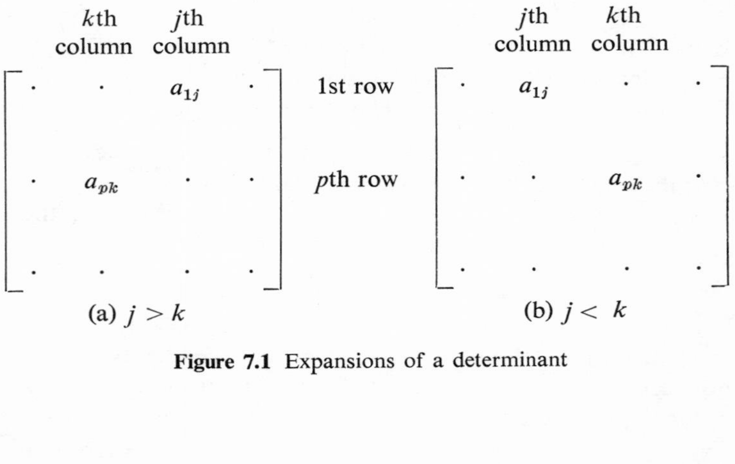

Figure 7.1 Expansions of a determinant

$(k-1)$th row of M_{1j}. If $j < k$, then a_{pk} is in the $(p-1)$th column and $(k-1)$th row of M_{1j}. We next single out the term containing $a_{pk}a_{1j}$. This is given by $(-1)^{p+k}$ times the coefficient of a_{1j} in the expansion of M_{pk}, or

$$\left.\begin{array}{ll}(-1)^{p+k}(-1)^{1+j-1}M_{p1,kj}, & (j > k),\\ (-1)^{p+k}(-1)^{1+j}M_{p1,kj}, & (j < k).\end{array}\right\}$$

This is precisely the same as (7.11), so that (7.10) is proved.

(c) On applying the result in (b) to the transpose of **A**, we see that expansion of det **A** by its qth column gives the same result as expansion by its first column.

This concludes the proof of Theorem 7.1.

The same method can be used to prove:

THEOREM 7.2. *If* **B** *is the matrix obtained from a square matrix* **A** *by interchanging any two rows (or any two columns), then*

$$\det \mathbf{B} = -\det \mathbf{A}. \tag{7.12}$$

Proof: We first prove that the result is true if the 1st and pth rows of $\mathbf{A} = [a_{ij}]$ are interchanged. The coefficient of $a_{1j}a_{pk}$ in the determinant on the right of (7.12) is given by (7.11). The matrix $\mathbf{B} = [b_{ij}]$ is obtained by interchanging the 1st and pth rows of **A** so that $b_{ij} = a_{ij}$ except when $i = 1$, p, in which case

$$b_{1j} = a_{pj}, \qquad b_{pj} = a_{1j}, \qquad (j = 1 \text{ to } n).$$

Hence, the coefficient of $a_{1j}a_{pk}$ in the determinant on the left of (7.12) is the coefficient of $b_{pj}b_{1k}$, which is found by replacing j by k and k by j in (7.11):

$$\left.\begin{array}{ll}(-1)^{k+1}(-1)^{p+j-1}M_{1p,kj}, & (k > j),\\ (-1)^{k+1}(-1)^{p-1+j-1}M_{1p,kj}, & (k < j).\end{array}\right\} \tag{7.13}$$

The minor $M_{1p,kj}$ that occurs in this expression is identical with that in (7.11) since **A** and **B** are the same apart from the 1st and pth rows. On comparing (7.11), (7.13) we see that one is precisely minus the other, which is the required result. Suppose next that **C** is the matrix obtained by interchanging the pth and qth rows of **A**. We can go from **A** to **C** by three interchanges of rows: 1st and pth, new 1st and qth, new 1st and pth. This produces a sign change of $(-1)^3 = -1$. A similar argument holds for columns. This completes the proof of the theorem.

7.3 Basic Properties of Determinants

Many of the properties of determinants follow directly from Theorems 7.1, 7.2 proved in the last section. We remind the reader that, from this point onwards, when we refer to the determinant of a matrix, it is implicitly assumed that the matrix is square, since determinants are defined only for square matrices.

THEOREM 7.3. (i) *The determinant of the transpose of a matrix is equal to the determinant of the matrix:*

$$|\mathbf{A}^T| = |\mathbf{A}|. \tag{7.14}$$

(ii) *If all the elements of any row or any column of a matrix are zero, then the determinant of the matrix is zero.*

(iii) *If the elements of one row or one column of a matrix are multiplied by a constant c, then the determinant is multiplied by c. If* **A** *is* $n \times n$, *then*

$$|c\mathbf{A}| = c^n\,|\mathbf{A}|. \tag{7.15}$$

(iv) *If* **A** *and* **B** *differ only in their kth columns, then* det **A** + det **B** = det **C** *where* **C** *is a matrix whose columns are the same as those of* **A** (*or* **B**) *except that the kth column of* **C** *is the sum of the kth columns of* **A** *and* **B**. *In symbols, partitioning in columns,*

$$\det[\mathbf{c}_1, \ldots, \mathbf{c}_k, \ldots, \mathbf{c}_n] + \det[\mathbf{c}_1, \ldots, \boldsymbol{\gamma}_k, \ldots, \mathbf{c}_n] = \det[\mathbf{c}_1, \ldots, \mathbf{c}_k + \boldsymbol{\gamma}_k, \ldots, \mathbf{c}_n]. \tag{7.16}$$

A similar result holds for rows.

(v) *If a determinant has two equal rows* (*or columns*), *then its value is zero. If any row* (*or column*) *of a matrix is a multiple of any other row* (*or column*), *then its determinant is zero.*

(vi) *The value of a determinant is unchanged if a multiple of one row* (*or column*) *is added to another row* (*or column*). *For* $j \neq q$,

$$\begin{vmatrix} a_{11} & \ldots & a_{1j} & \ldots & a_{1n} \\ & & \ldots & & \\ a_{n1} & \ldots & a_{nj} & \ldots & a_{nn} \end{vmatrix} = \begin{vmatrix} a_{11} & \ldots & a_{1j} + ca_{1q} & \ldots & a_{1n} \\ & & \ldots & & \\ a_{n1} & \ldots & a_{nj} + ca_{nq} & \ldots & a_{nn} \end{vmatrix}.$$

Proof: To prove (i) we note that expansion of $\mathbf{A}^T$ by its first row is the same as expanding **A** by its first column, so that the result follows from Theorem 7.1. Part (ii) also follows from Theorem 7.1 on expanding the determinant by the row or column containing the zero elements. The first part of (iii) follows similarly on expanding by the row or column whose elements are multiplied by c. The last part follows on noting that $c\mathbf{A}$ is $[ca_{ij}]$ by definition, and $|c\mathbf{A}|$ can be found in terms of **A** by applying the first part of (iii) to each of the n rows of $c\mathbf{A}$. To prove (iv), expand the determinant on the right of (7.16) by the jth column, and the result is obvious. The first part of (v) follows because interchange of the equal rows (or columns) leaves the matrix unchanged, but changes the sign of its determinant, from Theorem 7.2. Hence $|\mathbf{A}| = -|\mathbf{A}|$, so that $|\mathbf{A}| = 0$. The last part of (v) follows on combining this result and the first part of (iii). Part (vi) follows from (iv) and (v) since, if the final determinant is expanded by (iv), one of the determinants in the sum is zero by the second part of (v).

There is a great deal of material in the above theorem and perhaps the best way to illustrate some of the implications is to work a numerical example. Part (vi) of the theorem is the main tool used in the practical evaluation of determinants when the elements are whole numbers or contain symbols. Consider

$$|\mathbf{A}| = \begin{vmatrix} 2 & -3 & 2 & 5 \\ 1 & -1 & 1 & 2 \\ 3 & 2 & 2 & 1 \\ 1 & 1 & -3 & -1 \end{vmatrix}.$$

We reduce the first element in the first, third, and fourth rows to zero by subtracting suitable multiples of the second row from each of these other rows. (The second row was chosen since the numbers in it are very simple. In particular, the first element of the second row is unity.) By subtracting twice the second row from the first, and so on, we obtain

$$|\mathbf{A}| = \begin{vmatrix} 0 & -1 & 0 & 1 \\ 1 & -1 & 1 & 2 \\ 0 & 5 & -1 & -5 \\ 0 & 2 & -4 & -3 \end{vmatrix}. \tag{7.17}$$

It is important to remember that the row which we are adding to the other rows must itself remain unchanged. We now expand (7.17) by the first column. This is the point of reducing all the elements in the first column to zero except one, since the expansion is now simple:

$$|\mathbf{A}| = -\begin{vmatrix} -1 & 0 & 1 \\ 5 & -1 & -5 \\ 2 & -4 & -3 \end{vmatrix}.$$

On adding the last column to the first, we see that

$$|\mathbf{A}| = -\begin{vmatrix} 0 & 0 & 1 \\ 0 & -1 & -5 \\ -1 & -4 & -3 \end{vmatrix} = +\begin{vmatrix} 0 & 1 \\ -1 & -5 \end{vmatrix} = +1,$$

where we have now expanded by the last element in the first column.

In this method of evaluating determinants we use essentially two results:

(a) We use part (vi) of Theorem 7.3, which says that the value of a determinant is unchanged if a multiple of one row is added to another. By repeated application of this result we reduce all the elements except one in some row or column to zero. (If the elements of the determinant are integers, there is usually considerable scope for ingenuity in doing this in such a way that the arithmetic is as simple as possible.)

(b) Having carried out (a), Theorem 7.1 tells us that if all the elements in the ith row (or the jth column) of $\mathbf{A}$ are zero except a_{ij}, then

$$|\mathbf{A}| = a_{ij}A_{ij} = (-1)^{i+j}a_{ij}M_{ij}, \tag{7.18}$$

where M_{ij} is the minor corresponding to a_{ij}.

7.4 Determinants and Elementary Row Operations

Many of the operations on the rows or columns of determinants described in the last section (for example, adding a multiple of one row to another) are obviously closely related to the elementary row and column operations described earlier, which led to the definition of elementary matrices in Section 3.8, Definition 3.6. In this section we develop some of the implications of the connection between determinants and elementary operations.

THEOREM 7.4.

(i) $\det \mathbf{I} = 1$.
(ii) $\det \mathbf{E}_{pq} = -1$.
(iii) $\det \mathbf{E}_p(c) = c$.
(iv) $\det \mathbf{E}_{pq}(c) = 1$.

In these equations, $\mathbf{E}_{pq}$, $\mathbf{E}_p(c)$, $\mathbf{E}_{pq}(c)$ *are the elementary matrices defined in Definition* 3.6.

Proof: If $\mathbf{I}_m$ denotes the unit matrix of order m, expansion by its first row shows that $\det \mathbf{I}_m = \det \mathbf{I}_{m-1}$. Since $\det \mathbf{I}_1 = 1$, we see that $\det \mathbf{I}_m = 1$. Since $\mathbf{E}_{pq}$ is obtained from the unit matrix $\mathbf{I}$ by interchanging rows p and q, part (i) follows immediately from Theorem 7.2, using the fact that $\det \mathbf{I} = 1$. Part (ii) is obvious since $\mathbf{E}_p(c)$ is diagonal. Part (iii) follows from Theorem 7.3(vi) since $\mathbf{E}_{pq}(c)$ is obtained by adding c times the qth row of the unit matrix to the pth row.

THEOREM 7.5. *If* $\mathbf{E}$ *is any elementary matrix and* $\mathbf{A}$ *is an arbitrary matrix, then*

$$\det \mathbf{EA} = \det \mathbf{E} \det \mathbf{A}. \tag{7.19}$$

Proof: If $\mathbf{E} = \mathbf{E}_{pq}$, then $\mathbf{E}_{pq}\mathbf{A}$ is the matrix obtained by interchanging the pth and qth rows of $\mathbf{A}$, so that $\det(\mathbf{E}_{pq}\mathbf{A}) = -\det \mathbf{A}$. From Theorem 7.4(ii), $\det \mathbf{E}_{pq} = -1$ so that (7.19) is true for $\mathbf{E} = \mathbf{E}_{pq}$. Similarly, if $\mathbf{E} = \mathbf{E}_p(c)$, then $\mathbf{EA}$ is the matrix obtained by multiplying the pth row of $\mathbf{A}$ by c, so that $\det(\mathbf{E}_p(c)\mathbf{A}) = c \det \mathbf{A}$, and the truth of (7.19) for this case follows on using Theorem 7.4(iii). Finally, if $\mathbf{E} = \mathbf{E}_{pq}(c)$, then $\mathbf{E}_{pq}(c)\mathbf{A}$ is the matrix obtained by adding c times the qth row of $\mathbf{A}$ to the pth row so that, from Theorem 7.3(vi), $\det(\mathbf{E}_{pq}(c)\mathbf{A}) = \det \mathbf{A}$, and the truth of (7.19) follows, on using Theorem 7.4(iv).

THEOREM 7.6. *If* $\mathbf{A}$ *is nonsingular then* $\det \mathbf{A} \neq 0$, *and conversely. If* $\mathbf{A}$ *is singular then* $\det \mathbf{A} = 0$, *and conversely.*

Proof: From Theorem 5.8(ii), if $\mathbf{A}$ is nonsingular, then we can write $\mathbf{A}$ as a product of elementary matrices:

$$\mathbf{A} = \mathbf{E}_1\mathbf{E}_2 \ldots \mathbf{E}_k. \tag{7.20}$$

By repeated application of Theorem 7.5,

$$\begin{aligned}\det \mathbf{A} &= \det \mathbf{E}_1 \det \mathbf{E}_2\mathbf{E}_3 \ldots \mathbf{E}_k \\ &= \det \mathbf{E}_1 \det \mathbf{E}_2 \ldots \det \mathbf{E}_k.\end{aligned}$$

From Theorem 7.4, the determinant of any elementary matrix is nonzero. Hence, det **A** is nonzero. To prove the second half of the theorem, we note that Theorem 5.8(i) states that if **U** denotes the row-echelon form of **A**, then **A** can be written in the form

$$\mathbf{A} = \mathbf{E}_1\mathbf{E}_2 \ldots \mathbf{E}_k\mathbf{U}, \tag{7.21}$$

where the $\mathbf{E}_i$ are elementary matrices. Theorem 7.5 then gives

$$\det \mathbf{A} = \det \mathbf{E}_1 \det \mathbf{E}_2 \ldots \det \mathbf{E}_k \det \mathbf{U}.$$

Since **A** is singular, the last row of its row-echelon form **U** is zero. Hence, det **U** is zero [Theorem 7.3(ii)], so that det $\mathbf{A} = 0$.

The truth of the converse statements in the theorem follows from the direct statements. Thus, if det $\mathbf{A} = 0$, then **A** cannot be nonsingular, and the only other possibility is that **A** must be singular. Similarly, if det $\mathbf{A} \neq 0$ then **A** cannot be singular, so that it must be nonsingular.

THEOREM 7.7. *The determinant of the product of two square matrices is equal to the product of the determinants*

$$\det \mathbf{AB} = \det \mathbf{A} \det \mathbf{B}. \tag{7.22}$$

Proof: We consider two cases (a) **A** nonsingular (b) **A** singular. If **A** is nonsingular, then, as in (7.20), **A** can be expressed as the product of elementary matrices:

$$\mathbf{A} = \mathbf{E}_1\mathbf{E}_2 \ldots \mathbf{E}_k. \tag{7.23}$$

On repeated application of Theorem 7.5,

$$\begin{aligned}\det \mathbf{AB} &= \det (\mathbf{E}_1\mathbf{E}_2 \ldots \mathbf{E}_k\mathbf{B}) \\ &= \det \mathbf{E}_1 \det \mathbf{E}_2 \ldots \det \mathbf{E}_k \det \mathbf{B} \\ &= \det (\mathbf{E}_1\mathbf{E}_2 \ldots \mathbf{E}_k) \det \mathbf{B} \\ &= \det \mathbf{A} \det \mathbf{B}.\end{aligned}$$

If **A** is singular then, as in (7.21), **A** can be written

$$\mathbf{A} = \mathbf{E}_1\mathbf{E}_2 \ldots \mathbf{E}_k\mathbf{U}, \tag{7.24}$$

where the last row of **U** is a row of zeros. Hence,

$$\mathbf{AB} = \mathbf{E}_1\mathbf{E}_2 \ldots \mathbf{E}_k(\mathbf{UB}),$$

where the last row of **UB** is a row of zeros, so that det $\mathbf{UB} = 0$, and

$$\det \mathbf{AB} = \det \mathbf{E}_1 \det \mathbf{E}_2 \ldots \det \mathbf{E}_k \det \mathbf{UB} = 0.$$

Hence, in all cases det **AB** = det **A** det **B** and the theorem is proved.

7.5 The Solution of Linear Equations by Determinants

We next explain how the solution of a set of n simultaneous linear equations in n unknowns can be expressed in terms of determinants. The following theorem will play a central role:

THEOREM 7.8.

$$\sum_{i=1}^{n} a_{ij}A_{ip} = \begin{cases} \det \mathbf{A}, & j = p, \\ 0, & j \neq p. \end{cases} \tag{7.25}$$

Proof: We have already met the part $j = p$ of (7.25) in Theorem 7.1, which states that the sum of the products of the elements in the jth column of a matrix times their cofactors equals the determinant of the matrix. The remaining part $j \neq p$ of (7.25) states that the sum of the products of the elements in the jth column of $\mathbf{A}$ times the cofactors of the corresponding elements in *another* column of $\mathbf{A}$ is zero. This result is almost obvious since it is the expansion by the pth column of a matrix $\mathbf{B}$ whose pth column is the same as its jth:

$$\mathbf{B} = \begin{bmatrix} a_{11} & \cdots & \overset{\substack{j\text{th}\\ \downarrow}}{a_{1j}} & \cdots & \overset{\substack{p\text{th}\\ \downarrow}}{a_{1j}} & \cdots & a_{1n} \\ a_{21} & \cdots & a_{2j} & \cdots & a_{2j} & \cdots & a_{2n} \\ & & & \cdots & & & \\ a_{n1} & \cdots & a_{nj} & \cdots & a_{nj} & \cdots & a_{nn} \end{bmatrix}.$$

Hence, the value of the sum in (7.25) when $j \neq p$ is equal to the determinant of a matrix with two identical columns, and this is zero.

Ex. 7.1. As a numerical illustration, consider

$$|\mathbf{A}| = \begin{vmatrix} 2 & -3 & 2 & 5 \\ 1 & -1 & 1 & 2 \\ 3 & 2 & 2 & 1 \\ 1 & 1 & -3 & -1 \end{vmatrix}. \tag{7.26}$$

By straightforward evaluation of 3×3 determinants we find, for example,

$$A_{13} = -5, \qquad A_{23} = 13, \qquad A_{33} = -1, \qquad A_{43} = 0.$$

We verify (7.25):

$$\begin{aligned} 2(-5) + (13) + 3(-1) + 1(0) &= 0 \\ -3(-5) - (13) + 2(-1) + 1(0) &= 0 \\ 2(-5) + (13) + 2(-1) - 3(0) &= 1 \\ 5(-5) + 2(13) + (-1) - 1(0) &= 0. \end{aligned}$$

The value of the determinant agrees with that found previously in Section 7.3.

We now use Theorem 7.8 to obtain *Cramer's rule* for the solution of a system of n equations in n unknowns. For simplicity, we first examine the special case where $n = 3$:

$$\begin{aligned} a_{11}x_1 + a_{12}x_2 + a_{13}x_3 &= b_1 \\ a_{21}x_1 + a_{22}x_2 + a_{23}x_3 &= b_2 \\ a_{31}x_1 + a_{32}x_2 + a_{33}x_3 &= b_3. \end{aligned} \tag{7.27}$$

We multiply the first equation by A_{11}, the second by A_{21}, the third by A_{32}, and add. The coefficients of x_2 and x_3 vanish from Theorem 7.8 and we find

$$(a_{11}A_{11} + a_{21}A_{21} + a_{31}A_{31})x_1 = (b_1A_{11} + b_2A_{21} + b_3A_{31}) \tag{7.28}$$

or

$$\begin{vmatrix} a_{11} & a_{12} & a_{13} \\ a_{21} & a_{22} & a_{23} \\ a_{31} & a_{32} & a_{33} \end{vmatrix} x_1 = \begin{vmatrix} b_1 & a_{12} & a_{13} \\ b_2 & a_{22} & a_{23} \\ b_3 & a_{32} & a_{33} \end{vmatrix}. \tag{7.29}$$

This introduces the following theorem:

THEOREM 7.9. (*Cramer's rule*). *If* $\det \mathbf{A} \neq 0$, *then the solution of the system of linear equations* $\mathbf{Ax} = \mathbf{b}$ *is given by*

$$x_i = \frac{\Delta_i}{\Delta}, \qquad i = 1 \quad \text{to} \quad n, \tag{7.30}$$

where $\Delta = \det \mathbf{A}$ *and* $\Delta_i = \det \mathbf{A}^{(i)}$, *where* $\mathbf{A}^{(i)}$ *is the matrix obtained by replacing the ith column of* $\mathbf{A}$ *by* $\mathbf{b}$.

Proof: The equations $\mathbf{Ax} = \mathbf{b}$ are

$$\sum_{j=1}^{n} a_{ij}x_j = b_i, \qquad i = 1, 2, \ldots, n. \tag{7.31}$$

We multiply the ith equation by A_{ip}, and sum over i:

$$\sum_{i=1}^{n} A_{ip} \sum_{j=1}^{n} a_{ij}x_j = \sum_{i=1}^{n} A_{ip}b_i.$$

On interchanging orders of summation

$$\sum_{j=1}^{n} \left\{ \sum_{i=1}^{n} a_{ij}A_{ip} \right\} x_j = \sum_{i=1}^{n} A_{ip}b_i.$$

We have just shown in Theorem 7.8, Equation (7.25), that the inner sum on the left is zero unless $j = p$, in which case it has the value $\det \mathbf{A}$. Hence,

$$(\det \mathbf{A})x_p = \sum_{i=1}^{n} A_{ip}b_i. \tag{7.32}$$

The expression on the right is the expansion by the pth column, of the determinant of the matrix given by replacing the pth column of $\mathbf{A}$ by $\mathbf{b}$. This matrix is $\mathbf{A}^{(p)}$ in the notation used in the theorem, so that (7.32) gives, since det $\mathbf{A} \neq 0$,

$$x_p = \frac{\det \mathbf{A}^{(p)}}{\det \mathbf{A}},$$

which is (7.30).

We next express the inverse matrix in terms of the cofactors of the elements of the original matrix. Suppose that $\mathbf{A}^{-1}$ is defined by the equation $\mathbf{AA}^{-1} = \mathbf{I}$, and that the columns of $\mathbf{A}^{-1}$ are denoted by $\boldsymbol{\alpha}_1, \boldsymbol{\alpha}_2, \ldots, \boldsymbol{\alpha}_n$, the ith element of $\boldsymbol{\alpha}_j$ being α_{ij}:

$$\mathbf{A}\boldsymbol{\alpha}_j = \mathbf{e}_j,$$

where $\mathbf{e}_j$ is the unit column matrix whose jth element is unity, and all other elements are zero. Hence, from Cramer's rule,

$$\alpha_{ij} = \frac{\Delta_{ij}}{\Delta},$$

where $\Delta = |\mathbf{A}|$ and Δ_{ij} is the determinant obtained by replacing the ith *column* of $\mathbf{A}$ by $\mathbf{e}_j$, i.e., Δ_{ij} is the determinant of a matrix with unity in the (j, i)th position, and zeros in the other positions in the ith column. Hence, Δ_{ij} is simply A_{ji}, the cofactor of the element a_{ji} in $\mathbf{A}$, so that

$$\alpha_{ij} = \frac{A_{ji}}{\Delta}. \tag{7.33}$$

This result states that the inverse matrix is $(1/\Delta)$ times the transpose of the matrix whose elements are the cofactors of the elements of the original matrix.

We restate and give a second proof of this result:

DEFINITION 7.3. If $\mathbf{A} = [a_{ij}]$ is a square matrix and A_{ij} is the cofactor of a_{ij}, then the transpose of the matrix of cofactors is known as the *adjoint* of the matrix $\mathbf{A}$, denoted by adj $\mathbf{A}$,

$$\text{adj } \mathbf{A} = [A_{ji}]. \tag{7.34}$$

THEOREM 7.10. *If* $\mathbf{A}$ *is nonsingular, the inverse of* $\mathbf{A}$ *is given by*

$$\mathbf{A}^{-1} = \frac{1}{\det \mathbf{A}} \text{adj } \mathbf{A}. \tag{7.35}$$

Proof: We have

$$\mathbf{A} \text{ adj } \mathbf{A} = \left[\sum_{k=1}^{n} a_{ik} b_{kj}\right],$$

where b_{kj} is the (k, j)th element of adj $\mathbf{A}$, i.e., A_{jk}. Hence,

$$\mathbf{A}\,\text{adj}\,\mathbf{A} = \left[\sum_{k=1}^{n} a_{ik}A_{jk}\right]$$

$$= \begin{bmatrix} |\mathbf{A}| & 0 & \dots & 0 \\ 0 & |\mathbf{A}| & \dots & 0 \\ & & \dots & \\ 0 & 0 & \dots & |\mathbf{A}| \end{bmatrix} = |\mathbf{A}|\,\mathbf{I},$$

where we have used (7.25). Since $|\mathbf{A}| \neq 0$, this gives

$$\mathbf{A}\left\{\frac{1}{|\mathbf{A}|}\,\text{adj}\,\mathbf{A}\right\} = \mathbf{I},$$

and (7.35) follows.

We conclude by mentioning that many of the results concerning square matrices that were proved earlier by means of elementary row operations could also be proved by means of determinants. In fact, the theory of matrices could have been developed using the theory of determinants. For instance it is clear, on the basis of Theorem 7.10, that if det $\mathbf{A} \neq 0$, then $\mathbf{A}$ must possess both left- and right-inverses, whereas if det $\mathbf{A} = 0$, $\mathbf{A}$ possesses neither a left- nor a right-inverse. In some ways this is a more direct statement than those made earlier.

7.6 Gaussian Elimination

In the remainder of this chapter we consider some practical aspects of the solution of k sets of simultaneous linear equations in n unknowns, with the same coefficient matrix $\mathbf{A}$ but different right-hand sides $\mathbf{b}_j$:

$$\mathbf{A}\mathbf{x}_j = \mathbf{b}_j, \qquad j = 1, 2, \dots, k. \tag{7.36}$$

This includes the problem of matrix inversion for which $k = n$ and the $\mathbf{b}_j$ are the unit column matrices $\mathbf{e}_j$.

The method of Gaussian elimination has already been described in Sections 3.2, 3.4. We simplify the situation by assuming that $\mathbf{A}$ is nonsingular, so that our equations always have a unique solution.

We introduce notation that will be used in the remainder of this chapter. Suppose that we consider one set of equations, $\mathbf{A}\mathbf{x} = \mathbf{b}$,

$$\begin{aligned} a_{11}x_1 + a_{12}x_2 + \dots + a_{1n}x_n &= b_1 \\ a_{21}x_1 + a_{22}x_2 + \dots + a_{2n}x_n &= b_2 \\ \dots & \\ a_{n1}x_1 + a_{n2}x_2 + \dots + a_{nn}x_n &= b_n. \end{aligned} \tag{7.37}$$

Suppose that a_{11} is nonzero. (If a_{11} is zero, we can interchange the first equation and one of the later equations so as to obtain a first equation with a nonzero coefficient for x_1, since the matrix of coefficients is assumed to be nonsingular.) In Chapter 3 (e.g., Section 3.4) the next step was to divide the first equation by a_{11}. In this chapter we use a procedure that is slightly different but mathematically equivalent. We divide the coefficients of x_1 in the last $n - 1$ equations by a_{11} to obtain multiplying factors

$$m_{i1} = \frac{a_{i1}}{a_{11}}, \qquad i = 2, \ldots, n.$$

We subtract m_{i1} times the first equation from the ith equation for $i = 2, \ldots, n$ to obtain the first derived system,

$$\begin{aligned} a_{11}x_1 + a_{12}x_2 + \ldots + a_{1n}x_n &= b_1 \\ a_{22}^{(2)}x_2 + \ldots + a_{2n}^{(2)}x_n &= b_2^{(2)} \\ \ldots \\ a_{n2}^{(2)}x_2 + \ldots + a_{nn}^{(2)}x_n &= b_n^{(2)}, \end{aligned} \tag{7.38}$$

where

$$a_{ij}^{(2)} = a_{ij} - m_{i1}a_{ij}, \qquad b_i^{(2)} = b_i - m_{i1}b_1, \qquad (i, j = 1, \ldots, n).$$

If $a_{22}^{(2)} = 0$, we can again interchange one of the later equations with the second equation so as to obtain a nonzero element in the (2, 2) position, since **A** is nonsingular. Assuming therefore that $a_{22}^{(2)}$ is nonzero, we divide the coefficients of x_2 in the last $n - 2$ equations by $a_{22}^{(2)}$, obtaining multipliers

$$m_{i2} = \frac{a_{i2}^{(2)}}{a_{22}}, \qquad i = 3, \ldots, n.$$

We subtract m_{i2} times the second equation from the ith equation for $i = 3, \ldots, n$, obtaining

$$\begin{aligned} a_{11}x_1 + a_{12}x_2 + a_{13}x_3 + \ldots + a_{1n}x_n &= b_1 \\ a_{22}^{(2)}x_2 + a_{23}^{(2)}x_3 + \ldots + a_{2n}^{(2)}x_n &= b_2^{(2)} \\ a_{33}^{(3)}x_3 + \ldots + a_{3n}^{(3)}x_n &= b_3^{(3)} \\ \ldots \\ a_{n3}^{(3)}x_3 + \ldots + a_{nn}^{(3)}x_n &= b_n^{(3)}. \end{aligned} \tag{7.39}$$

On repeating this procedure we obtain, finally,

$$\begin{aligned} a_{11}x_1 + a_{12}x_2 + \ldots + a_{1n}x_n &= b_1 \\ a_{22}^{(2)}x_2 + \ldots + a_{2n}^{(2)}x_n &= b_2^{(2)} \\ \ldots \\ a_{nn}^{(n)}x_n &= b_n^{(n)}. \end{aligned} \tag{7.40}$$

The unknowns are easily found from these equations by back-substitution.

Ex. 7.2. Show that the equations obtained by the procedure in Section 3.4 are simply (7.40) divided by the diagonal elements $a_{rr}^{(r)}$. (There is no special reason why we have used the slightly different sequence of operations described here, in preference to the method of Section 3.4. In the row-echelon form it is convenient to reduce the pivot elements to unity so that the key columns are unit vectors. In numerical work on a computer the magnitudes of the pivots are important, as we see later, and these are displayed explicitly in (7.40). On the other hand, we could keep track of the sizes of the $a_{rr}^{(r)}$ even though we divided through by them to obtain the row-echelon form.)

The procedure described above can be summarized by saying that we produce $n - 1$ sets of equations equivalent to $\mathbf{Ax} = \mathbf{b}$, say

$$\mathbf{A}^{(r)}\mathbf{x} = \mathbf{b}^{(r)}, \qquad r = 2, \ldots, n,$$

where the original equations $\mathbf{Ax} = \mathbf{b}$ can be considered to be the case $r = 1$. The cases $r = 2, 3, n$ are displayed in (7.38), (7.39), (7.40). The final matrix $\mathbf{A}^{(n)}$ is upper triangular.

The general equations for calculating the elements of $\mathbf{A}^{(r+1)}$, $\mathbf{b}^{(r+1)}$ from those of $\mathbf{A}^{(r)}$, $\mathbf{b}^{(r)}$ are:

$$m_{ir} = \frac{a_{ir}^{(r)}}{a_{rr}^{(r)}}, \qquad i = r + 1, \ldots, n, \tag{7.41}$$

$$a_{ij}^{(r+1)} = a_{ij}^{(r)} - m_{ir}a_{rj}^{(r)}, \qquad i, j = r + 1, \ldots, n, \tag{7.42}$$

$$b_i^{(r+1)} = b_i^{(r)} - m_{ir}b_r^{(r)}, \qquad i = r + 1, \ldots, n, \tag{7.43}$$

where, for $r = 1$, we must take $a_{ij}^{(1)} = a_{ij}$, $b_i^{(r)} = b_i$.

In order to obtain some idea of the amount of work involved in Gaussian elimination, we count the number of additions and multiplications required. (For simplicity, additions and subtractions are lumped together as "additions," multiplications and divisions are lumped together as "multiplications.") Consider the solution of k sets of equations, as in (7.36). The calculation of the elements of $\mathbf{A}^{(r+1)}$, $\mathbf{b}_j^{(r+1)}$ from $\mathbf{A}^{(r)}$, $\mathbf{b}_j^{(r)}$ involves the following:

(a) Computations of the m_{ir} from (7.41), involving $n - r$ divisions.

(b) Computation of the $a_{ij}^{(r+1)}$ from (7.42), involving $(n - r)^2$ multiplications and additions.

(c) Computation of k sets of $b_i^{(r+1)}$ from (7.43), involving $k(n - r)$ multiplications and additions.

The forward elimination to obtain (7.40) therefore requires

$$\sum_{r=1}^{n-1}\{(n - r)^2 + (k + 1)(n - r)\} = n\{(\tfrac{1}{3}n^2 - \tfrac{1}{3}) + \tfrac{1}{2}k(n - 1)\} \quad \text{multiplications,}$$

$$\sum_{r=1}^{n-1}\{(n - r)^2 + k(n - r)\} = n\{(\tfrac{1}{3}n^2 - \tfrac{1}{2}n + \tfrac{1}{6}) + \tfrac{1}{2}k(n - 1)\} \quad \text{additions,}$$

where we have used the standard results

$$\sum_{s=1}^{m} s = \tfrac{1}{2}m(m + 1), \qquad \sum_{s=1}^{m} s^2 = \tfrac{1}{6}m(m + 1)(2m + 1).$$

In the solution of (7.40) by back-substitution, the determination of x_r involves $n - r$ multiplications and additions, and one division. Regarding the division as equivalent to a multiplication, k back-substitutions involve

$$\left.\begin{aligned} k(1 + 2 + \ldots + n) &= \tfrac{1}{2}kn(n+1) \quad \text{multiplications,} \\ k(1 + 2 + \ldots + n - 1) &= \tfrac{1}{2}kn(n-1) \quad \text{additions.} \end{aligned}\right\} \tag{7.44}$$

The overall totals for the complete solution are:

$$\left.\begin{aligned} n(\tfrac{1}{3}n^2 - \tfrac{1}{3} + kn) \quad &\text{multiplications,} \\ n\{\tfrac{1}{3}n^2 - \tfrac{1}{2}n + \tfrac{1}{6} + k(n-1)\} \quad &\text{additions.} \end{aligned}\right\} \tag{7.45}$$

When inverting $\mathbf{A}$, we start with n unit vectors $\mathbf{e}_j$ on the right. The matrices $\mathbf{A}^{(r)}$, $\mathbf{e}_j^{(r)}$ for the case $r = 3$, $n = 5$ are of the form

$$[\mathbf{A}^{(3)}\mathbf{e}_1^{(3)}\mathbf{e}_2^{(3)}\mathbf{e}_3\mathbf{e}_4\mathbf{e}_5] = \begin{bmatrix} \times & \times & \cdot & \times & \times & \times & \cdot & 1 & 0 & \cdot & 0 & 0 & 0 \\ 0 & \times & \cdot & \times & \times & \times & \cdot & \times & 1 & \cdot & 0 & 0 & 0 \\ \cdot & \cdot & \cdot & \cdot & \cdot & \cdot & \cdot & \cdot & \cdot & \cdot & \cdot & \cdot & \cdot \\ 0 & 0 & \cdot & \times & \times & \times & \cdot & \times & \times & \cdot & 1 & 0 & 0 \\ 0 & 0 & \cdot & \times & \times & \times & \cdot & \times & \times & \cdot & 0 & 1 & 0 \\ 0 & 0 & \cdot & \times & \times & \times & \cdot & \times & \times & \cdot & 0 & 0 & 1 \end{bmatrix}$$

The unit vectors on the right-hand side become, successively,

$$\begin{array}{llllll} r = 2, & \mathbf{e}_1^{(2)} & \mathbf{e}_2 & \mathbf{e}_3 & \mathbf{e}_4 & \mathbf{e}_5 \\ r = 3, & \mathbf{e}_1^{(3)} & \mathbf{e}_2^{(3)} & \mathbf{e}_3 & \mathbf{e}_4 & \mathbf{e}_5 \\ r = 4, & \mathbf{e}_1^{(4)} & \mathbf{e}_2^{(4)} & \mathbf{e}_3^{(4)} & \mathbf{e}_4 & \mathbf{e}_5 \\ r = 5, & \mathbf{e}_1^{(5)} & \mathbf{e}_2^{(5)} & \mathbf{e}_3^{(5)} & \mathbf{e}_4^{(5)} & \mathbf{e}_5 \end{array}$$

The vector $\mathbf{e}_r^{(j)}$ remains the vector $\mathbf{e}_r$ for $j \leq r$. If we ignore the work involved in multiplication by unity and addition to zero, then no work is required to form $\mathbf{e}_r^{(r+1)}$ from $\mathbf{e}_r^{(r)} = \mathbf{e}_r$. The formation of $\mathbf{e}_k^{(r+1)}$ from $\mathbf{e}_k^{(r)}$ for $r \geq 2$ involves $n - r$ multiplications and additions and this applies for $k = 1, \ldots, r - 1$. Hence the number of multiplications and additions required for the right-hand side part of the forward elimination is

$$\sum_{r=2}^{n-1} (r-1)(n-r) = \tfrac{1}{6}n(n-1)(n-2).$$

The corresponding work on the left is obtained by setting $k = 0$ in (7.45), and by adding these figures it is found that the total work for the forward elimination amounts to

$$\left.\begin{aligned} \tfrac{1}{2}n^2(n-1) \quad &\text{multiplications,} \\ \tfrac{1}{2}n(n-1)^2 \quad &\text{additions.} \end{aligned}\right\} \tag{7.46}$$

In the back-substitution, from (7.44), each right-hand column $\mathbf{e}_j^{(n)}$ involves $\frac{1}{2}n(n+1)$ multiplications, or $\frac{1}{2}n^2(n+1)$ in all. For the additions, from (7.44), we should have $\frac{1}{2}n(n-1)$ for each right-hand column if the vectors on the right were arbitrary, but there are $\frac{1}{2}n(n-1)$ zeros on the right, so that only

$$\tfrac{1}{2}n^2(n-1) - \tfrac{1}{2}n(n-1) = \tfrac{1}{2}n(n-1)^2$$

additions are required. By adding these numbers for back-substitution to the numbers (7.46) for forward elimination, we obtain the following totals required for inversion:

$$\left.\begin{aligned} n^3 &\quad \text{multiplications,} \\ n^3 - 2n^2 + n &\quad \text{additions.} \end{aligned}\right\} \tag{7.47}$$

The important conclusions to be drawn from the numbers in (7.45) and (7.47) for Gaussian elimination are

(a) The numbers of multiplications and additions required to solve a single set of equations are of order $\frac{1}{3}n^3$.

(b) The numbers of multiplications and additions required to invert a matrix are of order n^3.

It does not seem possible to do better than this. Although the exact figures can be altered slightly by rearranging the details of the calculation, the dominant terms are always $n^3/3$ and n^3. Note that

(1) The amount of work is proportional to n^3, so that if we double the number of equations we have to do eight times the amount of work. The amount of work involved rapidly becomes prohibitive as the size of the system increases.

(2) About three times the amount of work is involved when inverting a matrix, compared with solving a single set of equations, not n times, as we might expect. The ratio is independent of the size of the system.

One tends to forget that multiplying two matrices of order n together requires n^3 multiplications and additions. Hence, the amount of work required to form A^{-1} is of the same order of magnitude as the amount of work required to form A^2 or A^TA.

By hand it is laborious to solve 5 equations in 5 unknowns. On present day computers it is quite practical to solve 100 equations in 100 unknowns, with all 10^4 coefficients nonzero. The arithmetic operations take about 10 secs, and the cost is less than a dollar. This is why digital computers are revolutionizing the way in which we formulate problems in the applied sciences (Section 2.3). However we would still hesitate before tackling a system with $n = 1000$ unless most of the coefficients were zero.

Ex. 7.3. Show that the Gauss-Jordan procedure (Section 3.2) requires roughly $\frac{1}{2}n^3$ multiplications and additions to solve a single set of equations, so that the work required is 50% greater than for Gaussian elimination. Show however, that inversion can be performed with approximately n^3 multiplications and additions so that the Gauss-Jordan and Gauss procedures involve comparable amounts of work for inversion.

7.7 Triangular Decomposition

In this section we consider a method for solving simultaneous equations that will turn out to be equivalent to Gaussian elimination. The method depends on the decomposition given in Theorem 7.12 below. We require some preliminary results.

DEFINITION 7.4. A *lower triangular matrix* **L** is a square matrix with zero elements above the principal diagonal. An *upper triangular matrix* **U** is a square matrix with zero elements below the principal diagonal:

$$\mathbf{L} = \begin{bmatrix} l_{11} & 0 & \dots & 0 \\ l_{21} & 0 & & 0 \\ & & \dots & \\ l_{n1} & l_{n2} & \dots & l_{nn} \end{bmatrix}, \qquad \mathbf{U} = \begin{bmatrix} u_{11} & u_{12} & \dots & u_{1n} \\ 0 & u_{22} & \dots & u_{2n} \\ & & \dots & \\ 0 & 0 & & u_{nn} \end{bmatrix}.$$

Triangular matrices have various convenient properties:

THEOREM 7.11. (i) *The product of two upper (lower) triangular matrices is again an upper (lower) triangular matrix. The diagonal elements of the product are given by the product of the corresponding diagonal elements of the original matrices.*

(ii) *A triangular matrix is nonsingular if and only if all the diagonal elements are nonzero. If one or more diagonal elements are zero, then the triangular matrix is singular.*

(iii) *The inverse of an upper (lower) triangular matrix is also an upper (lower) triangular matrix. The diagonal elements of the inverse of a triangular matrix are the inverses of the diagonal elements of the original matrix.*

Proof: The proof of (i) is left to the reader. To prove (ii), we remark that if all the diagonal elements of a triangular matrix are nonzero, the matrix is row-reducible to the unit matrix, and therefore nonsingular. If at least one diagonal element is zero, the matrix is row-reducible.to a matrix with a row of zeros, so that the matrix is singular. For (iii), to show that the inverse of a lower triangular matrix **L** is also lower triangular, consider the equation **LM** = **I**. Since **L** is assumed to have an inverse, its diagonal elements must be nonzero. In multiplying out **LM** and equating the elements above the diagonal to zero we can show that **M** must be a lower triangular matrix. Equating the diagonal elements of **LM** to unity shows that the diagonal elements of **M** must be the inverses of those of **L**.

The basic theorem we require is the following:

THEOREM 7.12. *Suppose that* $\mathbf{A} = [a_{ij}]$ *is an* $n \times n$ *matrix and that* $\mathbf{A}_k$ *denotes the matrix formed by the first* k *rows and columns of* $\mathbf{A}$. *If* $\mathbf{A}_1, \mathbf{A}_2, \ldots, \mathbf{A}_{n-1}, \mathbf{A}_n = \mathbf{A}$ *are all nonsingular, then:*

(i) $\mathbf{A}$ *can be decomposed uniquely in the form*

$$\mathbf{A} = \mathbf{CDB}, \tag{7.48}$$

where $\mathbf{C}$ *and* $\mathbf{B}$ *are lower and upper triangular matrices with units along their principal diagonals, and* $\mathbf{D}$ *is a diagonal matrix.*

(ii) *If* $\mathbf{C}_k$, $\mathbf{D}_k$, $\mathbf{B}_k$ *are the matrices formed by the first* k *rows and columns of* $\mathbf{C}$, $\mathbf{D}$, $\mathbf{B}$, *then*

$$\mathbf{A}_k = \mathbf{C}_k\mathbf{D}_k\mathbf{B}_k, \qquad k = 1, \ldots, n. \tag{7.49}$$

(iii) *The diagonal elements of* $\mathbf{D}$ *(and therefore of the* $\mathbf{D}_k$*) are the pivots* $a_{ii}^{(i)}$ *in Gaussian elimination* [*see* (7.40)]. *Also,*

$$\det \mathbf{A}_k = a_{11}a_{22}^{(2)} \ldots a_{kk}^{(k)}.$$

In particular, $\det \mathbf{A}$ *is given by the product of the pivots.*

Proof: The statement that $\mathbf{A}_1$ is nonsingular means that $a_{11} \neq 0$. Consider the matrix

$$\mathbf{A}_2 = \begin{bmatrix} a_{11} & a_{12} \\ a_{21} & a_{22} \end{bmatrix}.$$

Since a_{11} is nonzero, we can reduce $\mathbf{A}_2$ to an upper triangular form by subtracting a_{21}/a_{11} times the first row from the second row, to obtain

$$\begin{bmatrix} a_{11} & a_{12} \\ 0 & \alpha_{22} \end{bmatrix},$$

where α_{22} must be nonzero since $\mathbf{A}_2$ is nonsingular (see Theorems 5.14, 7.11(ii)). Similarly, on considering

$$\mathbf{A}_3 = \begin{bmatrix} a_{11} & a_{12} & a_{13} \\ a_{21} & a_{22} & a_{23} \\ a_{31} & a_{32} & a_{33} \end{bmatrix},$$

if we subtract the same multiple of the first row from the second row, and also a_{31}/a_{11} times the first row from the third row, we obtain

$$\begin{bmatrix} a_{11} & a_{12} & a_{13} \\ 0 & \alpha_{22} & \alpha_{23} \\ 0 & \beta_{32} & \beta_{33} \end{bmatrix}.$$

We have already shown that α_{22} is nonzero, so that, on subtracting β_{32}/α_{22} times the second row from the third row, the matrix $\mathbf{A}_3$ is reduced to the form

$$\begin{bmatrix} a_{11} & a_{12} & a_{13} \\ 0 & \alpha_{22} & \alpha_{23} \\ 0 & 0 & \alpha_{33} \end{bmatrix}.$$

Since $\mathbf{A}_3$ is nonsingular, α_{33} must be nonzero, from Theorem 7.11(ii). Continuing in this way, we can reduce $\mathbf{A}$ to an upper triangular matrix by means of elementary row operations. In symbols,

$$\mathbf{E}_k\mathbf{E}_{k-1}\ldots\mathbf{E}_1\mathbf{A} = \mathbf{U}, \tag{7.50}$$

where $\mathbf{U}$ represents an upper triangular matrix. The important thing about the elementary row operations that are involved is that they are of only one single type, namely addition of a multiple of one row to a *later* row. This means that $\mathbf{E}_1, \ldots, \mathbf{E}_k$ in the above equations are all *lower* triangular with units along their principal diagonals. This means that [Theorem 7.11(i)] Equation (7.50) can be written $\mathbf{EA} = \mathbf{U}$, where $\mathbf{E}$ is lower triangular with units on its principal diagonal. Hence,

$$\mathbf{A} = \mathbf{LU} \tag{7.51}$$

where $\mathbf{L} = \mathbf{E}^{-1}$ is lower triangular with units on its principal diagonal [Theorem 7.11(iii)]. We next note that we can write $\mathbf{U} = \mathbf{DB}$, where $\mathbf{D}$ is diagonal and $\mathbf{B}$ is upper triangular with units on its principal diagonal. Substituting in (7.51), we obtain (7.48). We still have to prove that the decomposition (7.48) is unique. Suppose that we have two decompositions of the form (7.48):

$$\mathbf{A} = \mathbf{CDB} = \mathbf{C}'\mathbf{D}'\mathbf{B}',$$

where $\mathbf{C}'$, $\mathbf{B}'$ have units on their diagonal, and $\mathbf{D}'$ is diagonal. Then

$$\mathbf{DB}(\mathbf{B}')^{-1} = \mathbf{C}^{-1}\mathbf{C}'\mathbf{D}'.$$

The matrices on the left and right are upper and lower triangular, respectively. Hence, each must be diagonal. Hence, $\mathbf{B}(\mathbf{B}')^{-1}$ and $\mathbf{C}^{-1}\mathbf{C}'$ must be diagonal. But each of these products must have units on their diagonals so that

$$\mathbf{B}(\mathbf{B}')^{-1} = \mathbf{I}, \qquad \mathbf{C}^{-1}\mathbf{C}' = \mathbf{I},$$

or $\mathbf{B} = \mathbf{B}'$, $\mathbf{C} = \mathbf{C}'$. This concludes the proof of part (i). Part (ii) follows immediately since $\mathbf{B}_k$, $\mathbf{C}_k$, $\mathbf{D}_k$ are obtained from $\mathbf{A}_k$ in exactly the same way as $\mathbf{B}$, $\mathbf{C}$, $\mathbf{D}$ are obtained from $\mathbf{A}$. The steps in the reduction of $\mathbf{A}$ to the upper triangular matrix $\mathbf{U}$ in the proof of part (ii) are exactly the steps used to produce the matrix of coefficients in (7.40), so that the diagonal elements of $\mathbf{U}$, i.e., of $\mathbf{D}$, are precisely $a_{ii}^{(i)}$, det $\mathbf{A}$ = det $\mathbf{C}$ det $\mathbf{D}$ det $\mathbf{B}$ = det $\mathbf{D}$. Completion of the details of the proof of part (iii) are left to the reader.

Suppose now that a matrix $\mathbf{A}$ satisfying the conditions of Theorem 7.12 is decomposed in the form

$$\mathbf{A} = \mathbf{LU},$$

where $\mathbf{L}$ is a lower triangular matrix and $\mathbf{U}$ is an upper triangular matrix. From Theorem 7.12, the decomposition is unique if we arrange that $\mathbf{L}$ has units along its diagonal:

$$\mathbf{L} = \begin{bmatrix} 1 & 0 & \dots & 0 \\ l_{21} & 1 & \dots & 0 \\ & & \dots & \\ l_{n1} & l_{n2} & \dots & 1 \end{bmatrix}, \qquad \mathbf{U} = \begin{bmatrix} u_{11} & u_{12} & \dots & u_{1n} \\ 0 & u_{22} & \dots & u_{2n} \\ & & \dots & \\ 0 & 0 & \dots & u_{nn} \end{bmatrix}. \tag{7.52}$$

(There are various other ways of arranging the split. For instance, we could arrange that **U** has units along the diagonal instead of **L**. The reason for choosing the above form for **L** is that, as we shall see later, it is possible to link up the formulae for the elements of **L** and **U** with the formulae for Gaussian elimination obtained in the last section.)

It is easy to show that the elements of **L**, **U** can be calculated by a sequential procedure. The product **LU** is given by

$$\mathbf{A} = \mathbf{LU} = \begin{bmatrix} u_{11} & u_{12} & u_{13} & \dots \\ l_{21}u_{11} & l_{21}u_{12} + u_{22} & l_{21}u_{13} + u_{23} & \dots \\ l_{31}u_{11} & l_{31}u_{12} + l_{32}u_{22} & l_{31}u_{13} + l_{32}u_{23} + u_{33} & \dots \\ & & \dots & \end{bmatrix}.$$

On equating the individual elements in **A** to the elements in this last matrix, we find that **U**, **L** can be calculated in the following order:

(a) The first row of **U**:

$$u_{1j} = a_{1j}, \qquad j = 1, 2, \dots, n.$$

(b) The first column of **L**:

$$l_{i1} = \frac{a_{i1}}{u_{11}}, \qquad i = 1, 2, \dots, n.$$

(c) The second row of **U**:

$$u_{2j} = a_{2j} - l_{21}u_{1j}, \qquad j = 2, 3, \dots, n.$$

(d) The second column of **L**:

$$l_{i2} = \frac{a_{i2} - l_{i1}u_{12}}{u_{22}}, \qquad i = 2, 3, \dots, n.$$

(e) The third row of **U**:

$$u_{3j} = a_{3j} - l_{31}u_{1j} - l_{32}u_{2j}, \qquad j = 3, 4, \dots, \text{and so on.}$$

The importance of doing the computations in this order is that the quantities required to compute the value of an element at any stage of the calculation have already been calculated at some previous stage. The general formulae are:

$$u_{pj} = a_{pj} - \sum_{k=1}^{p-1} l_{pk}u_{kj}, \qquad j = p, p+1, \dots, n, \tag{7.53}$$

$$l_{iq} = \frac{a_{iq} - \sum_{k=1}^{q-1} l_{ik}u_{kq}}{u_{qq}}, \qquad i = q+1, \dots, n. \tag{7.54}$$

Before examining the structure of these equations (which turns out to be quite simple) we apply the decomposition $\mathbf{A} = \mathbf{LU}$ to the solution of $\mathbf{Ax} = \mathbf{b}$. We wish to solve

$$\mathbf{LUx} = \mathbf{b}. \tag{7.55}$$

If we introduce

$$\mathbf{y} = \mathbf{Ux}, \tag{7.56}$$

then (7.55) gives

$$\mathbf{Ly} = \mathbf{b}. \tag{7.57}$$

The procedure is to solve (7.57) for $\mathbf{y}$ and then solve (7.56) for $\mathbf{x}$. Each of these is a triangular set of equations:

$$\begin{aligned} u_{11}x_1 + u_{12}x_2 + \ldots + u_{1n}x_n &= y_1 \\ u_{22}x_2 + \ldots + u_{2n}x_n &= y_2 \\ \ldots \qquad & \\ u_{nn}x_n &= y_n, \\ y_1 \qquad\qquad &= b_1 \\ l_{21}y_1 + l_{22}y_2 \qquad &= b_2 \\ \ldots \qquad & \\ l_{n1}y_1 + l_{n2}y_2 + \ldots + l_{nn}y_n &= b_n. \end{aligned}$$

It is easy to solve the second set for $y_1, \ldots, y_n$ in succession, and then to solve the first set for $x_n, \ldots, x_1$ in succession. The general formula for y_p is

$$y_p = b_p - \sum_{k=1}^{p-1} l_{pk}y_k. \tag{7.58}$$

This is precisely (7.53) with u_{kj} in (7.53) replaced by y_k, and a_{pj} by b_p.

If the reader visualizes the situation, he will see that the formulae (7.53), (7.54), (7.58) are simple and systematic, in spite of the apparent complexity of the symbols. We can write $\mathbf{L}$, $\mathbf{U}$, $\mathbf{b}$ together in a single "auxiliary matrix" in the following form.

$$\begin{bmatrix} u_{11} & u_{12} & \ldots & u_{1n} & y_1 \\ l_{21} & u_{22} & \ldots & u_{2n} & y_2 \\ & & \ldots & & \\ l_{n2} & l_{n2} & \ldots & l_{nn} & y_n \end{bmatrix}.$$

This corresponds to the original "augmented matrix"

$$\begin{bmatrix} a_{11} & a_{12} & \ldots & a_{1n} & b_1 \\ a_{21} & a_{22} & \ldots & a_{2n} & b_2 \\ & & \ldots & & \\ a_{n1} & a_{n2} & \ldots & a_{nn} & b_n \end{bmatrix}.$$

The elements of the auxiliary matrix can be computed in the following order:

(a) Elements of the first row, u_{1j}, y_1.
(b) Elements of the first column below the diagonal, l_{i1}.
(c) Elements of the second row on and to the right of the diagonal, u_{2j}, y_2.
(d) Elements of the second column below the diagonal, l_{i2}.
(e) Elements of the third row on and to the right of the diagonal, u_{3j}, y_3.

The elements of the auxiliary matrix are determined by the following general rule, which simply expresses (7.53), (7.54), (7.58) in words: Each element on or to the right of the diagonal is equal to the corresponding element in the original augmented matrix minus the sum of products of elements in its row times the corresponding elements in its column, where these products involve only previously computed elements. Each element below the diagonal is obtained by exactly the same rule except that finally we divide by the diagonal element in the same column. If the matrix **A** is symmetrical, labor can be saved by noting that each element l_{ij} of **L** is equal to the symmetrically situated element u_{ji} of **U** divided by the diagonal element u_{jj}.

Ex. 7.4. As an example, we apply the above method to the set considered in Section 3.2. The original augmented matrix is

$$\begin{bmatrix} 2 & -3 & 2 & 5 & 3 \\ 1 & -1 & 1 & 2 & 1 \\ 3 & 2 & 2 & 1 & 0 \\ 1 & 1 & -3 & -1 & 0 \end{bmatrix}.$$

The auxiliary matrix is found to be

$$\begin{bmatrix} 2 & -3 & 2 & 5 & 3 \\ 0.5 & 0.5 & 0 & -0.5 & -0.5 \\ 1.5 & 13 & -1 & 0 & 2 \\ 0.5 & 5 & 4 & -1 & -7 \end{bmatrix}.$$

The system $\mathbf{Ux} = \mathbf{y}$ is therefore given by

$$\begin{aligned} 2x_1 - 3x_2 + 2x_3 + 5x_4 &= 3 \\ -0.5x_2 \qquad - 0.5x_4 &= -0.5 \\ -x_3 \qquad &= 2 \\ -x_4 &= -7. \end{aligned}$$

Back-substitution leads to the solution $x_1 = -5$, $x_2 = 6$, $x_3 = -2$, $x_4 = 7$.

Perhaps surprisingly, formulae that are precisely equivalent to the basic equations (7.53), (7.54), (7.58) for the triangular decomposition method can be obtained from the fundamental relations (7.41)–(7.43) for Gaussian elimination derived in the last section. On writing out (7.42), (7.43) with $r-1, r-2, \ldots,$ 1 in place of r, in turn, we obtain, remembering that $a_{ij}^{(1)} = a_{ij}$, $b_i^{(1)} = b_i$,

$$\begin{aligned} a_{ij}^{(r)} &= a_{ij}^{(r-1)} - m_{i,r-1}a_{r-1,j}^{(r-1)}, & b_i^{(r)} &= b_i^{(r-1)} - m_{i,r-1}b_{r-1}^{(r-1)},\\ a_{ij}^{(r-1)} &= a_{ij}^{(r-2)} - m_{i,r-2}a_{r-2,j}^{(r-2)}, & b_i^{(r-1)} &= b_i^{(r-2)} - m_{i,r-2}b_{r-2}^{(r-2)}\\ &\cdots & &\cdots\\ a_{ij}^{(2)} &= a_{ij} - m_{i1}a_{ij}^{(1)}, & b_i^{(2)} &= b_i - m_{i1}b_1^{(1)}. \end{aligned}$$

Addition of these equations gives

$$a_{ij}^{(r)} = a_{ij} - \sum_{k=1}^{r-1} m_{ik}a_{kj}^{(k)}, \tag{7.59}$$

$$b_i^{(r)} = b_i - \sum_{k=1}^{r-1} m_{ik}b_k^{(k)}. \tag{7.60}$$

On setting $j = r$ in (7.59), we obtain

$$a_{ir}^{(r)} = a_{ir} - \sum_{k=1}^{r-1} m_{ik}a_{kr}^{(k)}.$$

Equation (7.41) then gives

$$m_{ir} = \frac{a_{ir} - \sum_{k=1}^{r-1} m_{ik}a_{kr}^{(k)}}{a_{rr}^{(r)}}. \tag{7.61}$$

On setting $i = r$ in (7.59), (7.60), we obtain

$$a_{rj}^{(r)} = a_{rj} - \sum_{k=1}^{r-1} m_{rk}a_{kj}^{(k)}, \tag{7.62}$$

$$b_r^{(r)} = b_r - \sum_{k=1}^{r-1} m_{rk}b_k^{(k)}. \tag{7.63}$$

We can identify (7.61), (7.62), (7.63) with (7.54), (7.53), (7.58), respectively, by making the following correspondences in notation:

$$a_{rj}^{(r)} \equiv u_{rj}, \qquad b_r^{(r)} \equiv y_r, \qquad m_{ir} \equiv l_{ir}. \tag{7.64}$$

The meaning of this result is that the equations for the methods of triangular decomposition and Gaussian elimination are essentially identical. The method of triangular decomposition is simply a compact form of Gauss elimination in which it is not necessary to write down each of the successive arrays in the Gauss method, but we must accumulate sums like (7.61), (7.62), (7.63). The numbers of additions and multiplications are the same in the two methods, but under some circumstances there may be advantages in using the compact method, as discussed later.

There are several variants of the compact triangular decomposition method discussed here associated, for example, with the names of Cholesky, Doolittle, Crout, and Banachiewicz. Although the distinctions between these may be important for the professional computer, from our point of view they are not essentially different, and we shall not discuss them further (see Ex. 7.34).

Miscellaneous Exercises 7

Ex. 7.5. Suppose that **A** is an $n \times n$ matrix such that in each row and in each column there is precisely one nonzero element, which is unity. Show that $\det \mathbf{A} = \pm 1$.

Ex. 7.6. Show that

$$\begin{vmatrix} 2 & 0 & 3 \\ 10 & 1 & 17 \\ 7 & 12 & -4 \end{vmatrix} = -77.$$

Verify that the same result is obtained by expanding by any row or column.

Ex. 7.7. Verify that the determinant of the following matrix is -36.

$$\begin{bmatrix} 1 & 1 & 3 & 0 & 2 \\ 3 & 1 & 0 & 1 & 2 \\ 0 & 1 & 3 & 0 & 2 \\ 4 & -2 & 3 & 1 & 0 \\ 5 & 1 & 0 & 0 & 6 \end{bmatrix}.$$

Ex. 7.8. Verify that, if $\theta_1 + \theta_2 + \theta_3 = 3\pi/2$,

$$\begin{vmatrix} 1 & \sin\theta_1 & \sin\theta_2 \\ \sin\theta_1 & 1 & \sin\theta_3 \\ \sin\theta_2 & \sin\theta_3 & 1 \end{vmatrix} = 0.$$

Ex. 7.9. If

$$k_p = \begin{vmatrix} a_1 & 1 & 0 & \dots & 0 \\ 1 & a_2 & 1 & \dots & 0 \\ 0 & 1 & a_3 & \dots & 0 \\ & & \dots & & \\ 0 & 0 & 0 & \dots & a_p \end{vmatrix},$$

show that

$$k_p = a_p k_{p-1} - k_{p-2}, \qquad (p \geq 3).$$

If $a_i = 2\cos\theta$ for all i, deduce that $k_n = \operatorname{cosec}\theta \sin(n+1)\theta$.

Ex. 7.10. Evaluate the Vandermonde determinant:

$$\begin{vmatrix} 1 & x_1 & \dots & x_1^{n-1} \\ 1 & x_2 & \dots & x_2^{n-1} \\ & & \dots & \\ 1 & x_n & \dots & x_n^{n-1} \end{vmatrix} = \prod_{i<j} (x_j - x_i).$$

Ex. 7.11. If $\mathbf{A} = [a_{ij}]$, where $a_{ij} = (\alpha_i + \beta_j)^{-1}$, show that

$$\det \mathbf{A} = \frac{\prod_{i=1}^{n-1} p_i q_i}{\prod_{r=1}^{n}\prod_{s=1}^{n} (\alpha_r + \beta_s)},$$

where

$$p_i = \prod_{r=i+1}^{n} (\alpha_i - \alpha_r), \qquad q_i = \prod_{r=i+1}^{n} (\beta_i - \beta_r).$$

Deduce an explicit form for the inverse of the generalized Hilbert matrix,

$$a_{ij} = (i + j - \gamma)^{-1}, \qquad 0 < \gamma \le 1.$$

Ex. 7.12. Show that the straight line through two points (x_1, y_1) and (x_2, y_2) is given by

$$\begin{vmatrix} x & y & 1 \\ x_1 & y_1 & 1 \\ x_2 & y_2 & 1 \end{vmatrix} = 0.$$

Deduce the familiar formula

$$\frac{x - x_1}{x_1 - x_2} = \frac{y - y_1}{y_1 - y_2}.$$

Ex. 7.13. Show that the area of the triangle whose vertices are the points (x_1, y_1), (x_2, y_2), (x_3, y_3) is given by the formula

$$A = \frac{1}{2}\begin{vmatrix} x_1 & y_1 & 1 \\ x_2 & y_2 & 1 \\ x_3 & y_3 & 1 \end{vmatrix},$$

if the vertices are numbered 1, 2, 3 in the counterclockwise direction. How must this expression be altered if the vertices are numbered clockwise?

Ex. 7.14. Show that the equation of the circle through three given points (x_i, y_i), $i = 1, 2, 3$, is

$$\begin{vmatrix} x^2 + y^2 & x & y & 1 \\ x_1^2 + y_1^2 & x_1 & y_1 & 1 \\ x_2^2 + y_2^2 & x_2 & y_2 & 1 \\ x_3^2 + y_3^2 & x_3 & y_3 & 1 \end{vmatrix} = 0.$$

Ex. 7.15. If $\mathbf{A}$ is skew-symmetric (i.e., $\mathbf{A}^T = -\mathbf{A}$), prove that

$$\det \mathbf{A} = (-1)^n \det \mathbf{A}.$$

Deduce that the determinant of a skew-symmetric matrix of odd order is zero.

Ex. 7.16. If $\mathbf{A}$ is hermitian (i.e., $\mathbf{A} = \bar{\mathbf{A}}^T = \mathbf{A}^H$), prove that $\det \mathbf{A}$ is real. If $\mathbf{A}$ is a general square matrix, prove that $\det \mathbf{A}^H\mathbf{A}$ is real.

Ex. 7.17. If $\mathbf{A}$ is singular, prove that

$$\mathbf{A} \operatorname{adj} \mathbf{A} = \mathbf{0}.$$

Ex. 7.18. Prove that

$$\det(\operatorname{adj} \mathbf{A}) = (\det \mathbf{A})^{n-1}, \qquad \det(\mathbf{A}^{-1}) = (\det \mathbf{A})^{n-2},$$

where in the second result we assume $\det \mathbf{A} \neq 0$.

Ex. 7.19. Prove that $\partial \det \mathbf{A}/\partial a_{ij} = A_{ij}$, where A_{ij} is the cofactor of a_{ij}.

Ex. 7.20. If each element of the determinant of a matrix **A** of order n is a function of a variable t, show that $\partial \det \mathbf{A}/\partial t$ is equal to the sum of the determinants of n matrices $\mathbf{B}_i$, where $\mathbf{B}_i$ is the same as **A** except for the ith row, which consists of elements $\partial a_{ij}/\partial t$ ($j = 1, \ldots, n$).

Ex. 7.21. If **A**, **D** are square matrices of orders m, n, respectively, show that

$$\det \begin{bmatrix} \mathbf{A} & \mathbf{0} \\ \mathbf{C} & \mathbf{D} \end{bmatrix} = \det \mathbf{A} \det \mathbf{D}.$$

Ex. 7.22. Prove that $\det \mathbf{A} = \det \mathbf{A}_1 + \det \mathbf{A}_2$, where

$$\mathbf{A}_1 = \begin{bmatrix} a_{11} & \mathbf{0} \\ \mathbf{b} & \mathbf{B} \end{bmatrix}, \qquad \mathbf{A}_2 = \begin{bmatrix} 0 & \mathbf{a} \\ \mathbf{b} & \mathbf{B} \end{bmatrix},$$

where $\mathbf{a} = [a_{12}, \ldots, a_{1n}]$.

Ex. 7.23. Let $L_{ij,pq}$ denote the determinant of the 2×2 submatrix consisting of the rows i, j and columns p, q of a square matrix **A**, and let $M_{ij,pq}$ denote the determinant of the submatrix of order $n - 2$ obtained by omitting rows i, j and columns p, q from **A**. Prove that if we select two rows i, j of **A**,

$$\det \mathbf{A} = \sum_{p,q} (-1)^{i+j+p+q} L_{ij,pq} M_{ij,pq},$$

where the sum is taken over all possible pairs p, q. Generalize to the case where we select any r rows of **A**. (This is known as *Laplace's expansion*, and it is a generalization of Theorem 7.1.)

Ex. 7.24. If **A**, **D** are nonsingular matrices of orders m, n, and **B**, **C** are $m \times n$, $n \times m$, respectively, show that

$$\det \mathbf{A} \det (\mathbf{D} + \mathbf{C}\mathbf{A}^{-1}\mathbf{B}) = \det \mathbf{D} \det (\mathbf{A} + \mathbf{B}\mathbf{D}^{-1}\mathbf{C}).$$

Ex. 7.25. Show that, if **u**, **v** are $m \times 1$ column vectors,

$$\det (\mathbf{I} + \mathbf{u}\mathbf{v}^T) = 1 + \mathbf{v}^T\mathbf{u}.$$

Ex. 7.26. If **D** is a diagonal matrix of order m whose ith diagonal element is d_i, and **u** is an $m \times 1$ column matrix, show that

$$\det (\mathbf{D} + \mathbf{u}\mathbf{u}^T) = \det \mathbf{D} \left\{ 1 + \sum_{i=1}^{m} \frac{u_i^2}{d_i} \right\}.$$

Deduce that

$$\begin{vmatrix} d_1 + 1 & 1 & \ldots & 1 \\ 1 & d_2 + 1 & \ldots & 1 \\ & \ldots & & \\ 1 & 1 & \ldots & d_m + 1 \end{vmatrix} = d_1 d_2 \ldots d_m \left\{ 1 + \sum_{i=1}^{m} \frac{1}{d_i} \right\}.$$

Ex. 7.27. Show that if $a_{ii} = a$, $i = 1, \ldots, n$, and $a_{ij} = b$ $(i \neq j)$, then

$$\det \mathbf{A} = (a - b)^{n-1}[a + (n - 1)b].$$

Ex. 7.28. Deduce directly from Definition 7.1 that

$$\det \mathbf{A} = \sum_{\sigma} (\mathrm{sgn}) a_{\sigma(1),1} a_{\sigma(2),2} \ldots a_{\sigma(n),n},$$

where $\sigma(1), \ldots, \sigma(n)$ are a *permutation* of the integers $1, \ldots, n$ (i.e., these integers arranged in some order), where the sum is taken over all such permutations. The symbol (sgn) denotes $+1$ if the integers $\sigma(1), \ldots, \sigma(n)$ can be converted into $1, \ldots, n$ by an *even* number of interchanges; otherwise (sgn) $= -1$. [It can be shown that (sgn) is independent of the way in which the interchanges are done.]

Ex. 7.29. Consider det **AB**, where **A** is $m \times n$ and **B** is $n \times m$. If $m = n$, we know from Theorem 7.7 that det **AB** = det **A** det **B**. Show that if $m > n$, det **AB** = 0, and that if $m < n$,

$$\det \mathbf{AB} = \sum_p \det \mathbf{A}_p \det \mathbf{B}_p,$$

where $\mathbf{A}_p$ is the square matrix obtained by choosing any m columns of **A**, $\mathbf{B}_p$ is the matrix obtained by choosing the corresponding rows of **B**, and the sum is taken over all such possible choices.

Solution: If $m > n$, we note that

$$\mathbf{AB} = [\mathbf{A}\ \mathbf{0}_1]\begin{bmatrix}\mathbf{B}\\ \mathbf{0}_2\end{bmatrix},$$

where $\mathbf{0}_1$, $\mathbf{0}_2$ are $m \times (m - n)$ and $(m - n) \times m$ null matrices. The determinant of the right-hand side is the product of the determinants of two singular square matrices, which is zero. If $m < n$, we first of all consider the case $m = 2$, $n = 3$, say

$$\mathbf{A} = \begin{bmatrix} a_1 & b_1 & c_1 \\ a_2 & b_2 & c_2 \end{bmatrix}, \qquad \mathbf{B} = \begin{bmatrix} \alpha_1 & \alpha_2 \\ \beta_1 & \beta_2 \\ \gamma_1 & \gamma_2 \end{bmatrix},$$

so that

$$\det \mathbf{AB} = \begin{vmatrix} a_1\alpha_1 + b_1\beta_1 + c_1\gamma_1 & a_1\alpha_2 + b_1\beta_2 + c_1\gamma_2 \\ a_2\alpha_1 + b_2\beta_1 + c_2\gamma_1 & a_2\alpha_2 + b_2\beta_2 + c_2\gamma_2 \end{vmatrix}.$$

If we expand this determinant and pick out the terms involving, say, b_1c_2 and b_2c_1, we find that they give a contribution

$$(b_1c_2 - b_2c_1)(\beta_1\gamma_2 - \beta_2\gamma_1) = \begin{vmatrix} b_1 & c_1 \\ b_2 & c_2 \end{vmatrix}\begin{vmatrix} \beta_1 & \gamma_1 \\ \beta_2 & \gamma_2 \end{vmatrix} = (b_1c_2)(\beta_1\gamma_2),$$

where we introduce a short-hand self-explanatory notation for the determinants. Proceeding in this way, we find that

$$\det \mathbf{AB} = (a_1b_2)(\alpha_1\beta_2) + (b_1c_2)(\beta_1\gamma_2) + (c_1a_2)(\gamma_1\alpha_2),$$

which verifies the required result for this particular case. In the general case we set

$$\mathbf{A} = \begin{bmatrix} a_1 \ldots k_1 \ldots s_1 \\ a_n \ldots k_n \ldots s_n \end{bmatrix}, \qquad \mathbf{B} = \begin{bmatrix} \alpha_1 \ldots \kappa_1 \ldots \sigma_1 \\ \alpha_n \ldots \kappa_n \ldots \sigma_n \end{bmatrix},$$

where if k is the nth letter, a typical term in the expansion of det **AB** is $(a_1 \ldots k_1)(\alpha_1 \ldots \kappa_1)$. This includes all terms in the expansion involving the roman letters $a \ldots k$ and no other roman letters. The full expansion is obtained by adding the terms involving all possible combinations of roman letters, and this is the theorem.

Ex. 7.30. Given any nonsingular matrix, the rows can be rearranged in such a way that, if $\mathbf{A}_k$ denotes the square matrix of order k in the top left corner of the resulting matrix, all the $\mathbf{A}_k$ are nonsingular, $k = 1, \ldots, n$.

Ex. 7.31. Prove Theorem 7.12 by induction as follows. Let $\mathbf{A}_k$ denote the square matrix of order k in the top left corner of $\mathbf{A}$, and suppose that the theorem has been proved from some value of $k < n$, i.e.,

$$\mathbf{A}_k = \mathbf{C}_k\mathbf{D}_k\mathbf{B}_k,$$

where $\mathbf{C}_k$ and $\mathbf{B}_k$ are upper and lower triangular matrices with units along their diagonals, and $\mathbf{D}_k$ is diagonal. We shall show that $\mathbf{A}_{k+1}$ can be decomposed in the same way. We try to find a $1 \times k$ matrix $\mathbf{p}$, a $k \times 1$ matrix $\mathbf{q}$, and a scalar d_{k+1} such that

$$\mathbf{C}_{k+1} = \begin{bmatrix} \mathbf{C}_k & \mathbf{0} \\ \mathbf{p} & 1 \end{bmatrix}, \qquad \mathbf{D}_{k+1} = \begin{bmatrix} \mathbf{D}_k & \mathbf{0} \\ \mathbf{0} & d_{k+1} \end{bmatrix}, \qquad \mathbf{B}_{k+1} = \begin{bmatrix} \mathbf{B}_k & \mathbf{q} \\ \mathbf{0} & 1 \end{bmatrix}.$$

On multiplying these together we find

$$\mathbf{C}_{k+1}\mathbf{D}_{k+1}\mathbf{B}_{k+1} = \begin{bmatrix} \mathbf{C}_k\mathbf{D}_k\mathbf{B}_k & \mathbf{C}_k\mathbf{D}_k\mathbf{q} \\ \mathbf{p}\mathbf{D}_k\mathbf{B}_k & \mathbf{p}\mathbf{D}_k\mathbf{q} + d_{k+1} \end{bmatrix}.$$

If $\mathbf{A}_{k+1}$ is partitioned in a similar way,

$$\mathbf{A}_{k+1} = \begin{bmatrix} \mathbf{A}_k & \mathbf{r} \\ \mathbf{s} & a_{k+1,k+1} \end{bmatrix},$$

we see that $\mathbf{p}$, $\mathbf{q}$, d_{k+1} must satisfy the equations

$$\begin{aligned} \mathbf{C}_k\mathbf{D}_k\mathbf{q} &= \mathbf{r}, \\ \mathbf{p}\mathbf{D}_k\mathbf{B}_k &= \mathbf{s}, \\ \mathbf{p}\mathbf{D}_k\mathbf{q} + d_{k+1} &= a_{k+1,k+1}. \end{aligned}$$

It is left to the reader to verify that $\mathbf{p}$, $\mathbf{q}$, d_{k+1} can indeed be determined uniquely from these equations, and that the condition that the $\mathbf{A}_k$ are nonsingular is necessary and sufficient for the proof of the theorem. To complete the induction it is necessary to state that the theorem is obviously true for $k = 1$.

Ex. 7.32. Let $\mathbf{A}$ be the *tridiagonal* or *band* matrix ($a_{ij} = 0$ for $|i - j| > 1$)

$$\mathbf{A} = \begin{bmatrix} a_1 & c_1 & 0 & \ldots & 0 \\ b_2 & a_2 & c_2 & \ldots & 0 \\ & & \ldots & & \\ 0 & 0 & 0 & \ldots & a_n \end{bmatrix}.$$

If the elements satisfy $|a_1| > |c_1| > 0$, $|a_n| > |b_n| > 0$, and $|a_i| > |b_i| + |c_i|$, b_i, c_i not both zero, $i = 2, \ldots, n - 1$, prove that $\mathbf{A}$ is nonsingular, and $\mathbf{A}$ can be factored into the form $\mathbf{LU}$ where $\mathbf{L}$, $\mathbf{U}$ are bidiagonal:

$$\mathbf{L} = \begin{bmatrix} \alpha_1 & 0 & \ldots & 0 \\ b_2 & \alpha_2 & \ldots & 0 \\ & & \ldots & \\ 0 & 0 & \ldots & \alpha_n \end{bmatrix}, \qquad \mathbf{U} = \begin{bmatrix} 1 & \gamma_1 & \ldots & 0 \\ 0 & 1 & \ldots & 0 \\ & & \ldots & \\ 0 & 0 & \ldots & 1 \end{bmatrix},$$

where $\alpha_1 = a_1$, $\alpha_i = a_i - b_i\gamma_{i-1}$ $(i = 2, \ldots, n)$, $\gamma_i = \dfrac{c_i}{\alpha_i}$ $(i = 1, \ldots, n - 1)$ with $|\gamma_i| < 1$, $|a_i| - |b_i| < |\alpha_i| < |a_i| + |b_i|$. Show that if this decomposition is used to solve a system $\mathbf{Ax} = \mathbf{b}$, then only $5n - 4$ multiplications and divisions are required. Prove that the number of operations required to invert $\mathbf{A}$ is of order $3n^2$.

Ex. 7.33. Let

$$\mathbf{M} = \begin{bmatrix} \mathbf{A} & \mathbf{B} \\ \mathbf{C} & \mathbf{0} \end{bmatrix},$$

where $\mathbf{A}$ is $n \times n$, $\mathbf{B}$ is $n \times p$, $\mathbf{C}$ is $q \times n$. Prove that if the triangular decomposition method of Section 7.7 is applied to the first n rows and columns of $\mathbf{M}$ this leads to the triangular decomposition

$$\begin{bmatrix} \mathbf{L} & \mathbf{0} \\ \mathbf{CU}^{-1} & \mathbf{0} \end{bmatrix} \begin{bmatrix} \mathbf{U} & \mathbf{L}^{-1}\mathbf{B} \\ \mathbf{0} & \mathbf{0} \end{bmatrix}$$

(This is a convenient method for computing $\mathbf{CU}^{-1}$ and/or $\mathbf{L}^{-1}\mathbf{B}$ for any $\mathbf{C}$, $\mathbf{B}$. To obtain $\mathbf{U}^{-1}$, for instance, choose $\mathbf{C} = \mathbf{I}$.)

Ex. 7.34. Write an essay on the methods for solving linear simultaneous equations associated with the names of Banachiewicz, Cholesky, Crout, and Doolittle, showing the distinction between these methods and their close connection with the methods of Gaussian elimination and triangular decomposition. (See [54].)

8 The Numerical Solution of Simultaneous Linear Equations

8.1 Introduction

As illustrated in Chapter 2, many problems in the applied sciences can be formulated in terms of a system of n linear equations in n unknowns. It is often necessary to find the numerical solution of such systems. We have already considered two aspects of this problem:

(a) The theory in Chapter 3 (Section 3.9) gave a clear-cut answer to the question of whether a solution exists or not: A unique solution exists if and only if the matrix of coefficients is nonsingular. When the coefficient matrix is singular, an infinite number of solutions may exist if the right-hand side satisfies special conditions, but in general the equations are contradictory (no solution exists).

(b) It is desirable to find an *efficient* procedure for solving the equations. In Section 7.6 it was shown that the method of successive elimination requires approximately $\frac{1}{3}n^3$ additions and multiplications to solve a set of n equations in n unknowns. In the 150 years since Gauss published this method, a great deal of effort has been expended in trying to find a more efficient procedure. The end result of all this work is that, unless the matrix has a very special structure (for example, a large number of zero elements) the method of successive elimination is still the best, provided that proper precautions are taken.

In this chapter we consider two further aspects of the problem of the numerical solution of linear equations:

(c) One important complication that we have not considered so far is that the solution of the equations may be very sensitive to small changes in the coefficients. This phenomenon, known as *ill-conditioning*, is related to the fact that the matrix of coefficients in the linear equations is nearly singular. This complex of ideas is the subject of Sections 8.2–4.

(d) One of the most important of the "proper precautions" mentioned in the last sentence in (b) is the correct choice of pivots. This is examined in Sections 8.5–6.

If $\hat{\mathbf{x}}$ is an approximate solution of $\mathbf{Ax} = \mathbf{b}$, the errors $\mathbf{r} = \mathbf{b} - \mathbf{A}\hat{\mathbf{x}}$ are called the *residuals*. The significance of residuals is examined in Section 8.7. Some comments on avoiding ill-conditioning, if possible, are made in Section 8.8. In Section 8.9 we summarize the recommended procedures and precautions when solving linear equations numerically in practice.

The situation that we visualize when considering the numerical solution of linear equations is the following:

(a) There exists a set of equations whose solutions we wish to find:

$$\mathbf{A}^*\mathbf{x}^* = \mathbf{b}^*, \tag{8.1}$$

where $\mathbf{A}^*$, $\mathbf{b}^*$ are matrices whose elements are exact, although these exact values may not be known to us. If the elements are determined experimentally, for instance, then we will know only approximations to $\mathbf{A}^*$, $\mathbf{b}^*$.

(b) Instead of the exact set (8.1), we in fact start with a set

$$\mathbf{Ax} = \mathbf{b}. \tag{8.2}$$

For instance, $\mathbf{A}$, $\mathbf{b}$ might be the matrices stored in a computer, which differ from the exact $\mathbf{A}^*$, $\mathbf{b}^*$ due to rounding errors in computing the coefficients, and in binary-decimal conversion. As mentioned under (a), there will also be experimental errors if $\mathbf{A}$, $\mathbf{b}$ are determined experimentally.

(c) By an *exact* solution of a set of equations we mean a solution that satisfies the equations exactly, provided that the computations involved in the substitution are performed exactly. Unfortunately, we can very seldom find the exact solution of (8.2), since calculations are usually performed to a finite number of significant figures, and rounding errors occur. If we denote by $\hat{\mathbf{x}}$ the solution of (8.2) obtained by a digital computer (or by hand calculation), then $\hat{\mathbf{x}}$ will not be the same as $\mathbf{x}$, the exact solution of (8.2), in general.

In this discussion we have introduced three "solutions": $\mathbf{x}^*$, the exact solution of the exact equations (8.1); $\mathbf{x}$, the exact solution of the approximate equations (8.2); and $\hat{\mathbf{x}}$, the approximate solution of the approximate equations (8.2). The error that is the main concern of the numerical analyst is $\mathbf{x} - \hat{\mathbf{x}}$, the difference between the exact and approximate solutions of the approximate equations we start from. This chapter deals with some technical aspects of minimizing $\mathbf{x} - \hat{\mathbf{x}}$. However, it is important to realize that the applied scientist usually wishes to minimize $\mathbf{x}^* - \hat{\mathbf{x}}$, the difference between the exact answer of the exact equations, and the solution given by the computer. The moral here is that there is no point in going to excessive trouble to make $\mathbf{x} - \hat{\mathbf{x}}$ small, if $\mathbf{x}^* - \mathbf{x}$ is likely to be large. Such situations arise when the solution is very sensitive to small changes in the coefficients of the original system, or to rounding errors introduced in the course of the solution, as discussed in the next section.

8.2 Ill-Conditioning

A set of equations is said to be *ill-conditioned* (or badly conditioned) if the solutions are very sensitive to small changes in the coefficients of the equations. Similarly, equations are said to be *well-conditioned* if the solutions are not sensitive to small changes in the coefficients. One of the difficulties here is to clarify what we mean by the crucial words "sensitive" and "small." We illustrate first of all by numerical examples.

As an example of a well-conditioned set of equations, consider

$$\begin{aligned} x_1 + x_2 &= 3, \\ x_1 - x_2 &= 1, \end{aligned} \tag{8.3}$$

with solution $x_1 = 2$, $x_2 = 1$. We change the second element on the right by a small amount to obtain

$$\begin{aligned} x_1' + x_2' &= 3 \\ x_1' - x_2' &= 1.0001, \end{aligned} \tag{8.4}$$

with solution $x_1' = 2.00005$, $x_2' = 0.99995$. A change of 1 in 10^{-4} in one coefficient produces changes that are less than 1 in 10^{-4} in the solutions. More generally, if we consider

$$\begin{aligned} x_1'' + x_2'' &= 3 \\ x_1'' - x_2'' &= 1 + \delta, \end{aligned} \tag{8.5}$$

we find solutions $x_1'' = 2 + \frac{1}{2}\delta$, $x_2'' = 1 - \frac{1}{2}\delta$. It is reasonable to say that "small" changes δ produce "small" changes in the solution.

In order to illustrate the need for care when using the word "small," consider, instead of (8.5),

$$\begin{aligned} y_1 + y_2 &= 3.10^{10} \\ y_1 - y_2 &= (1 + \delta)10^{10}, \end{aligned} \tag{8.6}$$

with solution $y_1 = (2 + \frac{1}{2}\delta)10^{10}$, $y_2 = (1 - \frac{1}{2}\delta)10^{10}$. If δ changes from zero to 10^{-4}, as in going from (8.3) to (8.4), then y_1 and y_2 change by $\frac{1}{2}10^6$ which is large compared with unity. However, the *relative* changes are still small. (By the relative change, we mean the ratio of the change to the original value of the quantity changed.) In fact, the relative changes produced in the solution of (8.5) and (8.6) by a given δ are the same.

As an example of an ill-conditioned set of equations, consider

$$\begin{aligned} x_1 + x_2 &= 2 \\ x_1 + 1.00001x_2 &= 2.00001, \end{aligned} \tag{8.7}$$

with solution $x_1 = x_2 = 1$. Compare

$$\begin{aligned} x_1' + x_2' &= 2 \\ x_1' + 1.00001x_2' &= 1.99990, \end{aligned} \tag{8.8}$$

with solution $x_1' = 12$, $x_2' = -10$. A change of 1 in 20,000 in one coefficient has completely changed the solution. The reason is clear if we examine the situation algebraically:

$$\begin{aligned} x_1'' + x_2'' &= 2 \\ x_1'' + 1.00001x_2'' &= 2.00001 + \delta, \end{aligned} \tag{8.9}$$

with solution

$$x_1'' = 1 - \frac{\delta}{0.00001}, \qquad x_2'' = 1 + \frac{\delta}{0.00001}.$$

The importance of these ideas is that the coefficients in equations are not usually known exactly; for example, they may have been obtained by rounding exact numbers, or they may have been given by experiment. In the terminology of Section 8.1, we work with **A** in (8.2), not $\mathbf{A}^*$ in (8.1). If the equations are ill-conditioned, then $\mathbf{x}^* - \mathbf{x}$ and $\mathbf{x} - \hat{\mathbf{x}}$ may be "large" even though $\mathbf{A}^* - \mathbf{A}$ and $\mathbf{b}^* - \mathbf{b}$ are "small."

It should be emphasized that the discussion in this section does not depend in any way on rounding errors made in the course of the computations. All the calculations in this section are *exact*.

It is instructive to consider the following generalization of (8.9):

$$\begin{aligned} z_1 + z_2 &= 2 \\ z_1 + (1 + \varepsilon)z_2 &= 2 + \delta, \end{aligned} \tag{8.10}$$

with solution

$$z_1 = 2 - \frac{\delta}{\varepsilon}, \qquad z_2 = \frac{\delta}{\varepsilon}. \tag{8.11}$$

There are no solutions when $\varepsilon = 0$, and an infinity of solutions when $\varepsilon = \delta = 0$. When $\varepsilon \neq 0$, the solution is very sensitive to variations in ε around zero. The difficulty is connected with the fact that the coefficient matrix is close to the singular matrix

$$\begin{bmatrix} 1 & 1 \\ 1 & 1 \end{bmatrix},$$

when ε is small. Mathematically, there is a clear-cut distinction between singular and nonsingular matrices. A matrix is either singular or it is not. Unfortunately, if the elements of a matrix are not known exactly, we may not know whether the matrix should be regarded as singular or not. The clear-cut distinction is blurred. In the same way, the mathematical theory tells us that a set of equations has no solution, a unique solution, or an infinity of solutions. If the coefficients in the equations are not known exactly, and the equations are ill-conditioned, we may find it difficult to decide which of the three possibilities applies to one set of equations. This should be clear from the example (8.10). Even if we know that the equations have a unique solution, ill-conditioning will mean that small uncertainties in the coefficients will result in large uncertainties in the answers we compute, and this is connected with the fact that we are near the "singular" cases where no solution or an infinity of solutions exist. There is a connection between the terms "ill-conditioned" and "nearly-singular."

We are now in a position to consider the general case. Suppose that

$$\mathbf{Ax} = \mathbf{b}, \tag{8.12}$$

where $\mathbf{A}$ is nonsingular. Let $\mathbf{A}$ be changed to $\mathbf{A} + \delta\mathbf{A}$, and $\mathbf{b}$ to $\mathbf{b} + \delta\mathbf{b}$ where $\delta\mathbf{A} = [\delta a_{ij}]$, $\delta\mathbf{b} = [\delta b_j]$. Suppose that $\mathbf{A} + \delta\mathbf{A}$ is nonsingular. Denote the solution of the resulting equations by $\mathbf{x}' = \mathbf{x} + \delta\mathbf{x}$, where $\delta\mathbf{x} = [\delta x_j]$, so that

$$(\mathbf{A} + \delta\mathbf{A})\mathbf{x}' = (\mathbf{A} + \delta\mathbf{A})(\mathbf{x} + \delta\mathbf{x}) = \mathbf{b} + \delta\mathbf{b}. \tag{8.13}$$

Subtracting (8.12) from (8.13) and rearranging,

$$\mathbf{A}\delta\mathbf{x} = \delta\mathbf{b} - \delta\mathbf{A}\mathbf{x}',$$

or

$$\delta\mathbf{x} = \mathbf{A}^{-1}(\delta\mathbf{b} - \delta\mathbf{A}\mathbf{x}'). \tag{8.14}$$

In a later chapter we shall find an "average" estimate for the sizes of the elements of $\delta\mathbf{x}$, but at this stage it is more instructive to proceed in the following way. Suppose first of all that the only change we make is to alter one element b_k to $b_k + \delta b_k$. Then $\delta\mathbf{A}$ is zero, and (8.14) gives

$$\delta x_j = \alpha_{jk}\delta b_k, \tag{8.15}$$

where α_{jk} is the (j, k)th element of $\mathbf{A}^{-1}$.

We now have to make a basic decision as regards whether we are interested in *relative* or *absolute* changes: Are we interested in the ratio $|\delta x_j/x_j|$ or in the absolute value $|\delta x_j|$? The answer to this question will depend on circumstances. Digital computers represent numbers in floating-point and, as explained later in Section 8.5, if we are concerned with rounding error, we are usually interested in *relative* errors. On the other hand, if numbers are obtained from physical measurements, we are often interested in *absolute*, not relative, errors. Thus if two measurements yield estimates of two numbers x and y that lie in the ranges $a - \Delta \le x \le a + \Delta, b - \Delta \le y \le b + \Delta$, then the resulting estimate of $x - y$ will lie in the range $a - b - 2\Delta \le x - y \le a - b + 2\Delta$. We will often be interested in the absolute value of the maximum error in $x - y$, namely 2Δ, rather than the relative value $2\Delta/(x - y)$ which may be very large if $x - y$ is small. At the same time we have to bear relative error in mind. For instance a change δx in a distance x may look large if x is measured in inches, but small if x

is measured in miles. Unfortunately, the answer to the question of whether a set of equations is sensitive to small changes in coefficients depends (as we shall see) on whether we specify absolute or relative changes, and sometimes it is not clear which of these we are interested in. The sharp distinction between relative and absolute errors seems convenient for expository purposes, but in practice it may be necessary to decide the appropriate measure of error for each individual quantity involved. In spite of these remarks, we introduce the following definitions.

DEFINITION **8.1.** Suppose that a small change in a parameter from α to $\alpha + \delta\alpha$ produces a change from x to $x + \delta x$ in the calculation of a quantity x. If, for small $\delta\alpha$,

$$|\delta x| = C\,|\delta\alpha|, \tag{8.16}$$

then C is called the *condition number for absolute changes in x caused by absolute changes in* α. If, for small $\delta\alpha$,

$$\left|\frac{\delta x}{x}\right| = K\left|\frac{\delta\alpha}{\alpha}\right|, \tag{8.17}$$

then K is called the *condition number for relative changes in x caused by relative changes in* α. The statement "for small $\delta\alpha$" means "in the limit as δx tends to zero." An equivalent definition is to let $\delta\alpha$ tend to zero in the above formulae and define

$$C = \left|\frac{dx}{d\alpha}\right|, \qquad K = \left|\frac{\alpha}{x}\frac{dx}{d\alpha}\right|. \tag{8.18}$$

We have preferred the forms (8.16), (8.17) because we shall usually obtain condition numbers by analysis leading to equations like (8.14).

Returning to the result (8.15), we see that the condition number for absolute changes in x_j caused by absolute changes in b_k is given by

$$C_{jk} = |\alpha_{jk}| = \frac{|A_{kj}|}{|\Delta|}, \tag{8.19}$$

whereas the condition number for relative changes is given by

$$K_{jk} = \frac{|\alpha_{jk}b_k|}{|x_j|} = \frac{|A_{kj}b_k|}{|x_j\Delta|}, \tag{8.20}$$

where $\Delta = \det \mathbf{A}$, and A_{kj} is the cofactor of a_{kj}, so that α_{jk}, the (j, k)th element of $\mathbf{A}^{-1}$, is A_{kj}/Δ.

As a numerical example, if we wish to examine the dependence of x_2 on changes in b_2 for the set of equations (8.7), we have $A_{22} = 1$, $\Delta = 0.00001$, $b_2 = 2.00001$, $x_2 = 1$, so that $C_{22} \approx 10^5$, $K_{22} \approx 2.10^5$, and x_2 is very sensitive to changes in b_2, in either the absolute or the relative sense. On the other hand, in

Equation (8.3), $A_{22} = 1$, $\Delta = -2$, $b_2 = 1$, $x_2 = 1$, and $C_{22} = K_{22} = \frac{1}{2}$. In this case, x_2 is not sensitive to changes in b_2.

Using the notation in Definition 8.1, it is clear that if either C or K is large compared with unity, then x will be sensitive to changes in α, in the appropriate sense. This leads to

DEFINITION 8.2. Let p, P be two arbitrary numbers that are at our disposal in any particular problem. The number P will usually be taken to be much larger than unity (say 10^4 upwards), and p is usually taken to be not much larger than unity (say 10 or 100). If, using the notation in Definition 8.1, $C \geq P$ or $K \geq P$, we say that x is *ill-conditioned with respect to variations in* α, the variations being understood in the absolute sense for C, and the relative sense for K. Similarly, if $C \leq p$ or $K \leq p$, we say that x is *well-conditioned with respect to variations in* α, the variations being understood in the appropriate sense.

We have not specified the values of p and P precisely in this definition. This vagueness is deliberate since the question of whether we consider a set of equations to be ill-conditioned or not often depends on circumstances. If we can obtain a solution that is adequate for our purposes, with the computing equipment at our disposal, without too much trouble, we usually regard the equations as well-conditioned. This statement in itself indicates why the definition of ill-conditioning must contain some degree of arbitrariness. As a corollary, it follows that we do not usually wish to determine condition numbers very precisely. The order of magnitude is usually sufficient.

Ex. 8.1. Suppose that in (8.14) the only change present is a change in a_{pq} to $a_{pq} + \delta a_{pq}$ for some particular p, q. Show that, in the limit as δa_{pq} tends to zero, the condition numbers for the resulting changes in x_j are given by:

$$C_{j,pq} = |\alpha_{jp} x_q| = \frac{|A_{pj} x_q|}{|\Delta|}, \tag{8.21}$$

$$K_{j,pq} = \frac{|\alpha_{jp} a_{pq} x_q|}{|x_j|} = \frac{|A_{pj} a_{pj}|}{|\Delta|} \frac{|a_{pq} x_q|}{|a_{pj} x_j|}. \tag{8.22}$$

Show that the x_j in (8.7) are ill-conditioned with respect to variations in the a_{pq}, but in (8.6), the x_j are well-conditioned.

It is instructive to note the following conditions under which the condition numbers K in (8.20) and (8.22) are large. We have

$$\Delta = \det \mathbf{A} = \sum_{i=1}^{n} A_{ij} a_{ij}, \tag{8.23}$$

and we see that the term $A_{pj}a_{pj}$ in the numerator of (8.22) is one of the terms in the sum (8.23). Hence, if $a_{pq}x_q$ is comparable with $a_{pj}x_j$ (these both occur in the pth equation), then $K_{j,pq}$ will be large only if cancellation occurs when forming the sum in (8.23). Similarly, from Cramer's rule,

$$x_j\Delta = \Delta_j = \sum_{i=1}^{n} A_{ij}b_i \tag{8.24}$$

where Δ_j is the determinant of the matrix obtained by replacing the jth column of **A** by **b**, and we have expanded this determinant by the jth column. We see that K_{jk} defined in (8.20) will be large if and only if cancellation occurs when the terms in (8.24) are summed.

Even though no cancellation occurs when forming the sum for det **A** in (8.23), the condition numbers $K_{j,pq}$ in (8.22) will be large if $|x_j|$ is small compared with $|\alpha_{jp}a_{pq}x_q|$. It will always be possible to find some right-hand side **b** for which this is true. (An example is given in another connection in Ex. 8.13.) We should suspect that this is occurring if one of the unknowns is small compared with the others, or if one of the $|a_{ij}x_j|$ is small compared with the others (i fixed, j variable). However the question of scaling, discussed in the next section, is relevant, and the ultimate check is to compute the condition numbers themselves.

The definitions of "condition number" and "ill-conditioned" are now precise, but the reader will notice that we have not said that a set of equations is ill-conditioned, but only that one unknown x_j is ill-conditioned with respect to variations in a particular a_{pq} or b_k. In practice, one of two things usually happens. Either many of the condition numbers are large, or all the condition numbers are small. In the former case, we say that the equations are ill-conditioned, and, in the latter case, that they are well-conditioned. The term "ill-conditioned" in this general sense is used somewhat loosely as a term of abuse. However there is one important proviso that must be made. Our previous discussion indicated that large condition numbers arise from two causes:

(a) det **A** is much smaller than the individual terms in the sum (8.23) because cancellation occurs.

(b) The right-hand side **b** is such that some of the unknowns are "small" in some sense.

The second situation under which large condition numbers arise is accidental in that ill-conditioning then depends on special **b**. Also it tends to occur when the unknowns are "small" and then consideration of relative error may be misleading. (If an unknown is zero its relative error is meaningless.) For these reasons, *when we refer to "ill-conditioned equations" we usually refer to large condition numbers caused by* (*a*), *namely cancellation in forming* det **A**, *not* (*b*), *the occurrence of "small" unknowns.* As an overall measure of condition in this sense we might take

$$\max_{i,j} |\alpha_{ij}a_{ji}|, \quad \text{or} \quad \sum_{i=1}^{n}\sum_{j=1}^{n} |\alpha_{ij}a_{ji}|,$$

where $\alpha_{ij} = A_{ji}/\Delta$, the (i, j)th element of $\mathbf{A}^{-1}$. (See also Theorem 8.3 below and the discussion connected with (8.45). We return to the question of "average" condition numbers in Chapter 13.)

In order to ensure that the basic result in this section is clear, we state it in the form of a theorem:

THEOREM 8.1. *When solving* $\mathbf{Ax} = \mathbf{b}$, *the condition numbers for absolute changes in* x_j *caused by small absolute changes in* b_k *and* a_{pq} *are given by* C_{jk} *and* $C_{j,pq}$ *defined in* (8.19) *and* (8.21), *respectively. The condition numbers for relative changes in* x_j *caused by small relative changes in* b_k, a_{pq} *are given by* K_{jk}, $K_{j,pq}$ *defined in* (8.20), (8.22), *respectively.*

Proof: Follows directly from the derivation of (8.14) and Definition 8.1.

Although we have concentrated so far on expressing condition numbers in terms of determinants, in numerical examples we would use (8.14) directly, as in the following exercise.

Ex. 8.2. Find the condition numbers of the following equations for relative changes in the b_k and a_{pq}, and deduce that the equations are well-conditioned with respect to relative changes when $|\varepsilon| \ll 1$.

$$\begin{aligned} 2x_1 + x_2 + x_3 &= 1 \\ x_1 + \varepsilon x_2 + \varepsilon x_3 &= 2\varepsilon \\ x_1 + \varepsilon x_2 - \varepsilon x_3 &= \varepsilon. \end{aligned} \tag{8.25}$$

Solution: A straightforward calculation shows that

$$\det \mathbf{A} = 2\varepsilon(1 - 2\varepsilon), \tag{8.26}$$

$$\mathbf{A}^{-1} = \begin{bmatrix} -\dfrac{\varepsilon}{1-2\varepsilon} & \dfrac{1}{1-2\varepsilon} & 0 \\ \dfrac{1}{1-2\varepsilon} & -\dfrac{(1+2\varepsilon)}{2\varepsilon(1-2\varepsilon)} & \dfrac{1}{2\varepsilon} \\ 0 & \dfrac{1}{2\varepsilon} & -\dfrac{1}{2\varepsilon} \end{bmatrix} \tag{8.27}$$

$$x_1 = \frac{\varepsilon}{1-2\varepsilon}, \qquad x_2 = \frac{1}{2} - \frac{2\varepsilon}{1-2\varepsilon}, \qquad x_3 = \tfrac{1}{2}. \tag{8.28}$$

Since we are interested in relative changes, we introduce the notation

$$\frac{\delta a_{ij}}{a_{ij}} = \delta_{ij}, \qquad \frac{\delta b_k}{b_k} = \delta_k.$$

We apply Equation (8.14). Assuming that, to a sufficient degree of accuracy, $\mathbf{x}'$ can be replaced by $\mathbf{x}$, we have

$$\delta\mathbf{b} - \delta\mathbf{A}\mathbf{x}' \approx \begin{bmatrix} \delta_1 - 2\delta_{11}x_1 - \delta_{12}x_2 - \delta_{13}x_3 \\ 2\varepsilon\delta_2 - \delta_{21}x_1 - \varepsilon\delta_{22}x_2 - \varepsilon\delta_{23}x_3 \\ \varepsilon\delta_3 - \delta_{31}x_1 - \varepsilon\delta_{32}x_2 + \varepsilon\delta_{33}x_3 \end{bmatrix},$$

and

$$\frac{\delta x_1}{x_1} \approx \frac{\alpha_{11}}{x_1}(\delta_1 - 2\delta_{11}x_1 - \delta_{12}x_2 - \delta_{13}x_3) + \frac{\alpha_{12}}{x_1}(2\varepsilon\delta_2 - \delta_{21}x_1 - \varepsilon\delta_{22}x_2 - \varepsilon\delta_{23}x_3), \quad (8.29)$$

with similar equations for $\delta x_2/x_2$ and $\delta x_3/x_3$, where α_{ij} is the (i, j)th element of $\mathbf{A}^{-1}$. (From (8.27), $\alpha_{13} = 0$ in this case.) Direct substitution of values from (8.27), (8.28), assuming that $|\varepsilon| \ll 1$ and keeping only the dominant part of each coefficient to show the results more clearly, gives

$$\frac{\delta x_1}{x_1} \approx -\delta_1 + 2\varepsilon\delta_{11} - \tfrac{1}{2}\delta_{12} - \tfrac{1}{2}\delta_{13} + 2\delta_2 - \delta_{21} - \tfrac{1}{2}\delta_{22} - \tfrac{1}{2}\delta_{23}.$$

None of the coefficients of δ_k or δ_{pq} are large compared with unity, so that x_1 is well-conditioned with respect to relative variations in any of the coefficients. It is left to the reader to check that the same is true of x_2 and x_3.

Ex. 8.3. Find the condition numbers for absolute changes in b_k and a_{pq} for the equations (8.25), and deduce that the equations are badly conditioned with respect to absolute changes when $|\varepsilon| \ll 1$. [Actually, this is obvious by inspection. If $\varepsilon = 0$, the matrix of coefficients is singular which, from the discussion following (8.10), indicates that the equations are ill-conditioned with respect to absolute changes.]

Ex. 8.4. Show that for a 2×2 set of equations, (8.14) gives

$$\frac{\delta x_1}{x_1} = s\frac{\delta b_1}{b_1} + (1 - s)\frac{\delta b_2}{b_2} - \frac{x_1'}{x_1}\left\{(1 + p)\frac{\delta a_{11}}{a_{11}} - p\frac{\delta a_{21}}{a_{21}}\right\} - \frac{1}{q}(1 + p)\frac{x_2'}{x_2}\left\{\frac{\delta a_{12}}{a_{12}} - \frac{\delta a_{22}}{a_{22}}\right\}, \quad (8.30)$$

$$p = \frac{a_{12}a_{21}}{a_{11}a_{22} - a_{12}a_{21}}, \qquad q = \frac{a_{11}x_1}{a_{12}x_2}, \qquad s = (1 + p)\left(1 + \frac{1}{q}\right). \quad (8.31)$$

Find the corresponding result for $\delta x_2/x_2$.

This last example illustrates nicely the distinction already made between inherent ill-conditioning due to cancellation when evaluating det $\mathbf{A}$ which will result in large p, and accidental ill-conditioning due to particular x_i resulting from a given $\mathbf{b}$. In line with our previous comments, if we say that a 2×2 set of equations is ill-conditioned we mean that p is large.

8.3 Scaling and the Recognition of Ill-Conditioning

The discussion in the last section has given a method for deciding whether $\mathbf{Ax} = \mathbf{b}$ is ill-conditioned. However, as illustrated in Ex. 8.1, the method is laborious. We should like to have some easy way of recognizing whether a set of equations is ill-conditioned. Examination of the condition numbers (8.19)–(8.22) suggests two situations under which ill-conditioning occurs:

(a) When the elements of the inverse are "large" [since $\mathbf{A}^{-1}$ appears in (8.14), and the elements of the inverse occur in the numerators of (8.19)–(8.22)].

(b) When the determinant of coefficients is "small" [since this occurs in the denominators of (8.19)–(8.22)].

However, we have to be careful. If we multiply each of the equations in (8.3) by 10^{-10}, we have

$$\begin{aligned} 10^{-10}x_1 + 10^{-10}x_2 &= 3 \cdot 10^{-10} \\ 10^{-10}x_1 - 10^{-10}x_2 &= 10^{-10}. \end{aligned}$$

The elements of the inverse are of order 10^{10} and the determinant is $-2 \cdot 10^{-10}$, but the equations are still well-conditioned. The answer is of course that the condition numbers depend on the *ratios* of certain numbers, not on their absolute values. This introduces the question of *scaling*.

DEFINITION 8.3. By *scaling a set of equations* we mean

(a) multiplying any equation by a nonzero constant,

(b) replacing any unknown by a new unknown which is a multiple of the old one.

By *scaling a matrix* we mean multiplying the rows and columns by any nonzero constants.

It is obvious that, in matrix notation, if the original matrix is denoted by $\mathbf{A}$, and the scaled matrix by $\mathbf{B}$, then $\mathbf{B} = \mathbf{PAQ}$, where $\mathbf{P}$ and $\mathbf{Q}$ are diagonal matrices. Similarly, if the original set of equations is $\mathbf{Ax} = \mathbf{b}$, and we multiply the ith equation by p_i, and set $x_j = q_j x_j'$, then the scaled equations are

$$\mathbf{A}'\mathbf{x}' = \mathbf{b}', \qquad \mathbf{A}' = \mathbf{PAQ}, \qquad \mathbf{x}' = \mathbf{Q}^{-1}\mathbf{x}, \qquad \mathbf{b}' = \mathbf{Pb}. \tag{8.32}$$

If the original equations have no solution, a unique solution, or an infinity of solutions, the same property holds for the scaled equations. Also:

THEOREM 8.2. *When solving* $\mathbf{Ax} = \mathbf{b}$, *the relative condition numbers for changes in* x_j *produced by changes in* b_k, a_{pq}, *are independent of scaling.*

Proof: The relative condition numbers are given by (8.20), (8.22). Using primes for quantities connected with the scaled equations, we have [see (8.32)]:

$$K'_{jk} = \frac{|A'_{kj}b'_k|}{|x'_j\Delta'|} = \frac{|q_jA'_{kj}p_kb_k|}{|x_j\Delta'|} = \frac{|A_{kj}b_k|}{|x_j\Delta|} = K_{jk}.$$

It is left to the reader to show similarly that $K'_{j,pq} = K_{j,pq}$.

Consider the definition of the condition number $K_{jk} = |\alpha_{jk}b_k|/|x_j|$ given in (8.20). If $|b_k|$ and $|x_j|$ are of order unity, it is true that if the element of the inverse α_{jk} is large, then K_{jk} is large. However b_k and x_j can be altered at will by rescaling. This indicates that statement (a) at the beginning of this section ought to read something like "If the equations are scaled properly, then ill-conditioning (in a relative sense) is indicated when the elements of the inverse are large." The difficulty here is to indicate what we mean by saying that the equations are "properly" scaled. The best we can do is to give some cautionary examples.

It is often suggested that equations should be scaled so that the largest element in each row and column of the augmented matrix is of order unity. In Ex. 8.2, equations (8.25), with $|\varepsilon| \ll 1$, are a set for which this criterion is satisfied, the determinant of coefficients is very small, some of the elements of the inverse are very large, and yet the equations are very well-conditioned in a relative sense. This shows that the criterion that the largest element in each row and column is of order unity is not *sufficient* to ensure that we can see whether a set of equations is ill-conditioned by inspection of the size of the determinant or the elements of the inverse.

In connection with Ex. 8.2, the following result is of interest:

Ex. 8.5. Show that Equations (8.25) can be rescaled so that the largest elements in each row and column of the augmented matrix are still of order unity, and the determinant and the elements of the inverse are of order unity ($|\varepsilon| \ll 1$).

Solution: Introduce new unknowns $z_1 = x_1/\varepsilon$, $z_2 = x_2$, $z_3 = x_3$, and divide the resulting second and third equations by ε. This gives

$$\begin{aligned} 2\varepsilon z_1 + z_2 + z_3 &= 1 \\ z_1 + z_2 + z_3 &= 2 \\ z_1 + z_2 - z_3 &= 1. \end{aligned} \tag{8.33}$$

Denoting this new matrix of coefficients by $\mathbf{A}'$, we find

$$\det \mathbf{A}' = 2(1 - 2\varepsilon),$$

$$(\mathbf{A}')^{-1} = \frac{1}{(1-2\varepsilon)} \begin{bmatrix} -1 & 1 & 0 \\ 1 & -\frac{1}{2}(1+2\varepsilon) & \frac{1}{2}(1-2\varepsilon) \\ 0 & \frac{1}{2}(1-2\varepsilon) & -\frac{1}{2}(1-2\varepsilon) \end{bmatrix}. \tag{8.34}$$

The chief result in this section has been negative: If we wish to see whether a set of equations is ill-conditioned, the safest method is to use the full machinery of Theorem 8.1, exemplified in Ex. 8.1. The size of the determinant or the elements of the inverse are unreliable measures of ill-conditioning in themselves. They are suitable if the equations are scaled "properly," but this is difficult to define precisely. The best criterion produced so far seems to be a condition like the one derived in Section 13.5, that the absolute row-sums of **A** and $\mathbf{A}^{-1}$ are constants:

$$\sum_{j=1}^{n} |a_{ij}| = \xi, \qquad \sum_{j=1}^{n} |\alpha_{ij}| = \eta, \tag{8.35}$$

where ξ and η are independent of i. The value of ξ can be chosen arbitrarily, and it is convenient to choose this to be unity. In order to find out whether this criterion is satisfied, we need the inverse $\mathbf{A}^{-1}$. No satisfactory criterion is known for deciding whether **A** is properly scaled by inspection of **A** alone. The condition that the largest elements in each row and column of $[\mathbf{A}, \mathbf{b}]$ are of the same order (unity for convenience) is certainly desirable though not sufficient. A better criterion when solving $\mathbf{Ax} = \mathbf{b}$ seems to be: Arrange that in $[\mathbf{A}, \mathbf{b}]$ there are $n + 1$ elements, one from each column, no two of the elements from **A** occurring in the same row, and each of the $n + 1$ elements being of order unity. Equations (8.33) satisfy this criterion but equations (8.25) do not.

We shall use several times, in later sections, the criterion that *if equations are properly scaled* (in particular, if the largest elements in **A** are of order unity in the sense discussed in the last paragraph), then a small value of det **A** (i.e., a value small compared with unity) indicates that the equations are badly conditioned. The chief reason for using this criterion is simply that it is extremely convenient, but it should be clear from the discussion that it is a reasonable criterion in many cases, rather than a criterion based on a rigorous theorem.

8.4 Nearly-Singular Matrices and Numerical Rank

DEFINITION **8.4.** A square matrix **A** is said to be *nearly-singular* if it is possible to find some matrix $\delta\mathbf{A}$ such that $\mathbf{A} + \delta\mathbf{A}$ is singular, where, if we are concerned with absolute (relative) variations, then, for some given ε

$$|\delta a_{ij}| \le \varepsilon, \qquad \left(\left|\frac{\delta a_{ij}}{a_{ij}}\right| \le \varepsilon\right), \qquad \text{for all } i, j. \tag{8.36}$$

To obtain a criterion for deciding whether a matrix is nearly-singular, we start from the relation that, since $\mathbf{A} + \delta\mathbf{A}$ is singular,

$$\det(\mathbf{A} + \delta\mathbf{A}) = 0.$$

Each column of $\mathbf{A} + \delta\mathbf{A}$ is the sum of columns of **A** and $\delta\mathbf{A}$, so this determinant can be expanded by repeated applications of Theorem 7.3(iv). The expansion rapidly becomes complicated, but if we neglect second-order terms involving products of the δa_{ij}, we readily find, for small δa_{ij},

$$\det(\mathbf{A} + \delta\mathbf{A}) \approx \det \mathbf{A} + \sum_{i=1}^{n}\sum_{j=1}^{n} \delta a_{ij} A_{ij}. \tag{8.37}$$

The values of the δa_{ij} are at our disposal and we wish to choose them in such a way as to make $\det(\mathbf{A} + \delta\mathbf{A})$ zero. This leads to the following theorem:

THEOREM 8.3. *The square matrix* $\mathbf{A}$ *is nearly-singular if and only if* $C > 1/\varepsilon$, *where* ε *is the parameter in Definition* 8.4 *and*

(i) *for absolute variations:*

$$C = \sum_{i=1}^{n}\sum_{j=1}^{n} |\alpha_{ij}|, \tag{8.38}$$

(ii) *for relative variations:*

$$C = \sum_{i=1}^{n}\sum_{j=1}^{n} |a_{ij}\alpha_{ji}|, \tag{8.39}$$

where in both cases α_{ij} *is the* (i, j)*th element of* $\mathbf{A}^{-1}$.

Proof: If we are interested in absolute variations in a_{ij}, suppose that we choose $|\delta a_{ij}| = \mu$ for all i, j, where μ is a constant to be determined, and choose the sign of δa_{ij} to be opposite to that of $A_{ij}/\det \mathbf{A}$. Then, from (8.37), the condition that $\det(\mathbf{A} + \delta\mathbf{A})$ be zero gives, approximately, $\mu = 1/C$, where

$$C = \frac{\left(\sum_{i=1}^{n}\sum_{j=1}^{n} |A_{ij}|\right)}{|\det \mathbf{A}|} = \sum_{i=1}^{n}\sum_{j=1}^{n} |\alpha_{ji}|, \tag{8.40}$$

where $\alpha_{ji} = A_{ij}/\det \mathbf{A}$ is the (j, i)th element of $\mathbf{A}^{-1}$. The point of this is that μ is the *smallest* constant such that δa_{ij} can be chosen with $|\delta a_{ij}| \le \mu$ for all i, j, and $\mathbf{A} + \delta\mathbf{A}$ singular. This remark proves the part of the theorem dealing with absolute variations. If we are interested in relative variations, we choose $|\delta a_{ij}/a_{ij}| = \mu$ for all i, j, and choose the sign of δa_{ij} so that δa_{ij} and $a_{ij}A_{ij}/\det \mathbf{A}$ have opposite signs. Then $\det(\mathbf{A} + \delta\mathbf{A})$ is zero if $\mu = 1/C$, where

$$C = \frac{\left(\sum_{i=1}^{n}\sum_{j=1}^{n} |a_{ij}A_{ij}|\right)}{|\det \mathbf{A}|} = \sum_{i=1}^{n}\sum_{j=1}^{n} |a_{ij}\alpha_{ji}|.$$

This μ is the smallest constant such that a_{ij} can be chosen with $|\delta a_{ij}/a_{ij}| \le \mu$ for all i, j, and $\mathbf{A} + \delta\mathbf{A}$ singular. Hence, the part of the theorem dealing with relative variations is true.

Ex. 8.6. Is the coefficient matrix for Equations (8.25) nearly-singular, where ε is much smaller than unity, $|\varepsilon| \ll 1$?

Solution: From the explicit inverse (8.27) we see that, for absolute changes, (8.38) gives $C \approx 2/\varepsilon$, and, for relative changes, (8.39) gives $C \approx 4$. Hence, the coefficient matrix is nearly-singular for absolute changes, but not nearly-singular for relative changes.

In practice the problem of determining whether a matrix is nearly-singular or not often appears in connection with experimental error.

Ex. 8.7. Investigate whether the following matrix is nearly-singular, if each of its elements is uncertain to within ± 0.01.

$$\begin{bmatrix} 12.39 & 7.59 & 4.64 \\ 11.71 & 6.21 & 3.46 \\ 4.41 & 1.95 & 0.89 \end{bmatrix}. \qquad (8.41)$$

Solution: The inverse of this matrix is, to two decimal places,

$$\begin{bmatrix} -2.57 & 4.84 & -5.39 \\ 10.20 & -19.90 & 24.18 \\ -9.60 & 19.64 & -25.18 \end{bmatrix}. \qquad (8.42)$$

We are interested in absolute changes, so we use (8.38) which gives $C = 121.5$, $1/C \approx 0.008$, which is less than 0.01. Hence, the matrix is nearly-singular, according to the strict definition, although it could more accurately be described as a borderline case.

Since a singular matrix has a zero determinant, we might expect that:

(a) A nearly-singular matrix must have a small determinant.
(b) A small determinant is a sign of a nearly-singular matrix.
(c) A large determinant indicates a matrix that is not nearly-singular.

However, none of these statements is necessarily true. The difficulty is that we need to be clear about what we mean by "large" and "small." In particular, are we interested in absolute or relative variations? The following examples are instructive. Note that in each case the matrices are scaled so that the largest element in each row and column is of order unity.

Ex. 8.8. Show that the coefficient matrix in (8.25), where $|\varepsilon| \ll 1$, is an example where the determinant of the matrix, (8.26), is small, and the elements of the inverse, (8.27), are large, yet the matrix is *not* nearly-singular with respect to relative variations.

Ex. 8.9. Show that the following upper triangular matrix of order n, with units along its principal diagonal and -1 for all elements above the diagonal, is nearly-singular for absolute variations, if n is sufficiently large.

$$\mathbf{A} = \begin{bmatrix} 1 & -1 & -1 & \dots & -1 & -1 \\ 0 & 1 & -1 & \dots & -1 & -1 \\ 0 & 0 & 1 & \dots & -1 & -1 \\ & & & \dots & & \\ 0 & 0 & 0 & \dots & 1 & -1 \\ 0 & 0 & 0 & \dots & 0 & 1 \end{bmatrix}. \tag{8.43}$$

Solution: The inverse in the 5×5 case, for instance, is

$$\mathbf{A}^{-1} = \begin{bmatrix} 1 & 1 & 2 & 4 & 8 \\ 0 & 1 & 1 & 2 & 4 \\ 0 & 0 & 1 & 1 & 2 \\ 0 & 0 & 0 & 1 & 1 \\ 0 & 0 & 0 & 0 & 1 \end{bmatrix}. \tag{8.44}$$

In the general case it is easy to see that $\alpha_{1n} = 2^{n-2}$. Theorem 8.3, (8.38), immediately tells us that $\mathbf{A}$ is nearly-singular for absolute variations in its elements, when n is large.

The point of this example is that det $\mathbf{A}$ is always unity, so that a nearly-singular matrix does not necessarily have a small determinant.

It is instructive to ask whether, if $\mathbf{A}$ is a nearly-singular matrix, the corresponding set of equations $\mathbf{Ax} = \mathbf{b}$ is ill-conditioned in the sense of Section 8.2. For absolute variations, if $\mathbf{A}$ is nearly-singular, the sum (8.38) is large and at least one of the condition numbers defined in (8.19), and perhaps some of those in (8.21), will be large. Hence, the equations must be ill-conditioned in some sense. For relative variations, if $\mathbf{A}$ is nearly-singular, (8.39) indicates that at least one of the numbers $|a_{ij}\alpha_{ji}|$ is large. However, from (8.20), (8.22), ill-conditioning of $\mathbf{Ax} = \mathbf{b}$ with respect to relative changes depends on the numbers

$$K_{ji} = |a_{ij}\alpha_{ji}| \frac{|b_i|}{|a_{ij}x_j|}, \qquad K_{j,iq} = |a_{ij}\alpha_{ji}| \frac{|a_{iq}x_q|}{|a_{ij}x_j|}. \tag{8.45}$$

The situation is not quite so straightforward as for absolute variations. If $\mathbf{A}$ is nearly singular for relative variations, at least one of the condition numbers $|a_{ij}\alpha_{ji}|$ is large, and the equations will be ill-conditioned in some sense since at least $K_{j,ij}$ will be large. The discussion in the paragraphs preceding Theorem 8.1 is relevant, where two causes (a), (b) of large condition numbers are listed. We were careful to say that the general phrase "ill-conditioned equations" usually refers to cause (a), namely cancellation when evaluating determinants. In this sense ill-conditioned equations imply nearly-singular matrices, and vice-versa. However large relative condition numbers do not imply a nearly singular coefficient matrix since cause (b) may be operative.

The question of whether a matrix is nearly-singular is connected with the problem of the rank of a general matrix when the elements of the matrix may be in error. We illustrate the problem by an example.

Ex. 8.10. The elements of the following matrix are experimental results with errors that can be as much as 0.01 in absolute value.

$$\mathbf{A} = \begin{bmatrix} 12.39 & 7.59 & 4.64 & 2.35 & 1.25 \\ 11.71 & 6.21 & 3.46 & 1.96 & 1.17 \\ 10.21 & 6.63 & 4.20 & 2.03 & 1.02 \\ 4.40 & 1.93 & 0.91 & 0.62 & 0.45 \\ 4.41 & 1.95 & 0.89 & 0.61 & 0.44 \end{bmatrix}. \tag{8.46}$$

Determine the rank of the matrix. [This is the matrix already quoted in Section 5.5, (5.12), except that rows and columns have been interchanged so that pivoting on the (1, 1) and (2, 2) elements is convenient. The question of choice of pivots is considered in the next two sections.]

Solution: We use elementary row operations to reduce the matrix to a simpler form. We subtract multiples of the first row from the others to reduce the $(i, 1)$ elements to zero, $i = 2$ to 5. This gives

$$\begin{bmatrix} 12.39 & 7.59 & 4.64 & 2.35 & 1.25 \\ 0 & -0.963 & -0.925 & -0.261 & -0.011 \\ 0 & 0.376 & 0.376 & 0.094 & -0.010 \\ 0 & -0.765 & -0.738 & -0.215 & -0.006 \\ 0 & -0.752 & -0.762 & -0.226 & -0.005 \end{bmatrix}. \tag{8.47}$$

Numbers have been rounded to three decimals but we are keeping one guarding figure and rounding errors are not important. We next subtract multiples of the second row in (8.47) from the later rows to reduce the $(i, 2)$ elements to zero, $i = 3, 4, 5$:

$$\begin{bmatrix} 12.39 & 7.59 & 4.64 & 2.35 & 1.25 \\ 0 & -0.963 & -0.925 & -0.261 & -0.011 \\ 0 & 0 & 0.016 & -0.008 & -0.015 \\ 0 & 0 & -0.003 & 0.007 & 0.015 \\ 0 & 0 & -0.040 & -0.023 & 0.004 \end{bmatrix}. \tag{8.48}$$

We can now see the difficulty very clearly. If we accept these numbers at their face value, we can proceed further with the reduction, and we will end up with the result that (8.46) is of rank 5. However, the numbers in the last three rows of (8.48) are comparable with 0.01 in size. This suggests that we might be able to vary the elements of (8.46) by amounts less than 0.01 in such a way that all the submatrices of order 3 are singular. In the terminology of Definition 8.4, the problem is to find out whether all the submatrices of order 3 are nearly-singular in the absolute sense, with $\varepsilon = 0.01$. It is possible to set this up as a linear programming problem by using the approach leading to Theorem 8.3, but this lies outside the scope of this book. For our purposes, it is sufficient to concentrate on the least-singular submatrix of order 3, obtained from rows 1, 2, 5 and columns 1, 2, 3, of (8.46), since the (5, 3) element in (8.48) is the largest in the last three rows. The question of whether this matrix is nearly-singular was investigated in Ex. 8.7, where it was concluded that it could be made singular by changes in its elements less than or equal to 0.008. Since the criterion that *all* submatrices must be nearly-singular is more stringent than the criterion that the worst one be nearly-singular, the fact that 0.008 is close to 0.01 indicates that we have a borderline case on our hands. However, the size of the largest determinant corresponding to a submatrix of order 2 is about 12, and this is so much larger than the largest determinant corresponding to a submatrix of order 3, namely 12×0.04, that an applied scientist would have no hesitation in saying that it is consistent with the numerical results to assume that (8.46) is an approximation to a matrix of rank 2. (If necessary, he would say that the uncertainty 0.01 in the elements may well have been underestimated.)

The above discussion suggests:

DEFINITION 8.5. A general $m \times n$ matrix $\mathbf{A}$ has *numerical rank k* if:

(a) It is possible to find some $\delta\mathbf{A}$ such that $\mathbf{A} + \delta\mathbf{A}$ is of rank k where, if we are concerned with absolute (relative) errors, then, for some specified ε,

$$|\delta a_{ij}| \le \varepsilon, \qquad \left(\left|\frac{\delta a_{ij}}{a_{ij}}\right| \le \varepsilon\right), \qquad \text{for } all\ i, j. \tag{8.49}$$

(b) There is no other $\delta\mathbf{A}$ with elements satisfying condition (8.49) such that the rank of $\mathbf{A} + \delta\mathbf{A}$ is $k - 1$.

8.5 Rounding and the Choice of Pivots

In this section we turn our attention to a problem that has been ignored so far, namely the fact that, when solving linear equations numerically, it is essential to choose the pivots correctly in order to obtain accurate numerical results. The reason for this comes from the fact that when calculations are performed on a digital computer (or by hand), only a finite number of digits can be carried. For example, $\frac{1}{3} = 0.333\ldots$, but when computing we must round this number to a finite number of decimals. (To *round* a number, retain the required digits and discard the remainder. If the discarded part is less than half a unit in the last place retained, leave the last digit unchanged; if it is greater than half a unit, increase the last digit by one; if it is exactly half a unit, round to the nearest even digit.)

In order to illustrate that the choice of pivots is important, consider the equations

$$\begin{aligned} x_1 - x_2 &= 0 \\ 10^{-2}x_1 + x_2 &= 1, \end{aligned} \tag{8.50}$$

which have the exact solution $x_1 = x_2 = \frac{100}{101}$. Suppose that we solve these numerically, working to two significant figures, using the sequence of operations discussed in Section 7.6. We multiply the first equation by 10^{-2}, and subtract from the second:

$$-1.01x_2 = -1. \tag{8.51}$$

However, we are working to two significant figures, so 1.01 will be rounded to 1.0, and this equation is computed as $\hat{x}_2 = 1$, where a cap is used to denote "computed value." Back-substitution in the first equation gives $\hat{x}_1 = 1$, and we have obtained a reasonable approximate solution of the equations, accurate to 1%.

Suppose, however, that we pivot on the (2, 1) element instead of the (1, 1) element. This is equivalent to solving the system

$$\begin{aligned} 10^{-2}x_1 + x_2 &= 1 \\ x_1 - x_2 &= 0 \end{aligned} \tag{8.52}$$

in the natural order. In this case, we multiply the first equation by 10^2 and subtract from the second which gives, as before, $1.01x_2 = 1$, or, on rounding, $\hat{x}_2 = 1$. Back-substitution in the first equation gives $\hat{x}_1 = 0$. In this case, the computed solution is no longer a reasonable approximation to the exact solution. The only difference in the procedure has been the choice of pivots, and this illustrates that the choice of pivots is important.

A detailed analysis of the situation would be out of place here, but we give a brief treatment of the 2×2 case. We assume that calculations are being performed in *floating-point* in which numbers are represented to a fixed number of decimal places, $x = a \cdot 10^b$, where a is called the *fractional part* (mantissa) and b is the *exponent*. The exponent is an integer. The fractional part is always normalized so that

$$0.1 \le |a| < 1.$$

We consider floating-point working rather than fixed-point (in which numbers are represented to a fixed number of decimal places) since digital computers work in floating-point. When rounding a floating-point number, the fractional part is rounded to a fixed number of decimals. The rounded form of a floating-point number z will be denoted by $\mathrm{fl}\,(z) = \hat{z}$, where we again use a cap to denote "computed value."

The reader may have subconsciously gained the impression that the reason why the first solution of (8.50) was satisfactory whereas (8.52) was unsatisfactory is connected with the fact that the pivot 1 used to solve (8.50) is much larger than the pivot 10^{-2} used to solve (8.52). It is easy to show that this is not true when we are working in floating-point. Suppose that we *rescale* (8.50) by multiplying the first equation by 10^{-2}, the second by 10^2, and setting $x_1 = 10^2 z_1$, $x_2 = 10^{-2} z_2$. The equations become

$$\begin{aligned} z_1 - 10^{-4} z_2 &= 0 \\ 10^2 z_1 + \quad z_2 &= 10^2. \end{aligned} \tag{8.53}$$

If we pivot on the "large" coefficient 10^2, we find, working to two significant figures in floating-point, $z_2 = 10^2$, $z_1 = 0$, which gives $x_2 = 1$, $x_1 = 0$, i.e., the same unsatisfactory solution found from (8.52).

Ex. 8.11. Show that any of the other three pivots in (8.53), including the "small" pivot 10^{-4}, gives satisfactory approximations for x_1, x_2 when working in floating-point to two significant figures.

In order to understand the situation, we give a theoretical analysis. If n is an approximation to a number N which is known exactly, the *error* δ of n is defined by $n = N + \delta$, and the *relative error* ε is defined by δ/N, i.e.,

$$\varepsilon = \frac{(n - N)}{N} \quad \text{or} \quad n = N(1 + \varepsilon). \tag{8.54}$$

Suppose that x is an exact number represented in the form $a \cdot 10^b$, where b is an integer and a has t decimal places, with $0.1 \le |a| < 1$. The rounded value fl (x) will differ from x by no more than $(0.5 \cdot 10^{-t})10^b$, so that

$$|x - \text{fl}\,(x)| \le (0.5 \cdot 10^{-t})10^b,$$

$$\frac{|x - \text{fl}\,(x)|}{|\text{fl}\,(x)|} \le 5 \cdot 10^{-t}.$$

The value of t for digital computers is usually greater than 8, so that to a close approximation we can replace fl (x) by x in the denominator of this expression. It is then convenient to rewrite the resulting expression in the form

$$\text{fl}\,(x) = x(1 + \varepsilon), \qquad |\varepsilon| \le 5 \cdot 10^{-t}. \tag{8.55}$$

Summing up: We make the *basic assumption* that *if x is an exact number and* fl (x) *is the rounded form of x, then*

$$\text{fl}\,(x) = x(1 + \varepsilon), \qquad |\varepsilon| \le e, \tag{8.56}$$

where e is some number independent of x. If we are working in floating-point to t decimals, then the bound e is $5 \cdot 10^{-t}$. On comparing the forms of (8.56) and (8.54), we see that if we are working in floating-point, the important thing is the *relative*, not the absolute, errors introduced by rounding. Of course, we have to be careful under certain circumstances. When the number being computed is zero (for instance, if we try to compute sin π from the series for sin x), the relative error is not appropriate.

The above basic assumption immediately gives the following results for addition, subtraction, multiplication, and division:

$$\mathrm{fl}\,(x \pm y) = (x \pm y)(1 + \varepsilon), \tag{8.57}$$

$$\mathrm{fl}\,(xy) = xy(1 + \varepsilon), \qquad \mathrm{fl}\left(\frac{x}{y}\right) = \frac{x}{y}(1 + \varepsilon), \tag{8.58}$$

where ε is bounded as in (8.56). These results do not need proof since they are simply restatements of the basic assumption. However, the reader must be careful to interpret the notation properly. Thus, fl $(x - y)$ means that x, y are exact, that $x - y$ must be formed *exactly*, and that, finally, this exact form of $x - y$ is rounded. Thus, if $x = 0.43 \cdot 10^1$, $y = 0.27 \cdot 10^{-1}$, and we work to two figures,

$$x - y = 4.3 - 0.027 = 4.273, \qquad \mathrm{fl}\,(x - y) = 0.43 \cdot 10^1.$$

It may be noted in passing that if we are subtracting two nearly equal numbers, the result may be exact, i.e., no rounding errors may be involved. This is sufficiently illustrated by an example. Working to two figures, with $x = 0.15 \cdot 10^2$, $y = 0.83 \cdot 10^1$,

$$x - y = 150 - 83 = 67 = 0.67 \cdot 10^2, \qquad \mathrm{fl}\,(x - y) = 0.67 \cdot 10^2.$$

The point is that cancellation of leading figures means that rounding is not necessary. When cancellation occurs, we find fl $(x - y) = x - y$, i.e., $\varepsilon = 0$ in (8.56). In spite of this, *cancellation of significant figures when forming $x - y$ is the main reason for loss of accuracy when computing in floating-point.* This may seem to contradict the statement we have just made, that no rounding errors are involved in the formation of $x - y$. The loss of accuracy occurs because of a factor that we have not yet considered, namely that x and y may themselves be inaccurate. (We have been assuming so far that x and y are exact.) We examine this in detail, since it provides an elementary example of the theoretical analysis of error. Suppose that $x = x_0(1 + \varepsilon_1)$, $y = y_0(1 + \varepsilon_2)$, where $|\varepsilon_1| \le e$, $|\varepsilon_2| \le e$. Then

$$x + y = (x_0 + y_0) + (x_0\varepsilon_1 + y_0\varepsilon_2).$$

If we write fl $(x + y) = (x + y)(1 + \varepsilon)$, it is easy to show that, assuming no rounding is necessary,

$$|\varepsilon| \le \frac{|x_0|\,|\varepsilon_1| + |y_0|\,|\varepsilon_2|}{|x_0 + y_0|} \le \frac{|x_0| + |y_0|}{|x_0 + y_0|}\,e. \tag{8.59}$$

If x_0 and y_0 are nearly equal and of opposite signs, then $|x_0 + y_0|$ may be much smaller than $|x_0|$ or $|y_0|$ separately, and the factor multiplying e in (8.59) may be very large, even though no rounding error is present.

Ex. 8.12. If $x_0 = 0.343169 \cdot 10^0$, $y_0 = 0.341946 \cdot 10^0$, and these are rounded to four figures, giving numbers denoted by x and y, show by performing the calculations that $x - y$ is more than 5% different from $x_0 - y_0$, even though x, y are individually only about 0.01% different from x_0, y_0. Show that we should expect this from formula (8.59).

8.6 Choice of Pivots (continued)

We examine theoretically the rounding errors involved when solving the system

$$\begin{aligned} a_{11}x_1 + a_{12}x_2 &= b_1 \\ a_{21}x_1 + a_{22}x_2 &= b_2 \end{aligned} \tag{8.60}$$

by Gaussian elimination. The order in which operations are performed is important. We use the method described in Section 7.6, in which we first compute a multiplying factor

$$m_{21} = \frac{a_{21}}{a_{11}}, \tag{8.61}$$

and then subtract m_{21} times the first equation from the second, which gives x_2, and then back-substitute in the first equation to find x_1. Introducing the notation

$$a_{22}^{(2)} = a_{22} - m_{21}a_{12}, \qquad b_2^{(2)} = b_2 - m_{21}b_1, \tag{8.62}$$

we find

$$x_2 = \frac{b_2^{(2)}}{a_{22}^{(2)}}, \qquad x_1 = \frac{(b_1 - a_{12}x_2)}{a_{11}}. \tag{8.63}$$

The computed value of m_{21}, which we denote by $\hat{m}_{21}$, is related to the exact value (8.61) by

$$\hat{m}_{21} = m_{21}(1 + \varepsilon_{21}), \qquad |\varepsilon_{21}| \le e, \tag{8.64}$$

where e is the known bound introduced in (8.56). We assume that when computing $\hat{a}_{22}^{(2)}$, the number $a_{22} - \hat{m}_{21}a_{12}$ is computed exactly, and the result is rounded, i.e., there is no intermediate rounding when $\hat{m}_{21}a_{12}$ is formed. (The expert will recognize that this is known as *partial double-precision* working.) This gives

$$\hat{a}_{22}^{(2)} = (a_{22} - \hat{m}_{21}a_{12})(1 + \varepsilon_{22}), \qquad |\varepsilon_{22}| \le e.$$

Similarly,

$$\hat{b}_2^{(2)} = (b_2 - \hat{m}_{21}b_1)(1 + \varepsilon_2), \qquad |\varepsilon_2| \le e.$$

Hence, from (8.63), we find

$$\hat{x}_2 = \mathrm{fl}\left\{\frac{\hat{b}_2^{(2)}}{\hat{a}_{22}^{(2)}}\right\} = \frac{(b_2 - \hat{m}_{21}b_1)(1 + \varepsilon_3)}{(a_{22} - \hat{m}_{21}a_{12})}, \tag{8.65}$$

$$\hat{x}_1 = \mathrm{fl}\left\{\frac{\mathrm{fl}\,[b_1 - a_{12}\hat{x}_2]}{a_{11}}\right\} = \frac{\{(b_1a_{22} - b_2a_{12}) - a_{12}(b_2 - \hat{m}_{21}b_1)\varepsilon_3\}(1 + \varepsilon_4)}{a_{11}(a_{22} - \hat{m}_{21}a_{12})}, \tag{8.66}$$

where, for convenience, we have introduced ε_3 and ε_4 defined by

$$1 + \varepsilon_3 = \frac{(1 + \varepsilon_2)(1 + \varepsilon_2')}{1 + \varepsilon_{22}}, \qquad 1 + \varepsilon_4 = (1 + \varepsilon_1)(1 + \varepsilon_1'), \tag{8.67}$$

where ε_2' and ε_1, ε_1' are introduced by the roundings in (8.65), (8.66), respectively, and all the ε's are bounded by the same quantity e introduced in (8.56).

Equations (8.65), (8.66) lead, after some laborious algebra, to

$$\frac{\hat{x}_2 - x_2}{x_2} \approx \varepsilon_3 - \left(\frac{a_{12}a_{21}}{a_{11}a_{22}^{(2)}}\right)\left(\frac{a_{11}x_1}{a_{12}x_2}\right)\varepsilon_{21}, \tag{8.68}$$

$$\frac{\hat{x}_1 - x_1}{x_1} \approx \varepsilon_4 + \left(\frac{a_{12}a_{21}}{a_{11}a_{22}^{(2)}}\right)\varepsilon_{21} - \left(\frac{a_{12}x_2}{a_{11}x_1}\right)\varepsilon_3. \tag{8.69}$$

In deriving these results we have retained only the most important terms, using the approximations listed in the following theorem. This theorem is a direct consequence of (8.68), (8.69).

THEOREM 8.4. *If equations* (8.60) *are solved by the procedure involving the sequence of operations and rounding rules specified above, the relative errors in the unknowns are given exactly by* (8.68), (8.69). *If the relative errors in the computed values are small so that* $\hat{a}_{22}^{(2)} \approx a_{22}^{(2)}$, $\hat{b}_2^{(2)} \approx b_2$, $\hat{x}_2 \approx x_2$, *and* $|e| \ll 1$, *then*

$$\frac{\hat{x}_1 - x_1}{x_1} \approx \varepsilon_4 - \frac{1}{q}\varepsilon_3 + p\varepsilon_{21}, \tag{8.70}$$

$$\frac{\hat{x}_2 - x_2}{x_2} \approx \varepsilon_3 - pq\varepsilon_{21}, \tag{8.71}$$

where

$$p = \frac{a_{12}a_{21}}{a_{11}a_{22} - a_{12}a_{21}}, \qquad q = \frac{a_{11}x_1}{a_{12}x_2}, \tag{8.72}$$

and approximate upper bounds for ε_3, ε_4, ε_{21} *are* $3e$, $2e$, e, *respectively.*

We can draw some important conclusions from these results. Consider the question of whether to pick a_{11} or a_{21} as pivot. The choice of a_{21} is equivalent to interchanging the order in which we solve the equations, i.e., the solutions x_1 and x_2 are unchanged, but we interchange a_{11} and a_{21}, a_{12} and a_{22}, b_1 and b_2. Instead of (8.70), (8.71), we have

$$\frac{x_1' - x_1}{x_1} \approx \varepsilon_4' - \frac{1}{q'}\varepsilon_3' + p'\varepsilon_{21}', \qquad \frac{x_2' - x_2}{x_2} \approx \varepsilon_3' - p'q'\varepsilon_{21}', \tag{8.73}$$

where it turns out that

$$p' = -\frac{a_{11}a_{22}}{a_{12}a_{21}}\,p, \qquad q' = \frac{a_{12}a_{21}}{a_{11}a_{22}}\,q. \tag{8.74}$$

The values of the ε_3', ε_4', ε_{21}', in (8.73) will not be the same as the values of the ε_3, ε_4, ε_{21}, in (8.70), (8.71). However, if we imagine a repetition of the calculations for many different sets of a_{ij} and b_i, we should expect that ε_3 and ε_3' would be comparable in size, and similarly for ε_4, ε_4', ε_{21}, ε_{21}'. The question of whether the errors in (8.73) are less than those in (8.70), (8.71) on the average, therefore depends on the relation of p, q to p', q'. If $|a_{12}a_{21}| < |a_{11}a_{22}|$, equation (8.74) shows that

$$|p| < |p'|, \qquad \left|\frac{1}{q}\right| < \left|\frac{1}{q'}\right|, \qquad |pq| = |p'q'|.$$

Hence, the relative errors (8.70), (8.71) will be less than the errors (8.73), on the average. However, if $|a_{12}a_{21}| \approx |a_{11}a_{22}|$, equation (8.74) shows that it is immaterial whether we pivot on a_{11} or a_{22} rather than a_{12} or a_{21}. We have proved:

THEOREM 8.5. *If the set of two equations in two unknowns* (8.60) *is solved, using the specified elimination method and rounding rules, and if* $|a_{12}a_{21}| < |a_{11}a_{22}|$, *the errors in the computed solutions due to rounding are minimized if we pivot on* a_{11} *or* a_{22} *rather than* a_{12} *or* a_{21}. *If* $|a_{12}a_{21}| \approx |a_{11}a_{22}|$, *and in particular if the equations are ill-conditioned in the sense that p is large, the rounding errors are comparable on the average whether we pivot on one of the pairs* a_{11}, a_{22} *or one of the pairs* a_{12}, a_{21}.

As an example, consider (8.53). We have $a_{11}a_{22} = 1$, $a_{12}a_{21} = -10^{-2}$. This tells us that we must avoid the large pivot 10^2.

Our discussion of pivoting is not quite complete. If $|a_{12}a_{21}| < |a_{11}a_{22}|$, and, following the above theorem, we decide to pivot on a_{11} or a_{22}, is it better to pivot on a_{11} or a_{22}? If we pivot on a_{11}, the errors are given by (8.70), (8.71). If we pivot on a_{22}, a permutation of symbols leads to the result, after some algebra, that

$$\frac{\hat{x}_1'' - x_1}{x_1} \approx \varepsilon_3'' - \frac{1+p}{q}\varepsilon_{21}'', \qquad \frac{\hat{x}_2'' - x_2}{x_2} \approx \varepsilon_4'' - \frac{pq}{1+p}\varepsilon_3'' + p\varepsilon_{21}''. \quad (8.75)$$

A comparison of these results with (8.70), (8.71) shows that an enumeration of possibilities is not particularly illuminating.

We can draw the following conclusions concerning conditions under which the errors due to rounding will tend to be large, even though we use the optimum choice of pivots. (The reason for making probabilistic statements like "the errors tend to be large" is simply that the rounding errors ε_{21}, etc., may be zero or small for particular examples.)

THEOREM 8.6. *If* (8.60) *is solved by the specified elimination method and rounding rules, and if* $|a_{12}a_{21}| < |a_{11}a_{22}|$:

(i) *The errors introduced by rounding during the course of the solution tend to produce relative errors in the unknowns comparable to those that would be produced by making relative changes in the* a_{ij} *and* b_k *of the order of magnitude of the maximum relative rounding error* e *introduced in* (8.56).

(ii) *If the equations are ill-conditioned in the sense specified in the last sentence in Section* 8.2 (*i.e.,* p *large*), *the relative errors in the unknowns due to rounding tend to be large.*

(iii) *The relative error in* x_1 *or* x_2 *tends to be large if* $|a_{11}x_1| \ll |a_{12}x_2|$ *or* $|a_{22}x_2| \ll |a_{21}x_1|$, *respectively.*

Proof: Relative errors in the unknowns due to rounding errors are given in (8.70), (8.71), (8.75). Errors produced by making small relative errors in the a_{ij} and b_i have been investigated in Ex. 8.4 [e.g., (8.30)]. The coefficients that occur involve only the constants p, q, and these occur in such a way that the errors specified in the first two sentences will tend to be comparable in size. [Remember that $|a_{12}a_{21}| < |a_{11}a_{22}|$ implies that $1/(1 + p)$ cannot be large.] This proves (i). Part (ii) is true because ill-conditioned equations mean that p is large, and then at least one coefficient in each of the equations in (8.70), (8.71), (8.75) will be large. Part (iii) is true because if $|a_{11}x_1| \ll |a_{12}x_2|$ this means that $1/q$ is large, so that one of the coefficients in the error in the computed estimate of x_1 is large, from (8.70), (8.75). Proof that a coefficient in the error estimate for x_2 is large if $|a_{22}x_2| \ll |a_{21}x_1|$ is left to the reader.

Ex. 8.13. Illustrate Theorem 8.6 (iii) by considering

$$0.98x_1 + 0.43x_2 = 0.91$$
$$-0.61x_1 + 0.23x_2 = 0.48.$$

(Note that these are well-conditioned in the sense that p is small, but the computed value of one of the unknowns has a large relative inaccuracy).

It is important to realize that scaling by powers of 10 does not essentially alter the rounding errors when we are working in floating-point.

THEOREM 8.7. *If the* 2×2 *set* (8.60) *is scaled as in* (8.32), *where the* p_i *and* q_j *are of the form* 10^{α}, *the* α *being positive or negative integers, the relative rounding errors in the computed solution derived from the scaled equations will be exactly the same as the relative rounding errors in the solution computed from the original equations.* (*The specified elimination method and rounding rules are assumed to be the same in both cases.*)

Proof: The essential point is that scaling by integer powers of 10 changes the exponents but not the fractional parts, and the rounding errors depend only on the fractional parts. Algebraically, if $p_1 = 10^m, p_2 = 10^n, q_1 = 10^r, q_2 = 10^s$, the scaled equations are

$$\begin{aligned} 10^{m+r}a_{11}z_1 + 10^{m+s}a_{12}z_2 &= 10^m b_1 \\ 10^{n+r}a_{21}z_1 + 10^{n+s}a_{22}z_2 &= 10^n b_2, \end{aligned} \tag{8.76}$$

where $z_1 = 10^{-r}x_1$, $z_2 = 10^{-s}x_2$. To solve these we first compute a multiplying factor

$$\hat{m}_{21} = \mathrm{fl}\left\{\frac{10^{n+r}a_{21}}{10^{m+r}a_{11}}\right\} = 10^{n-m}\,\mathrm{fl}\left\{\frac{a_{21}}{a_{11}}\right\} = 10^{n-m}m_{21}(1 + \varepsilon_{21}),$$

where m_{21} and ε_{21} are *precisely* those defined in (8.64) for the unscaled equations. Similarly, we can show that all the other relative rounding errors that occur are unchanged, and this proves the theorem. Another way of stating the proof is to say that p, q in (8.72) are independent of the scaling, and the rounding errors ε_{21}, etc., are all unchanged by scaling.

All our theorems on pivoting have been proved only for the 2×2 case (8.60) partly because a discussion of the general $n \times n$ case would take us too far afield. The 2×2 case has illustrated the essential points.

The whole question of the best pivotal strategy in floating-point is difficult since, as we have pointed out, the absolute magnitudes of individual elements depend on scaling, and it is only ratios independent of scaling that are important. The solution to the best pivotal strategy in the 2×2 case has been given in Theorem 8.5, but one of the major difficulties in the $n \times n$ case is that the correct generalization of Theorem 8.5 is not yet known.

Instead of computing ratios in order to decide which elements should be chosen as pivots (which we do not know how to do in the general case), the recommended method in practice is to *first scale the equations* and then use one of the following methods of choosing pivots:

(a) *Partial pivoting*, in which the unknowns are eliminated in their natural order $x_1, x_2, \ldots$, and at the rth stage the pivot is taken to be the coefficient of largest modulus of x_r in the remaining $n - r + 1$ equations.

(b) *Complete pivoting*, in which, at the rth stage, we select as pivot the coefficient of largest modulus of all the $n - r + 1$ unknowns in the remaining $n - r + 1$ equations.

Experience seems to indicate that it is sufficient to use partial pivoting in practice; the theoretical advantages of complete pivoting tend to be outweighed by the bookkeeping required for its implementation.

The preliminary scaling is important because *the numbers that are chosen as pivots if we use complete or partial pivoting will depend on the scaling*. Unfortunately, scaling by simply adjusting the largest element in each row or column to be of order unity does not ensure that either complete or partial pivoting will give a suitable choice of pivots. A simple counterexample is given by setting $x_1 = 200z$, in (8.50), and dividing the first equation by 200. On the other hand, the rule (8.35) does lead to a satisfactory choice of pivots in the 2×2 case. In Ex. 13.11 it is proved that in the 2×2 case the rule (8.35) leads to

$$\begin{aligned} z_1 + \alpha z_2 &= \beta_1 \\ \pm\alpha z_1 + \quad z_2 &= \beta_2, \end{aligned}$$

with $0 \leq \alpha \leq 1$. In this case, either complete or partial pivoting will lead to the (1, 1) and (2, 2) elements as pivots, in agreement with Theorem 8.5. This gives the theorem: In the 2×2 case, complete or partial pivoting on equations scaled according to (8.35) will lead to a choice of pivots that minimizes rounding errors. In Chapter 13 we show by a roundabout argument that a similar result holds for the $n \times n$ case (see the paragraph preceding Definition 13.4). However no direct proof similar to that just given for the 2×2 case is known. One difficulty is that the correct generalization of the pivoting criterion in Theorem 8.5 is not known.

The situation in practice as regards choice of pivots is not as bad as it might seem from this discussion. After all, millions of large linear systems have been solved successfully on digital computers. The position seems to be that most systems that arise in practice have a built-in "natural" scaling that prevents a disastrous choice of pivots. In surveying problems we do not measure some distances in inches and others in miles. On the other hand, when distances and angles occur together, it is advisable to scale so that coefficients are comparable in size. The other factor that should be mentioned is that it is not necessary to find the very best choice of pivots—the essential thing is to avoid very bad choices of pivots. The problem of finding an automatic method for scaling (so that partial pivoting will avoid a bad choice of pivots) is becoming more acute as the size of problems is becoming greater and the intervention of human beings in complicated calculations is becoming less.

Ex. 8.14. Show that neither partial nor complete pivoting will lead to a suitable choice of pivots in (8.25), but either form of pivoting will be successful in the rescaled form (8.33). [Note that each of the coefficient matrices satisfies the condition that the largest element in each row and column is of order unity. However, in (8.33) it is possible to choose one element of order unity from each row of $\mathbf{A}$, no two of these elements being in the same column. This is not true of (8.25).]

8.7 Residuals

There is a tendency to think that if we evaluate the *residuals*

$$\mathbf{r} = \mathbf{b} - \mathbf{A}\hat{\mathbf{x}} \tag{8.77}$$

using an approximate solution $\hat{\mathbf{x}}$, and if these residuals turn out to be small, then the approximate solution $\hat{\mathbf{x}}$ must in some sense be close to the exact solution $\mathbf{x}$

of $\mathbf{Ax} = \mathbf{b}$. It is easy to see that this may not be true. Substitution of $\mathbf{b} = \mathbf{Ax}$ in (8.77) gives

$$\mathbf{A}(\mathbf{x} - \hat{\mathbf{x}}) = \mathbf{r}, \qquad \mathbf{x} - \hat{\mathbf{x}} = \mathbf{A}^{-1}\mathbf{r}.$$

If the elements of $\mathbf{A}^{-1}$ are large, then the elements of $\mathbf{x} - \hat{\mathbf{x}}$ may be large even though the elements of $\mathbf{r}$ are small.

Consider the following equations:

$$\begin{aligned} 0.89x_1 + 0.53x_2 &= 0.36 \\ 0.47x_1 + 0.28x_2 &= 0.19. \end{aligned} \tag{8.78}$$

The approximate solution $\hat{x}_1 = 0.47$, $\hat{x}_2 = -0.11$ gives the following residuals exactly:

$$r_1 = 0.0000, \qquad r_2 = 0.0001.$$

Since the exact product of a pair of two-decimal numbers is a four-decimal number, no other two-decimal solution can give smaller residuals except the exact solution, provided that this solution consists of two-decimal numbers, in which case $r_1 = r_2 = 0$. How accurate is the above approximate solution? The exact solution is $x_1 = 1$, $x_2 = -1$! It should be noted that the equations are badly conditioned. Thus, if we change b_2 in (8.78) from 0.19 to 0.20, the solution changes to $x_1 = -50$, $x_2 = 88$. It is characteristic of badly conditioned equations that inaccurate answers can give small residuals.

As a second example, consider the badly conditioned equations

$$\begin{aligned} x_1 \qquad + x_2 &= 2 \\ x_1 + 1.00001x_2 &= 2.00001, \end{aligned} \tag{8.79}$$

with exact solution $x_1 = x_2 = 1$. If we set $\hat{x}_1 = 1 + \xi$, $\hat{x}_2 = 1 + \eta$, we find

$$r_1 = -(\xi + \eta), \qquad r_2 = -(\xi + 1.00001\eta).$$

Suppose that ξ, η are chosen so that $\xi + \eta = 0$. Then

$$r_1 = 0, \qquad r_2 = -0.00001\eta.$$

In this case, the residuals can be extremely small even though the approximate solutions are quite inaccurate. In contrast, consider the well-conditioned equations

$$\begin{aligned} x_1 + x_2 &= 2 \\ x_1 - x_2 &= 0, \end{aligned} \tag{8.80}$$

with exact solution $x_1 = x_2 = 1$. If we set $\hat{x}_1 = 1 + \xi$, $\hat{x}_2 = 1 + \eta$, we now find

$$r_1 = -(\xi + \eta), \qquad r_2 = -\xi + \eta,$$

and at least one of the residuals will be of the order of the errors ξ, η.

We are *not* saying that *all* approximate solutions of ill-conditioned equations give small residuals, but only that *some* approximate solutions of ill-conditioned equations give surprisingly small residuals. This means that if residuals for an approximate solution $\hat{\mathbf{y}}$ are smaller than residuals for a second approximate solution $\hat{\mathbf{z}}$, this does *not* mean that $\hat{\mathbf{y}}$ is closer to the exact solution $\mathbf{x}$ than $\hat{\mathbf{z}}$. To illustrate this, consider the following approximate solutions for the ill-conditioned equations (8.79).

$$\hat{\mathbf{y}} = \begin{bmatrix} 2 \\ 0 \end{bmatrix}, \qquad \text{residuals} \begin{bmatrix} 0 \\ 0.00001 \end{bmatrix},$$
$$\hat{\mathbf{z}} = \begin{bmatrix} 1.01 \\ 1.01 \end{bmatrix}, \qquad \text{residuals} \begin{bmatrix} -0.02 \\ -0.02 \end{bmatrix}.$$

The residuals for $\hat{\mathbf{y}}$ are much smaller than those for $\hat{\mathbf{z}}$, even though $\hat{\mathbf{z}}$ is much closer to the exact solution $x_1 = x_2 = 1$.

We next compute the residuals for the solution of the 2×2 set (8.60) computed by the Gaussian elimination method (8.61)–(8.63), with the rounding rules (8.64)–(8.66). From (8.70), (8.71), after some algebra, we find

$$\begin{aligned} r_1 &= b_1 - a_{11}\hat{x}_1 - a_{12}\hat{x}_2 \approx -a_{11}x_1\varepsilon_4 \\ r_2 &= b_2 - a_{21}\hat{x}_1 - a_{22}\hat{x}_2 \approx a_{21}x_1(\varepsilon_{21} - \varepsilon_4) + a_{22}x_2(\eta - 1)\varepsilon_3, \end{aligned} \tag{8.81}$$

where $\eta = a_{12}a_{21}/a_{11}a_{22}$. The factor η will be less than 1 in absolute value if and only if we follow the optimum pivotal strategy in Theorem 8.5. One important feature of (8.81) is that the coefficients of the errors are independent of the numbers p, q, defined in (8.31) which determine whether a 2×2 set of equations is ill-conditioned. This means that the residuals can be small even though the equations are ill-conditioned. It is instructive to rewrite (8.81) in the form

$$\begin{aligned} a_{11}(1 - \varepsilon_4)\hat{x}_1 + \qquad\qquad\quad a_{12}\hat{x}_2 &\approx b_1, \\ a_{21}(1 + \varepsilon_{21} - \varepsilon_4)\hat{x}_1 + a_{22}(1 + \xi\varepsilon_3)\hat{x}_2 &\approx b_2, \end{aligned}$$

where $\xi = \eta - 1$ and we produce only second-order errors by replacing x_1, x_2 on the right of (8.81) by $\hat{x}_1$, $\hat{x}_2$. This proves (since $|\eta| < 1$ if $|a_{12}a_{21}| < |a_{11}a_{22}|$):

THEOREM 8.8. *If the* 2×2 *set* (8.60) *is solved using the specified elimination method and rounding rules, the residual* r_i *will always be small relative to the larger of* $|a_{i1}x_1|$, $|a_{i2}x_2|$, *for* $i = 1, 2$, *if we use the optimum pivotal strategy of Theorem* 8.5.

If residuals are not small in the sense in the theorem, this indicates that nonoptimum pivoting has been used. The reason for this in the above example is that large residuals (where "large" is used in the sense in the theorem) can occur only when $|\eta| \gg 1$, i.e., when nonoptimal pivoting has been used.

It is interesting to note that Gaussian elimination applied to ill-conditioned 2×2 equations always produces small residuals. This is true because ill-conditioning means that p defined in (8.72) is large, and p can be large only if

$\eta \approx 1$. Large residuals in the 2×2 case indicate that answers are inaccurate due to nonoptimum pivoting in well-conditioned equations.

This discussion can be summarized by saying that fortunately or unfortunately (depending on the point of view) Gaussian elimination tends to produce approximate solutions that have residuals that are small relative to the largest $|a_{ij}x_j|$ for fixed $i, j = 1, \ldots, n$, irrespective of the accuracy of the solution. We have proved this only for the 2×2 case.

If $\mathbf{C}$ is an approximate right-inverse of $\mathbf{A}$ such that the residuals $\mathbf{r} = \mathbf{I} - \mathbf{AC}$ are small we say that $\mathbf{C}$ is a good right-inverse of $\mathbf{A}$. This equation gives

$$\mathbf{A}^{-1} - \mathbf{C} = \mathbf{A}^{-1}\mathbf{r}, \qquad \mathbf{I} - \mathbf{CA} = \mathbf{A}^{-1}\mathbf{rA}.$$

The first equation shows that small $\mathbf{r}$ does not imply that $\mathbf{C}$ is close to $\mathbf{A}^{-1}$, so that the word "good" has to be understood in a special sense. The second equation shows that if $\mathbf{C}$ is an approximate right-inverse of $\mathbf{A}$ such that $\mathbf{AC}$ is very nearly equal to the unit matrix, this is no guarantee that $\mathbf{CA}$ will be nearly equal to the unit matrix. As an example, consider

$$\mathbf{A} = \begin{bmatrix} 1.00 & 1.00 \\ 1.00 & 0.99 \end{bmatrix}, \qquad \mathbf{C} = \begin{bmatrix} -89 & 100 \\ 90 & -100 \end{bmatrix}. \tag{8.82}$$

Then

$$\mathbf{AC} = \begin{bmatrix} 1.0 & 0.0 \\ 0.1 & 1.0 \end{bmatrix}, \qquad \mathbf{CA} = \begin{bmatrix} 11 & 10 \\ -10 & -9 \end{bmatrix}. \tag{8.83}$$

A good right-inverse may not be a good left-inverse, and vice versa. The situation in numerical work is quite different from the situation in the mathematical theory where left- and right-inverses are the same. The above trouble often occurs when an approximate inverse is found by solving $\mathbf{Ax}_i = \mathbf{e}_i$, $i = 1, \ldots, n$ where the $\mathbf{e}_i$ are unit vectors, which is the method we have recommended so far. If the equations are solved by Gaussian elimination with suitable choice of pivots, this will produce approximate solutions $\hat{\mathbf{x}}_i$ such that the residuals $\mathbf{e}_i - \mathbf{Ax}_i$ are small, i.e., the approximate inverse $\mathbf{C}$ will be such that $\mathbf{I} - \mathbf{AC}$ is small. This means that $\mathbf{C}$ will be a good right-inverse. There is no guarantee that $\mathbf{I} - \mathbf{CA}$ is small, i.e., that $\mathbf{C}$ is a good left-inverse. To get a good left-inverse we must solve $\mathbf{A}^T\mathbf{y}_i = \mathbf{e}_i$, where the $\mathbf{y}_i$ will give the rows of the approximate inverse. We have to be particularly careful if a library subroutine claims to improve the accuracy of an inverse by an iterative procedure. It may even happen that the subroutine may decrease the residuals $\mathbf{I} - \mathbf{AC}$ but increase the residuals $\mathbf{I} - \mathbf{CA}$.

The reason for making these remarks is that to obtain an accurate solution of $\mathbf{Ax} = \mathbf{b}$ using an approximate inverse $\mathbf{C}$ we should use a good left-inverse. To see this, consider the difference between the exact and approximate solutions:

$$\mathbf{x} - \hat{\mathbf{x}} = (\mathbf{A}^{-1} - \mathbf{C})\mathbf{b} = (\mathbf{I} - \mathbf{CA})\mathbf{x} = \mathbf{A}^{-1}(\mathbf{I} - \mathbf{AC})\mathbf{b}.$$

The second last equation indicates that if $\mathbf{C}$ is a good left-inverse, the relative error in the estimates of the largest unknowns will be small. On the other hand the last equation does not guarantee the smallness of $\mathbf{x} - \hat{\mathbf{x}}$ even if $\mathbf{C}$ is a good right-inverse.

To conclude this section we mention an iterative procedure for improving the accuracy of an approximate solution. We first explain what is meant by *double-precision working* on a digital computer. The normal mode of working in floating-point, in which every addition, subtraction, multiplication, and division is rounded to, say, t decimals, is known as single-precision. It is possible to arrange that all calculations are carried out and numbers are stored using approximately $2t$ decimals. This is known as double-precision. Assume then that the residuals $\mathbf{r} = \mathbf{b} - \mathbf{A}\hat{\mathbf{x}}$ have been computed to double-precision. (This is essential if the residuals are to mean anything, since Gaussian elimination tends to produce answers that give very small residuals as we have seen in Theorem 8.8. The rounding errors involved if residuals are computed to single-precision will make the results meaningless.) We set $\mathbf{x} = \hat{\mathbf{x}} + \boldsymbol{\delta}$, where $\mathbf{x}$ is the exact solution, $\hat{\mathbf{x}}$ is the known approximate solution that we wish to improve, and $\boldsymbol{\delta}$ is the correction that we wish to determine. Since $\mathbf{Ax} = \mathbf{b}$, we have $\mathbf{A}(\hat{\mathbf{x}} + \boldsymbol{\delta}) = \mathbf{b}$, or

$$\mathbf{A}\boldsymbol{\delta} = \mathbf{b} - \mathbf{A}\hat{\mathbf{x}} = \mathbf{r}.$$

It will not be possible to solve these equations exactly, but we can obtain an approximation $\hat{\boldsymbol{\delta}}$ to $\boldsymbol{\delta}$, which gives a new estimate $\hat{\mathbf{x}} + \hat{\boldsymbol{\delta}}$ for $\mathbf{x}$. The process can then be repeated. Setting this up as an iterative procedure, we have

$$\hat{\mathbf{x}}_{i+1} = \hat{\mathbf{x}}_i + \hat{\boldsymbol{\delta}}_i$$

where $\hat{\boldsymbol{\delta}}_i$ is the computed estimate for the solution of

$$\mathbf{A}\boldsymbol{\delta}_i = \mathbf{r}_i = \mathbf{b} - \mathbf{A}\hat{\mathbf{x}}_i,$$

where $\mathbf{r}_i$ is computed in double-precision. The iteration is started by taking $\mathbf{x}_1$ to be the solution of $\mathbf{Ax} = \mathbf{b}$ found by single-precision working. The equations $\mathbf{A}\boldsymbol{\delta}_i = \mathbf{r}_i$ are of course solved in single-precision. This is a relatively cheap way of improving the accuracy, since we are solving sets of equations with the same coefficient matrix and different right-hand sides. Each iteration takes only an extra n^2 multiplications and n^2 additions (double-precision) to compute residuals, and n^2 multiplications and n^2 additions to solve $\mathbf{A}\boldsymbol{\delta}_i = \mathbf{r}_i$.

If the iterative procedure converges, then the convergence is ultimately linear, i.e., each additional iteration gives a fixed number of extra figures. This will be true in practice only until we reach the "noise level" of the calculation, beyond which no further improvement will be possible. The worse the conditioning of the equations, the slower the rate of convergence of the iteration. For very ill-conditioned equations, the process may not converge at all, and this indicates that the first approximation $\mathbf{x}_1$ is meaningless, and that the set of equations $\mathbf{Ax} = \mathbf{b}$ cannot be solved by single-precision arithmetic. This raises the question of whether the solution of such a set would mean anything even if it were obtained by double-precision arithmetic. This remark serves as a good introduction to the next section.

8.8 The Avoidance of Ill-Conditioning; a Least-Squares Example

The motto of anyone faced with really ill-conditioned equations should be (to quote J. W. Tukey): "If a thing is not worth doing, it is not worth doing well." If a set of equations is very badly conditioned, and the coefficients are not known to sufficient accuracy, the results are going to be meaningless, however accurately we solve the equations on a computer. Rather than struggle with the profitless task of solving a badly conditioned set accurately, we should ask ourselves where the equations come from, and try to *reformulate the original problem* in terms of a reasonably well-conditioned set of equations.

The basic point concerning accuracy has already been made in Section 8.1. The equations we solve are usually an approximation (8.2) to an exact set (8.1). In practice we compute an approximation $\hat{\mathbf{x}}$ to the exact solution $\mathbf{x}$ of (8.2), which in turn is an approximation to the exact solution $\mathbf{x}^*$ of (8.1). There is a temptation to compute $\mathbf{x}$ very accurately by various technical devices (iterative correction, double-precision, and so on). In this way we reduce $\mathbf{x} - \hat{\mathbf{x}}$, but there is very little point in making $\mathbf{x} - \hat{\mathbf{x}}$ much smaller than $\mathbf{x} - \mathbf{x}^*$. Probably the main reason for making $\mathbf{x} - \hat{\mathbf{x}}$ very small is that the size of $\mathbf{x} - \mathbf{x}^*$ may not be known, so if we make $\mathbf{x} - \hat{\mathbf{x}}$ negligible, at least we have removed this source of inaccuracy. However, this begs the real question, namely that we wish to find $\mathbf{x}^*$, not $\mathbf{x}$. If we start from (8.2), we can only find $\mathbf{x}$, but in a really badly conditioned situation this is not worth doing anyway, so it is not worth doing well. The logical conclusion is that if we wish to find $\mathbf{x}^*$ accurately, we must start from some set of equations different from (8.2) but exactly equivalent to (8.1) and not so ill-conditioned as (8.2).

To illustrate these remarks we consider first of all an example involving the notorious Hilbert matrix $\mathbf{H} = [(i + j - 1)^{-1}]$. Suppose that we wish to find a function

$$f(t) = \sum_{j=1}^{n} x_j t^{j-1} + t^n, \qquad 0 \le t \le 1,$$

where the constants x_j are determined by

$$\int_0^1 f(t) t^{i-1}\, dt = 0, \qquad i = 1, \ldots, n.$$

On applying these conditions to $f(t)$ we find that the x_j are determined by equations $\mathbf{Hx} = \mathbf{b}$. These are extremely ill-conditioned. Difficulties arise if the order n is comparable with the number of significant figures in the calculation.

We can avoid these equations altogether if we realize that the x_j can be derived from the Legendre polynomial of order n, for which we have an explicit formula. The reader may object that this is cheating but this is precisely the point we are trying to make. The best way to overcome ill-conditioning is to avoid it. (Even if we had to deal with the problem directly we could improve the condition of the computation by the simple expedient of considering the equivalent problem obtained by replacing t by $t - \frac{1}{2}$ in the above formulation. This is equivalent to a simple transformation on $\mathbf{H}$.)

Ill-conditioning in physical applications can often be avoided by formulating the problem differently. As an example, consider the pin-jointed framework in Figure 2.1. One method for solving this is to start by solving the "statically determinate" framework that is left when three of the members are omitted. If the members 2, 3, 4 are omitted, the remaining members 1, 5 form a rigid frame and it will be found that the corresponding linear equations are well-conditioned. If 3, 4, 5 are omitted, the frame formed by the remaining members 1, 2 is such that small applied forces cause large deflections and it will be found that the corresponding linear equations are ill-conditioned. If we use this type of method we must start by omitting members 2, 3, 4 if we wish to avoid ill-conditioned equations. This is well known to mechanical engineers. Physical intuition helps to avoid ill-conditioning.

If an experiment gives rise to ill-conditioned equations, the answer is to design the experiment differently. A good example is discussed in [91], Chapter 11.

In the remainder of this section we discuss ill-conditioning in least-squares equations. The vector $\mathbf{x}$ that minimizes the sum of squares of residuals $S = \mathbf{r}^T\mathbf{r}$, $\mathbf{r} = \mathbf{b} - \mathbf{A}\mathbf{x}$, for an inconsistent set $\mathbf{A}\mathbf{x} = \mathbf{b}$, is given by [Theorem 5.17, equation (5.14)]:

$$\mathbf{A}^T\mathbf{A}\mathbf{x} = \mathbf{A}^T\mathbf{b}. \tag{8.84}$$

The practical difficulty in finding $\mathbf{x}$ from these equations is that they are often ill-conditioned. The reason for this can be understood by considering the case in which $\mathbf{A}$ is square. In the spirit of the discussion in the last paragraph of Section 8.3, if $\mathbf{A}$ is scaled properly, the condition of the set $\mathbf{A}\mathbf{x} = \mathbf{b}$ is indicated by the size of det $\mathbf{A}$. Similarly, the condition of the set $\mathbf{A}^T\mathbf{A}\mathbf{x} = \mathbf{A}^T\mathbf{b}$ is indicated by the size of det $(\mathbf{A}^T\mathbf{A}) = (\det \mathbf{A})^2$. If det $\mathbf{A}$ is small compared with unity (say 10^{-6}), then $(\det \mathbf{A})^2$ is much smaller still. The largest elements of $\mathbf{A}^T\mathbf{A}$ will lie along the diagonal, and they will be of order unity, so that $\mathbf{A}^T\mathbf{A}$ should be reasonably well scaled. Under these circumstances, if $\mathbf{A}\mathbf{x} = \mathbf{b}$ is ill-conditioned, then the condition of $\mathbf{A}^T\mathbf{A}\mathbf{x} = \mathbf{A}^T\mathbf{b}$ is much worse than that of $\mathbf{A}\mathbf{x} = \mathbf{b}$. This argument can be extended to the case where $\mathbf{A}$ is $m \times n$ $(m > n)$ by using the result in Ex. 7.29:

$$\det \mathbf{A}^T\mathbf{A} = \sum_p (\det \mathbf{A}_p)^2, \tag{8.85}$$

where $\mathbf{A}_p$ is an $n \times n$ matrix obtained by selecting any n rows of $\mathbf{A}$, and the sum is taken over the square of the determinant of all such matrices. If the largest such determinant is small compared with unity, then det $\mathbf{A}^T\mathbf{A}$ will, in general, be much smaller still. If $\mathbf{A}_1$ is the submatrix corresponding to the largest such determinant, then the condition of $\mathbf{A}^T\mathbf{A}\mathbf{x} = \mathbf{A}^T\mathbf{b}$ is much worse than the condition of the subset of equations in $\mathbf{A}\mathbf{x} = \mathbf{b}$ that have coefficient matrix $\mathbf{A}_1$, say $\mathbf{A}_1\mathbf{x} = \mathbf{b}_1$. The object of the method we describe below is to produce an algorithm for solving the least-squares equations by a method involving solution of equations whose condition is comparable with that of $\mathbf{A}_1\mathbf{x} = \mathbf{b}_1$.

Before going on, we emphasize that there is no claim that the method to be described is necessarily the best in practice (see Ex. 8.18 and its answer).

Consider the equations

$$\mathbf{A}\mathbf{x} = \mathbf{b}, \tag{8.86}$$

where $\mathbf{A}$ is $m \times n$ $(m > n)$, of rank n. We partition $\mathbf{A}$ and $\mathbf{b}$ in the form

$$\mathbf{A} = \begin{bmatrix} \mathbf{A}_1 \\ \mathbf{A}_2 \end{bmatrix}, \qquad \mathbf{b} = \begin{bmatrix} \mathbf{b}_1 \\ \mathbf{b}_2 \end{bmatrix}, \tag{8.87}$$

where $\mathbf{A}_1$ is $n \times n$ and $\mathbf{b}_1$ is $n \times 1$. There is a considerable amount of freedom in the way in which this partitioning can be done since clearly the order of the original equations (8.86) can be changed without affecting the solutions, so that the rows of $\mathbf{A}$ can be rearranged in any way before partitioning. The main assumption that we make is that $\mathbf{A}_1$ is nonsingular. This can always be arranged, since the rank of $\mathbf{A}$ is n. In practice, we should also try to arrange that det $\mathbf{A}_1$ is as large as possible, as we shall see later.

Since $\mathbf{A}$ has rank n, the last $m - n$ rows of $\mathbf{A}$ can be expressed as linear combinations of the first n rows. In the notation of (8.87) this means that we can find a matrix $\mathbf{P}$ such that

$$\mathbf{A}_2 = \mathbf{P}\mathbf{A}_1, \tag{8.88}$$

that is,

$$\mathbf{A} = \begin{bmatrix} \mathbf{I} \\ \mathbf{P} \end{bmatrix}\mathbf{A}_1. \tag{8.89}$$

On inserting this expression for $\mathbf{A}$, together with $\mathbf{b}$ from (8.87), in the least-squares equations $\mathbf{A}^T\mathbf{A}\mathbf{x} = \mathbf{A}^T\mathbf{b}$, we find

$$\mathbf{A}_1^T[\mathbf{I}, \mathbf{P}^T]\begin{bmatrix} \mathbf{I} \\ \mathbf{P} \end{bmatrix}\mathbf{A}_1\mathbf{x} = \mathbf{A}_1^T[\mathbf{I}, \mathbf{P}^T]\begin{bmatrix} \mathbf{b}_1 \\ \mathbf{b}_2 \end{bmatrix},$$

that is,

$$\mathbf{A}_1^T[\mathbf{I} + \mathbf{P}^T\mathbf{P}]\mathbf{A}_1\mathbf{x} = \mathbf{A}_1^T[\mathbf{b}_1 + \mathbf{P}^T\mathbf{b}_2].$$

Since $\mathbf{A}_1$ is nonsingular, we can multiply through by $(\mathbf{A}_1^T)^{-1}$:

$$[\mathbf{I} + \mathbf{P}^T\mathbf{P}]\mathbf{A}_1\mathbf{x} = \mathbf{b}_1 + \mathbf{P}^T\mathbf{b}_2. \tag{8.90}$$

Although it may not be obvious at this point, it is precisely this step that has improved the conditioning of the original least-squares equations $\mathbf{A}^T\mathbf{A}\mathbf{x} = \mathbf{A}^T\mathbf{b}$, since we, in effect, perform an inversion analytically, thus obviating the loss of accuracy which occurs when this is (implicitly) built into a numerical procedure, as when we solve $\mathbf{A}^T\mathbf{A}\mathbf{x} = \mathbf{A}^T\mathbf{b}$ instead of (8.90).

The condition of the system (8.90) is determined by

$$\det[\mathbf{I} + \mathbf{P}^T\mathbf{P}]\mathbf{A}_1 = \det[\mathbf{I} + \mathbf{P}^T\mathbf{P}] \det \mathbf{A}_1. \tag{8.91}$$

Since $\mathbf{A}^T\mathbf{A} = \mathbf{A}_1^T[\mathbf{I} + \mathbf{P}^T\mathbf{P}]\mathbf{A}_1$, we have

$$\det[\mathbf{I} + \mathbf{P}^T\mathbf{P}] = \frac{\det \mathbf{A}^T\mathbf{A}}{(\det \mathbf{A}_1)^2}.$$

From the expression (8.85) for $\det \mathbf{A}^T\mathbf{A}$, since $\mathbf{A}_1$ is one of the matrices $\mathbf{A}_p$ in (8.85), we see that

$$\det[\mathbf{I} + \mathbf{P}^T\mathbf{P}] \geq 1. \tag{8.92}$$

Hence, not only is $\mathbf{I} + \mathbf{P}^T\mathbf{P}$ nonsingular, but it is a well-conditioned matrix. From (8.91) this means that the condition of the equations (8.90) is determined by the size of $\det \mathbf{A}_1$. This is the reason for the remark made earlier that $\mathbf{A}_1$ should be chosen in such a way that $\det \mathbf{A}_1$ is as large as possible. The condition of the original system (8.84) is indicated by the size of $\det \mathbf{A}^T\mathbf{A}$, and (8.85) shows that this is likely to be much smaller than the maximum value of the $\det \mathbf{A}_p$, if this maximum value is much less than unity.

The reason why (8.90) is a satisfactory set of equations can be seen from a slightly different point of view by rearranging (8.90) in the form

$$[\mathbf{I} + \mathbf{P}^T\mathbf{P}]\mathbf{A}_1\mathbf{x} = [\mathbf{I} + \mathbf{P}^T\mathbf{P}]\mathbf{b}_1 + \mathbf{P}^T[\mathbf{b}_2 - \mathbf{P}\mathbf{b}_1],$$

or

$$\mathbf{A}_1\mathbf{x} = \mathbf{b}_1 + [\mathbf{I} + \mathbf{P}^T\mathbf{P}]^{-1}\mathbf{P}^T[\mathbf{b}_2 - \mathbf{P}\mathbf{b}_1]. \tag{8.93}$$

If the last $m - n$ equations in $\mathbf{A}\mathbf{x} = \mathbf{b}$ are simply linear combinations of the first n equations, this means that if $\mathbf{P}$ is defined as in (8.88), then we must have also

$$\mathbf{b}_2 = \mathbf{P}\mathbf{b}_1.$$

This means that the second term on the right of (8.93) vanishes, and we find the least-squares solution by simply solving

$$\mathbf{A}_1\mathbf{x} = \mathbf{b}_1,$$

as we should expect. If the equations $\mathbf{A}\mathbf{x} = \mathbf{b}$ arise in a physical situation, then we should expect that the last $m - n$ equations would be nearly equal to linear combinations of the first n, i.e., $\mathbf{b}_2$ would be nearly equal to $\mathbf{P}\mathbf{b}_1$, and the last term in (8.93) will be a small correction to $\mathbf{b}_1$.

There are several ways of implementing this procedure in practice. Consider the matrix

$$\begin{bmatrix} \mathbf{A}_1 & \mathbf{b}_1 & \mathbf{I} \\ \mathbf{A}_2 & \mathbf{b}_2 & \mathbf{0} \end{bmatrix}, \tag{8.94}$$

where the notation is as in (8.87). Suppose that the Gauss-Jordan procedure is applied to reduce $\mathbf{A}_1$ to the unit matrix and at the same time multiples of the resulting rows are subtracted from the last $m - n$ rows to reduce $\mathbf{A}_2$ to zero. This means that (8.94) will be reduced to the form

$$\begin{bmatrix} \mathbf{I} & \mathbf{A}_1^{-1}\mathbf{b}_1 & \mathbf{A}_1^{-1} \\ \mathbf{0} & \mathbf{b}_2 - \mathbf{P}\mathbf{b}_1 & -\mathbf{P} \end{bmatrix}, \tag{8.95}$$

where $\mathbf{P}$ is defined by $\mathbf{A}_2 - \mathbf{P}\mathbf{A}_1 = \mathbf{0}$, i.e., $\mathbf{P}$ is precisely the matrix introduced in (8.88). The matrices we require for (8.90) or (8.93) are available in (8.95). There is one other point to be noted. In order to ensure that $\mathbf{A}_1$ is as well-conditioned as possible, we try to pick the n rows of $\mathbf{A}$ that constitute $\mathbf{A}_1$ so that det $\mathbf{A}_1$ is as large as possible. If we are using partial pivoting, we run down the first column of $\mathbf{A}$ and pick the largest element. The corresponding row of $\mathbf{A}$ is used as the first row of (8.94), and so on. The procedure is illustrated in the following example.

Ex. 8.15. Solve the following least-squares equations by the above procedure, working to two significant figures in floating-point.

$$\begin{aligned} 1.1x_1 + 0.9x_2 &= 2.2 \\ 1.2x_1 + x_2 &= 2.3 \\ x_1 + x_2 &= 2.1. \end{aligned}$$

Solution: The largest element in the first column is 1.2, so we start with the matrix [compare (8.94)]

$$\begin{bmatrix} 1.2 & 1 & 2.3 & 1 \\ 1.1 & 0.9 & 2.2 & 0 \\ 1 & 1 & 2.1 & 0 \end{bmatrix},$$

where we have added only one unit column vector for a reason that will appear later. Divide the first row by 1.2, and reduce the (1, 2) and (1, 3) elements to zero, rounding where necessary. (There is no particular reason why we have used the procedure of Chapter 3 rather than the slightly different procedure of Section 7.6 that involves dividing the first column by 1.2. The two procedures are of course not quite equivalent numerically.)

$$\begin{bmatrix} 1.0 & 0.83 & 1.9 & 0.83 \\ 0 & -0.013 & 0.11 & -0.91 \\ 0 & 0.17 & 0.20 & -0.83 \end{bmatrix}.$$

The (3, 2) element is larger than the (2, 2), so we rearrange and add a unit column:

$$\begin{bmatrix} 1.0 & 0.83 & 1.9 & 0.83 & 0 \\ 0 & 0.17 & 0.20 & -0.83 & 1 \\ 0 & -0.013 & 0.11 & -0.91 & 0 \end{bmatrix}.$$

We did not add the fifth column until this point because we did not know which row would be the second. We now divide the second row by 0.17 and reduce the (1, 2) and (3, 2) elements to zero:

$$\begin{bmatrix} 1.0 & 0 & 0.90 & 4.9 & -4.9 \\ 0 & 1.0 & 1.2 & -4.9 & 5.9 \\ 0 & 0 & 0.13 & -0.97 & 0.077 \end{bmatrix}.$$

From this,

$$\mathbf{I} + \mathbf{P}^T\mathbf{P} = \mathbf{I} + \begin{bmatrix} 0.97 \\ -0.077 \end{bmatrix} [0.97 \ -0.077] = \begin{bmatrix} 1.9 & -0.075 \\ -0.075 & 1.0 \end{bmatrix},$$

and the second term on the right of (8.93) is given by solving

$$\begin{bmatrix} 1.9 & -0.075 \\ -0.075 & 1.0 \end{bmatrix} \begin{bmatrix} y_1 \\ y_2 \end{bmatrix} = 0.13P^T = \begin{bmatrix} 0.13 \\ -0.010 \end{bmatrix},$$

which yields $y_2 = -0.0049$, $y_1 = 0.068$. Hence, using (8.93) and (8.95),

$$\begin{bmatrix} x_1 \\ x_2 \end{bmatrix} = \begin{bmatrix} 0.90 \\ 1.2 \end{bmatrix} + \begin{bmatrix} 4.9 & -4.9 \\ -4.9 & 5.9 \end{bmatrix} \begin{bmatrix} 0.068 \\ -0.0049 \end{bmatrix} = \begin{bmatrix} 1.26 \\ 0.84 \end{bmatrix}.$$

The exact solution of the exact least-squares equations $\mathbf{A}^T\mathbf{A}\mathbf{x} = \mathbf{A}^T\mathbf{b}$ is $x_1 = 1.30$, $x_2 = 0.79$. If $\mathbf{A}^T\mathbf{A}$ and $\mathbf{A}^T\mathbf{b}$ are found to full precision and then rounded to two significant figures, and the rounded set is solved, working to two significant figures in floating-point, the solution is found to be $x_1 = 2.0$, $x_2 = 0.25$. The answer by the present method, $x_1 = 1.26$, $x_2 = 0.84$, is far closer to the exact answer.

In terms of the least-squares example in Section 2.4, the procedure we have described can be interpreted as follows. Solving $\mathbf{A}_1\mathbf{x} = \mathbf{b}_1$ alone in (8.93) corresponds to passing a line through the end points AB in Figure 2.8. The correction term on the right of (8.93) corresponds to making an adjustment to the line to take account of the other points. We try to choose $\mathbf{A}_1$ to be the best conditioned of all choices of n rows from $\mathbf{A}$. This corresponds to passing our first line through AB rather than CD, for instance, in Figure 2.8.

8.9 A Summary of the Practical Procedure

So many points have been mentioned that it may be helpful to summarize some of the factors that should be borne in mind when solving simultaneous linear equations in practice. We assume we are interested in relative error.

(a) *Check the scaling of the equations.* The maximum elements in each row and column of $\mathbf{A}$ should certainly be of order unity (unity being chosen for convenience). If this is true and we compute $\mathbf{A}^{-1}$, then the maximum elements in each row and column of $\mathbf{A}^{-1}$ should be comparable. [A criterion of this type was stated more precisely in connection with (8.35) above.] The difficulty is that we may not be willing to carry out a preliminary computation of the inverse merely to scale the matrix. The main reason for scaling is to ensure that partial or complete pivoting will give a satisfactory choice of pivots. Proper scaling will also help when trying to recognize ill-conditioning. Scaling by powers of 10 is sufficient, since it is orders of magnitude that are important. (These remarks on scaling are not definitive since the problem is not completely solved.)

(b) *Use the triangular decomposition method of Section* 7.7, which is equivalent to Gaussian elimination. (There are many variants of the elimination method that are equally satisfactory.) A point that was mentioned in the sentence following (8.64) arises here, namely that it is usually recommended that the sums in (7.53), (7.54) be accumulated in double-precision, the final sums being rounded to single-precision.

(c) *Incorporate partial or complete pivoting.* This can be omitted only when we have a guarantee that pivoting in some given way, for example, along the principal diagonal, will not lead to unsatisfactory pivots. When solving least-squares equations $\mathbf{A}^T\mathbf{A}\mathbf{x} = \mathbf{A}^T\mathbf{b}$, it is sometimes permissible to work straight down the principal diagonal, and this has the advantage that we can halve the storage space required, by taking advantage of the symmetry. If $\mathbf{A}$ is scaled so that the largest element in each row and column is of order unity, and we use triangular decomposition $\mathbf{A} = \mathbf{LU}$ with partial pivoting where $\mathbf{L}$ has unit diagonal elements, then if $\mathbf{U}$ has elements much larger than unity this indicates that we are in trouble [Ex. 8.25, equation (8.98)]. Complete pivoting may help [Ex. 8.17].

(d) *Incorporate the iterative improvement procedure* described at the end of Section 8.7, since this is not expensive and the rate of convergence gives some indication of the condition.

(e) The *residuals* computed to double-precision on a t-decimal machine [which are found in (d)] should be of order 10^{-t} times the maximum $|a_{ij}x_j|$ over j, for each i. Larger values indicate that the choice of pivots may not be satisfactory.

(f) *Check the pivots* and print these if they are not all large. (When working with equations whose properties are unknown, it is a good idea to print the pivots anyway.) Pivots that gradually decrease to zero, say $1, 0.1, 0.01, 0.001, \ldots$ indicate ill-conditioning. Rank-deficiency (rank less than n) is indicated when the pivots start by being more or less constant, then suddenly go down to a very small value.

(g) It may be helpful to compute *condition numbers* but this is laborious and involves the inverse or its equivalent. The method in Ex. 8.2 is usually impractical in which case we have to be content with some "average" condition number. The discussion in Chapter 13 connected with Definition 13.4 is relevant, and it is instructive to compute and compare (8.39) and (13.31). The number (8.39) is recommended as a practical measure of relative condition.

(h) It is impossible to be definitive about the "best" procedure since this depends on striking a balance between the degree of certainty required, and the expense. At least one should incorporate partial pivoting, iterative improvement (with a check on the number of iterations), and a check on pivots.

Having said all this, the worrisome thing is that we can think of situations in practice where we are still going to be in trouble. Thus, consider a digital computer operating on (8.25),

$$\begin{bmatrix} 2 & 1 & 1 \\ 1 & \varepsilon & \varepsilon \\ 1 & \varepsilon & -\varepsilon \end{bmatrix}. \tag{8.96}$$

If we subtract multiples of the first row from the second and third to reduce the (2, 1) and (3, 1) elements to zero, and ε is so small that it is lost when the resulting numbers are rounded, we obtain

$$\begin{bmatrix} 2 & 1 & 1 \\ 0 & -\frac{1}{2} & -\frac{1}{2} \\ 0 & -\frac{1}{2} & -\frac{1}{2} \end{bmatrix} \to \begin{bmatrix} 2 & 1 & 1 \\ 0 & -\frac{1}{2} & -\frac{1}{2} \\ 0 & 0 & 0 \end{bmatrix},$$

where the matrix on the right is obtained by then reducing the (3, 2) element to zero. The third pivot suddenly goes down to zero, and we are in the second situation in (f) above. Our rule of thumb would indicate rank-deficiency. However, we have shown that if ε is known to a high degree of relative accuracy, the matrix is *not* nearly-singular (Ex. 8.8). We showed in Ex. 8.14 that our troubles in this case are due to the fact that (8.96) is not scaled properly. Here we cannot apply the check on scaling that the absolute row sums of $\mathbf{A}^{-1}$ should be approximately the same, *since our machine tells us that* **A** *does not have an inverse.* If we suspected the true situation, then we should be justified in using double-precision to compute the inverse. (This does not contradict the statement at the beginning of Section 8.8 that it is not usually worthwhile to go to a lot of trouble to compute accurate solutions for badly conditioned equations with inaccurate solutions. Here we are in a different situation.)

If we try to solve equations (8.25) on our computer, we obtain

$$\begin{aligned} 2x_1 + x_2 + \phantom{\tfrac{1}{2}}x_3 &= 1 \\ -\tfrac{1}{2}x_2 - \tfrac{1}{2}x_3 &= -\tfrac{1}{2}. \end{aligned}$$

Hence, $x_1 = 0$, $x_2 = k$, $x_3 = 1 - k$, for arbitrary k. The residuals are 0, ε, ε but the maximum $|a_{ij}x_j|$ for $i = 2, 3, j = 1, 2, 3$ are of order ε, so our suspicions are aroused. [See (e) above.]

In conclusion, we reiterate two important points (see Figure 8.1):

(a) In practice we have to look out for three sources of difficulty: *ill-conditioning*, *rank-deficiency*, and *wrong choice of pivots*. It is impossible to distinguish between these when solving simultaneous linear equations (or even to know whether we are in trouble) simply by inspection of the estimates of the unknowns produced by a computer. This is why it is so important to carry out the iterative improvement procedure, and check pivots and residuals, as in (d)–(f) above.

(b) In cases where either ill-conditioning or rank-deficiency is indicated, it is helpful to go back to the origin of the equations. If ill-conditioning is present

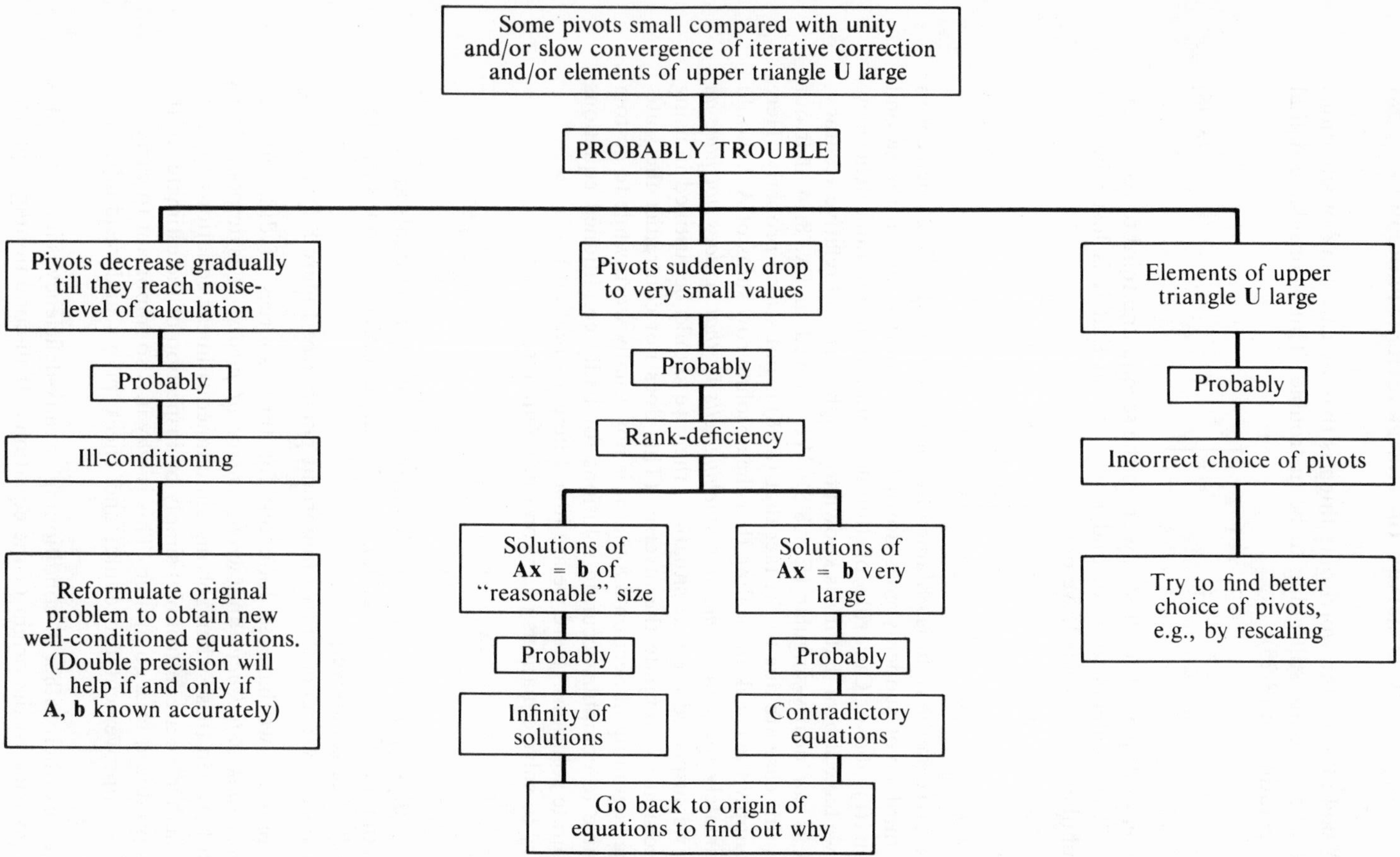

Figure 8.1 Summary of warning signs present when solving $\mathbf{Ax} = \mathbf{b}$ by Gaussian elimination, with partial or complete pivoting. $\mathbf{A} = \mathbf{LU}$ with elements of $\mathbf{L}$ less than unity. $[\mathbf{A}, \mathbf{b}]$ scaled, e.g., so that largest element in each row and column is of order unity. The discussion on p. 267 illustrates one reason why the word "probably" is necessary.

and unacceptable, it may be possible to reformulate in terms of a well-conditioned set of equations. If rank-deficiency is present we should understand the reason and either find the solution in a well-defined form (Exs. 8.22, 8.23) or reformulate in terms of a set of equations with a unique solution.

Some further discussion concerning the numerical solution of linear simultaneous equations is given in Sections 13.3–5.

Miscellaneous Exercises 8

Ex. 8.16. Show that

$$\begin{bmatrix} -\varepsilon & 0.1 & 2\varepsilon \\ 0.2 & 1.0 & 0.1 \\ \varepsilon & 0.2 & \varepsilon \end{bmatrix}$$

is badly scaled if we are interested in relative errors. Here ε is a number with small relative error, and $|\varepsilon| \ll 1$.

Ex. 8.17. Show that, if the system

$$\begin{bmatrix} 1 & 0 & 0 & 0 & 1 \\ 1 & 1 & 0 & 0 & -1 \\ -1 & 1 & 1 & 0 & 1 \\ 1 & -1 & 1 & 1 & -1 \\ -1 & 1 & -1 & 1 & 1 \end{bmatrix} \begin{bmatrix} x_1 \\ x_2 \\ x_3 \\ x_4 \\ x_5 \end{bmatrix} = \begin{bmatrix} 1 \\ -1 \\ 1 \\ -1 \\ 1 \end{bmatrix}$$

is solved by partial pivoting, the last pivot is 16. In the case of a matrix of order n with the same structure, show that the last pivot would be 2^{n-1}. Show that if the (n, n) element is altered by an amount δ, the last pivot changes to $2^{n-1} + \delta$. Why does this tell that it will be difficult to solve equations of this type on a computer, using partial pivoting? Show that the difficulty disappears if we use complete pivoting.

Ex. 8.18. Which of the following procedures for solving the least-squares problem is preferable? Explain.

(a) Form $\mathbf{A}^T\mathbf{A}$ and $\mathbf{A}^T\mathbf{b}$ in double-precision, round the answers to single-precision, and solve $\mathbf{A}^T\mathbf{A}\mathbf{x} = \mathbf{A}^T\mathbf{b}$ using single-precision.

(b) Form $\mathbf{A}^T\mathbf{A}$ and $\mathbf{A}^T\mathbf{b}$ using single-precision, and solve $\mathbf{A}^T\mathbf{A}\mathbf{x} = \mathbf{A}^T\mathbf{b}$ using double-precision.

(c) Perform all the computations in single-precision.

(d) Perform *all* the computations in double-precision.

(e) Use the method of avoiding ill-conditioning described in Section 8.9.

(f) Use a slightly modified iterative correction scheme. Let $(\mathbf{A}^T\mathbf{A})^*$, $(\mathbf{A}^T\mathbf{b})^*$, $\mathbf{r}_i^*$ denote the result of computing $\mathbf{A}^T\mathbf{A}$, $\mathbf{A}^T\mathbf{b}$, $\mathbf{A}^T\mathbf{b} - \mathbf{A}^T\mathbf{A}\hat{\mathbf{x}}_i$ to double-precision and rounding to single-precision. Set $\hat{\mathbf{x}}_{i+1} = \hat{\mathbf{x}}_i + \hat{\boldsymbol{\delta}}_i$ where $\hat{\mathbf{x}}_0$ and $\hat{\boldsymbol{\delta}}_i$ are obtained by solving the following equations to single-precision:

$$(\mathbf{A}^T\mathbf{A})^*\mathbf{x}_0 = (\mathbf{A}^T\mathbf{b})^*, \qquad (\mathbf{A}^T\mathbf{A})^*\boldsymbol{\delta}_i = \mathbf{r}_i^*.$$

(g) Use the orthogonal transformation method described later in Ex. 10.35.

Ex. 8.19. Show that it is easy to incorporate partial pivoting but not complete pivoting into the triangular decomposition procedure of Section 7.7. (When forming the elements of **L** and **U**, the sums involved are performed in one operation.) Draw a flow-chart for the solution of $\mathbf{Ax} = \mathbf{b}$, incorporating some of the checks mentioned in Section 8.9, to distinguish between ill-conditioning and rank-deficiency.

Ex. 8.20. Check through the procedure for solving simultaneous linear equations given in [59], pp. 85–90, including the flow-charts. Summarize the procedure and give the reasons for each step.

Ex. 8.21. Suppose we are solving a set of equations for which we expect (for example, on physical grounds) that the answers will be of order unity. Suppose that we use a computer program that assumes that the equations have a unique solution. Show that if the equations are actually inconsistent, we should expect the computer to print out very large numbers as the solution, whereas if the equations have an infinity of solutions, we should expect the computer to print one of the infinity in which the numbers are of reasonable size. (In this latter case we may be misled into thinking that the equations have a unique solution.)

Ex. 8.22. Outline a procedure for computing the solution of a set of equations with an infinite number of solutions in the form

$$\mathbf{x} = \mathbf{x}_0 + \sum_{i=1}^{p} \alpha_i \mathbf{x}_i,$$

where the α_i are arbitrary constants and $\mathbf{x}_0$, $\mathbf{x}_i$ are *unique* vectors. (By this we mean that if we rescale the equations or change the order of the unknowns, the computer will come up with exactly the same $\mathbf{x}_0$, $\mathbf{x}_i$ as for the original problem, to within limits set by rounding errors.)

Ex. 8.23. Explain what is meant by saying that a set of equations with an infinity of solutions is well-conditioned. How would you test to check the condition of a set of equations with an infinite number of solutions? Do you see any connection between this context of ideas and the idea of "numerical rank"?

Ex. 8.24. If **A** and **C** are the matrices given in (8.82), show that $\mathbf{x} \approx \mathbf{Cb}$ is a very poor approximate solution for the equations $\mathbf{Ax} = \mathbf{b}$, whereas $\mathbf{y} \approx \mathbf{C}^T\mathbf{d}$ is a reasonable approximation to the solution of $\mathbf{A}^T\mathbf{y} = \mathbf{d}$. Explain on the basis of (8.83).

Ex. 8.25. Suppose that we are performing the triangular decomposition $\mathbf{A} = \mathbf{LU}$ using the formulae (7.53), (7.54), where the sums of products are accumulated in double-precision, so that the only rounding errors are those at the very end of the formation of u_{pj} or l_{iq}. This means that if the computed values of u_{pj} and l_{iq} are denoted by $\hat{u}_{pj}$ and $\hat{l}_{iq}$, we have

$$\hat{u}_{pj} = \left\{a_{pj} - \sum_{h=1}^{p-1} \hat{l}_{ph}\hat{u}_{hj}\right\}(1 + \varepsilon'_{pj}), \qquad j = p, p+1, \ldots, n,$$

$$\hat{l}_{iq} = \left\{\frac{a_{iq} - \sum_{h=1}^{q-1} \hat{l}_{ih}\hat{u}_{hq}}{\hat{u}_{qq}}\right\}(1 + \varepsilon'_{iq}), \qquad i = q+1, \ldots, n.$$

Suppose that $\hat{u}_{pj}$ and $\hat{l}_{iq}$ can be obtained by *exact* calculation from elements $\hat{a}_{ij}$ instead of the actual a_{ij}, i.e.,

$$\hat{u}_{pj} = \hat{a}_{pj} - \sum_{h=1}^{p-1} \hat{l}_{ph}\hat{u}_{hj}, \qquad j = p, p+1, \ldots, n,$$

$$\hat{l}_{iq} = \frac{\hat{a}_{iq} - \sum_{h=1}^{q-1} \hat{l}_{ih}\hat{u}_{hq}}{\hat{u}_{qq}}, \qquad i = q+1, \ldots, n.$$

Prove that

$$\hat{a}_{pj} = a_{pj} + \hat{u}_{pj}\varepsilon_{pj}, \qquad p \le j,$$
$$\hat{a}_{iq} = a_{iq} + \hat{l}_{iq}\hat{u}_{qq}\varepsilon_{iq}, \qquad i > q,$$

where $\varepsilon_{rs} = \varepsilon'_{rs}/(1 + \varepsilon'_{rs})$. This gives the remarkable result that the triangular reduction part of the solution of the linear simultaneous equations $\mathbf{Ax} = \mathbf{b}$, when the above rounding errors are present, gives triangles $\hat{\mathbf{L}}$, $\hat{\mathbf{U}}$ that would be obtained by exact computation with matrices $\mathbf{A} + \delta\mathbf{A}$, $\mathbf{b} + \delta\mathbf{b}$, in place of $\mathbf{A}$, $\mathbf{b}$, where

$$[\delta\mathbf{A}, \delta\mathbf{b}] = \begin{bmatrix} 0 & 0 & 0 & \cdots & 0 \\ \hat{l}_{21}\hat{u}_{11}\varepsilon_{21} & \hat{u}_{22}\varepsilon_{22} & \hat{u}_{23}\varepsilon_{23} & \cdots & \hat{u}_{2,n+1}\varepsilon_{2,n+1} \\ \hat{l}_{31}\hat{u}_{11}\varepsilon_{31} & \hat{l}_{32}\hat{u}_{22}\varepsilon_{32} & \hat{u}_{33}\varepsilon_{33} & \cdots & \hat{u}_{3,n+1}\varepsilon_{3,n+1} \\ & & \cdots & & \\ \hat{l}_{n1}\hat{u}_{11}\varepsilon_{n1} & \hat{l}_{n2}\hat{u}_{22}\varepsilon_{n2} & \hat{l}_{n3}\hat{u}_{33}\varepsilon_{n3} & \cdots & \hat{u}_{n,n+1}\varepsilon_{n,n+1} \end{bmatrix}. \qquad (8.97)$$

Two deductions are:

(a) We have an immediate a posteriori check on any computed $\mathbf{L}$, $\mathbf{U}$ by looking at the magnitudes of

$$\frac{\hat{l}_{ij}\hat{u}_{jj}}{a_{ij}}, \quad (i > j); \qquad \frac{\hat{u}_{ij}}{a_{ij}}, \quad \frac{\hat{u}_{i,n+1}}{b_i}, \quad (i \le j).$$

If none of these magnitudes is large compared with unity, this indicates that the computed $\mathbf{L}$, $\mathbf{U}$ are exact for a matrix $\mathbf{A} + \delta\mathbf{A}$ which is (relatively) very close to $\mathbf{A}$.

(b) We can see why partial pivoting should help. Suppose that, when we have computed the first $q - 1$ columns of $\mathbf{L}$ and rows of $\mathbf{U}$, we compute

$$\left\{a_{iq} - \sum_{k=1}^{q-1} \hat{l}_{ik}\hat{u}_{kq}\right\}(1 + \varepsilon''_{iq}), \qquad i = q, q+1, \ldots, n,$$

and choose the largest of these as $\hat{u}_{qq}$, i.e., if the largest of these occurs for $i = r$, we interchange the qth and rth rows of **A** and **L**. If we compute $\hat{l}_{iq}$ for the resulting matrix, we have

$$|\hat{l}_{iq}| \leq 1, \qquad i = q + 1, \ldots, n.$$

Going back to (8.97), this means that, if $|\varepsilon_{ij}| \leq \varepsilon$,

$$|\delta a_{ij}| \leq \begin{cases} 0, & i = 1, \\ |\hat{u}_{ij}|\, \varepsilon, & i > 1, \quad i \leq j, \\ |\hat{u}_{ii}|\, \varepsilon, & i > 1, \quad i > j. \end{cases} \tag{8.98}$$

If none of the elements of **U** is much greater than unity in size, this indicates that the computed **L**, **U** are exact for a matrix $\mathbf{A} + \delta\mathbf{A}$ which is close to **A** in a relative sense. Experience in practice indicates that, if equations are scaled so that the largest element in each row and column is of order unity, and partial pivoting is used, the elements of **U** are not usually very large (even although this scaling is not theoretically perfect, and we can invent examples where our statement is not true, as in Ex. 8.17). This is especially true of ill-conditioned matrices, where a great deal of cancellation takes place (remember that $\det \mathbf{A} = u_{11} \ldots u_{nn}$ and $\det \mathbf{A}$ is much less than unity for ill-conditioned equations). Wilkinson has shown that if complete pivoting is used

$$\max \left|\frac{u_{ii}}{a_{11}}\right| \leq 1.8 n^{(1/4) \log n}$$

but no real matrix is known for which the left-hand side is greater than n, and for most matrices found in practice it is less than 10. (The problem of the best theoretical bound is an interesting open question.)

It is not difficult to extend the above type of *backward error analysis* to Gaussian elimination, where the sums for $\hat{u}_{pj}$ and $\hat{l}_{iq}$ are not accumulated in double-precision, and rounding errors are encountered at each stage of the reduction. Suppose that the formation of $\hat{u}_{pj}$ and $\hat{l}_{iq}$ involve, respectively, $p - 1$ and q roundings, and we use the scaling in the last paragraph and complete pivoting. Then $|\hat{l}_{iq}| \leq 1$ and $|\hat{u}_{pj}| \leq |\hat{u}_{pp}|$, and it is not too difficult to see that the absolute values of the δa_{ij} and δb_j are bounded by [compare (8.97), (8.98)]

$$\left\{\max_i |u_{ii}|\right\} \varepsilon \begin{bmatrix} 0 & 0 & 0 & \ldots & 0 & 0 & . & 0 \\ 1 & 1 & 1 & \ldots & 1 & 1 & . & 1 \\ 1 & 2 & 2 & \ldots & 2 & 2 & . & 2 \\ 1 & 2 & 3 & \ldots & 3 & 3 & . & 3 \\ & & & & \ldots & & & \\ 1 & 2 & 3 & \ldots & n-2 & n-2 & . & n-2 \\ 1 & 2 & 3 & \ldots & n-1 & n-1 & . & n-1 \end{bmatrix}. \tag{8.99}$$

Elementary derivations of the bound (8.99) can be found in *Modern Computing Methods* [58] and:

E. L. Albasiny, article in *Error in Digital Computation*, Vol. I, ed. L. B. Rall, Wiley (1965), pp. 131–184.

See also Forsythe and Moler [53], who assume that additional rounding errors are made when forming $\hat{u}_{pj}$ and $\hat{l}_{iq}$, so that the matrix given on p. 103 of their book is larger than that quoted above. These references also deal with the errors in back-substitution.

More sophisticated treatments of backward error analysis can be found in Isaacson and Keller [57], and Wilkinson [61].

9 Eigenvalues and Eigenvectors

9.1 Introduction: A Physical Example

In order to introduce the subject of eigenvalues and eigenvectors, we consider a physical example involving the vibration of beads on a string. The reader who prefers a geometrical example can read Section 12.1, and then return to the discussion of the properties of eigenvalues and eigenvectors that begins in Section 9.2. The mathematical developments in Section 9.2 do not depend on the examples in this section or in Section 12.1, which are intended as motivation. The reader who wishes to skip the technical details of the formulation of the problem in this section can go directly to equation (9.3).

We first of all remind the reader of the differential equation for simple harmonic motion. If a particle of mass m moves in a straight line and is attracted to a point in the line by a force which is proportional to the distance X of the particle from the point, then the equation of motion of the particle is given by

$$m\frac{d^2X}{dt^2} + pX = 0, \tag{9.1}$$

where p is a constant of proportionality. To solve this equation we set, in the usual way,

$$X = xe^{i\omega t}$$

where ω is the angular frequency of the vibration and x is a constant representing the amplitude of vibration. Equation (9.1) gives

$$(-m\omega^2 + p)xe^{i\omega t} = 0. \tag{9.2}$$

Since the particle is assumed to be moving, $x \neq 0$. Also, $e^{i\omega t}$ is nonzero for all t. Hence, (9.2) implies that

$$m\omega^2 = p \quad \text{or} \quad \omega = \left(\frac{p}{m}\right)^{1/2}.$$

This means physically that there is only one frequency of free vibration.

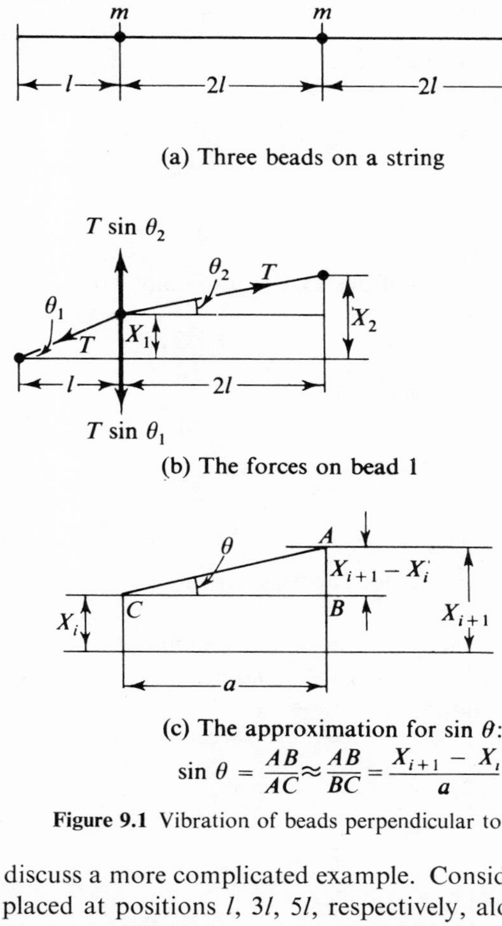

(a) Three beads on a string

(b) The forces on bead 1

(c) The approximation for sin θ:

$$\sin\theta = \frac{AB}{AC} \approx \frac{AB}{BC} = \frac{X_{i+1} - X_i}{a}$$

Figure 9.1 Vibration of beads perpendicular to string.

We now discuss a more complicated example. Consider three particles, each of mass m, placed at positions l, $3l$, $5l$, respectively, along an elastic string of length $6l$, as in Figure 9.1(a). The string is fixed at both ends, and is under a tension T. Suppose that the particles execute small transverse vibrations under no external forces, the displacements of the three particles in a direction perpendicular to the equilibrium line of the string being X_1, X_2, X_3, respectively.

The forces on bead 1 are shown in Figure 9.1(b). The resultant force perpendicular to the line of equilibrium is

$$T(\sin\theta_2 - \sin\theta_1).$$

We assume that the displacements are small so that the tension T can be taken to be constant, and $\sin\theta_1$, $\sin\theta_2$ can be approximated by $\tan\theta_1$, $\tan\theta_2$ as shown in Figure 9.1(c). Newton's second law of motion, that the mass times the acceleration is equal to the force on the particle, gives, for bead 1, on using the above results,

$$m\frac{d^2X_1}{dt^2} = -\frac{TX_1}{l} + \frac{T(X_2 - X_1)}{2l}.$$

Similarly, for the motion of beads 2, 3, we obtain

$$m\frac{d^2X_2}{dt^2} = -\frac{T(X_2 - X_1)}{2l} + \frac{T(X_3 - X_2)}{2l},$$

$$m\frac{d^2X_3}{dt^2} = -\frac{T(X_3 - X_2)}{2l} - \frac{TX_3}{l}.$$

We now assume that all quantities vary sinusoidally with time, and set

$$X_r = x_r e^{i\omega t}, \qquad (r = 1, 2, 3).$$

Then the above equations become

$$\begin{aligned} (3-\lambda)x_1 \quad -x_2 \qquad\qquad &= 0 \\ -x_1 + (2-\lambda)x_2 \qquad -x_3 &= 0 \\ -x_2 + (3-\lambda)x_3 &= 0, \end{aligned} \tag{9.3}$$

where $\lambda = 2\omega^2 ml/T$. These equations are the starting point for the mathematical developments in this chapter.

Equations (9.3) are a set of homogeneous simultaneous linear equations and we know from the theory in earlier chapters that, in general, these will possess only the trivial solution $x_1 = x_2 = x_3 = 0$. However, nonzero solutions will exist if the determinant of coefficients is zero, i.e.,

$$\begin{vmatrix} 3-\lambda & -1 & 0 \\ -1 & 2-\lambda & -1 \\ 0 & -1 & 3-\lambda \end{vmatrix} = 0. \tag{9.4}$$

Expansion in terms of the first row gives

$$(3-\lambda)\begin{vmatrix} 2-\lambda & -1 \\ -1 & 3-\lambda \end{vmatrix} + \begin{vmatrix} -1 & -1 \\ 0 & 3-\lambda \end{vmatrix} = 0.$$

Further expansion shows immediately that $3 - \lambda$ is a factor and the remaining quadratic can be factorized to give

$$(1-\lambda)(3-\lambda)(4-\lambda) = 0. \tag{9.5}$$

Hence, there are three possible values for λ, and we examine each of these in turn:

(a) $\lambda = 1$. Equations (9.3) reduce to

$$\begin{aligned} 2x_1 - x_2 \qquad &= 0 \\ -x_1 + x_2 - \ x_3 &= 0 \\ -x_2 + 2x_3 &= 0. \end{aligned}$$

These equations are consistent and yield $x_1 = \frac{1}{2}x_2 = x_3$, i.e.,

$$\lambda = 1, \qquad x_1 : x_2 : x_3 = 1:2:1. \tag{9.6}$$

(b) $\lambda = 3$. Then (9.3) yields $x_2 = 0$, $x_1 = -x_3$, or

$$\lambda = 3, \qquad x_1 : x_2 : x_3 = 1:0:-1. \tag{9.7}$$

(c) $\lambda = 4$. Equations (9.3) then yield $x_1 = -x_2 = x_3$,

$$\lambda = 4, \qquad x_1 : x_2 : x_3 = 1:-1:1. \tag{9.8}$$

The interesting and important thing about these results is that equations (9.3) possess nonzero solutions for three and only three values of λ. If we set λ equal to any value other than 1, 3, 4, we shall find that the equations possess only the trivial solution $x_1 = x_2 = x_3 = 0$. Thus, if we set $\lambda = 2$, equations (9.3) become

$$\begin{aligned} x_1 - x_2 \qquad &= 0 \\ - x_3 &= 0 \\ - x_2 + x_3 &= 0. \end{aligned}$$

From the first and second equations we obtain $x_2 = x_1$, $x_3 = -x_1$ and if these are substituted in the third equation, we find $-2x_1 = 0$, or $x_1 = 0$, which implies that also $x_2 = x_3 = 0$.

The physical meaning of the results of the above analysis is the following. Corresponding to $\lambda = 1$, for example, there is a free vibration with angular frequency ω given by $\omega^2 = \frac{1}{2}T/ml$, and corresponding to this frequency of vibration there is a mode of oscillation given by (9.6) such that the ratios $x_1 : x_2 : x_3$ are $1:2:1$. Similarly for $\lambda = 3$ and $\lambda = 4$. The modes of vibration are illustrated graphically in Figure 9.2. These three frequencies and modes of vibration are the only ones that can exist.

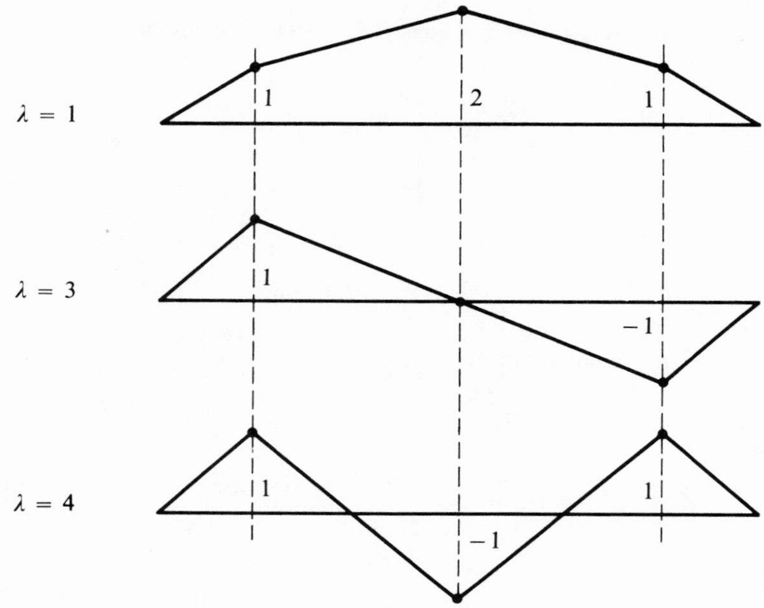

Figure 9.2 Modes of vibration.

Ex. 9.1. Find the eigenvalues and eigenvectors of the matrices

$$\begin{bmatrix} 2 & 2 \\ 1 & 3 \end{bmatrix}, \qquad \begin{bmatrix} 4 & -20 & -10 \\ -2 & 10 & 4 \\ 6 & -30 & -13 \end{bmatrix}.$$

Ex. 9.2. Obtain the determinantal equation corresponding to (9.4) for the case of n particles of masses m_i ($i = 1$ to n) at arbitrary positions along a string with fixed ends.

9.2 Definitions and Basic Properties

We express the ideas in Section 9.1 in more general terminology. Generalizing (9.3), we consider a system of n homogeneous equations in n unknowns:

$$\begin{aligned} (a_{11} - \lambda)x_1 + a_{12}x_2 + \ldots + a_{1n}x_n &= 0 \\ a_{21}x_1 + (a_{22} - \lambda)x_2 + \ldots + a_{2n}x_n &= 0 \\ &\ldots \\ a_{n1}x_1 + a_{n2}x_2 + \ldots + (a_{nn} - \lambda)x_n &= 0. \end{aligned} \tag{9.9}$$

In an obvious matrix notation, these are

$$(\mathbf{A} - \lambda\mathbf{I})\mathbf{x} = \mathbf{0} \tag{9.10}$$

or

$$\mathbf{A}\mathbf{x} = \lambda\mathbf{x}. \tag{9.11}$$

This homogeneous set of equations possesses only the trivial solution $\mathbf{x} = \mathbf{0}$ unless the determinant of coefficients is zero,

$$\det(\mathbf{A} - \lambda\mathbf{I}) = \begin{vmatrix} a_{11} - \lambda & a_{12} & \dots & a_{1n} \\ a_{21} & a_{22} - \lambda & \dots & a_{2n} \\ & & \dots & \\ a_{n1} & a_{n2} & \dots & a_{nn} - \lambda \end{vmatrix} = 0. \tag{9.12}$$

This is a polynomial equation in λ of degree n, known as the *characteristic* (or *secular*) equation of **A**. The roots of this equation are special values of λ for which the simultaneous equations (9.9) possess nonzero solutions. They are called the *eigenvalues* of **A**, and will be denoted by λ_i $(i = 1, 2, \dots, n)$. The λ_i are sometimes called latent roots, characteristic roots, or proper values. Corresponding to each of the λ_i there will be a solution of (9.9) of the form $c\mathbf{x}_i$, where $\mathbf{x}_i$ is a nonzero vector, and c is an arbitrary constant. These solutions are called the *eigenvectors* (or latent vectors, characteristic vectors, or proper vectors). No confusion should arise from the use of $\mathbf{x}_1, \dots, \mathbf{x}_n$ to denote the n eigenvectors, and $x_1, \dots, x_n$ to denote the elements of a given eigenvector.

DEFINITION 9.1. The polynomial $f(\lambda) = \det(\mathbf{A} - \lambda\mathbf{I})$ is called the *characteristic polynomial* and the equation $f(\lambda) = 0$ is called the *characteristic equation* of **A**. The *eigenvalues* of **A** are the scalars λ for which $\mathbf{A}\mathbf{x} = \lambda\mathbf{x}$ possess nonzero solutions. The corresponding nonzero solutions **x** are the *eigenvectors* of **A**.

We obtain directly from this definition of eigenvalues and eigenvectors the following basic formula:

$$\mathbf{A}\mathbf{x}_i = \lambda_i\mathbf{x}_i, \qquad (i = 1, \dots, n). \tag{9.13}$$

Ex. 9.3. Transforming the results in the previous section into the above language, show that the matrix

$$\mathbf{A} = \begin{bmatrix} 3 & -1 & 0 \\ -1 & 2 & -1 \\ 0 & -1 & 3 \end{bmatrix} \tag{9.14}$$

has the eigenvalues $\lambda_1 = 1$, $\lambda_2 = 3$, $\lambda_3 = 4$, with corresponding eigenvectors

$$\mathbf{x}_1 = \begin{bmatrix} 1 \\ 2 \\ 1 \end{bmatrix}, \quad \mathbf{x}_2 = \begin{bmatrix} 1 \\ 0 \\ -1 \end{bmatrix}, \quad \mathbf{x}_3 = \begin{bmatrix} 1 \\ -1 \\ 1 \end{bmatrix}. \tag{9.15}$$

Some useful results concerning the characteristic polynomial are summarized in the next theorem. We remind the reader of the definition of the *trace*, tr **A**, of a square matrix **A**, which is simply the sum of the diagonal elements (see Ex. 1.57).

THEOREM 9.1. *The characteristic polynomial of a square matrix of order n is a polynomial of degree n with leading coefficient* $(-1)^n$, *and constant term* det **A**. *The coefficient of* λ^{n-1} *is* $(-1)^{n-1}$ tr **A**. *There are n eigenvalues, and if these are* $\lambda_1, \lambda_2, \ldots, \lambda_n$, *then*

$$\sum_{i=1}^{n} \lambda_i = \sum_{i=1}^{n} a_{ii} = \text{tr}\,\mathbf{A} \tag{9.16}$$

$$\lambda_1 \lambda_2 \ldots \lambda_n = \det \mathbf{A}. \tag{9.17}$$

Proof: If we expand det $(\mathbf{A} - \lambda\mathbf{I})$ in terms of elements in the first row, we see that

$$f(\lambda) = \det(\mathbf{A} - \lambda\mathbf{I}) = (a_{11} - \lambda)B_{11} + \sum_{j=2}^{n} a_{1j}B_{1j}, \tag{9.18}$$

where B_{1j} is the cofactor of the (i, j)th element in $\mathbf{A} - \lambda\mathbf{I}$. There are only $n - 2$ elements $a_{ii} - \lambda$ involving λ in the B_{1j} for $j = 2, \ldots, n$, so that the largest power of λ that can be obtained by expansion of these is λ^{n-2}. Hence, (9.18) gives

$$f(\lambda) = (a_{11} - \lambda)B_{11} + \{\text{terms of degree } n - 2 \text{ or less in } \lambda\}.$$

The same argument can be applied to B_{11}, and by repetition we see that

$$\begin{aligned} f(\lambda) &= (a_{11} - \lambda)(a_{22} - \lambda) \ldots (a_{nn} - \lambda) + \{\text{terms of degree } n - 2 \text{ or less in } \lambda\} \\ &= (-1)^n\lambda^n + (-1)^{n-1}\lambda^{n-1} \sum_{i=1}^{n} a_{ii} + \{\text{terms of degree } n - 2 \text{ or less in } \lambda\}. \end{aligned} \tag{9.19}$$

Hence the characteristic polynomial is of degree n, and the coefficients of λ^n and λ^{n-1} agree with those stated in the theorem. To see that the constant term in $f(\lambda)$ is det **A** we set $\lambda = 0$ in the definition $f(\lambda) = \det(\mathbf{A} - \lambda\mathbf{I})$. The λ_i are the roots of the characteristic polynomial, so that

$$\begin{aligned} f(\lambda) = \det(\mathbf{A} - \lambda\mathbf{I}) &= (\lambda_1 - \lambda)(\lambda_2 - \lambda) \ldots (\lambda_n - \lambda) \\ &= (-1)^n\lambda^n + (-1)^{n-1}\lambda^{n-1} \sum_{i=1}^{n} \lambda_i + \ldots . \end{aligned} \tag{9.20}$$

A comparison of this result with (9.19) gives (9.16). To obtain (9.17), we simply set $\lambda = 0$ in (9.20).

The eigenvalues of a matrix of order n are the roots of a polynomial degree n, and there is no reason why these should be distinct, in the general case. As a simple example, consider the situation when $\mathbf{A}$ is the unit matrix $\mathbf{I}$. Then the characteristic polynomial is given by

$$\det(\mathbf{A} - \lambda\mathbf{I}) = \det(1 - \lambda)\mathbf{I} = (1 - \lambda)^n \det \mathbf{I} = (1 - \lambda)^n$$

and the eigenvalues of $\mathbf{I}$ are $\lambda = 1$ repeated n times. This example is also interesting because *any* vector is an eigenvector,

$$\mathbf{Ax} = \mathbf{Ix} = \mathbf{x} = \lambda_i \mathbf{x},$$

for any λ_i, since all the λ_i are equal to unity.

DEFINITION **9.2.** If the roots of the characteristic equation are such that the value of λ_i is repeated k times, then λ_i is said to be an eigenvalue of *multiplicity* k. If λ_i occurs only once, i.e., if its multiplicity is one, then λ_i is said to be *simple*.

THEOREM **9.2.** (i) *There exists at least one eigenvector corresponding to each eigenvalue.*

(ii) *The eigenvectors corresponding to a given eigenvalue constitute a vector space.*

Proof: To find an eigenvector corresponding to λ_i we have to solve

$$(\mathbf{A} - \lambda_i \mathbf{I})\mathbf{x} = \mathbf{0}.$$

Since $\det(\mathbf{A} - \lambda_i \mathbf{I}) = 0$, this is a set of n homogeneous equations in n unknowns, the coefficient matrix having rank less than n. Hence a nonzero solution exists, which gives an eigenvector. This proves (i). If $\mathbf{u}$ and $\mathbf{v}$ are two eigenvectors corresponding to λ_i, then

$$\mathbf{Au} = \lambda_i \mathbf{u}, \qquad \mathbf{Av} = \lambda_i \mathbf{v},$$

so that

$$\begin{aligned} \mathbf{A}(\alpha\mathbf{u} + \beta\mathbf{v}) &= \alpha\mathbf{Au} + \beta\mathbf{Av} \\ &= \alpha\lambda_i\mathbf{u} + \beta\lambda_i\mathbf{v} = \lambda_i(\alpha\mathbf{u} + \beta\mathbf{v}). \end{aligned}$$

Hence, $\alpha\mathbf{u} + \beta\mathbf{v}$ is also an eigenvector, and this proves (ii).

THEOREM **9.3.** (i) *Eigenvectors corresponding to distinct eigenvalues are linearly independent.*

(ii) *If* $\mathbf{A}$ *has n distinct eigenvalues, there exist exactly n linearly independent eigenvectors, one associated with each eigenvalue.*

Proof: Suppose that $\mathbf{x}_1, \ldots, \mathbf{x}_s$ are eigenvectors corresponding to distinct eigenvalues $\lambda_1, \ldots, \lambda_s$ of $\mathbf{A}$. Suppose that the $\mathbf{x}_i$ are linearly dependent, and that s is the smallest number for which this is true. Then

$$\alpha_1\mathbf{x}_1 + \alpha_2\mathbf{x}_2 + \ldots + \alpha_s\mathbf{x}_s = \mathbf{0}, \tag{9.21}$$

where all the α_i are nonzero (since s is the *smallest* number for which the vectors are linearly dependent). Multiplying through by $\mathbf{A}$, and using the fact that $\mathbf{A}\mathbf{x}_i = \lambda_i \mathbf{x}_i$, we see that

$$\alpha_1 \lambda_1 \mathbf{x}_1 + \alpha_2 \lambda_2 \mathbf{x}_2 + \ldots + \alpha_s \lambda_s \mathbf{x}_s = \mathbf{0}. \tag{9.22}$$

If one of the λ_i is zero, this equation gives a dependence relation between $s - 1$ eigenvectors, which is impossible by the definition of s. If all the λ_i are nonzero, we subtract λ_1 times (9.21) from (9.22), which gives

$$\alpha_2(\lambda_2 - \lambda_1)\mathbf{x}_2 + \ldots + \alpha_s(\lambda_s - \lambda_1)\mathbf{x}_s = \mathbf{0}.$$

Since $\lambda_i - \lambda_1 \neq 0$ for $i = 2, \ldots, s$, this means that we have again obtained a linear relation between $s - 1$ eigenvectors, which contradicts the definition of s. This proves (i). To prove (ii), we know from Theorem 9.2(i) that there exist n eigenvectors $\mathbf{x}_1, \ldots, \mathbf{x}_n$ corresponding to $\lambda_1, \ldots, \lambda_n$. Suppose that a second eigenvector, say $\mathbf{u}$, corresponds to λ_i. From (i), the vectors $\mathbf{x}_1, \ldots, \mathbf{x}_n$ are linearly independent. Hence, they span the space of $n \times 1$ column vectors, and we can write

$$\mathbf{u} = \beta_1 \mathbf{x}_1 + \ldots + \beta_n \mathbf{x}_n. \tag{9.23}$$

Multiplication by $\mathbf{A}$ gives

$$\lambda_i \mathbf{u} = \beta_1 \lambda_1 \mathbf{x}_1 + \ldots + \beta_n \lambda_n \mathbf{x}_n. \tag{9.24}$$

Subtract λ_i times (9.23) from (9.24),

$$\mathbf{0} = \beta_1(\lambda_1 - \lambda_i)\mathbf{x}_1 + \ldots + \beta_n(\lambda_n - \lambda_i)\mathbf{x}_n.$$

The vectors $\mathbf{x}_i$ are linearly independent, so that $\beta_j = 0$ ($i = 1$ to n, $j \neq i$). From (9.23) this means that $\mathbf{u} = \beta_i \mathbf{x}_i$, so that $\mathbf{u}$ is linearly dependent on $\mathbf{x}_i$, and this proves part (ii).

The last two theorems do not tell the whole story. From Theorem 9.2(i) we know that to each eigenvalue there corresponds at least one eigenvector. If the eigenvalue is of multiplicity k, we might hope that there would be k linearly independent eigenvectors. Unfortunately, this is not true. For instance, in Chapter 11, Exs. 11.5–11.7, we give examples to show that, corresponding to an eigenvalue of multiplicity 3, there may be precisely 1, 2, or 3 linearly independent eigenvectors.

We saw that in order to discover the properties of a matrix with reference to the linear dependence or independence of rows or columns, it was convenient to reduce the matrix to a standard form called the row-echelon normal form. In a similar way, in order to investigate the properties of a matrix vis-à-vis its eigenvalues and eigenvectors it is desirable to transform the matrix into certain standard forms. This will prove to be a laborious but instructive task. The next few sections introduce ideas that will lead to a systematic study of transformations in Chapters 10 and 11. First some examples.

Ex. 9.4. Show that the matrix

$$\begin{bmatrix} 2 & -1 & 0 \\ -1 & 2 & -1 \\ 0 & -1 & 2 \end{bmatrix}$$

has eigenvalues 2, $2 \pm \sqrt{2}$, and find the corresponding eigenvectors.

Ex. 9.5. Find two linearly independent eigenvectors of the matrix

$$\begin{bmatrix} 2 & 2 & -6 \\ 2 & -1 & -3 \\ -2 & -1 & 1 \end{bmatrix}$$

corresponding to the eigenvalue $\lambda = -2$. Find the other eigenvalue and eigenvector.

Ex. 9.6. Prove that $\lambda = 0$ is an eigenvalue of a matrix **A** if and only if **A** is singular.

Ex. 9.7. Prove: (a) The transpose of **A** has the same eigenvalues as **A**.
(b) The matrix $k\mathbf{A}$ has the eigenvalues $k\lambda_i$.
(c) The matrix $\mathbf{A}^p$, where p is a positive integer, has the eigenvalues λ_i^p.
(d) If **A** is nonsingular, $\mathbf{A}^{-1}$ has the eigenvalues $1/\lambda_i$.
(e) The matrix $\mathbf{A} + k\mathbf{I}$ has the eigenvalues $\lambda_i + k$.

Ex. 9.8. If $f(x)$ is a polynomial in n, then $f(\mathbf{A})$ denotes the matrix obtained by replacing x by the (square) matrix **A**. If λ is an eigenvalue of **A**, show that $f(\lambda)$ is an eigenvalue of $f(\mathbf{A})$.

Ex. 9.9. If **A** is a real square matrix, show that the eigenvalues of **A** are real or complex conjugate in pairs. Also, if **A** is odd, show that it has at least one real eigenvalue.

9.3 *Inner Products and Hermitian Matrices*

The ideas we are now going to introduce may seem at first sight to be quite divorced from the subject matter of the first two sections in this chapter. However, we shall quickly see that inner products provide a useful tool for the investigation of eigenvalues and eigenvectors.

The notions of length and angle are fundamental in ordinary two- and three-dimensional space, although we did not require these ideas when we discussed vector spaces in Chapter 4. It is natural to try to introduce concepts analogous to length and angle into our general vector space framework. We first of all consider the ordinary three-dimensional case with which we are familiar.

As in Figure 9.3, let U, V be two points with coordinates (u_1, u_2, u_3), (v_1, v_2, v_3), the vectors from O to U and V being represented by $\vec{u}$, $\vec{v}$, respectively. The *scalar product* or *dot product* of $\vec{u}$ and $\vec{v}$ is defined to be

$$\vec{u} \cdot \vec{v} = u_1v_1 + u_2v_2 + u_3v_3. \tag{9.25}$$

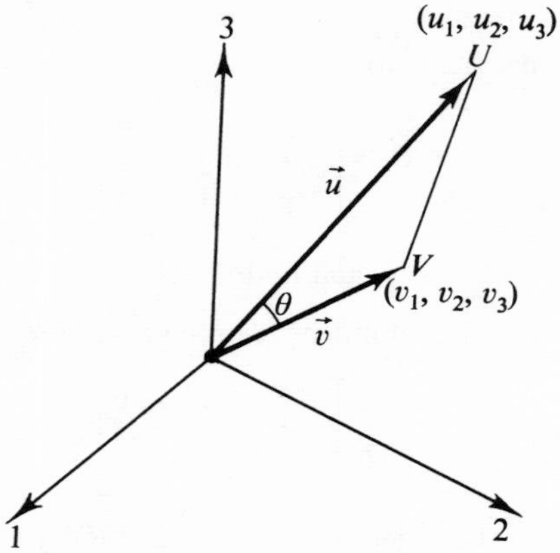

Figure 9.3 Vectors in three-dimensional space.

The length of a vector can be expressed in terms of this dot product. If $|\vec{u}|$ represents the length of $\vec{u}$, we have

$$|\vec{u}| = (u_1^2 + u_2^2 + u_3^2)^{1/2} = (\vec{u} \cdot \vec{u})^{1/2}. \tag{9.26}$$

The distance between U and V can also be expressed in terms of the dot product:

$$\begin{aligned} UV^2 &= (u_1 - v_1)^2 + (u_2 - v_2)^2 + (u_3 - v_3)^2 \\ &= |\vec{u} - \vec{v}|^2 = |\vec{u}|^2 + |\vec{v}|^2 - 2\vec{u} \cdot \vec{v}. \end{aligned} \tag{9.27}$$

The well-known formula for expressing a side of a triangle in terms of the opposite angle, say θ, and the sides adjacent to that angle, gives

$$UV^2 = |\vec{u}|^2 + |\vec{v}|^2 - 2\,|\vec{u}|\,|\vec{v}| \cos \theta. \tag{9.28}$$

On comparing (9.27) and (9.28) we see that

$$\cos \theta = \frac{\vec{u} \cdot \vec{v}}{|\vec{u}|\,|\vec{v}|}. \tag{9.29}$$

By using these results as a guide, we are in a position to introduce the concepts of length and angle into vector spaces. The basic idea is to generalize the notion of the scalar product (9.25). We first suppose that our vectors have real elements. (We give the following definition for clarity, although it will be superseded almost immediately by the more general Definition 9.4.)

DEFINITION **9.3.** The *inner product* (or *scalar product*) of two real $n \times 1$ column vectors $\mathbf{u}$, $\mathbf{v}$ is the scalar quantity $(\mathbf{u}, \mathbf{v})$ defined by

$$(\mathbf{u}, \mathbf{v}) = u_1v_1 + u_2v_2 + \ldots + u_nv_n. \tag{9.30}$$

The *length* or *norm* of $\mathbf{u}$, denoted by $\|\mathbf{u}\|$, is defined to be

$$\|\mathbf{u}\| = (\mathbf{u}, \mathbf{u})^{1/2} = +(u_1^2 + u_2^2 \ldots + u_n^2)^{1/2}. \tag{9.31}$$

The *angle* θ between $\mathbf{u}$ and $\mathbf{v}$ is defined by

$$\cos\theta = \frac{(\mathbf{u}, \mathbf{v})}{\|\mathbf{u}\|\;\|\mathbf{v}\|}.$$

It is convenient to summarize certain important properties of the inner product. The results are very simple but they are useful because they avoid the necessity of going back to the definition every time we use inner products.

THEOREM 9.4. *The inner product of real vectors has the following properties:*

(i) *Linearity:*

$$(\alpha\mathbf{u} + \beta\mathbf{w}, \mathbf{v}) = \alpha(\mathbf{u}, \mathbf{v}) + \beta(\mathbf{w}, \mathbf{v}),$$
$$(\mathbf{u}, \alpha\mathbf{v} + \beta\mathbf{w}) = \alpha(\mathbf{u}, \mathbf{v}) + \beta(\mathbf{u}, \mathbf{w}).$$

(ii) *Symmetry:*

$$(\mathbf{u}, \mathbf{v}) = (\mathbf{v}, \mathbf{u}).$$

(iii) *Positive-definiteness:*

$$(\mathbf{u}, \mathbf{u}) > 0 \quad \textit{if} \quad \mathbf{u} \neq \mathbf{0},$$
$$(\mathbf{u}, \mathbf{u}) = 0 \quad \textit{implies} \quad \mathbf{u} = \mathbf{0}.$$

Proof: The proof follows directly from the definition.

We next consider what happens when the elements of the vectors are complex. If we use Definition 9.3, equation (9.31), to find the length of the vector $(i = \sqrt{-1})$,

$$\mathbf{u} = \begin{bmatrix} 1 \\ i \end{bmatrix},$$

we find

$$\|\mathbf{u}\| = (1 - 1)^{1/2} = 0,$$

i.e., a nonzero vector has zero length, and we have lost property (iii) in Theorem 9.4. When using inner products, it will turn out that it is desirable to preserve this property. One way of doing this is to alter our definition of inner product slightly.

DEFINITION 9.4. The *inner product* (or *scalar product*) of two $n \times 1$ column vectors $\mathbf{u}$, $\mathbf{v}$ with real or complex elements is the scalar quantity $(\mathbf{u}, \mathbf{v})$ defined by

$$(\mathbf{u}, \mathbf{v}) = \bar{u}_1 v_1 + \bar{u}_2 v_2 + \ldots + \bar{u}_n v_n, \tag{9.32}$$

where $\bar{u}_i$ is the complex conjugate of u_i. The *norm* or *length* of $\mathbf{u}$, denoted by $\|\mathbf{u}\|$ is defined by

$$\|\mathbf{u}\| = (\mathbf{u}, \mathbf{u})^{1/2} = (\bar{u}_1 u_1 + \bar{u}_2 u_2 + \ldots + \bar{u}_n u_n)^{1/2}. \tag{9.33}$$

Note:

(a) This definition of $\|\mathbf{u}\|$ has the property that $\|\mathbf{u}\|$ is real, and $\|\mathbf{u}\| > 0$ if $\mathbf{u} \neq \mathbf{0}$.

(b) We could equally have defined $(\mathbf{u}, \mathbf{v})$ as the sum of the products $u_i\bar{v}_i$, with the complex conjugates on the second term. It does not matter which definition we use as long as we use the same convention consistently. We use the above convention because we shall often form the inner product of both sides of an equation, say $\mathbf{u} = \mathbf{v}$, with a third vector $\mathbf{w}$, to give $(\mathbf{w}, \mathbf{u}) = (\mathbf{w}, \mathbf{v})$ and it seems slightly more natural to take the complex conjugate of $\mathbf{w}$ rather than that of the equation $\mathbf{u} = \mathbf{v}$, if we are writing the result out explicitly. However, this is a matter of taste.

(c) Definition 9.4 reduces to the previous Definition 9.3 in the real case.

Although we have now preserved property (iii) in Theorem 9.4, the other two properties have to be modified slightly in the complex case. (The word "hermitian" in the theorem below is used merely as a label to remind the reader that we do not have linearity and symmetry in the ordinary sense. The reason for this term is simply that hermitian matrices, introduced immediately following the theorem, play a central role in the theory.)

THEOREM **9.5.** *The inner product has the following properties:*

(i) *Hermitian linearity:*

$$(\alpha\mathbf{u} + \beta\mathbf{w}, \mathbf{v}) = \bar{\alpha}(\mathbf{u}, \mathbf{v}) + \bar{\beta}(\mathbf{w}, \mathbf{v}),$$

$$(\mathbf{u}, \alpha\mathbf{v} + \beta\mathbf{w}) = \alpha(\mathbf{u}, \mathbf{v}) + \beta(\mathbf{u}, \mathbf{w}).$$

(ii) *Hermitian symmetry:*

$$(\mathbf{u}, \mathbf{v}) = \overline{(\mathbf{v}, \mathbf{u})}.$$

(iii) *Positive-definiteness:*

$$(\mathbf{u}, \mathbf{u}) > 0 \quad \textit{if} \quad \mathbf{u} \neq \mathbf{0}, \qquad (\mathbf{u}, \mathbf{u}) = 0 \quad \textit{implies} \quad \mathbf{u} = \mathbf{0}.$$

We remind the reader that a complex matrix is a matrix whose elements may be complex. We use the notation $\bar{\mathbf{A}}$ to denote the matrix whose elements are the complex conjugates of $\mathbf{A}$.

DEFINITION **9.5.** The *hermitian transpose* of a matrix $\mathbf{A}$, denoted by $\mathbf{A}^H$ is defined by $\mathbf{A}^H = \bar{\mathbf{A}}^T$, i.e., its elements are the complex conjugates of the elements of the transpose of $\mathbf{A}$. If $\mathbf{A}^H = \mathbf{A}$ (i.e., $a_{ij} = \bar{a}_{ji}$), the matrix is said to be *hermitian*.

The hermitian transpose possesses properties that are similar to those of the ordinary transpose:

THEOREM 9.6. (i) $(\mathbf{A}^H)^H = \mathbf{A}$.
(ii) $(\mathbf{AB})^H = \mathbf{B}^H\mathbf{A}^H$.
(iii) *If* $\mathbf{A}$ *is hermitian, then* $\mathbf{Q}^H\mathbf{AQ}$ *is hermitian, for arbitrary* $\mathbf{Q}$.

Proof: (i) $\mathbf{A}^H = \bar{\mathbf{A}}^T, \quad (\mathbf{A}^H)^H = \overline{(\bar{\mathbf{A}}^T)^T} = \overline{(\bar{\mathbf{A}})} = \mathbf{A}$.
(ii) $(\mathbf{AB})^H = \overline{(\mathbf{AB})}^T = (\bar{\mathbf{A}}\bar{\mathbf{B}})^T = \bar{\mathbf{B}}^T\bar{\mathbf{A}}^T = \mathbf{B}^H\mathbf{A}^H$.
(iii) $(\mathbf{Q}^H\mathbf{AQ})^H = \mathbf{Q}^H\mathbf{A}^H(\mathbf{Q}^H)^H = \mathbf{Q}^H\mathbf{AQ}$.

A simple example of a hermitian matrix is

$$\begin{bmatrix} 1 & 1+i \\ 1-i & 1 \end{bmatrix}.$$

Note that a hermitian matrix must have real elements along its principal diagonal.

Clearly, if $\mathbf{A}$ is real, the hermitian transpose is simply the ordinary transpose, and a hermitian matrix is simply a symmetric matrix. All the results we develop for the hermitian case will be true automatically for symmetric matrices with real elements. The main reason for introducing hermitian matrices is this: Symmetric real matrices have certain very convenient properties. However, we find that symmetric complex matrices do *not* possess these properties. Hermitian matrices *do* possess these convenient properties, so that hermitian matrices are the correct generalization of real symmetric matrices. The next point is that if we go through the details of the proofs for real symmetric matrices and then repeat the theory for hermitian matrices, we find that the proofs are almost the same except for certain annoying minor modifications consisting of adding complex conjugate bars where necessary. It is much simpler to prove the theorems for general hermitian matrices, and obtain the results for real symmetric matrices as special cases.

THEOREM 9.7. (i) $(\mathbf{u}, \mathbf{Av}) = (\mathbf{A}^H\mathbf{u}, \mathbf{v})$. (9.34)
(ii) *If* $\mathbf{A}$ *is hermitian, then*

$$(\mathbf{u}, \mathbf{Av}) = (\mathbf{Au}, \mathbf{v}). \tag{9.35}$$

Proof: To prove (i) we simply write out both sides in full,

$$(\mathbf{u}, \mathbf{Av}) = \sum_{r=1}^{n} \bar{u}_r\left(\sum_{s=1}^{n} a_{rs}v_s\right). \tag{9.36}$$

The general element of $\mathbf{A}^H\mathbf{u}$ is

$$\sum_{j=1}^{n} \bar{a}_{ji}u_j.$$

Hence,

$$(\mathbf{A}^H\mathbf{u}, \mathbf{v}) = \sum_{i=1}^{n} \left(\sum_{j=1}^{n} a_{ji}\bar{u}_j \right) v_i. \tag{9.37}$$

On identifying j and r and i with s in the terms on the right of (9.36), (9.37), we see that these are the same. This proves part (i), and part (ii) is an immediate consequence.

In the general case, since the eigenvalues are the roots of a polynomial equation, they may be complex. There is one very important case where we can prove that the eigenvalues are real, namely when the matrix is hermitian. This is one of the reasons why hermitian (and real symmetric) matrices have convenient properties.

THEOREM **9.8.** *The eigenvalues of a hermitian matrix are real.*

Proof: Suppose that λ is an eigenvalue of a hermitian matrix $\mathbf{A}$, the corresponding eigenvector being denoted by $\mathbf{x}$:

$$\mathbf{A}\mathbf{x} = \lambda\mathbf{x},$$

where λ and $\mathbf{x}$ may be complex. Form the inner product of both sides with $\mathbf{x}$,

$$(\mathbf{x}, \mathbf{A}\mathbf{x}) = \lambda(\mathbf{x}, \mathbf{x}). \tag{9.38}$$

We have already seen that the inner product has been defined so that $(\mathbf{x}, \mathbf{x})$ is real. Also, using Theorem 9.5(ii) and Theorem 9.7,

$$\overline{(\mathbf{x}, \mathbf{A}\mathbf{x})} = (\mathbf{A}\mathbf{x}, \mathbf{x}) = (\mathbf{x}, \mathbf{A}\mathbf{x}). \tag{9.39}$$

Hence, $(\mathbf{x}, \mathbf{A}\mathbf{x})$ is real. From (9.38), since $(\mathbf{x}, \mathbf{x}) \neq 0$, we see that λ is the ratio of real quantities, so that λ is real.

Ex. 9.10. Prove that $(\mathbf{x}, \mathbf{A}\mathbf{x})$ is real if $\mathbf{A}$ is hermitian by writing out the expression for the inner product explicitly as a double sum, and inspect individual terms. [This example will illustrate incidentally why we prefer the method of proof given in connection with (9.39).]

Ex. 9.11. A matrix is said to be *skew-hermitian* if $\bar{\mathbf{A}}^T = -\mathbf{A}$. Prove that if $\mathbf{A}$ is skew-hermitian then $i\mathbf{A}$ is hermitian. Prove that the eigenvalues of a skew-symmetric matrix are pure imaginary. Deduce that $\mathbf{I} + \mathbf{A}$ is nonsingular.

Ex. 9.12. If $\mathbf{A}$ is hermitian, show that $\bar{\mathbf{A}}$ and $\mathbf{A}^T$ are hermitian. If $\mathbf{A}$ is also nonsingular, show that $\mathbf{A}^{-1}$ is also hermitian. If $\mathbf{A} = \mathbf{B} + i\mathbf{C}$, where $\mathbf{B}$, $\mathbf{C}$ are real, show that $\mathbf{B}^T = \mathbf{B}$, $\mathbf{C}^T = -\mathbf{C}$.

Ex. 9.13. If $\mathbf{A}$ is hermitian, prove that its characteristic polynomial has real coefficients.

9.4 Orthogonality

In connection with the discussion of vectors in three-dimensional space given at the beginning of Section 9.3, we can deduce from equation (9.29) for the cosine of the angle between two vectors that two geometrical vectors are perpendicular to each other (or orthogonal) if the scalar product of the vectors is zero. We generalize this as follows.

DEFINITION 9.6. Two nonzero vectors $\mathbf{u}$, $\mathbf{v}$ are said to be *orthogonal* if

$$(\mathbf{u}, \mathbf{v}) = 0.$$

If a set of nonzero vectors $\mathbf{u}_1, \mathbf{u}_2, \ldots, \mathbf{u}_p$ are such that

$$(\mathbf{u}_i, \mathbf{u}_j) = 0, \qquad \text{all } i \neq j,$$

we say that they are *mutually orthogonal* and that we have an *orthogonal set.*

The reason for the name "orthogonal" can be illustrated by considering the following 2×1 matrices:

$$\mathbf{y} = \begin{bmatrix} \cos\theta \\ \sin\theta \end{bmatrix}, \qquad \mathbf{z} = \begin{bmatrix} -\sin\theta \\ \cos\theta \end{bmatrix}.$$

Geometrically in two dimensions these can be considered as vectors from the origin to the points $(\cos\theta, \sin\theta)$, $(-\sin\theta, \cos\theta)$. It is evident geometrically that these vectors are perpendicular to each other, i.e., orthogonal. The relation $(\mathbf{y}, \mathbf{z}) = 0$ is also satisfied, so that the vectors are also orthogonal in the sense of Definition 9.6.

The following theorem is one of the reasons why the concept of orthogonality is important in connection with eigenvectors.

THEOREM 9.9. *Eigenvectors corresponding to distinct eigenvalues of a hermitian matrix are orthogonal.*

Proof: Suppose that $\mathbf{x}_i$, $\mathbf{x}_j$ are eigenvectors corresponding to distinct eigenvalues λ_i, λ_j:

$$\mathbf{A}\mathbf{x}_i = \lambda_i\mathbf{x}_i, \qquad \mathbf{A}\mathbf{x}_j = \lambda_j\mathbf{x}_j. \tag{9.40}$$

If we form the inner product of the first equation with $\mathbf{x}_j$ and the second with $\mathbf{x}_i$, we obtain

$$(\mathbf{x}_j, \mathbf{A}\mathbf{x}_i) = \lambda_i(\mathbf{x}_j, \mathbf{x}_i), \qquad (\mathbf{x}_i, \mathbf{A}\mathbf{x}_j) = \lambda_j(\mathbf{x}_i, \mathbf{x}_j). \tag{9.41}$$

Interchanging elements in the inner products in the second equation,

$$\overline{(\mathbf{A}\mathbf{x}_j, \mathbf{x}_i)} = \lambda_j\overline{(\mathbf{x}_j, \mathbf{x}_i)}. \tag{9.42}$$

We take the complex conjugates of both sides, and use the fact that λ_j is real (Theorem 9.8) and that $(\mathbf{A}\mathbf{x}_j, \mathbf{x}_i) = (\mathbf{x}_j, \mathbf{A}\mathbf{x}_i)$ (Theorem 9.7). Then (9.42) becomes

$$(\mathbf{x}_j, \mathbf{A}\mathbf{x}_i) = \lambda_j(\mathbf{x}_j, \mathbf{x}_i).$$

Subtraction of this equation from the first equation in (9.41) yields

$$(\lambda_i - \lambda_j)(\mathbf{x}_j, \mathbf{x}_i) = 0.$$

Since $\lambda_i \neq \lambda_j$, this means that $(\mathbf{x}_j, \mathbf{x}_i) = 0$, which proves the theorem.

Ex. 9.14. Write out the proof of this theorem "longhand" by writing out the expressions in (9.41) in terms of the elements of $\mathbf{A}$, $\mathbf{x}_i$, $\mathbf{x}_j$.

Ex. 9.15. Show that the three eigenvectors in (9.15) form an orthogonal set. [Note that the matrix $\mathbf{A}$ in (9.14) is real symmetric.] For example,

$$(\mathbf{x}_1, \mathbf{x}_3) = 1(1) + 2(-1) + 1(1) = 0.$$

Similarly, check that $(\mathbf{x}_1, \mathbf{x}_2) = (\mathbf{x}_2, \mathbf{x}_3) = 0$.

If $\mathbf{z}_i$ is an eigenvector of $\mathbf{A}$ corresponding to the eigenvalue λ_i, then, since the defining equation $\mathbf{A}\mathbf{z}_i = \lambda_i\mathbf{z}_i$ is homogeneous, the vector $k\mathbf{z}_i$ is also an (equivalent) eigenvector for any nonzero constant k. It is convenient to choose k so that $\|\mathbf{x}_i\| = (\mathbf{x}_i, \mathbf{x}_i)^{1/2} = 1$, i.e., so that $k\bar{k}(\mathbf{z}_i, \mathbf{z}_i) = 1$. Usually we choose k to be real so that $k = 1/\|\mathbf{z}\|$, and

$$\mathbf{x}_i = \frac{\mathbf{z}_i}{\|\mathbf{z}_i\|}.$$

The resulting vector $\mathbf{x}_i$ is said to be *normalized.*

Ex. 9.16. Check that the normalized forms of the vectors in (9.15) are:

$$\mathbf{x}_1 = \frac{1}{\sqrt{6}}\begin{bmatrix}1\\2\\1\end{bmatrix}, \quad \mathbf{x}_2 = \frac{1}{\sqrt{2}}\begin{bmatrix}1\\0\\-1\end{bmatrix}, \quad \mathbf{x}_3 = \frac{1}{\sqrt{3}}\begin{bmatrix}1\\-1\\1\end{bmatrix}. \tag{9.43}$$

Geometrically, if we are replacing $\mathbf{z}$ by $\mathbf{x} = k\mathbf{z}$, where k is chosen so that $\|\mathbf{x}\| = 1$, we are replacing $\mathbf{z}$ by a vector $\mathbf{x}$ of unit length, in the same direction as $\mathbf{z}$.

DEFINITION **9.7.** If $(\mathbf{x}, \mathbf{x}) = \|\mathbf{x}\|^2 = 1$, the vector $\mathbf{x}$ is said to be *normalized.* If a set of vectors $\mathbf{x}_1, \ldots, \mathbf{x}_n$ is orthogonal and normalized [i.e., $(\mathbf{x}_i, \mathbf{x}_j) = 0$ $(i \neq j)$, $(\mathbf{x}_i, \mathbf{x}_i) = 1$], then the vectors are said to form an *orthonormal set.*

As an example, the vectors in (9.43) form an orthonormal set.

THEOREM **9.10.** *If a hermitian matrix has n distinct eigenvalues, the corresponding normalized eigenvectors form an orthonormal set.*

Proof: This theorem merely collects together various previous results. Theorem 9.2(i) tells us that the n corresponding eigenvectors exist, and Theorem 9.9 tells us that these form an orthogonal set.

Suppose next that $\mathbf{x}_i$ $(i = 1, \ldots, n)$ are n normalized eigenvectors corresponding to n distinct eigenvalues λ_i of a hermitian matrix $\mathbf{A}$ of order n. The matrix $\mathbf{P}$ whose ith column is $\mathbf{x}_i$ will play an important role in the development of the theory:

$$\mathbf{P} = [\mathbf{x}_1, \mathbf{x}_2, \ldots, \mathbf{x}_n]. \tag{9.44}$$

The matrix $\mathbf{P}$ possesses a remarkable property. We have

$$\mathbf{P}^H\mathbf{P} = \bar{\mathbf{P}}^T\mathbf{P} = \begin{bmatrix} \bar{\mathbf{x}}_1^T \\ \bar{\mathbf{x}}_2^T \\ \cdot \\ \cdot \\ \cdot \\ \bar{\mathbf{x}}_n^T \end{bmatrix} [\mathbf{x}_1, \mathbf{x}_2, \ldots, \mathbf{x}_n] = \begin{bmatrix} \bar{\mathbf{x}}_1^T\mathbf{x}_1, & \bar{\mathbf{x}}_1^T\mathbf{x}_2, & \ldots, & \bar{\mathbf{x}}_1^T\mathbf{x}_n \\ \bar{\mathbf{x}}_2^T\bar{\mathbf{x}}_1, & \bar{\mathbf{x}}_2^T\mathbf{x}_2, & \ldots, & \bar{\mathbf{x}}_2^T\mathbf{x}_n \\ & \cdots & & \\ \bar{\mathbf{x}}_n^T\mathbf{x}_1, & \bar{\mathbf{x}}_n^T\mathbf{x}_2, & \ldots, & \bar{\mathbf{x}}_n^T\mathbf{x}_n \end{bmatrix}.$$

The quantity $\bar{\mathbf{x}}_i^T\mathbf{x}_j$ is the 1×1 matrix with element $(\mathbf{x}_i, \mathbf{x}_j)$ and, from Theorem 9.9, this is 0 if $i \neq j$, and 1 if $i = j$. The product $\mathbf{P}\mathbf{P}^H$ can be considered similarly, leading to the result

$$\mathbf{P}\mathbf{P}^H = \mathbf{P}^H\mathbf{P} = \mathbf{I}, \tag{9.45}$$

where $\mathbf{I}$ is the unit matrix of order n. This gives the important result that the inverse of $\mathbf{P}$ is simply its hermitian transpose. In the special case where $\mathbf{A}$ is real symmetric, $\mathbf{P}$ is real and then we have the result that $\mathbf{P}\mathbf{P}^T = \mathbf{P}^T\mathbf{P} = \mathbf{I}$, or the inverse of $\mathbf{P}$ is its transpose.

Matrices that satisfy (9.45) are so important that they are given a special name.

DEFINITION **9.8.** A matrix $\mathbf{P}$ such that $\mathbf{P}^H\mathbf{P} = \mathbf{P}\mathbf{P}^H = \mathbf{I}$ is said to be a *unitary* matrix. As a special case, a real matrix $\mathbf{P}$ such that $\mathbf{P}^T\mathbf{P} = \mathbf{P}\mathbf{P}^T = \mathbf{I}$ is said to be an *orthogonal* matrix.

Ex 9.17. Verify that the following matrix is unitary.

$$\frac{1}{2}\begin{bmatrix} 1+i & -1+i \\ 1+i & 1-i \end{bmatrix}.$$

The result (9.45) has proved:

THEOREM 9.11. *The matrix* **P** *whose columns are the normalized eigenvectors of a hermitian (real symmetric) matrix with distinct eigenvalues is unitary (orthogonal).*

Ex. 9.18. Use Theorem 9.11, in conjunction with (9.14), (9.15), to show that

$$\mathbf{P} = \begin{bmatrix} \dfrac{1}{\sqrt{6}} & \dfrac{1}{\sqrt{2}} & \dfrac{1}{\sqrt{3}} \\ \dfrac{2}{\sqrt{6}} & 0 & -\dfrac{1}{\sqrt{3}} \\ \dfrac{1}{\sqrt{6}} & -\dfrac{1}{\sqrt{2}} & \dfrac{1}{\sqrt{3}} \end{bmatrix} \tag{9.46}$$

must be an orthogonal matrix. Verify that this is the case.

We now prove an important theorem that will be used in Section 9.5. Much of Chapters 10–12 will be concerned with elaborating and exploiting this theorem.

THEOREM 9.12. *Suppose that* **A** *has n linearly independent eigenvectors,* $\mathbf{A}\mathbf{x}_i = \lambda_i\mathbf{x}_i$, *and introduce:*

$$\mathbf{P} = [\mathbf{x}_1, \ldots, \mathbf{x}_n], \qquad \mathbf{\Lambda} = \begin{bmatrix} \lambda_1 & 0 & \ldots & 0 \\ 0 & \lambda_1 & \ldots & 0 \\ & & \ldots & \\ 0 & 0 & & \lambda_n \end{bmatrix}. \tag{9.47}$$

Then

$$\text{(i) } \mathbf{P}^{-1}\mathbf{A}\mathbf{P} = \mathbf{\Lambda}, \qquad \text{(ii) } \mathbf{A} = \mathbf{P}\mathbf{\Lambda}\mathbf{P}^{-1}. \tag{9.48}$$

If **P** *is unitary,*

$$\text{(iii) } \mathbf{P}^{H}\mathbf{A}\mathbf{P} = \mathbf{\Lambda}, \qquad \text{(iv) } \mathbf{A} = \mathbf{P}\mathbf{\Lambda}\mathbf{P}^{H}. \tag{9.49}$$

Proof: Since $\mathbf{A}\mathbf{x}_i = \lambda_i\mathbf{x}_i$, $i = 1, \ldots, n$, we see, using the standard rules for manipulating partitioned matrices, that

$$\begin{aligned} \mathbf{A}\mathbf{P} &= \mathbf{A}[\mathbf{x}_1, \ldots, \mathbf{x}_n] = [\mathbf{A}\mathbf{x}_1, \ldots, \mathbf{A}\mathbf{x}_n] \\ &= [\lambda_1\mathbf{x}_1, \ldots, \lambda_n\mathbf{x}_n] = \mathbf{P}\mathbf{\Lambda}. \end{aligned} \tag{9.50}$$

Since the $\mathbf{x}_i$ are independent, **P** can be inverted, and all the results stated in the theorem follow immediately.

The main reason why we mention separately the case when **P** is unitary is that this often occurs in practice. We have already shown that **P** can be chosen to be unitary when **A** is hermitian with distinct eigenvalues. We shall show in Chapter 11 that a unitary **P** exists for *any* hermitian matrix. The reason why a unitary **P** is extremely convenient is of course that in order to invert **P** we simply take its hermitian transpose.

It is important to realize that in this section (and the next) we concentrate on hermitian matrices with distinct eigenvalues merely because the exposition is then simple and clear. However, it is misleading to spend a great deal of time on this case because the general situation is more subtle. Elucidation of the general case is the objective of Chapters 10 and 11. Briefly, it will turn out that the most important property of a matrix in connection with the eigenproblem is whether it has *n linearly independent eigenvectors* or not. A hermitian matrix always has this property and this is one of the reasons why the theory of hermitian matrices is especially simple. This is fortunate since hermitian matrices occur frequently in applications.

In order to illustrate the usefulness of Theorem 9.12, we give an application to the evaluation of $\mathbf{A}^k$, where k is an arbitrary integer. We have, from (9.48),

$$\mathbf{A}^2 = (\mathbf{P\Lambda P}^{-1})(\mathbf{P\Lambda P}^{-1}) = \mathbf{P\Lambda}^2\mathbf{P}^{-1}.$$

Similarly,

$$\mathbf{A}^k = (\mathbf{P\Lambda P}^{-1})(\mathbf{P\Lambda P}^{-1}) \ldots k \text{ times} = \mathbf{P\Lambda}^k\mathbf{P}^{-1}. \tag{9.51}$$

Since $\mathbf{\Lambda}$ is a diagonal matrix, $\mathbf{\Lambda}^k$ is also diagonal, with ith element λ_i^k, so that $\mathbf{A}^k$ can be evaluated if $\mathbf{P}$, $\mathbf{\Lambda}$ are known.

Ex. 9.19. Verify that, since **P** in (9.46) corresponds to the matrix **A** in (9.14),

$$\begin{bmatrix} 3 & -1 & 0 \\ -1 & 2 & -1 \\ 0 & -1 & 3 \end{bmatrix}^k = \begin{bmatrix} 1/\sqrt{6} & 1/\sqrt{2} & 1/\sqrt{3} \\ 2/\sqrt{6} & 0 & -1/\sqrt{3} \\ 1/\sqrt{6} & -1/\sqrt{2} & 1/\sqrt{3} \end{bmatrix} \begin{bmatrix} 1 & 0 & 0 \\ 0 & 3^k & 0 \\ 0 & 0 & 4^k \end{bmatrix} \begin{bmatrix} 1/\sqrt{6} & 2/\sqrt{6} & 1/\sqrt{6} \\ 1/\sqrt{2} & 0 & -1/\sqrt{2} \\ 1/\sqrt{3} & -1/\sqrt{3} & 1/\sqrt{3} \end{bmatrix}$$

$$= \frac{1}{6}\begin{bmatrix} 1 + 3^\alpha + 2^\beta & 2 - 2^\beta & 1 - 3^\alpha + 2^\beta \\ 2 - 2^\beta & 4 + 2^\beta & 2 - 2^\beta \\ 1 - 3^\alpha + 2^\beta & 2 - 2^\beta & 1 + 3^\alpha + 2^\beta \end{bmatrix}$$

where $\alpha = k + 1$, $\beta = 2k + 1$.

Ex. 9.20. Find the eigenvalues and eigenvectors of the matrices

$$\begin{bmatrix} \cos\theta & -\sin\theta \\ \sin\theta & \cos\theta \end{bmatrix}, \qquad \begin{bmatrix} \cosh\theta & \sinh\theta \\ \sinh\theta & \cosh\theta \end{bmatrix}.$$

Deduce, using (9.51), a simple formula for the nth powers of these matrices. (Compare Ex. 1.31.)

Ex. 9.21. Construct the matrix with eigenvalues 2, 1, -1 and corresponding eigenvectors

$$\begin{bmatrix} 1 \\ 2 \\ -1 \end{bmatrix}, \quad \begin{bmatrix} 1 \\ -1 \\ 3 \end{bmatrix}, \quad \begin{bmatrix} 1 \\ 0 \\ 2 \end{bmatrix}.$$

9.5 *Orthogonal Expansions, with an Application to Forced Vibration*

The concept of orthogonality introduced in the last section is of fundamental importance in many branches of applied mathematics.

As a simple application of orthogonality, we consider the problem of expanding a given vector $\mathbf{u}$ as a linear combination of an orthogonal set of vectors $\mathbf{x}_1, \ldots, \mathbf{x}_n$. We first require the following theorem.

THEOREM **9.13.** *The vectors in an orthogonal set are linearly independent.*

Proof: Suppose that $\mathbf{x}_1, \ldots, \mathbf{x}_n$ constitute an orthogonal set, and

$$\alpha_1\mathbf{x}_1 + \alpha_2\mathbf{x}_2 + \ldots + \alpha_n\mathbf{x}_n = \mathbf{0}.$$

Form the inner product with $\mathbf{x}_i$. Since $(\mathbf{x}_i, \mathbf{x}_j) = 0$, $i \neq j$, we see that

$$\alpha_i(\mathbf{x}_i, \mathbf{x}_i) = 0.$$

But $(\mathbf{x}_i, \mathbf{x}_i) \neq 0$ since $\mathbf{x}_i \neq \mathbf{0}$. Hence, $\alpha_i = 0$, and this is true for all i, $i = 1, \ldots, n$. This proves the theorem.

We can now prove the main theorem.

THEOREM **9.14.** *An arbitrary $n \times 1$ vector $\mathbf{u}$ can be expressed uniquely as a linear combination of a set of n orthogonal vectors $\mathbf{x}_i$. If*

$$\mathbf{u} = \alpha_1\mathbf{x}_1 + \alpha_2\mathbf{x}_2 + \ldots + \alpha_n\mathbf{x}_n \tag{9.52}$$

then

$$\alpha_i = \frac{(\mathbf{x}_i, \mathbf{u})}{(\mathbf{x}_i, \mathbf{x}_i)}. \tag{9.53}$$

If the $\mathbf{x}_i$ are normalized, then

$$\alpha_i = (\mathbf{x}_i, \mathbf{u}). \tag{9.54}$$

Proof: If the α_i in (9.52) are regarded as unknowns, then (9.52) is a set of n linear simultaneous equations for the n unknowns α_i. From Theorem 9.13, the columns of the matrix of coefficients are linearly independent so that the equations have a unique solution. This means that the expansion exists and is unique.

We can easily write down the solution of (9.52) explicitly. Form the inner product of (9.52) with $\mathbf{x}_i$. Since $(\mathbf{x}_i, \mathbf{x}_j) = 0$, $i \neq j$, we have

$$(\mathbf{x}_i, \mathbf{u}) = \alpha_i(\mathbf{x}_i, \mathbf{x}_i),$$

and this is precisely (9.53), since $\mathbf{x}_i$ is nonzero. Equation (9.54) follows immediately.

The point of the above theorem is that usually, if we wish to express $\mathbf{u}$ as a sum of multiples of the $\mathbf{x}_i$, as in (9.52), we should have to solve a set of n equations in n unknowns for the α_i. However, if the $\mathbf{x}_i$ are orthogonal, the α_i can be written down directly and explicitly.

Ex. 9.22. Find α_1, α_2, α_3 such that

$$\mathbf{u} = \begin{bmatrix} 3 \\ -5 \\ 2 \end{bmatrix} = \alpha_1\mathbf{x}_1 + \alpha_2\mathbf{x}_2 + \alpha_3\mathbf{x}_3,$$

where the $\mathbf{x}_i$ are the orthogonal set defined in (9.15).

Solution: We have

$$(\mathbf{x}_1, \mathbf{u}) = [1 \quad 2 \quad 1]\begin{bmatrix} 3 \\ -5 \\ 2 \end{bmatrix} = -5, \qquad (\mathbf{x}_1, \mathbf{x}_1) = [1 \quad 2 \quad 1]\begin{bmatrix} 1 \\ 2 \\ 1 \end{bmatrix} = 6.$$

Hence, from (9.53), $\alpha_1 = -\frac{5}{6}$. Similarly, we can show that $\alpha_2 = \frac{1}{2}$, $\alpha_3 = \frac{10}{3}$, and, from (9.52),

$$\begin{bmatrix} 3 \\ -5 \\ 2 \end{bmatrix} = -\frac{5}{6}\begin{bmatrix} 1 \\ 2 \\ 1 \end{bmatrix} + \frac{1}{2}\begin{bmatrix} 1 \\ 0 \\ -1 \end{bmatrix} + \frac{10}{3}\begin{bmatrix} 1 \\ -1 \\ 1 \end{bmatrix}.$$

The correctness of this expansion can, of course, be checked by inspection.

We now derive a remarkable (and useful) result, namely that under certain circumstances it is possible to write down a formula for the solution of the system of linear equations

$$(\mathbf{A} - \lambda\mathbf{I})\mathbf{x} = \mathbf{f},$$

where $\mathbf{A}$, $\mathbf{f}$ are given and λ is an arbitrary parameter. The form of the solution shows explicitly the dependence of $\mathbf{x}$ on the symbol λ. In the following theorem we investigate the situation for a hermitian matrix $\mathbf{A}$ with distinct eigenvalues. Analogous theorems hold for more general $\mathbf{A}$. The case of general hermitian matrices is considered in Ex. 9.23, and the case of any $\mathbf{A}$ in Exs. 10.37, 10.38.

THEOREM 9.15. *Consider the following set of n equations in n unknowns:*

$$(\mathbf{A} - \lambda\mathbf{I})\mathbf{x} = \mathbf{f}, \tag{9.55}$$

where $\mathbf{A}$ *is a hermitian matrix with distinct eigenvalues* $\lambda_1, \ldots, \lambda_n$.

(i) *If* $\lambda \neq \lambda_i$ *for any* $i = 1, \ldots, n$, *then*

$$\mathbf{x} = \sum_{i=1}^{n} \frac{(\mathbf{x}_i, \mathbf{f})\mathbf{x}_i}{\lambda_i - \lambda}. \tag{9.56}$$

(ii) *If* $\lambda = \lambda_j$ *for some j, then no solution exists unless* $(\mathbf{x}_j, \mathbf{f}) = 0$. *If this condition is satisfied, then there is an infinity of solutions, namely*

$$\mathbf{x} = \sum_{i=1}^{n}{}' \frac{(\mathbf{x}_i, \mathbf{f})\mathbf{x}_i}{\lambda_i - \lambda} + c\mathbf{x}_j, \tag{9.57}$$

where the prime on the summation sign indicates that the term $i = j$ *is omitted, and c is an arbitrary constant.*

Proof: We shall use (9.45) and (9.49), namely $\mathbf{P}^H\mathbf{P} = \mathbf{I}$ and $\mathbf{P}^H\mathbf{A}\mathbf{P} = \mathbf{\Lambda}$ where $\mathbf{\Lambda}$ is defined in (9.47). On multiplying (9.55) by $\mathbf{P}^H$, and inserting $\mathbf{P}\mathbf{P}^H$ between the bracket and $\mathbf{x}$, which is permissible since $\mathbf{P}\mathbf{P}^H = \mathbf{I}$, we obtain

$$\mathbf{P}^H(\mathbf{A} - \lambda\mathbf{I})\mathbf{P}\mathbf{P}^H\mathbf{x} = \mathbf{P}^H\mathbf{f},$$

or

$$(\mathbf{P}^H\mathbf{A}\mathbf{P} - \lambda\mathbf{P}^H\mathbf{P})\mathbf{P}^H\mathbf{x} = \mathbf{P}^H\mathbf{f},$$

or

$$(\mathbf{\Lambda} - \lambda\mathbf{I})\mathbf{P}^H\mathbf{x} = \mathbf{P}^H\mathbf{f}. \tag{9.58}$$

On using the form (9.44) for $\mathbf{P}$, where the $\mathbf{x}_i$ are now normalized, this equation gives

$$(\lambda_i - \lambda)(\mathbf{x}_i, \mathbf{x}) = (\mathbf{x}_i, \mathbf{f}), \qquad i = 1, \ldots, n. \tag{9.59}$$

From Theorem 9.14, remembering that now $(\mathbf{x}_i, \mathbf{x}_i) = 1$, equations (9.52), (9.54) give

$$\mathbf{x} = \sum_{i=1}^{n} \alpha_i \mathbf{x}_i, \qquad \alpha_i = (\mathbf{x}_i, \mathbf{x}). \tag{9.60}$$

The α_i can be determined from (9.59) if $\lambda \neq \lambda_i$ for any i. In this case, (9.59), (9.60) immediately yield (9.56). If $\lambda = \lambda_j$ for some j, then (9.59) gives a contradictory equation when $i = j$ unless $(\mathbf{x}_j, \mathbf{f}) = 0$, in which case the corresponding equation is simply an identity. Hence, equations (9.55) have no solution when $\lambda = \lambda_j$ for some j, unless $(\mathbf{x}_j, \mathbf{f}) = 0$, in which case a solution is given by (9.57). This completes the proof.

We conclude this section by giving an application of the above theorem to forced vibration. Suppose that external transverse forces $F_r \cos(\omega t + \alpha_r)$, $r = 1, 2, 3$, are applied to the particles on the string, discussed in Section 9.1. The equation of motion for the first mass becomes, for instance [cf. (9.2)],

$$m\frac{d^2X_1}{dt^2} + \frac{TX_1}{l} - \frac{T(X_2 - X_1)}{2l} = F_1 \cos(\omega t + \alpha_1) = \mathrm{Re}\,\{F_1 e^{i\omega t + i\alpha_1}\},$$

where Re stands for the real part of the expression in brackets. In the usual way we set

$$X_i = \text{Re}\,\{x_i e^{i\omega t}\}, \qquad F_i e^{i\alpha_i} = \frac{1}{2}\left(\frac{T}{l}\right) f_i,$$

say, $i = 1, 2, 3$. Instead of the system (9.3) we now find

$$\begin{aligned} (3-\lambda)x_1 \qquad -x_2 \qquad\qquad &= f_1 \\ -x_1 + (2-\lambda)x_2 \qquad -x_3 &= f_2 \\ -x_2 + (3-\lambda)x_3 &= f_3. \end{aligned} \tag{9.61}$$

These are a set of three equations in three unknowns which we write in matrix form as

$$(\mathbf{A} - \lambda\mathbf{I})\mathbf{x} = \mathbf{f}.$$

The equations have a unique solution if det $(\mathbf{A} - \lambda\mathbf{I}) \neq 0$. If det $(\mathbf{A} - \lambda\mathbf{I}) = 0$, either there is no solution or an infinity of solutions.

Physically the situation can be interpreted in the following way, using Theorem 9.15. We remind the reader that, from the analysis in Section 9.1, the eigenvalues of $\mathbf{A}$ correspond physically to the frequencies of free vibration of the system, and the corresponding eigenvectors represent the modes of vibration:

(a) If det $(\mathbf{A} - \lambda\mathbf{I}) \neq 0$, this means that λ is *not* one of the eigenvalues of $\mathbf{A}$, i.e., the frequency of the externally applied forces (the forcing frequency) does not coincide with a frequency of free vibration. In this case, the equations have a unique solution and the system will settle down to a unique mode of forced vibration.

(b) If det $(\mathbf{A} - \lambda\mathbf{I}) = 0$, i.e., the forcing frequency coincides with a frequency of free vibration, say $\lambda = \lambda_j$, there are two possibilities:

(i) If $(\mathbf{x}_j, \mathbf{f}) = 0$, i.e., the vector $\mathbf{f}$ representing the applied force is orthogonal to the vector representing the mode of free vibration, the equations can possess an infinity of solutions. From (9.57), the solution is determined to within an arbitrary multiple of the eigenvector corresponding to the mode of free vibration.

(ii) If $(\mathbf{x}_j, \mathbf{f}) \neq 0$, i.e., the applied force is not orthogonal to the mode of free vibration, then the equations are inconsistent, i.e., no solution exists. Physically this corresponds to the case where resonance occurs, and the amplitudes of vibration are infinite.

By means of Theorem 9.15, equation (9.56), we can write down the solution of the system (9.61) explicitly. The normalized eigenvectors $\mathbf{x}_i$ are given by

(9.43). Straightforward substitution in (9.56) yields

$$\begin{aligned}
x_1 &= \frac{1}{6}(f_1 + 2f_2 + f_3)\frac{1}{1-\lambda} + \frac{1}{2}(f_1 - f_3)\frac{1}{3-\lambda} + \frac{1}{3}(f_1 - f_2 + f_3)\frac{1}{4-\lambda} \\
x_2 &= \frac{1}{3}(f_1 + 2f_2 + f_3)\frac{1}{1-\lambda} \qquad\qquad\qquad - \frac{1}{3}(f_1 - f_2 + f_3)\frac{1}{4-\lambda} \\
x_3 &= \frac{1}{6}(f_1 + 2f_2 + f_3)\frac{1}{1-\lambda} - \frac{1}{2}(f_1 - f_3)\frac{1}{3-\lambda} + \frac{1}{3}(f_1 - f_2 + f_3)\frac{1}{4-\lambda}.
\end{aligned} \tag{9.62}$$

If, for example, we are given $f_1 = 6, f_2 = -3, f_3 = -6$, then this formula gives

$$\begin{aligned}
x_1 &= -\frac{1}{1-\lambda} + \frac{6}{3-\lambda} + \frac{1}{4-\lambda} \\
x_2 &= -\frac{2}{1-\lambda} \qquad\qquad - \frac{1}{4-\lambda} \\
x_3 &= -\frac{1}{1-\lambda} - \frac{6}{3-\lambda} + \frac{1}{4-\lambda}.
\end{aligned} \tag{9.63}$$

The beauty of this result is that we see easily and directly the way in which the x_i vary with the forcing frequency, which is related to λ. In particular, the occurrence of resonance at $\lambda = 1, 3, 4$, is very clearly illustrated.

A graph of x_1 against λ has been drawn in Figure 9.4. The exceptional behavior near $\lambda = 1, 3, 4$ is evident.

Equations (9.62) contain a great deal of information in a clear and explicit form. It is difficult to extract this information from the original equations (9.61),

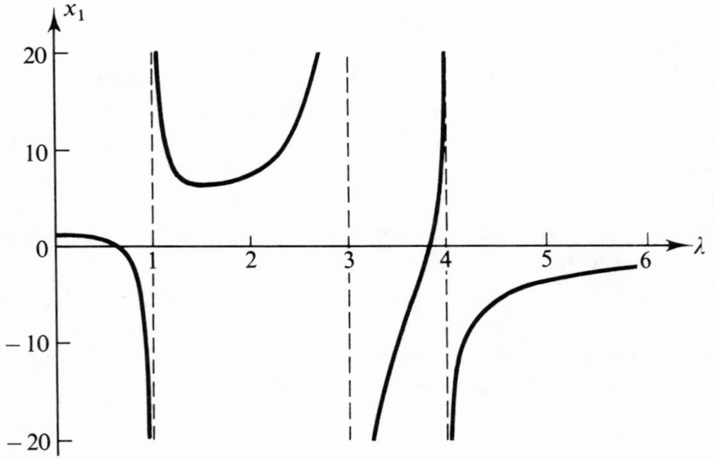

Figure 9.4 A graph of x_1 defined in (9.63) against λ.

and it would be difficult to obtain the solution (9.62) and graph like that in Figure 9.4 from (9.61) without using the theory of eigenvalues and eigenvectors.

Ex. 9.23. It will be shown later that a hermitian matrix always has a set of n orthonormal eigenvectors, whether its eigenvalues are distinct or not (Theorem 10.10). Show that Theorem 9.15(i) is true for any hermitian matrix and that part (ii) is true if all the terms corresponding to $\lambda = \lambda_j$ are omitted from the sum (9.57), and the additional term in this sum is replaced by a sum of arbitrary multiples of the eigenvectors corresponding to $\lambda = \lambda_j$.

9.6 Iterative Methods for Calculating Eigenvalues

In this section we deal briefly with the so-called power method for finding the largest eigenvalues of a matrix. The method is not very useful in practice unless we are interested in only a few eigenvalues of largest modulus, and these are well separated in modulus from the others. Even in this case complications will arise if an eigenvalue of large modulus of multiplicity k does not have k corresponding linearly independent eigenvectors. However, the method is conceptually simple, and it provides an instructive application of eigenvector expansions.

THEOREM **9.16.** *Let A be a real matrix with n linearly independent eigenvectors $\mathbf{x}_j$ corresponding to eigenvalues λ_j. Suppose that there is one eigenvalue of maximum modulus:*

$$|\lambda_1| > |\lambda_2| \geq |\lambda_3| \geq \ldots \geq |\lambda_n|. \tag{9.64}$$

Form the sequence

$$\mathbf{u}_{r+1} = \mathbf{A}\mathbf{u}_r, \qquad r = 0, 1, \ldots, \tag{9.65}$$

starting with an arbitrary real vector $\mathbf{u}_0$ satisfying the restriction (9.68) *below. Then*

$$\lim_{r\to\infty} \frac{(\mathbf{u}_{r+1})_i}{(\mathbf{u}_r)_i} = \lambda_1, \tag{9.66}$$

provided this limit exists, where $(\mathbf{u}_r)_i$ denotes the ith element of $\mathbf{x}_r$. Also $\mathbf{u}_r$ tends to the eigenvector corresponding to λ_1 as r tends to infinity.

Proof: Since the $\mathbf{x}_j$ are linearly independent, we can find constants α_i such that

$$\mathbf{u}_0 = \alpha_1\mathbf{x}_1 + \alpha_2\mathbf{x}_2 + \ldots + \alpha_n\mathbf{x}_n. \tag{9.67}$$

We impose the condition

$$\alpha_1 \neq 0. \tag{9.68}$$

From (9.67),

$$\mathbf{u}_r = \mathbf{A}^r\mathbf{u}_0 = \alpha_1\lambda_1^r\mathbf{x}_1 + \alpha_2\lambda_2^r\mathbf{x}_2 + \ldots + \alpha_n\lambda_n^r\mathbf{x}_n, \tag{9.69}$$

and

$$\frac{(\mathbf{u}_{r+1})_i}{(\mathbf{u}_r)_i} = \lambda_1 \frac{\alpha_1(\mathbf{x}_1)_i + \alpha_2(\lambda_2/\lambda_1)^{r+1}(\mathbf{x}_2)_i + \ldots + \alpha_n(\lambda_n/\lambda_1)^{r+1}(\mathbf{x}_n)_i}{\alpha_1(x_1)_i + \alpha_2(\lambda_2/\lambda_1)^r(\mathbf{x}_2)_i + \ldots + \alpha_n(\lambda_n/\lambda_1)^r(\mathbf{x}_n)_i}. \quad (9.70)$$

Since $|\lambda_s/\lambda_1| < 1$ for $s = 2, \ldots, n$, we see immediately that (9.66) is true. From (9.69),

$$\mathbf{u}_r = \lambda_1^r\left\{\alpha_1\mathbf{x}_1 + \alpha_2\left(\frac{\lambda_2}{\lambda_1}\right)^r\mathbf{x}_2 + \ldots + \alpha_n\left(\frac{\lambda_n}{\lambda_1}\right)^r\mathbf{x}_n\right\}$$

so that $\mathbf{u}_r$ becomes proportional to $\mathbf{x}_1$ as $r \to \infty$.

Ex. 9.24. Use the iterative method to approximate the largest eigenvalue of

$$\mathbf{A} = \begin{bmatrix} 3 & -1 & 0 \\ -1 & 2 & -1 \\ 0 & -1 & 3 \end{bmatrix}.$$

Solution: We modify the procedure in the proof of the theorem slightly by extracting the largest element from $\mathbf{u}_r$ at each stage. Using an obvious notation,

$$\mathbf{u}_0 = \begin{bmatrix} 1 \\ 1 \\ 1 \end{bmatrix}, \quad \mathbf{u}_1 = \mathbf{A}\mathbf{u}_0 = \begin{bmatrix} 2 \\ 0 \\ 2 \end{bmatrix} = 2\begin{bmatrix} 1 \\ 0 \\ 1 \end{bmatrix} = 2\mathbf{w}_1, \quad \mathbf{A}\mathbf{w}_1 = 3\begin{bmatrix} 1.000 \\ -0.667 \\ 1.000 \end{bmatrix} = 3\mathbf{w}_2,$$

$$\mathbf{A}\mathbf{w}_2 = 3.667\begin{bmatrix} 1.000 \\ -0.909 \\ 1.000 \end{bmatrix}, \quad \mathbf{A}\mathbf{w}_3 = 3.909\begin{bmatrix} 1.000 \\ -0.977 \\ 1.000 \end{bmatrix}, \quad \mathbf{A}\mathbf{w}_4 = 3.977\begin{bmatrix} 1.000 \\ -0.994 \\ 1.000 \end{bmatrix}.$$

The convergence towards the exact $\lambda_1 = 4$, $\mathbf{x}_1 = [1 \quad -1 \quad 1]^T$ is clear.

From (9.70) we see that the rate at which the ratio in that equation approaches λ_1 will depend on $|\lambda_2/\lambda_1|$. The smaller this ratio, the more rapid the rate of convergence. If $|\lambda_2|$ is nearly equal to $|\lambda_1|$, the ratio in (9.70) may approach λ_1 very slowly as r tends to infinity. Various methods are available for accelerating the rate of convergence in a given problem, but these lie in the domain of numerical analysis, outside the scope of this book. There exist numerous ingenious extensions of the above iterative method, for instance, to the calculation of the second largest root once the largest root has been found, or to the calculation of the two largest roots of a real matrix if these are complex conjugate. Some aspects are covered in the exercises, but the reader is referred to textbooks on numerical analysis for a detailed treatment.

Ex. 9.25. Show by performing the numerical work that when finding the dominant eigenvalue of the matrix

$$\begin{bmatrix} 2 & -1 & 0 \\ -1 & 2 & -1 \\ 0 & -1 & 2 \end{bmatrix},$$

by iterating with $u_0 = [1 \quad 1 \quad 1]^T$ the rate of convergence is more rapid than would be expected from the ratio λ_2/λ_1. Show that if we use $u_0 = [1 \quad 0 \quad 0]^T$, the rate of convergence of the estimates of the eigenvector is given by λ_2/λ_1, but the rate of convergence of the eigenvalue is again more rapid than would be expected. Explain the reasons for these results.

Ex. 9.26. Let μ_r, ν_r denote the roots of

$$\lambda^2 + \alpha\lambda + \beta = 0$$

where α, β can be found from

$$(\mathbf{u}_{r+1})_i + \alpha(\mathbf{u}_r)_i + \beta(\mathbf{u}_{r-1})_i = 0$$

$$(\mathbf{u}_r)_i + \alpha(\mathbf{u}_{r-1})_i + \beta(\mathbf{u}_{r-2})_i = 0,$$

the notation being the same as in (9.66). Prove that under certain circumstances (to be stated) μ_r and ν_r tend to the two eigenvalues of $\mathbf{A}$ of largest modulus as r tends to infinity.

9.7 *The Iterative Solution of Simultaneous Linear Equations*

The method of Gaussian elimination is a "direct" method for solving a set of simultaneous linear equations, in which the solution is obtained by a finite number of operations. In contrast, the methods we discuss in this section start with an initial guess $\mathbf{x}^{(0)}$ to the solution of $\mathbf{Ax} = \mathbf{b}$, and define a sequence of successive approximations $\mathbf{x}^{(1)}, \mathbf{x}^{(2)}, \ldots$, which hopefully converge to the exact solution $\mathbf{x}$.

We start by describing two special classical iterative procedures. Suppose that the equations $\mathbf{Ax} = \mathbf{b}$ are scaled so that all the diagonal elements a_{ii} of $\mathbf{A}$ are unity.

(a) In the method of *simultaneous corrections* (Jacobi iteration), if we know the approximations $x_i^{(r)}$ to x_i at the rth stage, we obtain the estimates at the $(r + 1)$th stage from

$$x_i^{(r+1)} = -a_{i,1}x_1^{(r)} - \ldots - a_{i,i-1}x_{i-1}^{(r)} - a_{i,i+1}x_{i+1}^{(r)} - \ldots - a_{i,n}x_n^{(r)} + b_i. \quad (9.71)$$

(b) In the method of *successive corrections* (Gauss-Seidel iteration), in order to compute $x_i^{(r+1)}$ we make use of the estimates at the $(r + 1)$th stage that are available at that point in the calculation:

$$x_i^{(r+1)} = -a_{i,1}x_1^{(r+1)} - \ldots - a_{i,i-1}x_{i-1}^{(r+1)} - a_{i,i+1}x_{i+1}^{(r)} - \ldots - a_{i,n}x_n^{(r)} + b_i. \tag{9.72}$$

A general class of iterative procedures that includes these as special cases can be discussed in the following way. We split the matrix $\mathbf{A}$ in the form $\mathbf{A} = \mathbf{E} - \mathbf{F}$ and rearrange $\mathbf{Ax} = \mathbf{b}$ in the form

$$\mathbf{Ex} = \mathbf{Fx} + \mathbf{b}. \tag{9.73}$$

The iterative procedure we wish to discuss is obtained by writing

$$\mathbf{Ex}^{(r+1)} = \mathbf{Fx}^{(r)} + \mathbf{b}, \tag{9.74}$$

where $\mathbf{x}^{(r)}$ is the approximation to $\mathbf{x}$ at the rth stage, and we start by choosing $\mathbf{x}^{(0)}$ to be an arbitrary column vector. The matrix $\mathbf{E}$ must obviously be chosen to be nonsingular and for practical reasons it is clear that $\mathbf{E}$ should be chosen so that it is easy to solve any system of the form $\mathbf{Ex} = \mathbf{G}$. In (a) above, $\mathbf{E}$ is the unit matrix and $\mathbf{F}$ has zeros on its diagonal. In (b) above, $\mathbf{E}$ is lower triangular with units on the diagonal and $\mathbf{F}$ is upper triangular with zeros on the diagonal.

Instead of working in terms of the $\mathbf{x}^{(r)}$ it is often more convenient to work in terms of the corrections

$$\mathbf{c}^{(r+1)} = \mathbf{x}^{(r+1)} - \mathbf{x}^{(r)}.$$

The advantage of this is that if we subtract from (9.74) the same equation with $r - 1$ in place of r, we find

$$\mathbf{Ec}^{(r+1)} = \mathbf{Fc}^{(r)}$$

$$\mathbf{x}^{(r+1)} = \mathbf{x}^{(0)} + \mathbf{c}^{(1)} + \ldots + \mathbf{c}^{r+1}.$$

If we subtract (9.73) from (9.74) and introduce

$$\boldsymbol{\delta}^{(r)} = \mathbf{x}^{(r)} - \mathbf{x}, \tag{9.75}$$

this gives

$$\mathbf{E}\boldsymbol{\delta}^{(r+1)} = \mathbf{F}\boldsymbol{\delta}^{(r)} \quad \text{or} \quad \boldsymbol{\delta}^{(r+1)} = \mathbf{H}\boldsymbol{\delta}^{(r)}, \tag{9.76}$$

where we have introduced

$$\mathbf{H} = \mathbf{E}^{-1}\mathbf{F}. \tag{9.77}$$

DEFINITION **9.9.** A sequence of matrices $\mathbf{K}^{(r)} = [k_{ij}^{(r)}]$ is said to *converge to a matrix* $\mathbf{K} = [k_{ij}]$ as $r \to \infty$ if $k_{ij}^{(r)} \to k_{ij}$ for all i, j as $r \to \infty$.

THEOREM **9.17.** *A necessary and sufficient condition for* $\mathbf{x}^{(r)}$ *in* (9.74) *to converge to* $\mathbf{x}$, *a solution of* $\mathbf{Ax} = \mathbf{b}$, *for all starting vectors* $\mathbf{x}^{(0)}$, *is that* $\mathbf{H}^r \to \mathbf{0}$ *as* $r \to \infty$, *where* $\mathbf{H}$ *is defined in* (9.77).

Proof: From (9.76) we see that

$$\boldsymbol{\delta}^{(r)} = \mathbf{H}^r\boldsymbol{\delta}^{(0)}. \tag{9.78}$$

If $\mathbf{H}^r \to \mathbf{0}$, as $r \to \infty$, then $\boldsymbol{\delta}^{(r)} \to \mathbf{0}$, which from (9.75) means that $\mathbf{x}^{(r)} \to \mathbf{x}$ as $r \to \infty$. If $\mathbf{x}^{(r)} \to \mathbf{x}$ as $r \to \infty$, this means that $\boldsymbol{\delta}^{(r)} \to \mathbf{0}$ as $r \to \infty$. Since $\mathbf{x}^{(0)}$ is arbitrary, $\boldsymbol{\delta}^{(0)}$ is arbitrary, and from (9.78) this means that $\mathbf{x}^{(r)}$ cannot tend to the zero vector as $r \to \infty$ unless $\mathbf{H}^r \to \mathbf{0}$. This completes the proof.

DEFINITION **9.10.** The *spectral radius* $\rho(\mathbf{A})$ of a matrix $\mathbf{A}$ is the value of the modulus of the eigenvalue of maximum modulus,

$$\rho(\mathbf{A}) = \max_i |\lambda_i|. \tag{9.79}$$

When examining iterative procedures, Theorem 9.17 makes it clear that conditions under which $\mathbf{H}^r \to \mathbf{0}$ as $r \to \infty$ are of direct interest. It turns out that $\mathbf{H}^r \to \mathbf{0}$ as $r \to \infty$ if and only if the spectral radius of $\mathbf{H}$ is less than unity (see Ex. 11.25). Our theory so far enables us to prove only a special case of this general result:

THEOREM **9.18.** *If* $\mathbf{H}$ *has n linearly independent eigenvectors, then* $\mathbf{H}^r \to \mathbf{0}$ *as* $r \to \infty$ *if and only if* $\rho(\mathbf{H}) < 1$.

Proof: Let the n linearly independent eigenvectors of $\mathbf{H}$ be denoted by $\mathbf{x}_i$. Then an arbitrary vector $\mathbf{x}$ can be expanded in the form

$$\mathbf{x} = \alpha_1\mathbf{x}_1 + \ldots + \alpha_n\mathbf{x}_n.$$

This gives

$$\mathbf{H}^r\mathbf{x} = \alpha_1\lambda_1^r\mathbf{x}_1 + \ldots + \alpha_n\lambda_n^r\mathbf{x}_n. \tag{9.80}$$

If $\rho(\mathbf{H}) < 1$, then $\mathbf{H}^r\mathbf{x} \to \mathbf{0}$ as $r \to \infty$ for any $\mathbf{x}$. Hence, $\mathbf{H}^r \to \mathbf{0}$ as $r \to \infty$ for any $\mathbf{x}$. Conversely, if $\mathbf{H}^r \to \mathbf{0}$ as $r \to \infty$, then $\mathbf{H}^r\mathbf{x} \to \mathbf{0}$ as $r \to \infty$ for any $\mathbf{x}$ which implies, from (9.80), that $|\lambda_i| < 1$ for all i. Hence, $\rho(\mathbf{H}) < 1$.

We now introduce the notation

$$\mathbf{A} = \mathbf{L} + \mathbf{I} + \mathbf{U}, \tag{9.81}$$

where $\mathbf{L}$ is a lower triangular matrix with zeros on the diagonal, $\mathbf{I}$ is a unit matrix, and $\mathbf{U}$ is an upper triangular matrix with zeros on the diagonal. In this notation the methods of simultaneous and successive corrections, (9.71), (9.72), read

$$\mathbf{x}^{(r+1)} = -(\mathbf{L} + \mathbf{U})\mathbf{x}^{(r)} + \mathbf{b}, \tag{9.82}$$

$$(\mathbf{L} + \mathbf{I})\mathbf{x}^{(r+1)} = -\mathbf{U}\mathbf{x}^{(r)} + \mathbf{b}. \tag{9.83}$$

We examine a generalization of (9.83) known as the method of *successive over-corrections*, or *over-relaxation*, or *accelerated Gauss-Seidel:*

$$(\mathbf{L} + p\mathbf{I})\mathbf{x}^{(r+1)} = -\{(1 - p)\mathbf{I} + \mathbf{U}\}\mathbf{x}^{(r)} + \mathbf{b}, \tag{9.84}$$

where p is a constant that will be determined so as to yield the fastest rate of convergence. If we rearrange (9.84) in the form

$$\mathbf{x}^{(r+1)} = \mathbf{x}^{(r)} + w\{-\mathbf{L}\mathbf{x}^{(r+1)} - (\mathbf{I} + \mathbf{U})\mathbf{x}^{(r)} + \mathbf{b}\}, \tag{9.85}$$

where $w = 1/p$ is known as the *over-relaxation factor*, we see that $\mathbf{x}^{(r+1)}$ is obtained by adding to $\mathbf{x}^{(r)}$ a multiple of the residual or error at the given point in the calculation. As we shall see, it often turns out that the optimum value of w for most rapid convergence is greater than unity, and this is the reason for the name *over*-correction. The method of successive corrections is the special case $w = 1$ of (9.85).

Equations (9.80) and (9.78) indicate that, when $\mathbf{H}$ has n linearly independent eigenvectors, the error $\boldsymbol{\delta}^{(r)}$ will tend to zero rather slowly if $\rho(\mathbf{H})$ is nearly equal to unity, and it will tend to zero rapidly if $\rho(\mathbf{H})$ is much smaller than unity. (This is also true for general $\mathbf{H}$ as we shall see in Chapter 11, Ex. 11.25.)

We can compare the rates of convergence of different iterative procedures if we can compare the spectral radii. An instructive elementary discussion of rates of convergence can be given for the special case of a tridiagonal matrix, the elements of which are zero except on the principal diagonal and the immediately adjacent diagonals. This means that in (9.81), $\mathbf{L}$ and $\mathbf{U}$ have the forms

$$\mathbf{L} = \begin{bmatrix} 0 & 0 & \dots & 0 & 0 \\ l_1 & 0 & \dots & 0 & 0 \\ & & \dots & & \\ 0 & 0 & \dots & 0 & 0 \\ 0 & 0 & \dots & l_{n-1} & 0 \end{bmatrix}, \qquad \mathbf{U} = \begin{bmatrix} 0 & u_1 & \dots & 0 & 0 \\ 0 & 0 & \dots & 0 & 0 \\ & & \dots & & \\ 0 & 0 & \dots & 0 & u_1 \\ 0 & 0 & \dots & 0 & 0 \end{bmatrix}. \tag{9.86}$$

We shall compare the rates of convergence of (9.82) and (9.84). From the discussion connected with (9.77) this means that we wish to compare the largest eigenvalues of

$$-(\mathbf{L} + \mathbf{U}) \quad \text{and} \quad (\mathbf{L} + p\mathbf{I})^{-1}\{(1 - p)\mathbf{I} + \mathbf{U}\}.$$

In other words, we wish to compare the eigenvalues λ, μ defined by the equations

$$[(\mathbf{L} + \mathbf{U}) + \lambda\mathbf{I}]\mathbf{u} = \mathbf{0}, \tag{9.87}$$

$$[\{(1 - p)\mathbf{I} + \mathbf{U}\} + \mu(\mathbf{L} + p\mathbf{I})]\mathbf{v} = \mathbf{0}. \tag{9.88}$$

THEOREM **9.19.** *The values of the eigenvalues* λ, μ *defined by* (9.87), (9.88) *are related by:*

$$\{(1 - p) + \mu p\}^2 = \mu\lambda^2. \tag{9.89}$$

Proof: Let $\mathbf{E}$, $\mathbf{F}$ be diagonal matrices with nonzero diagonal elements. The following eigenvalue problem is completely equivalent to (9.88):

$$\mathbf{E}[\{(1 - p)\mathbf{I} + \mathbf{U}\} + \mu(\mathbf{L} + p\mathbf{I})]\mathbf{F}(\mathbf{F}^{-1}\mathbf{v}) = \mathbf{0}. \tag{9.90}$$

We are going to show that **E** and **F** can be chosen so that the matrix multiplying $\mathbf{F}^{-1}\mathbf{v}$ in (9.90) is identical with the matrix multiplying **u** in (9.87), i.e.,

$$\mathbf{E}[\{(1-p)\mathbf{I}+\mathbf{U}\}+\mu(\mathbf{L}+p\mathbf{I})]\mathbf{F}=k\{(\mathbf{L}+\mathbf{U})+\lambda\mathbf{I}\}$$

for some constant k. Because of the nature of **L**, **I**, **U** this implies that we must have

$$\mathbf{EUF}=k\mathbf{U},\qquad \mu\mathbf{ELF}=k\mathbf{L},$$
$$\{(1-p)+\mu p\}\mathbf{EF}=k\lambda\mathbf{I}.$$

It is easy to check that these equations are satisfied if

$$e_i f_{i+1}=k,\qquad \mu e_{i+1}f_i=k,\qquad i=1,\ldots,n-1,$$
$$e_i f_i=q,\qquad q=\frac{k\lambda}{\{(1-p)+\mu p\}},\qquad i=1,\ldots,n,$$

where e_i, f_i are the diagonal elements of **E**, **F**. These equations are consistent if (9.89) is true, which proves the theorem.

THEOREM **9.20.** *If the methods of Jacobi and Gauss-Seidel are applied to a tridiagonal system, either both methods converge or both diverge. If both converge, Gauss-Seidel converges faster than Jacobi.*

Proof: The Gauss-Seidel method corresponds to taking $p = 1$ in (9.84). Hence, the relation between the eigenvalues λ in the Jacobi method and μ in the Gauss-Seidel method, for the matrices that determine the rate of convergence, is given by $p = 1$ in (9.89), i.e., $\mu = \lambda^2$. The results stated in the theorem follow immediately.

THEOREM **9.21.** *If the Jacobi method converges when applied to a tridiagonal system with real eigenvalues and largest eigenvalue λ_1, the optimum value of p in the accelerated Gauss-Seidel method is given by*

$$p=p_1=\tfrac{1}{2}\{1+(1-\lambda_1^2)^{1/2}\},\tag{9.91}$$

and the corresponding eigenvalue μ_1 that determines the rate of convergence of the accelerated method is given by

$$\mu_1=\frac{1-(1-\lambda_1^2)^{1/2}}{1+(1-\lambda_1^2)^{1/2}}.\tag{9.92}$$

Proof: We have to find the value of p in (9.89) that gives the smallest μ for a given λ, $0 \le |\lambda| < 1$. Equation (9.89) is a quadratic in μ. Of the two roots we must choose the one such that $\mu = \lambda^2$ when $p = 1$ since, if $p = 1$, (9.89) gives

$\mu = 0$ or λ^2 but the eigenvalue μ of largest modulus is certainly not zero. This gives

$$\mu = \tfrac{1}{2}\lambda^2 w^2 - w + 1 + \tfrac{1}{2}\,|\lambda w|\,\{\lambda^2 w^2 - 4w + 4\}^{1/2},$$

where $w = 1/p$. The value of μ decreases as w increases until μ becomes complex, which occurs for $w_1 < w < w_2$ where w_1 and w_2 are the zeros of the quadratic under the square root. We find

$$w_1 = \frac{2}{1 + (1 - \lambda^2)^{1/2}}, \qquad w_2 = \frac{2}{1 - (1 - \lambda^2)^{1/2}}. \tag{9.93}$$

The reader can verify that $|\mu| = w - 1$ for $w_1 < w < w_2$ so that $|\mu|$ is then increasing with w, and the increase continues for $w > w_2$. Hence the minimum $|\mu|$ occurs for $w = w_1$ and it is given by $|\mu| = w_1 - 1$. Each eigenvalue of the tridiagonal system gives rise to a μ. We must choose the largest, which corresponds to taking $\lambda = \lambda_1$ in (9.93). The results in the theorem follow.

The value of the accelerated Gauss-Seidel method can be illustrated by supposing that $\lambda_1 = 1 - \varepsilon$, where ε is very small so that the ordinary Gauss-Seidel method converges very slowly. Then (9.92) gives

$$\mu_1 \approx \{1 - \sqrt{(2\varepsilon)}\}\{1 + \sqrt{(2\varepsilon)}\}^{-1} \approx 1 - 2\sqrt{(2\varepsilon)}.$$

If $\lambda_1 = 0.995$, $\varepsilon = 0.005$, then $\mu_1 \simeq 0.8$ and a remarkable increase in the rate of convergence is achieved.

As a broad rule, it is profitable to use iterative methods in preference to direct methods for solving simultaneous linear equations *only* when the number of equations is very large (say $n > 100$ or 1000) and when the coefficient matrix is *sparse*, i.e., it contains a large number of zero elements. In most cases where iteration is effective, the nonzero elements are near the diagonal, and the matrices are *diagonally dominant*, i.e., remembering that in our notation the diagonal elements of **A** are unity as in (9.81),

$$\sum_{j=1}^{n}{}' \,|a_{ij}| < 1, \qquad i = 1, \ldots, n, \tag{9.94}$$

where the prime indicates that the term $i = j$ is omitted. Such matrices occur when solving partial differential equations. When the coefficient matrix is *dense*, i.e., nearly all the elements are nonzero, it is generally better to use direct methods, in particular, Gaussian elimination.

Ex. 9.27. In the Jacobi method, $\boldsymbol{\delta}^{(r+1)} = -(\mathbf{L} + \mathbf{U})\boldsymbol{\delta}^{(r)}$, where the notation has been defined in (9.75), (9.81). Let E_r denote the maximum component of the error vector $\boldsymbol{\delta}^{(r)}$ and let σ denote the maximum value of the left hand side of (9.94) over all i. Show that $E_r < \sigma^r E_0$ so that the Jacobi method converges for diagonally dominant matrices.

Miscellaneous Exercises 9

Ex. 9.28. Show that the following matrix has the eigenvectors indicated, corresponding to eigenvalues $a + ib$ and $a - ib$.

$$\mathbf{A} = \begin{bmatrix} a & b \\ -b & a \end{bmatrix}, \quad \mathbf{x}_1 = \begin{bmatrix} 1 \\ i \end{bmatrix}, \quad \mathbf{x}_2 = \begin{bmatrix} 1 \\ -i \end{bmatrix}.$$

Ex. 9.29. Prove that the eigenvalues of a triangular matrix are the diagonal elements, and find the corresponding eigenvectors.

Ex. 9.30. Show that the matrix

$$\begin{bmatrix} k & 1 & 0 & \dots & 0 \\ 1 & k & 1 & \dots & 0 \\ 0 & 1 & k & \dots & 0 \\ & & \dots & & \\ 0 & 0 & 0 & \dots & k \end{bmatrix}$$

has eigenvectors $\mathbf{x}_i$ whose jth element is given by $\sin \{ij\pi/(n + 1)\}$. Deduce the corresponding eigenvalues.

Ex. 9.31. If $\mathbf{A}^2 = \mathbf{I}$, show that $(\mathbf{I} + \mathbf{A})\mathbf{x}$ and $(\mathbf{I} - \mathbf{A})\mathbf{x}$ are eigenvectors of $\mathbf{A}$, corresponding to eigenvalues 1, -1, respectively, where $\mathbf{x}$ is an arbitrary vector. If

$$\mathbf{A} = \begin{bmatrix} 0 & 0 & 1 & 0 \\ 0 & 0 & 0 & -1 \\ 1 & 0 & 0 & 0 \\ 0 & -1 & 0 & 0 \end{bmatrix},$$

show by inspection of $(\mathbf{I} + \mathbf{A})\mathbf{x}$ and $(\mathbf{I} - \mathbf{A})\mathbf{x}$ that there are two independent eigenvectors corresponding to each of the eigenvalues 1, -1.

Ex. 9.32. If $\mathbf{A}$ is a real square matrix of even order and $\det \mathbf{A} < 0$, prove that $\mathbf{A}$ has two real eigenvalues.

Ex. 9.33. Prove that the characteristic polynomial of $\mathbf{A} = \begin{bmatrix} \mathbf{B} & \mathbf{0} \\ \mathbf{0} & \mathbf{C} \end{bmatrix}$, where $\mathbf{B}$, $\mathbf{C}$ are square, is the product of the characteristic polynomials of $\mathbf{B}$ and $\mathbf{C}$. Investigate the relationship between the eigenvectors of $\mathbf{A}$, $\mathbf{B}$, $\mathbf{C}$.

Ex. 9.34. If $\mathbf{A}$ is $m \times n$ and $\mathbf{B}$ is $n \times m$, and if $\mathbf{ABx} = \lambda\mathbf{x}$ where $\lambda \neq 0$, show that $\mathbf{Bx}$ is an eigenvector of $\mathbf{BA}$ corresponding to the same eigenvalue. Show that $\mathbf{AB}$ and $\mathbf{BA}$ have the same eigenvalues except that the product which is of larger order has $|m - n|$ extra zero eigenvalues.

Ex. 9.35. Show that $\mathbf{A}$ and $\mathbf{A}^T$ have precisely the same numbers of linearly independent eigenvectors corresponding to a given eigenvalue.

Ex. 9.36. A *principal minor* of a matrix $\mathbf{A}$ is a minor whose diagonal is part of the diagonal of $\mathbf{A}$. Prove that the coefficient of λ^r in the characteristic polynomial of $\mathbf{A}$ is equal to $(-1)^r$ times the sum of all $(n - r)$-rowed principal minors of $\mathbf{A}$. Write out in this form the coefficient of λ when $n = 3$.

Ex. 9.37. If λ_1 is an eigenvalue of multiplicity k of a matrix $\mathbf{A}$ of order n, then there are *at most* k independent eigenvectors corresponding to λ_1. Give an example to show that there may be less than k.

Ex. 9.38. Show that every polynomial equation is the characteristic equation of some matrix. More specifically, show that

$$(-1)^n \begin{vmatrix} -a_1 - \lambda & -a_2 & \dots & -a_{n-1} & -a_n \\ 1 & -\lambda & \dots & 0 & 0 \\ 0 & 1 & \dots & 0 & 0 \\ & & \dots & & \\ 0 & 0 & \dots & 1 & -\lambda \end{vmatrix} = \lambda^n + a_1\lambda^{n-1} + \dots + a_n.$$

Ex. 9.39. Show that the difference equation

$$x_{r+1} = \alpha x_r + \beta x_{r-1} + \gamma x_{r-2}, \qquad r = 2, 3, \dots,$$

where x_0, x_1, and x_2 are given, can be written

$$\begin{bmatrix} x_{r+1} \\ y_{r+1} \\ z_{r+1} \end{bmatrix} = \begin{bmatrix} \alpha & \beta & \gamma \\ 1 & 0 & 0 \\ 0 & 1 & 0 \end{bmatrix} \begin{bmatrix} x_r \\ y_r \\ z_r \end{bmatrix}.$$

Indicate how x_{r+1} can be expressed in terms of x_0, x_1, x_2 if the eigenvalues and eigenvectors of a certain 3×3 matrix are known. What is the connection between this example and Ex. 9.38?

Ex. 9.40. If the rank of $\mathbf{A}$ is r, show that at least $n - r$ eigenvalues of $\mathbf{A}$ are zero. Give an example to show that more than $n - r$ eigenvalues may be zero.

Ex. 9.41. If an $n \times 1$ vector $\mathbf{x}$ is orthogonal to n linearly independent vectors $\mathbf{x}_1, \dots, \mathbf{x}_n$, then $\mathbf{x} = \mathbf{0}$.

Ex. 9.42. If $\mathbf{s}_1, \dots, \mathbf{s}_p$ are an orthonormal set of $n \times 1$ vectors

$$\mathbf{I} - \sum_{i=1}^{p} \mathbf{s}_i\mathbf{s}_i^H = \prod_{j=1}^{p} (\mathbf{I} - \mathbf{s}_j\mathbf{s}_j^H).$$

Ex. 9.43. If A, B, C, D, E are the points $(\frac{1}{2}, \frac{1}{2}, \frac{1}{2})$, $(1, 0, 0)$, $(0, 1, 0)$, $(0, 0, 1)$ and $(1, 1, 1)$, respectively, deduce, using (9.29), that the angles between AB, AC, AD, AE are all the same. Interpret this result geometrically.

Ex. 9.44. Prove that a matrix obtained by interchanging the rows of the unit matrix in any way is orthogonal.

Ex. 9.45. Find α, β, γ so that the following matrix is orthogonal.

$$\frac{1}{3}\begin{bmatrix} 2 & \alpha & 5/\sqrt{5} \\ 1 & \beta & -2/\sqrt{5} \\ 2 & \gamma & -4/\sqrt{5} \end{bmatrix}.$$

Ex. 9.46. If $\mathbf{A}$ is a diagonal unitary (orthogonal) matrix, show that the diagonal elements of $\mathbf{A}$ are of the form $e^{i\theta}(\pm 1)$.

Ex. 9.47. Prove that for the matrix $\mathbf{A}$, equation (2.54), in the Markov chain example in Section 2.5, the eigenvalues are 1.0, 0.6, 0.5, and the corresponding eigenvectors are the columns of the following matrix **P**:

$$\mathbf{P} = \tfrac{1}{20}\begin{bmatrix} 9 & 5 & -4 \\ 7 & -5 & 8 \\ 4 & 0 & -4 \end{bmatrix}, \qquad \mathbf{P}^{-1} = \begin{bmatrix} 1 & 1 & 1 \\ 3 & -1 & -5 \\ 1 & 1 & -4 \end{bmatrix}.$$

Show that

$$\lim_{k\to\infty} \mathbf{\Lambda}^k = \begin{bmatrix} 1 & 0 & 0 \\ 0 & 0 & 0 \\ 0 & 0 & 0 \end{bmatrix}, \qquad \lim_{k\to\infty} \mathbf{A}^k = \tfrac{1}{20}\begin{bmatrix} 9 \\ 7 \\ 4 \end{bmatrix}[1\ 1\ 1]$$

Verify that this agrees with the results given in Section 2.5. [See results leading up to (2.58).]

Ex. 9.48. If $\omega = \exp(2\pi i/3) = \frac{1}{2}(-1 + i\sqrt{3})$ so that $\omega^3 = 1$, $\omega^2 + \omega + 1 = 0$, and

$$\mathbf{A} = \begin{bmatrix} a & b & c \\ c & a & b \\ b & c & a \end{bmatrix},$$

show that the eigenvalues of **A** are given by $a + b + c$, $a + \omega b + \omega^2 c$, and $a + \omega^2 b + \omega c$. Deduce the corresponding eigenvectors and check that $\mathbf{P}^{-1}\mathbf{A}\mathbf{P} = \mathbf{\Lambda}$ in the notation of Theorem 9.12.

Ex. 9.49. For the matrix in Ex. 2.15 find the eigenvalues and verify from the form of $\mathbf{P}^{-1}\mathbf{A}\mathbf{P}$ that $\mathbf{A}^3 = pqr\mathbf{I}$.

Ex. 9.50. Let **P** denote the *permutation matrix*

$$\begin{bmatrix} 0 & 0 & \ldots & 0 & 1 \\ 1 & 0 & \ldots & 0 & 0 \\ & & \ldots & & \\ 0 & 0 & \ldots & 1 & 0 \end{bmatrix}$$

for which $a_{i+1,i} = 1$, $a_{1n} = 1$, and all other elements are zero. Prove that the characteristic polynomial is $\lambda^n - 1 = 0$. If $\mu = \exp(2\pi i/n)$, show that the eigenvectors are given by

$$\mathbf{x}_r = [\mu^r, \mu^{2r}, \ldots, \mu^{nr}]^T, \qquad r = 1, \ldots, n$$

corresponding to eigenvalues μ^{n-r}, respectively. Prove that these are orthogonal. Prove that

$$\mathbf{P}\mathbf{e}_i = \mathbf{e}_{i+1}, \quad i = 1, \ldots, n-1; \qquad \mathbf{P}\mathbf{e}_n = \mathbf{e}_1.$$

Deduce that if **A** is the *circulant*

$$\mathbf{A} = \begin{bmatrix} c_0 & c_{n-1} & \ldots & c_1 \\ c_1 & c_0 & \ldots & c_2 \\ & & \ldots & \\ c_{n-1} & c_{n-2} & \ldots & c_0 \end{bmatrix},$$

then $\mathbf{A} = f(\mathbf{P})$ where $f(x) = c_0 + c_1 x + \ldots + c_{n-1}x^{n-1}$. Deduce that the eigenvalues of **A** are given by $f(\mu^{n-r})$, $r = 1, \ldots, n$, with corresponding eigenvectors $\mathbf{x}_r$ defined above. (See also Ex. 11.33.)

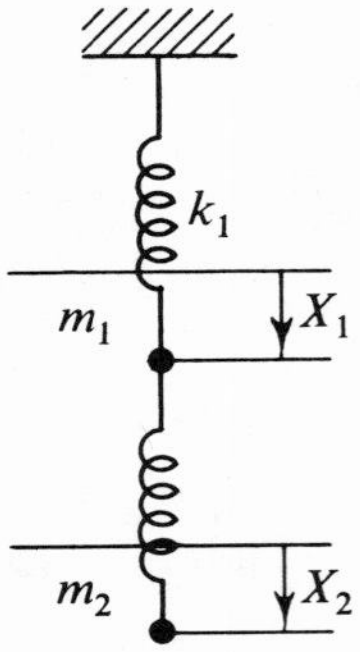

Figure 9.5 Masses on springs for Ex. 9.51.

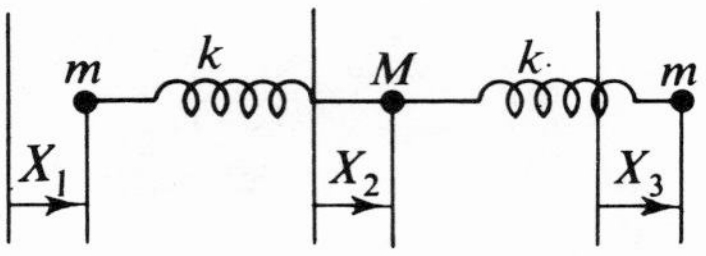

Figure 9.6 Linear triatomic molecule for Ex. 9.52.

Ex. 9.51. Two masses are suspended by weightless springs as shown in Figure 9.5. Show that the motion is governed by the equations

$$m_1 \frac{d^2X_1}{dt^2} = -k_1X_1 + k_2(X_2 - X_1),$$

$$m_2 \frac{d^2X_2}{dt^2} = -k_2(X_2 - X_1),$$

where k_1, k_2 are the spring constants. Show that the free vibrations of this system may be deduced from the solutions of an eigenvalue problem $\mathbf{Ax} = \lambda\mathbf{x}$, where

$$\mathbf{A} = \begin{bmatrix} \dfrac{(k_1 + k_2)}{m_1}, & \dfrac{-k_2}{m_1} \\ \dfrac{-k_2}{m_2}, & \dfrac{k_2}{m_2} \end{bmatrix}.$$

Find the frequencies and modes of free vibration if $m_1 = m_2$ and $k_1 = \frac{3}{2}k_2$.

Ex. 9.52. Establish the equations of motion for the linear triatomic molecule, shown diagrammatically in Figure 9.6 as two masses m attached by springs to a central mass M:

$$m \frac{d^2X_1}{dt^2} = -k(X_1 - X_2),$$

$$M \frac{d^2X_2}{dt^2} = k(X_1 - 2X_2 + X_3),$$

$$m \frac{d^2X_3}{dt^2} = -k(X_3 - X_2).$$

Deduce that there are three frequencies of free vibration given by

$$\omega_1 = 0, \qquad \omega_2 = \left(\frac{k}{m}\right)^{1/2}, \qquad \omega_3 = \left\{\frac{k(m + M)}{mM}\right\}^{1/2}.$$

What is the meaning of $\omega_1 = 0$? Find the modes of vibration.

Ex. 9.53. Consider the electrical circuit in Figure 9.7, for which the equations are

$$L_1 \frac{d^2 i_1}{dt^2} + M \frac{d^2 i_2}{dt^2} + \frac{i_1}{C_1} = 0,$$

$$M \frac{d^2 i_1}{dt^2} + L_2 \frac{d^2 i_2}{dt^2} + \frac{i_2}{C_2} = 0.$$

If we set $i_1 = x_1$, $i_2 = x_2$, $di_1/dt = x_3$, $di_2/dt = x_4$, show that the equations are equivalent to

$$\mathbf{B}\dot{\mathbf{x}} = \mathbf{E}\mathbf{x}, \qquad (*)$$

where

$$\mathbf{B} = \begin{bmatrix} \mathbf{I} & \mathbf{0} \\ \mathbf{0} & \mathbf{K} \end{bmatrix}, \qquad \mathbf{E} = \begin{bmatrix} \mathbf{0} & \mathbf{I} \\ \mathbf{C} & \mathbf{0} \end{bmatrix},$$

$$\mathbf{K} = \begin{bmatrix} L_1 & M \\ M & L_2 \end{bmatrix}, \qquad \mathbf{C} = \begin{bmatrix} -C_1^{-1} & 0 \\ 0 & -C_2^{-1} \end{bmatrix}.$$

Let $\Delta = L_1 L_2 - M^2$, and assume that $\Delta \neq 0$. (It is clear physically that $\Delta > 0$, and this assumption will be used later.) Then $\mathbf{K}^{-1}$ exists and (*) can be written

$$\dot{\mathbf{x}} = \mathbf{A}\mathbf{x},$$

$$\mathbf{A} = \mathbf{B}^{-1}\mathbf{E} = \begin{bmatrix} \mathbf{0} & \mathbf{I} \\ \mathbf{K}^{-1}\mathbf{C} & \mathbf{0} \end{bmatrix}.$$

Show that if the two eigenvalues of $\mathbf{K}^{-1}\mathbf{C}$ are denoted by λ_1, λ_2, the four eigenvalues of $\mathbf{A} - \lambda\mathbf{I}$ are given by $\pm\sqrt{\lambda_1}$, $\pm\sqrt{\lambda_2}$. Show that λ_1, λ_2 are the roots of the quadratic

$$\Delta C_1 C_2 \lambda^2 + (L_1 C_1 + L_2 C_2)\lambda + 1 = 0,$$

and that λ_1, λ_2 are real, unequal, and negative, on the assumption that $\Delta > 0$. Deduce that the solutions of the original differential equations are pure oscillations. [This result could be deduced more easily, of course, by simply substituting $i_r = a_r \exp(i\omega t)$, $r = 1, 2$, in the original differential equations. However, the present approach via eigenvalues and eigenvectors is valuable in more complicated situations, for instance, if we wish to compute transient solutions for given initial conditions, when resistance is present.]

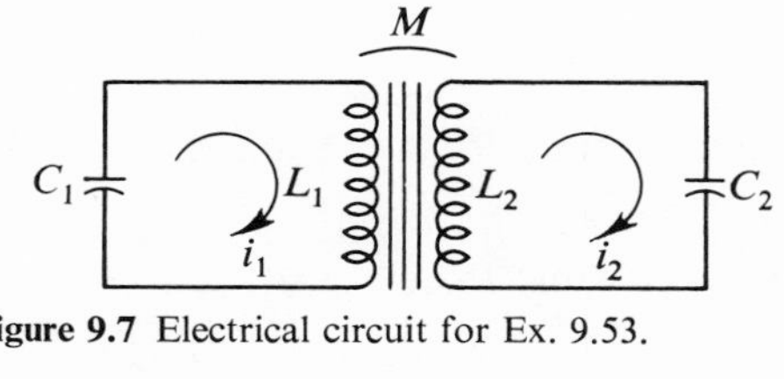

Figure 9.7 Electrical circuit for Ex. 9.53.

Ex. 9.54. Write an essay on applications of eigenvalues in any branch of applied science.

10 Unitary Transformations

10.1 Unitary Matrices

We remind the reader of the definition of a unitary matrix:

(DEFINITION 9.8.) A matrix $\mathbf{P}$ such that $\mathbf{P}^H\mathbf{P} = \mathbf{P}\mathbf{P}^H = \mathbf{I}$ is said to be a *unitary* matrix. As a special case, a real matrix $\mathbf{P}$ such that $\mathbf{P}^T\mathbf{P} = \mathbf{P}\mathbf{P}^T = \mathbf{I}$ is said to be an *orthogonal* matrix.

We have already met transformations of the type $\mathbf{P}^H\mathbf{A}\mathbf{P} = \mathbf{B}$ in Theorem 9.12. In this chapter we undertake a systematic study of such transformations.

DEFINITION **10.1.** If there exists a unitary matrix $\mathbf{P}$ such that $\mathbf{P}^H\mathbf{A}\mathbf{P} = \mathbf{B}$, the matrix $\mathbf{B}$ is said to be related to $\mathbf{A}$ by means of a *unitary transformation*.

One of the reasons why unitary transformations are important lies in the following theorem.

> THEOREM **10.1.** *If* $\mathbf{B}$ *is related to* $\mathbf{A}$ *through a unitary transformation then* $\mathbf{B}$ *and* $\mathbf{A}$ *have the same eigenvalues and the same characteristic equation.*

Proof: If $\mathbf{P}$ is unitary, then $\mathbf{P}^H\mathbf{P} = \mathbf{I}$ and $\det \mathbf{P}^H \det \mathbf{P} = 1$. If $\mathbf{P}^H\mathbf{A}\mathbf{P} = \mathbf{B}$, then

$$\begin{aligned}\det(\mathbf{B} - \lambda\mathbf{I}) &= \det(\mathbf{P}^H\mathbf{A}\mathbf{P} - \lambda\mathbf{I}) = \det \mathbf{P}^H(\mathbf{A} - \lambda\mathbf{I})\mathbf{P} \\ &= \det \mathbf{P}^H \det(\mathbf{A} - \lambda\mathbf{I}) \det \mathbf{P} = \det(\mathbf{A} - \lambda\mathbf{I}).\end{aligned}$$

Therefore $\mathbf{A}$ and $\mathbf{B}$ have the same characteristic equation, and hence the same eigenvalues.

As we shall see later, this theorem is the basis of many methods for computing eigenvalues, using a unitary transformation to change a matrix $\mathbf{A}$ into another matrix whose eigenvalues can be determined more easily. In particular, if $\mathbf{A}$ can be transformed into an upper triangular matrix $\mathbf{B}$, then the eigenvalues of $\mathbf{A}$ are simply the diagonal elements of $\mathbf{B}$.

The first part of this chapter leads up to the situation displayed diagrammatically in Figure 10.2 at the end of Section 10.3, where we characterize the matrices that can be reduced to diagonal form by means of a unitary transformation. Sections 10.5, 10.6 are concerned with unitary transformations that are useful for the computation of eigenvalues and eigenvectors. Section 10.7 introduces the concept of biorthogonality. Section 10.8 deals with singular values and vectors.

In the remainder of this section we list some properties of unitary matrices.

THEOREM **10.2.** (i) *The columns of a unitary (orthogonal) matrix constitute an orthonormal set. Similarly for the rows. Conversely, if a set of n orthonormal $n \times 1$ column vectors are assembled as the columns of a matrix, then the matrix is unitary (orthogonal if the vectors are real).*

(ii) *If* $\mathbf{P}$ *is unitary,* $|\det \mathbf{P}| = 1$.

(iii) *If* $\mathbf{P}$, $\mathbf{Q}$ *are unitary, so is* $\mathbf{PQ}$.

Proof: If $\mathbf{P} = [\mathbf{x}_1, \ldots, \mathbf{x}_n]$,

$$\mathbf{P}^H\mathbf{P} = \begin{bmatrix} \bar{\mathbf{x}}_1^T \\ \cdot \\ \cdot \\ \cdot \\ \bar{\mathbf{x}}_n^T \end{bmatrix} [\mathbf{x}_1, \ldots, \mathbf{x}_n] = \begin{bmatrix} (\mathbf{x}_1, \mathbf{x}_1) & (\mathbf{x}_1, \mathbf{x}_2) & \ldots & (\mathbf{x}_1, \mathbf{x}_n) \\ & & \ldots & \\ (\mathbf{x}_n, \mathbf{x}_1) & (\mathbf{x}_n, \mathbf{x}_2) & \ldots & (\mathbf{x}_n, \mathbf{x}_n) \end{bmatrix}.$$

If $\mathbf{P}$ is unitary, $\mathbf{P}^H\mathbf{P} = \mathbf{I}$ so that $(\mathbf{x}_i, \mathbf{x}_j) = 0$ $(i \neq j)$, 1 $(i = j)$, and the columns of $\mathbf{P}$ form an orthonormal set. Conversely, if the $\mathbf{x}_i$ form an orthonormal set, this gives $\mathbf{P}^H\mathbf{P} = \mathbf{I}$ so that $\mathbf{P}$ is unitary. For the rows, we consider $\mathbf{P}\mathbf{P}^H = \mathbf{I}$. To prove (ii), we note that since $\mathbf{P}^H\mathbf{P} = \mathbf{I}$ we have

$$\det \mathbf{P}^H\mathbf{P} = \det \mathbf{P}^H \det \mathbf{P} = |\det \mathbf{P}|^2 = 1.$$

To prove (iii),

$$(\mathbf{PQ})^H(\mathbf{PQ}) = \mathbf{Q}^H\mathbf{P}^H\mathbf{P}\mathbf{Q} = \mathbf{Q}^H\mathbf{Q} = \mathbf{I},$$

and similarly for $(\mathbf{PQ})(\mathbf{PQ})^H$, so that $\mathbf{PQ}$ is unitary.

THEOREM **10.3.** *Every eigenvalue of a unitary matrix has unit modulus.*

Proof: Let λ be an eigenvalue of a unitary matrix $\mathbf{A}$. Then $\mathbf{Ax} = \lambda\mathbf{x}$. Taking the complex conjugate of the transpose of both sides, we obtain $\bar{\mathbf{x}}^T\mathbf{A}^H = \bar{\lambda}\bar{\mathbf{x}}^T$. Hence,

$$(\bar{\lambda}\bar{\mathbf{x}}^T)(\lambda\mathbf{x}) = (\bar{\mathbf{x}}^T\mathbf{A}^H)(\mathbf{Ax}) = \bar{\mathbf{x}}^T\mathbf{x},$$

which gives $\bar{\lambda}\lambda = 1$, which is the result in the theorem.

Ex. 10.1. Show that if $\mathbf{A}$ is hermitian and $\mathbf{P}$ is unitary, then $\mathbf{P}^{-1}\mathbf{AP}$ is hermitian.

Ex. 10.2. If $\mathbf{P}$ is unitary, so are $\bar{\mathbf{P}}$, $\mathbf{P}^T$, and $\mathbf{P}^{-1}$.

Ex. 10.3. Verify that the following matrix $\mathbf{P}$ is unitary, and check that $|\det \mathbf{P}| = 1$, and that the eigenvalues of $\mathbf{P}$ have modulus unity.

$$\mathbf{P} = \frac{1}{2}\begin{bmatrix} 1+i & -1+i \\ 1+i & 1-i \end{bmatrix}.$$

Ex. 10.4. (i) If $\|\mathbf{Px}\| = \|\mathbf{x}\|$ for all $\mathbf{x}$, this implies that $(\mathbf{Px}, \mathbf{Py}) = (\mathbf{x}, \mathbf{y})$ for all $\mathbf{x}, \mathbf{y}$.

(ii) A matrix $\mathbf{P}$ is unitary if and only if $\|\mathbf{Px}\| = \|\mathbf{x}\|$ for all complex vectors $\mathbf{x}$.

(From Definition 9.3 if we interpret the equation $\mathbf{v} = \mathbf{Pu}$ as a transform of a vector $\mathbf{u}$ into a vector $\mathbf{v}$, these results mean that the transformation *leaves lengths and angles unchanged if and only if* $\mathbf{P}$ *is unitary, i.e., orthogonal in the real case.* In some sense $\mathbf{P}$ must therefore represent a "rotation" in n-dimensional space. This is explored further in the 2- and 3-dimensional case in Exs. 12.48–12.54.)

Ex. 10.5. If $\mathbf{P}$ is unitary, so is $\begin{bmatrix} \mathbf{I} & \mathbf{0} \\ \mathbf{0} & \mathbf{P} \end{bmatrix}$.

10.2 Gram-Schmidt Orthogonalization

Before we can make any further progress we require some additional results on orthogonal functions.

THEOREM **10.4.** (*Gram-Schmidt orthogonalization.*) *Given a set of s linearly independent vectors* $\mathbf{u}_1, \ldots, \mathbf{u}_s$ *we can construct an orthonormal set* $\mathbf{x}_1, \ldots, \mathbf{x}_s$ *where the* $\mathbf{x}_i$ *are suitable linear combinations of the* $\mathbf{u}_i$, $i = 1$ *to s.*

Proof: We shall prove this theorem by showing how the $\mathbf{x}_i$ can be constructed, using a method known as the *Gram-Schmidt orthogonalization procedure.* We shall form a sequence of functions $\mathbf{v}_1, \mathbf{v}_2, \ldots,$ in turn, from the $\mathbf{u}_i$, such that the $\mathbf{x}_i$ will be the normalized $\mathbf{v}_i$:

$$\mathbf{x}_i = \frac{\mathbf{v}_i}{\|\mathbf{v}_i\|}. \tag{10.1}$$

We start by choosing

$$\mathbf{v}_1 = \mathbf{u}_1, \qquad \mathbf{x}_1 = \frac{\mathbf{v}_1}{\|\mathbf{v}_1\|}.$$

We next choose the second vector $\mathbf{u}_2$ from the original set, and subtract from it a multiple of $\mathbf{x}_1$,

$$\mathbf{v}_2 = \mathbf{u}_2 - \alpha_1 \mathbf{x}_1, \tag{10.2}$$

where α_1 is chosen in such a way that $\mathbf{x}_1$ and $\mathbf{v}_2$ are orthogonal:

$$(\mathbf{x}_1, \mathbf{v}_2) = 0 = (\mathbf{x}_1, \mathbf{u}_2) - \alpha_1(\mathbf{x}_1, \mathbf{x}_1).$$

Since $(\mathbf{x}_1, \mathbf{x}_1) = 1$, this gives $\alpha_1 = (\mathbf{x}_1, \mathbf{u}_2)$ and

$$\mathbf{v}_2 = \mathbf{u}_2 - (\mathbf{x}_1, \mathbf{u}_2)\mathbf{x}_1, \qquad \mathbf{x}_2 = \frac{\mathbf{v}_2}{\|\mathbf{v}_2\|}. \tag{10.3}$$

The only way in which this construction would fail would be if $\mathbf{v}_2$ were identically zero. This, however, would imply the linear dependence of $\mathbf{u}_1$, $\mathbf{u}_2$, whereas it has been assumed in the theorem that $\mathbf{u}_1$ and $\mathbf{u}_2$ are independent. We next form $\mathbf{v}_3$ by subtracting multiples of $\mathbf{x}_1$ and $\mathbf{x}_2$ from the third given vector $\mathbf{u}_3$,

$$\mathbf{v}_3 = \mathbf{u}_3 - \alpha_2 \mathbf{x}_2 - \beta_1 \mathbf{x}_1, \tag{10.4}$$

where α_2, β_1 are determined in such a way that $\mathbf{v}_3$ is orthogonal to $\mathbf{x}_1$, $\mathbf{x}_2$. This gives

$$(\mathbf{x}_1, \mathbf{v}_3) = (\mathbf{x}_1, \mathbf{u}_3) - \beta_1 = 0, \qquad (\mathbf{x}_2, \mathbf{v}_3) = (\mathbf{x}_2, \mathbf{u}_3) - \alpha_2 = 0.$$

Hence,

$$\mathbf{v}_3 = \mathbf{u}_3 - (\mathbf{x}_2, \mathbf{u}_3)\mathbf{x}_2 - (\mathbf{x}_1, \mathbf{u}_3)\mathbf{x}_1, \qquad \mathbf{x}_3 = \frac{\mathbf{v}_3}{\|\mathbf{v}_3\|}. \tag{10.5}$$

Clearly the formula for the general $\mathbf{v}_r$ is

$$\mathbf{v}_r = \mathbf{u}_r - (\mathbf{x}_{r-1}, \mathbf{u}_r)\mathbf{x}_{r-1} - (\mathbf{x}_{r-2}, \mathbf{u}_r)\mathbf{x}_{r-2} - \cdots - (\mathbf{x}_1, \mathbf{u}_3)\mathbf{x}_1. \tag{10.6}$$

The only way in which this procedure could break down would be if $\mathbf{v}_r$ were identically zero for some r. From the method of formation of $\mathbf{v}_r$ it is clear that $\mathbf{v}_r$ is a linear combination of $\mathbf{u}_1, \ldots, \mathbf{u}_r$. If $\mathbf{v}_r$ is identically zero, this means that $\mathbf{u}_1, \ldots, \mathbf{u}_r$ are linearly dependent, contradicting the assumption in the theorem.

Two points should be noted in connection with the implementation of this theorem when solving simple numerical examples by hand:

(a) It is convenient to work throughout in terms of the $\mathbf{v}_r$, leaving the normalizations to the end, as illustrated in the following example. This means that the formulae we use are not quite the same as those developed in the proof.

(b) In any case, one should not try to memorize formulae for the method, since the principle behind the procedure tells us what to do at each stage.

Ex. 10.6. Form an orthonormal set from

$$\mathbf{u}_1 = \begin{bmatrix} 1 \\ 1 \\ 1 \\ -1 \end{bmatrix}, \qquad \mathbf{u}_2 = \begin{bmatrix} 2 \\ -1 \\ -1 \\ 1 \end{bmatrix}, \qquad \mathbf{u}_3 = \begin{bmatrix} -1 \\ 2 \\ 2 \\ 1 \end{bmatrix}.$$

Solution: We set $\mathbf{v}_1 = \mathbf{u}_1$ and then choose α so that

$$\mathbf{v}_2' = \mathbf{u}_2 - \alpha\mathbf{v}_1$$

is orthogonal to $\mathbf{v}_1$. (The reason for the prime will appear in a moment.) This gives $\alpha = (\mathbf{v}_1, \mathbf{u}_2)/(\mathbf{v}_1, \mathbf{v}_1)$, and we find $\alpha = -\frac{1}{4}$. For ease in computation, we compute $4\mathbf{v}_2'$ since then no fractions are involved.

$$4\mathbf{v}_2' = 4\mathbf{u}_2 + \mathbf{v}_1 = \begin{bmatrix} 9 \\ -3 \\ -3 \\ 3 \end{bmatrix} \quad \text{or} \quad \mathbf{v}_2 = \begin{bmatrix} 3 \\ -1 \\ -1 \\ 1 \end{bmatrix}.$$

The point here is that we are leaving normalizations to the end, so that we can choose, as $\mathbf{v}_2$, any convenient multiple of $\mathbf{v}_2'$. In a similar way we choose β, γ so that

$$\mathbf{v}_3' = \mathbf{u}_3 - \beta\mathbf{v}_1 - \gamma\mathbf{v}_2$$

is orthogonal to $\mathbf{v}_1$ and $\mathbf{v}_2$. This gives $\beta = \frac{1}{2}$, $\gamma = -\frac{1}{2}$, so we compute $2\mathbf{v}_3'$, again to avoid fractions:

$$2\mathbf{v}_3' = 2\mathbf{u}_3 - \mathbf{v}_1 + \mathbf{v}_2 = \begin{bmatrix} 0 \\ 2 \\ 2 \\ 4 \end{bmatrix} \quad \text{or} \quad \mathbf{v}_3 = \begin{bmatrix} 0 \\ 1 \\ 1 \\ 2 \end{bmatrix}.$$

Normalization of $\mathbf{v}_1$, $\mathbf{v}_2$, $\mathbf{v}_3$ gives, finally,

$$\mathbf{x}_1 = \frac{1}{2}\begin{bmatrix} 1 \\ 1 \\ 1 \\ -1 \end{bmatrix}, \quad \mathbf{x}_2 = \frac{1}{2\sqrt{3}}\begin{bmatrix} 3 \\ -1 \\ -1 \\ 1 \end{bmatrix}, \quad \mathbf{x}_3 = \frac{1}{\sqrt{6}}\begin{bmatrix} 0 \\ 1 \\ 1 \\ 2 \end{bmatrix}.$$

It is instructive to interpret the Gram-Schmidt procedure geometrically when $\mathbf{u}_1$, $\mathbf{u}_2$, $\mathbf{u}_3$ are 3×1 column vectors in three-dimensional space. The usual geometrical interpretation of scalar products already given at the beginning of Section 9.3 leads to the picture in Figure 10.1. The vectors $\overrightarrow{OP}$, $\overrightarrow{OQ}$ represent $\mathbf{u}_1$, $\mathbf{u}_2$ respectively, and $\mathbf{x}_1$ is a unit vector along OP. The line QR is perpendicular to OP so that

$$OR = OQ \cos\theta = (\mathbf{x}_1, \mathbf{u}_2),$$

where θ is the angle between $\mathbf{u}_1$ and $\mathbf{u}_2$. Hence, $(\mathbf{x}_1, \mathbf{u}_2)\mathbf{x}_1$ is a vector in the direction of $\mathbf{x}_1$ of length OR, i.e., it is the vector $\overrightarrow{OR}$ in Figure 10.1. The vector $\overrightarrow{OR}$ is known as the *projection* of $\overrightarrow{OQ}$ on $\overrightarrow{OP}$. We see that

$$\mathbf{v}_2 = \mathbf{u}_2 - (\mathbf{x}_1, \mathbf{u}_2)\mathbf{x}_1$$

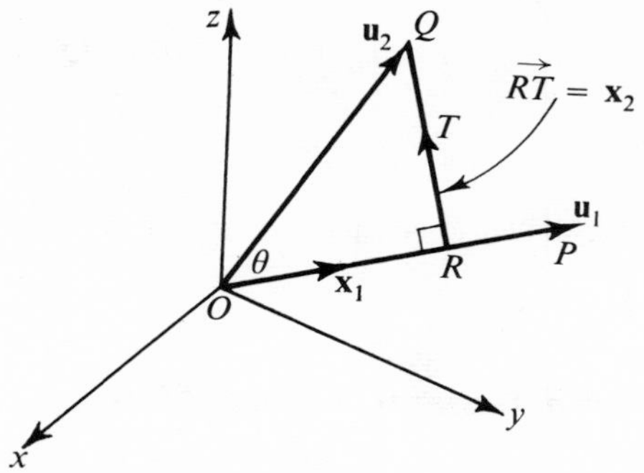

Figure 10.1 Gram-Schmidt orthogonalization.

is the vector $\overrightarrow{RQ}$ which, geometrically, is perpendicular to $\overrightarrow{OP}$, as we should expect. The vector $\mathbf{x}_2$ is a unit vector in the direction of $\overrightarrow{RQ}$. Summing up, the vector $\mathbf{x}_1$ is a unit vector in the direction of $\mathbf{u}_1$. The vector $\mathbf{x}_2$ is a unit vector in the plane of $\mathbf{u}_1$ and $\mathbf{u}_2$, perpendicular to $\mathbf{u}_1$. It is left to the reader to show similarly that $\mathbf{x}_3$ is a unit vector perpendicular to the plane of $\mathbf{u}_1$ and $\mathbf{u}_2$. What we are doing is constructing a set of three perpendicular unit vectors in three-space, starting from $\mathbf{u}_1, \mathbf{u}_2, \mathbf{u}_3$. The condition that $\mathbf{u}_1, \mathbf{u}_2, \mathbf{u}_3$ are linearly independent means geometrically that $\mathbf{u}_1, \mathbf{u}_2, \mathbf{u}_3$ are not coplanar, and this is a necessary condition for the construction to succeed.

We require one more theorem.

THEOREM **10.5.** *If* $\mathbf{u}_1, \ldots, \mathbf{u}_s$ *constitute an orthonormal set of* $n \times 1$ *vectors* $(s < n)$, *then vectors* $\mathbf{v}_1, \ldots, \mathbf{v}_{n-s}$ *exist such that*

$$\mathbf{Q} = [\mathbf{u}_1, \ldots, \mathbf{u}_s, \mathbf{v}_1, \ldots, \mathbf{v}_{n-s}] \tag{10.7}$$

is a unitary matrix.

Proof: Suppose that $\mathbf{w}_1, \ldots, \mathbf{w}_n$ are any linearly independent $n \times 1$ vectors. Consider the set of $n + s$ vectors

$$\mathbf{u}_1, \ldots, \mathbf{u}_s, \mathbf{w}_1, \ldots, \mathbf{w}_n.$$

We reduce this to a linearly independent set by the procedure described in the proof of Theorem 4.4(ii). The vectors $\mathbf{u}_1, \ldots, \mathbf{u}_s$ are linearly independent. If $\mathbf{w}_1$ is linearly independent of the preceding vectors $\mathbf{u}_1, \ldots, \mathbf{u}_s$, we include it in the set. Otherwise we exclude it. Proceeding in this way, we obtain a set of n vectors, say

$$\mathbf{u}_1, \ldots, \mathbf{u}_s, \mathbf{z}_1, \ldots, \mathbf{z}_{n-s}$$

such that any vector is linearly independent of the preceding vectors in the set. By means of the Gram-Schmidt orthogonalization procedure we can replace $\mathbf{z}_1, \ldots, \mathbf{z}_{n-s}$ by vectors $\mathbf{v}_1, \ldots, \mathbf{v}_{n-s}$ such that

$$\mathbf{u}_1, \ldots, \mathbf{u}_s, \mathbf{v}_1, \ldots, \mathbf{v}_{n-s}$$

is an orthonormal set. Hence, from Theorem 10.2, $\mathbf{Q}$ defined in (10.7) is a unitary matrix.

Ex. 10.7. Any k-dimensional space of $n \times 1$ column vectors possesses an orthonormal basis.

10.3 Reduction of a General Square Matrix to Triangular Form

It is clear that the formula $\mathbf{P}^H\mathbf{A}\mathbf{P} = \mathbf{\Lambda}$ (Theorem 9.12), which reduces a hermitian matrix $\mathbf{A}$ with distinct eigenvalues to diagonal form by means of a unitary transformation, is an extremely useful result. It is natural to ask:

(a) Are there any other types of matrix besides hermitian matrices with distinct eigenvalues that can be reduced to diagonal form by means of a unitary transformation?

(b) What is the simplest standard form to which a general matrix can be reduced by means of a unitary transformation?

In this section we first give a partial answer to the second question.

THEOREM **10.6.** *Any square matrix* $\mathbf{A}$ *can be reduced by a unitary transformation to an upper triangular matrix with the eigenvalues of* $\mathbf{A}$ *on the diagonal.*

Proof: Suppose that $\mathbf{A}$ has an eigenvalue λ_1 with a corresponding normalized eigenvector $\mathbf{x}_1$. In Theorem 10.5 we have shown that vectors $\mathbf{w}_2, \ldots, \mathbf{w}_n$ exist such that

$$\mathbf{Q} = [\mathbf{x}_1, \mathbf{w}_2, \ldots, \mathbf{w}_n] = [\mathbf{x}_1, \mathbf{W}] \tag{10.8}$$

is a unitary matrix, and this gives

$$\mathbf{Q}^H\mathbf{Q} = \begin{bmatrix} \mathbf{x}_1^H \\ \mathbf{W}^H \end{bmatrix} [\mathbf{x}_1, \mathbf{W}] = \begin{bmatrix} \mathbf{x}_1^H\mathbf{x}_1, & \mathbf{x}_1^H\mathbf{W} \\ \mathbf{W}^H\mathbf{x}_1, & \mathbf{W}^H\mathbf{W} \end{bmatrix} = \begin{bmatrix} 1 & \mathbf{0} \\ \mathbf{0} & \mathbf{I} \end{bmatrix},$$

so that $\mathbf{W}^H\mathbf{x}_1 = \mathbf{0}$. Hence, since $\mathbf{A}\mathbf{x}_1 = \lambda_1\mathbf{x}_1$,

$$\mathbf{Q}^H\mathbf{A}\mathbf{Q} = \begin{bmatrix} \mathbf{x}_1^H \\ \mathbf{W}^H \end{bmatrix} \mathbf{A}[\mathbf{x}_1, \mathbf{W}] = \begin{bmatrix} \mathbf{x}_1^H \\ \mathbf{W}^H \end{bmatrix} [\lambda_1\mathbf{x}_1, \mathbf{A}\mathbf{W}]$$

$$= \begin{bmatrix} \lambda_1 & \mathbf{A}\mathbf{W} \\ \mathbf{0} & \mathbf{W}^H\mathbf{A}\mathbf{W} \end{bmatrix} = \begin{bmatrix} \lambda_1 & \mathbf{B} \\ \mathbf{0} & \mathbf{C} \end{bmatrix}, \tag{10.9}$$

say. We proceed by induction. The theorem is true if $n = 2$ since (10.9) is already in the required form. Assume that $\mathbf{A}$ is $n \times n$ and the theorem is true for $n-1$. Then $\mathbf{C} = \mathbf{W}^H\mathbf{A}\mathbf{W}$ of (10.9) is of order $n-1$, and a unitary matrix $\mathbf{V}$ exists such that $\mathbf{V}^H\mathbf{C}\mathbf{V}$ is upper triangular. The matrix

$$\mathbf{U} = \begin{bmatrix} 1 & \mathbf{0} \\ \mathbf{0} & \mathbf{V} \end{bmatrix}$$

is unitary and

$$\mathbf{U}^H(\mathbf{Q}^H\mathbf{A}\mathbf{Q})\mathbf{U} = \begin{bmatrix} 1 & \mathbf{0} \\ \mathbf{0} & \mathbf{V}^H \end{bmatrix}\begin{bmatrix} \lambda_1 & \mathbf{B} \\ \mathbf{0} & \mathbf{C} \end{bmatrix}\begin{bmatrix} 1 & \mathbf{0} \\ \mathbf{0} & \mathbf{V} \end{bmatrix} = \begin{bmatrix} \lambda_1 & \mathbf{B}\mathbf{V} \\ \mathbf{0} & \mathbf{V}^H\mathbf{C}\mathbf{V} \end{bmatrix}.$$

Hence,

$$(\mathbf{Q}\mathbf{U})^H\mathbf{A}(\mathbf{Q}\mathbf{U})$$

is upper triangular. Since $\mathbf{QU}$ is unitary, $\mathbf{A}$ has been reduced to upper triangular form by a unitary transformation. The theorem follows by induction.

We are now in a position to characterize the class of matrices that can be reduced to diagonal form by a unitary transformation.

DEFINITION **10.2.** A matrix $\mathbf{A}$ is said to be *normal* if and only if

$$\mathbf{A}^H\mathbf{A} = \mathbf{A}\mathbf{A}^H.$$

Simple examples of normal matrices are unitary, hermitian, and skew-hermitian matrices, and diagonal matrices with arbitrary elements.

THEOREM **10.7.** *If* $\mathbf{P}$ *is unitary, then* $\mathbf{A}$ *is normal if and only if* $\mathbf{P}^H\mathbf{A}\mathbf{P}$ *is normal.*

Proof:

$$(\mathbf{P}^H\mathbf{A}\mathbf{P})^H(\mathbf{P}^H\mathbf{A}\mathbf{P}) = \mathbf{P}^H\mathbf{A}^H\mathbf{A}\mathbf{P},$$
$$(\mathbf{P}^H\mathbf{A}\mathbf{P})(\mathbf{P}^H\mathbf{A}\mathbf{P})^H = \mathbf{P}^H\mathbf{A}\mathbf{A}^H\mathbf{P}.$$

These show that if $\mathbf{A}^H\mathbf{A} = \mathbf{A}\mathbf{A}^H$, then $(\mathbf{P}^H\mathbf{A}\mathbf{P})^H(\mathbf{P}^H\mathbf{A}\mathbf{P}) = (\mathbf{P}^H\mathbf{A}\mathbf{P})(\mathbf{P}^H\mathbf{A}\mathbf{P})^H$, and conversely, which is the required result.

We now come to the basic result which answers question (a) at the beginning of this section.

THEOREM **10.8.** *A matrix* $\mathbf{A}$ *can be reduced to a diagonal matrix by a unitary transformation if and only if* $\mathbf{A}$ *is normal.*

Proof: Suppose that a unitary matrix $\mathbf{P}$ exists such that $\mathbf{P}^H\mathbf{A}\mathbf{P} = \mathbf{D}$, where $\mathbf{D}$ is a diagonal matrix. Then $\mathbf{A} = \mathbf{P}\mathbf{D}\mathbf{P}^H$ and

$$\mathbf{A}^H\mathbf{A} = \mathbf{P}\mathbf{D}^H\mathbf{D}\mathbf{P}, \qquad \mathbf{A}\mathbf{A}^H = \mathbf{P}\mathbf{D}\mathbf{D}^H\mathbf{P}.$$

But $\mathbf{D}^H\mathbf{D} = \mathbf{D}\mathbf{D}^H$ since diagonal matrices commute. Hence, $\mathbf{A}$ is normal. Conversely, suppose that $\mathbf{A}$ is normal. Theorem 10.6 shows that a unitary

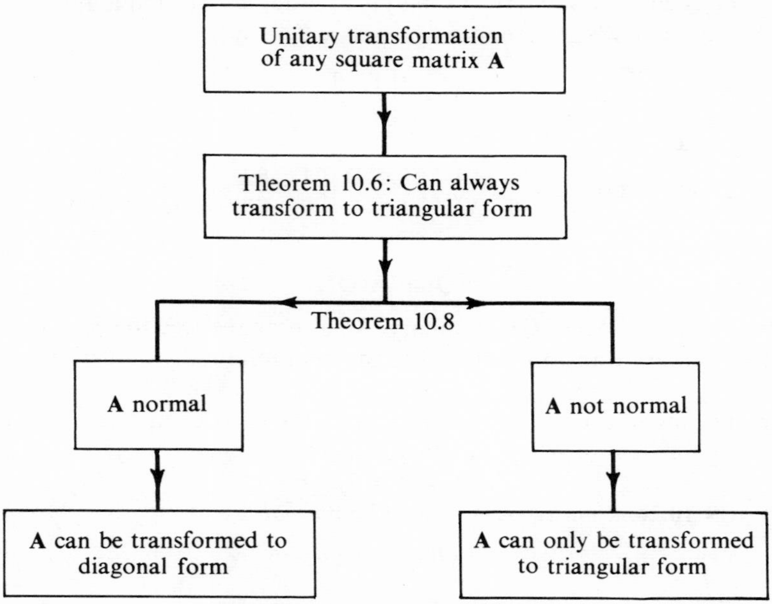

Figure 10.2 Unitary transformations.

matrix $\mathbf{Q}$ exists such that $\mathbf{Q}^H\mathbf{A}\mathbf{Q} = \mathbf{B}$, where $\mathbf{B}$ is upper triangular. From Theorem 10.7, $\mathbf{B}$ must also be normal. If $\mathbf{B} = [b_{ij}]$, we have $b_{ij} = 0$ for $i > j$, and we see that the (i, i) elements on the two sides of the equation $\mathbf{B}^H\mathbf{B} = \mathbf{B}\mathbf{B}^H$ give

$$\bar{b}_{ii}b_{ii} = \sum_{j=1}^{n} \bar{b}_{ij}b_{ij} = \bar{b}_{ii}b_{ii} + \sum_{j=i+1}^{n} |b_{ij}|^2.$$

Hence, $|b_{ij}| = 0$, $i < j$, so that $b_{ij} = 0$ for all off-diagonal elements of $\mathbf{B}$, which proves the required result.

Theorems 10.6, 10.8 give a comparatively simple answer to the question of what can be done by unitary transformations. The position is summarized in Figure 10.2.

Ex. 10.8. Prove that if $\mathbf{A}$ is normal with an eigenvector $\mathbf{x}_i$ corresponding to the eigenvalue λ_i, then $\mathbf{x}_i$ is also an eigenvector of $\mathbf{A}^H$, corresponding to the eigenvalue $\bar{\lambda}_i$. Eigenvectors of $\mathbf{A}$ associated with distinct eigenvalues are orthogonal.

Ex. 10.9. Prove that the number of independent eigenvectors of a normal matrix corresponding to an eigenvalue λ_i is equal to the multiplicity of λ_i. Give an example to show that this is not necessarily true if $\mathbf{A}$ is not normal.

10.4 Reduction of Hermitian Matrices to Diagonal Form

Since hermitian matrices are normal (Definition 10.2), we see immediately from Theorem 10.8 that a unitary transformation exists which reduces a hermitian matrix to a diagonal matrix. It is instructive to obtain this result more directly by modifying the proof of Theorem 10.6.

THEOREM **10.9.** *If* **A** *is hermitian, there exists a unitary matrix* **P** *such that* $\mathbf{P}^H\mathbf{AP}$ *is a diagonal matrix whose diagonal elements are the eigenvalues of* **A**.

Proof: We introduce the matrix **Q** defined in (10.8) and proceed as in the proof of Theorem 10.6 until we reach (10.9),

$$\mathbf{Q}^H\mathbf{AQ} = \begin{bmatrix} \lambda_1 & \mathbf{B} \\ \mathbf{0} & \mathbf{C} \end{bmatrix}.$$

Since **A** is hermitian, $\mathbf{Q}^H\mathbf{AQ}$ is hermitian [Theorem 9.6(iii)]. Hence, **B** must be zero and

$$\mathbf{Q}^H\mathbf{AQ} = \begin{bmatrix} \lambda_1 & \mathbf{0} \\ \mathbf{0} & \mathbf{C} \end{bmatrix}. \tag{10.10}$$

The proof then proceeds by induction, as in the proof of Theorem 10.6.

We can now prove

THEOREM **10.10.** (i) *A hermitian matrix of order n has n linearly independent eigenvectors.*

(ii) *A hermitian matrix of order n possesses an orthonormal set of eigenvectors.*

(iii) *If an eigenvalue* λ_1 *is of multiplicity s, it has associated with it precisely s linearly independent eigenvectors. These can be taken to be orthogonal.*

Proof: From Theorem 10.9, a unitary matrix **P** exists such that $\mathbf{P}^H\mathbf{AP} = \mathbf{\Lambda}$ where $\mathbf{\Lambda}$ is diagonal and $\mathbf{P}^H = \mathbf{P}^{-1}$. This gives

$$\mathbf{AP} = \mathbf{P\Lambda}. \tag{10.11}$$

If $\mathbf{P} = [\mathbf{x}_1, \ldots, \mathbf{x}_n]$ and the *i*th diagonal element of $\mathbf{\Lambda}$ is denoted by λ_i, then (10.11) yields

$$\mathbf{Ax}_i = \lambda_i\mathbf{x}_i$$

so that $\mathbf{x}_i$ is an eigenvector corresponding to an eigenvalue λ_i. Since **P** is nonsingular, the $\mathbf{x}_i$ are linearly independent, which completes the proof of (i). The eigenvectors are the columns of the unitary matrix **P**, so that they form an orthonormal set, which proves (ii). From Theorem 10.1 the matrices **A** and **Λ** have the same characteristic equation so that the eigenvalue λ_1 of multiplicity s must occur exactly s times along the diagonal of **Λ**, so that there are precisely s linearly independent (and orthogonal) eigenvectors associated with λ_1.

The reason for keeping (i) separate from (ii) in this theorem is that, in practice, when we are finding the eigenvectors associated with a repeated eigenvalue, it may be convenient to find a set of linearly independent vectors and then orthogonalize them by means of the Gram-Schmidt procedure.

Ex. 10.10. Find an orthonormal set of eigenvectors for

$$\mathbf{A} = \begin{bmatrix} 7 & -16 & -8 \\ -16 & 7 & 8 \\ -8 & 8 & -5 \end{bmatrix}. \tag{10.12}$$

Solution: The characteristic polynomial is found to be

$$\lambda^3 - 9\lambda^2 - 405\lambda - 2187 = 0,$$

with roots $\lambda_1 = 27$, $\lambda_2 = \lambda_3 = -9$. The equations $(\mathbf{A} - \lambda_1\mathbf{I})\mathbf{x} = \mathbf{0}$ readily yield precisely one eigenvalue, as we should expect, since λ_1 is a simple root:

$$\mathbf{x}_1 = \alpha\begin{bmatrix} -2 \\ 2 \\ 1 \end{bmatrix},$$

where α is an arbitrary constant. The equations $(\mathbf{A} - \lambda_2\mathbf{I})\mathbf{x} = \mathbf{0}$ reduce to a single equation

$$2x_1 - 2x_2 - x_3 = 0. \tag{10.13}$$

This gives a two-fold infinity of solutions as we should expect, since λ_2 has multiplicity 2. For $\mathbf{x}_2$ we can choose any solution of this equation, say

$$\mathbf{x}_2 = \beta\begin{bmatrix} 1 \\ 1 \\ 0 \end{bmatrix},$$

where β is an arbitrary constant. The third eigenvector must satisfy (10.13) and it must also be orthogonal to $\mathbf{x}_2$, i.e.,

$$x_1 + x_2 = 0. \tag{10.14}$$

The solution of (10.13), (10.14) gives

$$\mathbf{x}_3 = \gamma\begin{bmatrix} 1 \\ -1 \\ 4 \end{bmatrix},$$

where γ is an arbitrary constant. It is left to the reader to form **P** and verify that $\mathbf{P}^T\mathbf{A}\mathbf{P}$ is a diagonal matrix with diagonal elements 27, −9, −9.

10.5 The Methods of Jacobi and Givens

The only method we have given so far for the determination of the eigenvalues of a matrix is to evaluate its characteristic polynomial, and find the roots of this polynomial. There are two serious objections to this procedure when determining the eigenvalues of matrices on a digital computer:

(a) It is inefficient if the order of the matrix is greater than about four or five.

(b) It is ill-conditioned in a sense similar to that defined in connection with simultaneous linear equations. The results are inaccurate due to rounding errors even though the eigenvalues are well-defined by the given matrix.

A detailed discussion of the numerical determination of eigenvalues and eigenvectors lies outside this book, but it is relevant to the subject matter of this chapter to discuss the methods of Jacobi, Givens, and Householder, which use unitary transformations to reduce a matrix to a simpler form. Unitary transformations are particularly stable in numerical work. Intuitively this is because a unitary matrix **P** and its inverse have orthogonal rows and columns, maximum elements of order unity in each row and column, and determinants of magnitude unity. For simplicity, we consider only real symmetric matrices **A**.

Let e_{rs} denote the (r, s) element of the unit matrix. We define a *plane rotation matrix* $\mathbf{R}_{ij}$ to be a matrix obtained from the unit matrix by making the following replacements for the four elements in the ith and jth rows and columns of the unit matrix:

$$\begin{bmatrix} e_{ii} & e_{ij} \\ e_{ji} & e_{jj} \end{bmatrix} \rightarrow \begin{bmatrix} \cos\theta & -\sin\theta \\ \sin\theta & \cos\theta \end{bmatrix} \tag{10.15}$$

that is,

$$\mathbf{R}_{ij} = \begin{bmatrix} 1 & \cdots & 0 & \cdots & 0 & \cdots & 0 \\ & & & \cdots & & & \\ 0 & \cdots & \cos\theta & \cdots & -\sin\theta & \cdots & 0 \\ & & & \cdots & & & \\ 0 & \cdots & \sin\theta & \cdots & \cos\theta & \cdots & 0 \\ & & & \cdots & & & \\ 0 & \cdots & 0 & \cdots & 0 & \cdots & 1 \end{bmatrix}. \tag{10.16}$$

[The reason for the name "rotation matrix" is that, as we shall see in Section 12.1, the 2×2 matrix on the right of (10.15) represents a rotation of axes through an angle θ in two dimensions.]

It is easy to check that $\mathbf{R}_{ij}$ is orthogonal,

$$\mathbf{R}_{ij}\mathbf{R}_{ij}^T = \mathbf{R}_{ij}^T\mathbf{R}_{ij} = \mathbf{I}. \tag{10.17}$$

If we set

$$\mathbf{B} = \mathbf{R}^T\mathbf{A}\mathbf{R}, \tag{10.18}$$

the elements of **A** and **B** are the same except for the elements in the ith and jth rows and columns, for which

$$b_{ik} = b_{ki} = a_{ik}\cos\theta + a_{jk}\sin\theta, \qquad k \neq i, j, \tag{10.19}$$

$$b_{jk} = b_{kj} = -a_{ik}\sin\theta + a_{jk}\cos\theta, \qquad k \neq i, j, \tag{10.20}$$

$$b_{ii} = a_{ii}\cos^2\theta + 2a_{ij}\sin\theta\cos\theta + a_{jj}\sin^2\theta, \tag{10.21}$$

$$b_{jj} = a_{ii}\sin^2\theta - 2a_{ij}\sin\theta\cos\theta + a_{jj}\cos^2\theta, \tag{10.22}$$

$$b_{ij} = b_{ji} = a_{ij}\cos 2\theta + \tfrac{1}{2}(a_{jj} - a_{ii})\sin 2\theta. \tag{10.23}$$

We shall discuss the version of Jacobi's method in which we pick the largest off-diagonal element a_{ij}, and choose θ so that the (i, j) element in **B** is zero, i.e., from (10.23) we determine θ from

$$\tan 2\theta = \frac{2a_{ij}}{a_{ii} - a_{jj}}. \tag{10.24}$$

If the resulting matrix is denoted by $\mathbf{A}_1$, the procedure is repeated. Reduce the largest off-diagonal element of $\mathbf{A}_1$ to zero by an orthogonal transformation involving another plane rotation matrix. The (i, j) element that was reduced to zero in $\mathbf{A}_1$ will no longer be zero in $\mathbf{A}_2$. However, we prove in the following theorem that if this procedure is repeated indefinitely, the limit of the sequence $\mathbf{A}_r$ as r tends to infinity will be a diagonal matrix $\mathbf{\Lambda}$ with the eigenvalues of **A** as its diagonal elements.

THEOREM **10.11.** *Let* **A** *be real symmetric with eigenvalues* λ_i, *and define a sequence* $\mathbf{A}_1, \mathbf{A}_2, \ldots$ *by*

$$\mathbf{A}_{s+1} = \mathbf{R}_s^T\mathbf{A}_s\mathbf{R}_s, \qquad s = 0, 1, \ldots, \qquad \mathbf{A}_0 = \mathbf{A}, \tag{10.25}$$

where $\mathbf{R}_s$ *is a plane rotation matrix of the form* (10.16) *defined so that the maximum off-diagonal element of* $\mathbf{A}_s$ *is reduced to zero in* $\mathbf{A}_{s+1}$. *Then* $\mathbf{A}_s \to \mathbf{\Lambda}$ *as* $s \to \infty$, *where* $\mathbf{\Lambda}$ *is a diagonal matrix with diagonal elements* λ_i.

Proof: Consider (10.18). From (10.19), (10.20) we have

$$b_{ik}^2 + b_{jk}^2 = a_{ik}^2 + a_{jk}^2, \qquad k \neq i, j.$$

Since θ is chosen so that $b_{ij} = 0$, this gives

$$\sum b_{pq}^2 = \sum a_{pq}^2 - 2a_{ij}^2, \tag{10.26}$$

where the sums are taken over all off-diagonal elements. (Remember that $a_{\alpha\beta} = b_{\alpha\beta}$ if α, β are different from i, j.) Since a_{ij} is the largest off-diagonal element,

$$a_{ij}^2 \geq \frac{1}{n^2 - n}\sum a_{pq}^2, \tag{10.27}$$

so that (10.26) gives

$$\sum b_{pq}^2 \leq \left(1 - \frac{2}{n^2 - n}\right) \sum a_{pq}^2,$$

where in all cases the sums are taken over all off-diagonal elements. On applying these results to the sequence defined in (10.25), we see that

$$(\sum a_{pq}^2)_s \leq \left(1 - \frac{2}{n^2 - n}\right)^s (\sum a_{pq}^2)_0 \tag{10.28}$$

where $(\ )_s$ denotes the sum of the off-diagonal elements in $\mathbf{A}_s$. Since the right-hand side of (10.28) tends to zero as s tends to infinity, this means that the off-diagonal elements of $\mathbf{A}_s$ tend to zero as s tends to infinity, i.e., $\mathbf{A}_s$ tends to a diagonal form. Also,

$$\mathbf{A}_s = (\mathbf{R}_1 \ldots \mathbf{R}_s)^T \mathbf{A} (\mathbf{R}_1 \ldots \mathbf{R}_s) = \mathbf{P}_s^T \mathbf{A} \mathbf{P}_s \tag{10.29}$$

where $\mathbf{P}_s$ is orthogonal, so that the limit of $\mathbf{A}_s$ as s tends to infinity must be $\mathbf{\Lambda}$ as stated in the theorem.

Since a search to find the largest element is time-consuming, it is often more efficient to simply carry out the Jacobi process systematically, working along the elements in, say, the 1st, 2nd, . . . rows in turn. This is known as the *cyclic Jacobi procedure*. A complete sweep requires $\frac{1}{2}n(n - 1)$ plane rotations. In a variant known as the *threshold* Jacobi method, elements are reduced to zero only if they are greater than some prescribed value δ_s at the sth iteration, where δ_s can be decreased as s increases. It seems that if the diagonal elements in $\mathbf{A}$ are the largest in each row and column, less than about 10 sweeps will often reduce the off-diagonal elements to less than 10^{-6} of their original values, for matrices of order 20. The reason why convergence is very rapid once the off-diagonal elements begin to become small can be seen from the following example.

Ex. 10.11. If

$$\mathbf{A} = \begin{bmatrix} a_1 & \varepsilon_1 & \varepsilon_2 \\ \varepsilon_1 & a_2 & \varepsilon_3 \\ \varepsilon_2 & \varepsilon_3 & a_3 \end{bmatrix}$$

where all the ε_i are small compared with any of the a_i, show that the angle required to reduce the (1, 2) element to zero is given by $\theta \approx \varepsilon_1/(a_1 - a_2)$, so that $\sin\theta \approx \varepsilon_1/(a_1 - a_2)$. Show that

$$\mathbf{R}_{12}^T \mathbf{A} \mathbf{R}_{12} \approx \begin{bmatrix} a_1 + \dfrac{\varepsilon_1^2}{a_1 - a_2}, & 0, & \varepsilon_2 + \dfrac{\varepsilon_1\varepsilon_3}{a_1 - a_2} \\ 0, & a_2 - \dfrac{\varepsilon_1^2}{a_1 - a_2}, & \varepsilon_3 - \dfrac{\varepsilon_1\varepsilon_2}{a_1 - a_2} \\ \varepsilon_2 + \dfrac{\varepsilon_1\varepsilon_3}{a_1 - a_2}, & \varepsilon_3 - \dfrac{\varepsilon_1\varepsilon_2}{a_1 - a_2}, & a_3 \end{bmatrix}.$$

After a complete sweep, show that the transformed **A** has the form

$$\begin{bmatrix} a_1 + O(\varepsilon^2) & O(\varepsilon^2) & O(\varepsilon^2) \\ O(\varepsilon^2) & a_2 + O(\varepsilon^2) & O(\varepsilon^2) \\ O(\varepsilon^2) & O(\varepsilon^2) & a_3 + O(\varepsilon^2) \end{bmatrix},$$

where the notation $O(\varepsilon^2)$ means that if $\delta = O(\varepsilon^2)$, then $|\delta| \leq C\varepsilon^2$, for some constant C, where, in the present instance, $\varepsilon = \max(\varepsilon_1, \varepsilon_2, \varepsilon_3)$. In the terminology of iterative procedures, the meaning of this result is that the convergence of Jacobi iteration is *quadratic*, once the off-diagonal elements are small enough.

Ex. 10.12. Show that about $8n$ multiplications are required to form $\mathbf{P}_{s+1}$ and $\mathbf{A}_{s+1}$ from $\mathbf{P}_s$ and $\mathbf{A}_s$ [see (10.25), (10.29)]. Hence, if k sweeps are required to make the off-diagonal elements acceptably small, show that about $4kn^3$ multiplications are required to determine all the eigenvalues and eigenvectors.

In the Jacobi method the element b_{ij} in (10.18) was reduced to zero. In the Givens method a plane rotation is used to reduce a b_{rj} to zero, $r \neq i$. From (10.20) this means that θ is chosen so that

$$\tan \theta = \frac{a_{jr}}{a_{ir}}. \tag{10.30}$$

For simplicity, suppose that we always choose $r = i - 1$. Also $i \neq j$. Suppose that $\mathbf{A}_1 = \mathbf{R}_1^T\mathbf{A}\mathbf{R}_1$, where $\mathbf{R}_1$ is a plane rotation that reduces a_{13} to zero by choosing $r = 1, i = 2, j = 3$ in (10.30) and (10.19)–(10.23). Suppose that next we form $\mathbf{A}_2 = \mathbf{R}_2^T\mathbf{A}_1\mathbf{R}_2$, where $\mathbf{R}_2$ is a plane rotation that reduces the $(1, 4)$ element in $\mathbf{A}_1$ to zero, i.e., $r = 1, i = 2, j = 4$ in (10.30), etc. This will involve altering the second and fourth rows and columns in $\mathbf{A}_1$, i.e., the $(1, 3)$ element of $\mathbf{A}_1$, which is zero, *remains zero*. By repeating with $r = 1, i = 2, j = 5, 6, \ldots,$ we can use $n - 2$ plane rotations to transform **A** into a matrix in which the $n - 2$ elements in the $(1, 3), (1, 4), \ldots, (1, n)$ positions in the first row are zero. If we proceed to reduce the element in the $(2, 4)$ position in the resulting matrix to zero, by choosing $r = 2, i = 3, j = 4$, we find that the zero elements in the first row remain zero. Similarly for the $(2, 5)$ position and so on. The procedure can be repeated until **A** is reduced to a symmetric *band* or *tridiagonal* or *codiagonal* matrix:

$$\mathbf{P}^T\mathbf{A}\mathbf{P} = \begin{bmatrix} b_1 & c_1 & 0 & \ldots & 0 \\ c_1 & b_2 & c_2 & \ldots & 0 \\ 0 & c_2 & b_3 & \ldots & 0 \\ & & \ldots & & \\ 0 & 0 & 0 & \ldots & b_n \end{bmatrix}. \tag{10.31}$$

We cannot do better than this by plane rotations, choosing θ as in (10.30).

We have proved:

THEOREM **10.12.** *Let* **A** *be real symmetric and define a sequence* $\mathbf{A}_1$, $\mathbf{A}_2, \ldots$ *by*

$$\mathbf{A}_{s+1} = \mathbf{R}_s^T \mathbf{A}_s \mathbf{R}_s, \qquad s = 0, 1, \ldots, \qquad \mathbf{A}_0 = \mathbf{A},$$

where the plane rotation matrices $\mathbf{R}_0, \mathbf{R}_1, \ldots$ *reduce the following elements* (r, j) *to zero in turn:*

$$(1, 3), (1, 4), \ldots, (1, n), (2, 4), \ldots, (2, n), \ldots, (n-2, n),$$

using in each case a value of θ *given by* (10.30) *with* $i = r + 1$. *Then* $\mathbf{A}_k$, $k = \frac{1}{2}(n-1)(n-2)$, *is a tridiagonal matrix with the same eigenvalues as* **A**.

Having transformed **A** into the band form (10.31) which we denote by **B**, there remains the problem of finding the eigenvalues and eigenvectors of **B**. If we denote the determinant of the first k rows and columns of $\mathbf{B} - \lambda\mathbf{I}$ (the leading minor of order k of $\mathbf{B} - \lambda\mathbf{I}$) by $p_k(\lambda)$, it is a straightforward matter to show that

$$p_k(\lambda) = (b_k - \lambda)p_{k-1}(\lambda) - c_{k-1}^2 p_{k-2}(\lambda), \qquad k = 2, \ldots, n, \qquad (10.32)$$

with

$$p_0(\lambda) = 1, \qquad p_1(\lambda) = b_1 - \lambda.$$

This means that it is easy to evaluate $p_n(\lambda)$ for any given value of λ. The eigenvalues are the zeros of $p_n(\lambda)$, and techniques are available for determination of the λ_i by repeated evaluation of $p_n(\lambda)$.

Having determined the eigenvalues, it might seem that it would be a very easy matter to determine the corresponding eigenvectors by solving the corresponding tridiagonal systems

$$(\mathbf{B} - \lambda_i\mathbf{I})\mathbf{x} = \mathbf{0}, \qquad (10.33)$$

by omitting say the last equation, and solving the first $n - 1$ equations for $x_1, \ldots, x_{n-1}$ in terms of an arbitrary x_n. In fact, it turns out that even if a very good approximation to an eigenvalue is used, the corresponding approximate eigenvector determined in this way may be catastrophically in error. It is necessary to take special precautions to guarantee accuracy. The reader is referred to the literature for a detailed discussion (see Ex. 10.45).

Ex. 10.13. Apply the Givens method to

$$\mathbf{A} = \begin{bmatrix} 4 & 4 & 2 \\ 4 & 4 & 1 \\ 2 & 1 & 8 \end{bmatrix}. \qquad (10.34)$$

Solution: We can reduce only the (1, 3) element to zero and this is done by taking $r = 1$, $i = 2$, $j = 3$. Equation (10.30) gives $\tan\theta = \frac{1}{2}$,

$$\mathbf{R} = \begin{bmatrix} 1 & 0 & 0 \\ 0 & \dfrac{2}{\sqrt{5}} & -\dfrac{1}{\sqrt{5}} \\ 0 & \dfrac{1}{\sqrt{5}} & \dfrac{2}{\sqrt{5}} \end{bmatrix}, \qquad \mathbf{R}^T\mathbf{A}\mathbf{R} = \begin{bmatrix} 4 & 2\sqrt{5} & 0 \\ 2\sqrt{5} & 5.6 & 2.2 \\ 0 & 2.2 & 6.4 \end{bmatrix}.$$

The characteristic equation is found to be

$$\lambda^3 - 16\lambda^2 + 59\lambda + 4 = 0. \tag{10.35}$$

10.6 A Special Orthogonal Transformation, and Householder's Method

In the last section we used transformations consisting of plane rotations, specified by matrices of the form (10.16). In this section we consider a different type of transformation that can be motivated as follows (Figure 10.3). Suppose that we wish to transform a real arbitrary vector $\mathbf{u}$ into a second real vector $\mathbf{v}$ of the same length by means of an equation

$$\mathbf{v} = \mathbf{P}\mathbf{u}, \tag{10.36}$$

where $\mathbf{P}$ is a square matrix that will depend on $\mathbf{u}$ and $\mathbf{v}$. This can be done by noting that

$$\overrightarrow{OC} = \overrightarrow{OA} + 2\overrightarrow{AB},$$

where B is the midpoint of AC so that OB is perpendicular to AC and $\overrightarrow{AB}$ is *minus* the projection of OA on AB. The idea of a projection has already been mentioned in Section 10.2 in connection with Gram-Schmidt orthogonalization. If we introduce

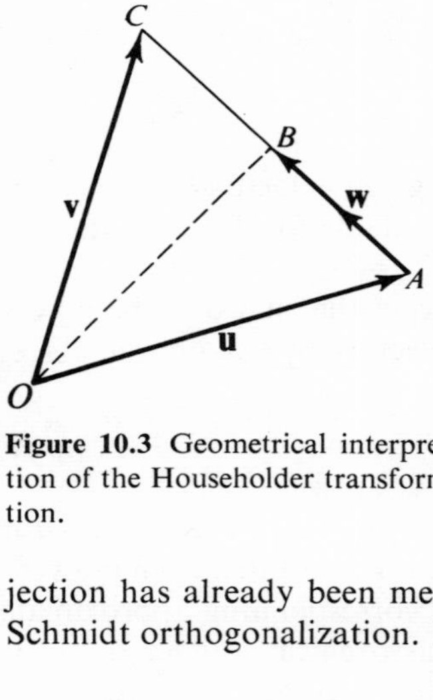

Figure 10.3 Geometrical interpretation of the Householder transformation.

$$\mathbf{w} = \frac{\mathbf{v} - \mathbf{u}}{\|\mathbf{v} - \mathbf{u}\|} \tag{10.37}$$

so that $\mathbf{w}$ is a unit vector along AC, then, remembering a minus because of the directions of the vectors $\mathbf{u}$ and $\mathbf{w}$,

$$\mathbf{v} = \mathbf{u} - 2(\mathbf{w}, \mathbf{u})\mathbf{w}. \tag{10.38}$$

It is easy to verify that

$$(\mathbf{w}, \mathbf{u})\mathbf{w} = \mathbf{w}\mathbf{w}^T\mathbf{u},$$

so that (10.38) gives

$$\mathbf{v} = (\mathbf{I} - 2\mathbf{w}\mathbf{w}^T)\mathbf{u}. \tag{10.39}$$

Summing up, we wish to consider what we shall call *Householder transformations* which are of the form (10.36) with

$$\mathbf{P} = \mathbf{I} - 2\mathbf{w}\mathbf{w}^T, \qquad \|\mathbf{w}\| = 1.$$

The vector **w** corresponding to given **u** and **v** is given by (10.37). We have derived these results by a geometrical argument but of course (10.36) is now an algebraic identity which can be verified directly. We have

$$\mathbf{P}\mathbf{u} = (\mathbf{I} - 2\mathbf{w}\mathbf{w}^T)\mathbf{u} = \mathbf{u} - \frac{2(\mathbf{v} - \mathbf{u})(\mathbf{v} - \mathbf{u})^T\mathbf{u}}{\|\mathbf{v} - \mathbf{u}\|^2}. \tag{10.40}$$

Since $\|\mathbf{u}\| = \|\mathbf{v}\|$,

$$\|\mathbf{v} - \mathbf{u}\|^2 = (\mathbf{v}, \mathbf{v}) - (\mathbf{v}, \mathbf{u}) - (\mathbf{u}, \mathbf{v}) + (\mathbf{u}, \mathbf{u}) = -2(\mathbf{v} - \mathbf{u}, \mathbf{u}).$$

Equation (10.40) therefore reduces to

$$\mathbf{P}\mathbf{u} = \mathbf{u} + (\mathbf{v} - \mathbf{u}) = \mathbf{v}.$$

Our geometrical derivation of **P** shows that the transformation represents a rotation from **u** to **v** around an axis through the origin O perpendicular to the plane of **u** and **v**. We therefore expect (see Ex. 10.4) that **P** should be orthogonal, and it is easy to verify that this is true. We have $\mathbf{P}^T = \mathbf{P}$ so that

$$\begin{aligned}\mathbf{P}^T\mathbf{P} = \mathbf{P}\mathbf{P}^T &= (\mathbf{I} - 2\mathbf{w}\mathbf{w}^T)^2 \\ &= \mathbf{I} - 4\mathbf{w}\mathbf{w}^T + 4\mathbf{w}\mathbf{w}^T\mathbf{w}\mathbf{w}^T = \mathbf{I}.\end{aligned}$$

As a first application of these ideas we show that we can premultiply a given real matrix **A** which is not necessarily symmetric by a real orthogonal matrix, to produce a matrix **B** in which all the elements in the first column are zero except the first,

$$\mathbf{B} = \mathbf{P}\mathbf{A} = \begin{bmatrix} b_{11} & \boldsymbol{\beta} \\ \mathbf{0} & \mathbf{B}_1 \end{bmatrix}. \tag{10.41}$$

We do this by means of a Householder transformation. If the first columns of **A** and **B** are denoted by $\mathbf{a}_1$ and $\mathbf{b}_1$, we wish to find an orthogonal matrix **P** such that

$$\mathbf{P}\mathbf{a}_1 = \mathbf{b}_1.$$

We must have $\|\mathbf{a}_1\| = \|\mathbf{b}_1\|$ and this condition tells us what the value of $|b_{11}|$ must be:

$$b_{11}| = \|\mathbf{a}_1\|.|$$

Also

$$\mathbf{w} = \frac{\mathbf{b}_1 - \mathbf{a}_1}{\|\mathbf{b}_1 - \mathbf{a}_1\|}.$$

The first element of $\mathbf{w}$ is proportional to

$$b_{11} - a_{11} = \pm\|\mathbf{a}_1\| - a_{11}.$$

We choose the sign which avoids cancellation when computing, which gives

$$b_{11} = -\frac{a_{11}}{|a_{11}|}\|\mathbf{a}_1\|.$$

Then

$$\begin{aligned}\|\mathbf{b}_1 - \mathbf{a}_1\|^2 &= (|a_{11}| + \|\mathbf{a}_1\|)^2 + \sum_{i=2}^{n} a_{i1}^2 \\ &= 2\,\|\mathbf{a}_1\|\,(|a_{11}| + \|\mathbf{a}_1\|) = S^2,\end{aligned}$$

say, so that

$$w_1 = -\frac{a_{11}}{|a_{11}|}\left(\frac{|a_{11}| + \|\mathbf{a}_1\|}{S}\right), \qquad w_i = -\frac{a_{i1}}{S}, \qquad i = 2, \ldots, n.$$

This type of transformation can be used to express an arbitrary matrix $\mathbf{A}$ in the form $\mathbf{QU}$, where $\mathbf{Q}$ is orthogonal and $\mathbf{U}$ is upper triangular (see Exs. 10.34 and 10.35).

For the determination of eigenvalues we are interested in transformations that reduce $\mathbf{P}^T\mathbf{AP}$ to as simple a form as possible. Although the form $\mathbf{PA}$ in (10.41) is simpler than the form of $\mathbf{A}$, the form of $\mathbf{P}^T\mathbf{AP}$ $(= \mathbf{PAP})$ is no simpler than that of $\mathbf{A}$. However, simplification can be achieved by means of the following strategy. Suppose that $\mathbf{Q}$ has the following form

$$\mathbf{Q} = \begin{bmatrix} 1 & \mathbf{0} \\ \mathbf{0} & \mathbf{P} \end{bmatrix},$$

where the square matrix $\mathbf{P}$ of order $n - 1$ is a Householder transformation. We assume that $\mathbf{A}$ is a real symmetric matrix. Partitioning $\mathbf{A}$ in an obvious way we see that

$$\mathbf{A} = \begin{bmatrix} a_{11} & \boldsymbol{\alpha}^T \\ \boldsymbol{\alpha} & \mathbf{A}_1 \end{bmatrix}, \qquad \mathbf{Q}^T\mathbf{AQ} = \begin{bmatrix} a_{11} & \boldsymbol{\alpha}^T\mathbf{P} \\ \mathbf{P}^T\boldsymbol{\alpha} & \mathbf{P}^T\mathbf{A}_1\mathbf{P} \end{bmatrix}.$$

Choose $\mathbf{P}$ to have the form $\mathbf{I} - 2\mathbf{ww}^T$ where $\mathbf{w}$ is chosen so that the last $n - 2$ elements in the $(n - 1) \times 1$ column vector $\mathbf{P}^T\boldsymbol{\alpha}$ $(= \mathbf{P}\boldsymbol{\alpha})$ are zero. The matrix $\mathbf{Q}^T\mathbf{AQ}$ reduces to the form

$$\begin{bmatrix} \times & \times & 0 & 0 & \ldots & 0 \\ \times & \times & \times & \times & \ldots & \times \\ 0 & \times & \times & \times & \ldots & \times \\ 0 & \times & \times & \times & \ldots & \times \\ & & \ldots & & & \\ 0 & \times & \times & \times & \ldots & \times \end{bmatrix}. \qquad (10.42)$$

We next show how repetition of a similar procedure will produce a matrix which is *tridiagonal*, i.e., elements such that $|i - j| > 1$ are zero. We produce a sequence of matrices $\mathbf{A}_1, \mathbf{A}_2, \ldots$, where $\mathbf{A}_{r+1}$ is produced from $\mathbf{A}_r$ by a transformation

$$\mathbf{A}_{r+1} = \mathbf{Q}_r^T \mathbf{A}_r \mathbf{Q}_r, \qquad \mathbf{Q}_r = \mathbf{I} - 2\boldsymbol{\omega}_r^T \boldsymbol{\omega}_r^T, \tag{10.43}$$

where $\mathbf{A}_r$ and $\boldsymbol{\omega}_r$ have the structure

$$\mathbf{A}_r = \begin{bmatrix} \mathbf{B}_r & \mathbf{0} \\ \mathbf{0} & \mathbf{C}_r \end{bmatrix}, \qquad \boldsymbol{\omega}_r = \begin{bmatrix} \mathbf{0} \\ \mathbf{w}_r \end{bmatrix}, \tag{10.44}$$

where $\mathbf{w}_r$ is an $(n - r) \times 1$ vector of the form $\mathbf{w}_r^T = [0, x_{r+1}, \ldots, x_n]$. For $r = 0$, the matrix $\mathbf{B}_0$ is nonexistent, $\mathbf{A}_0 = \mathbf{A}$, and we produce the matrix described in connection with (10.42). For $r > 0$ we obtain

$$\mathbf{Q}_r = \begin{bmatrix} \mathbf{I}_r & \mathbf{0} \\ \mathbf{0} & \mathbf{I}_{n-r} - 2\mathbf{w}_r\mathbf{w}_r^T \end{bmatrix} = \begin{bmatrix} \mathbf{I}_r & \mathbf{0} \\ \mathbf{0} & \mathbf{P}_r \end{bmatrix}, \tag{10.45}$$

where $\mathbf{P}_r = \mathbf{I}_{n-r} - 2\mathbf{w}_r\mathbf{w}_r^T$, and

$$\mathbf{A}_{r+1} = \mathbf{Q}_r^T \mathbf{A}_r \mathbf{Q}_r = \begin{bmatrix} \mathbf{B}_r & \mathbf{0} \\ \mathbf{0} & \mathbf{P}_r^T \mathbf{C}_r \mathbf{P}_r \end{bmatrix}.$$

We see that the elements that have been reduced to zero in $\mathbf{A}_r$ are still zero in $\mathbf{A}_{r+1}$. Also exactly the same method that was explained in connection with (10.42) can be used to choose $\mathbf{w}_r$ so that the elements in the first row and column of $\mathbf{P}_r^T\mathbf{C}_r\mathbf{P}_r$ are reduced to zero, except for the (1, 1), (1, 2) and (2, 1) elements. Generalizing (10.42) it is clear that the matrix $\mathbf{B}_r$ in (10.44) at each stage is tridiagonal. Also the matrix $\mathbf{A}_{n-2}$ is tridiagonal, and the process will terminate.

We have proved:

THEOREM **10.13.** *Let* **A** *be real symmetric, and define a sequence* $\mathbf{A}_0, \mathbf{A}_1, \ldots$ *by*

$$\mathbf{A}_{r+1} = \mathbf{Q}_r^T \mathbf{A}_r \mathbf{Q}_r, \qquad r = 0, 1, \ldots, \qquad \mathbf{A}_0 = \mathbf{A},$$

where $\mathbf{Q}_r$ *has the structure given in* (10.43)–(10.45). *Then the* $\mathbf{w}_r$ *can be chosen so that* $\mathbf{A}_{n-2}$ *is a tridiagonal matrix.*

Both the Givens and Householder methods reduce **A** to a tridiagonal matrix. It is of some interest that the final tridiagonal forms are essentially the same.

THEOREM **10.14.** *If* **A** *is real symmetric,* **Q** *is orthogonal with a given first column, and* $\mathbf{Q}^T\mathbf{A}\mathbf{Q} = \mathbf{B}$ *where* **B** *is tridiagonal, then this determines* **Q** *uniquely to within multipliers of* ± 1 *for each column.*

Proof: Let $\mathbf{q}_i$ denote the ith column of **Q**. Then $\mathbf{AQ} = \mathbf{QB}$ gives

$$\mathbf{A}[\mathbf{q}_1, \ldots, \mathbf{q}_n] = [\mathbf{q}_1, \ldots, \mathbf{q}_n] \begin{bmatrix} b_1 & c_1 & \ldots & 0 \\ c_1 & b_2 & \ldots & 0 \\ & & \ldots & \\ 0 & 0 & \ldots & b_n \end{bmatrix}.$$

Hence,

$$\begin{aligned} \mathbf{A}\mathbf{q}_1 &= b_1\mathbf{q}_1 + c_1\mathbf{q}_2, \\ \mathbf{A}\mathbf{q}_2 &= c_1\mathbf{q}_1 + b_2\mathbf{q}_2 + c_2\mathbf{q}_3, \text{ etc.} \end{aligned} \tag{10.46}$$

From (10.46), since $(\mathbf{q}_1, \mathbf{q}_1) = 1$, $(\mathbf{q}_1, \mathbf{q}_2) = 0$, we have $b_1 = (\mathbf{q}_1, \mathbf{A}\mathbf{q}_1)$, so that

$$c_1\mathbf{q}_2 = \mathbf{A}\mathbf{q}_1 - (\mathbf{q}_1, \mathbf{A}\mathbf{q}_1)\mathbf{q}_1 = \mathbf{s}_2,$$

where $\mathbf{s}_2$ is a known vector. Since $\|\mathbf{q}_2\| = 1$, this means that

$$\mathbf{q}_2 = \pm \frac{\mathbf{s}_2}{\|\mathbf{s}_2\|}, \qquad c_1 = \pm\|\mathbf{s}_2\|.$$

This proves that b_1, c_1, $\mathbf{q}_2$ are determined, apart from sign, once $\mathbf{q}_1$ is known. It is left to the reader to show similarly that the other elements in **B** and the columns of **Q** are also determined.

Since the Givens and Householder methods both use a matrix **Q** whose first column is the unit vector $\mathbf{e}_1$, this means that the tridiagonal matrix **B** obtained by either method is theoretically the same. Of course, it should not be concluded that the two methods are equivalent in numerical work. The Householder method is more efficient since it reduces a matrix to tridiagonal form using only half the number of operations required for the Givens method (Ex. 10.16). Also, the sequence of operations and therefore the rounding errors will be completely different in the two methods.

If the Givens and Householder methods are applied to a nonsymmetric matrix **A**, they can be used to reduce **A** to *Hessenberg* form **B** which is a matrix with the same structure as a tridiagonal matrix below the diagonal, but nonzero elements may occur in all positions above the diagonal (or vice versa), $b_{ij} = 0$ for $i + 2 \geq j$. It seems that the Householder method is the best method known for finding eigenvalues of a hermitian matrix. (We have considered only the real symmetric special case of this.) The question of the best method for nonsymmetric matrices is not settled.

Ex. 10.14. Show that, given two complex vectors $\mathbf{u}$, $\mathbf{v}$ such that $\|\mathbf{u}\| = \|\mathbf{v}\|$ and $(\mathbf{u}, \mathbf{v})$ is real, the vector $\mathbf{u}$ can be transformed into $\mathbf{v}$ by means of the transformation $\mathbf{v} = \mathbf{P}\mathbf{u}$ with $\mathbf{P} = \mathbf{I} - 2\mathbf{w}\mathbf{w}^H$, where $\mathbf{w}$ is the vector defined in (10.37). Show that this transformation can be used to reduce a hermitian matrix to tridiagonal form by the method used for real symmetric matrices in Section 10.6.

Ex. 10.15. Reduce (10.34), the matrix in Ex. 10.13, to tridiagonal form, using the Householder method.

Ex. 10.16. Show that the Givens and Householder methods require approximately $\frac{4}{3}n^3$ and $\frac{2}{3}n^3$ multiplications, respectively, to reduce a real symmetric matrix of order n to tridiagonal form.

10.7 Biorthogonality

When considering the question of the orthogonality of eigenvectors in Chapter 9, we considered only hermitian matrices **A**. Suppose now that **A** is a general $n \times n$ matrix. The main clue to the development of the theory is that we must consider the eigenvectors of the transpose of **A** as well as the eigenvectors of **A** itself. In the symmetric case these, of course, are the same. Even though the eigenvectors of **A** and $\mathbf{A}^T$ are different, their eigenvalues are identical.

THEOREM **10.15.** **A** *and* $\mathbf{A}^T$ *have the same eigenvalues.*

Proof: The eigenvalues of $\mathbf{A}^T$ are given by $\det(\mathbf{A}^T - \lambda\mathbf{I}) = 0$. Since the determinant of the transpose of a matrix is the same as the determinant of the original matrix, this implies that $\det(\mathbf{A} - \lambda\mathbf{I}) = 0$. Hence, the characteristic equations of **A** and $\mathbf{A}^T$ are the same, so that the eigenvalues are the same.

We now introduce the following definition.

DEFINITION **10.3.** Vectors $\mathbf{y}_i$ such that

$$\mathbf{y}_i^H\mathbf{A} = \lambda_i\mathbf{y}_i^H, \quad \text{i.e.,} \quad \mathbf{A}^H\mathbf{y}_i = \bar{\lambda}_i\mathbf{y}_i, \tag{10.47}$$

are called *left-eigenvectors* of **A**. To distinguish these from vectors $\mathbf{x}_i$ such that $\mathbf{A}\mathbf{x}_i = \lambda\mathbf{x}_i$, we call the $\mathbf{x}_i$ *right-eigenvectors* of **A**.

We use $\mathbf{y}^H$ and $\mathbf{A}^H$ rather than $\mathbf{y}^T$ and $\mathbf{A}^T$ in (10.47) because we make extensive use of inner products, for which $(\mathbf{u}, \mathbf{A}\mathbf{v}) = (\mathbf{A}^H\mathbf{u}, \mathbf{v})$ [see Theorem 9.7(i)]. Since $\mathbf{A}^H = \bar{\mathbf{A}}^T$, Theorem 10.15 states that if λ_i is an eigenvalue of **A**, $\bar{\lambda}_i$ is an eigenvalue of $\mathbf{A}^H$.

It is important to realize that when **A** is not symmetric, the right-eigenvectors are *not* mutually orthogonal (nor are the left-eigenvectors). However, there is a "cross-orthogonality."

THEOREM **10.16.** *A right-eigenvector* $\mathbf{x}_i$ *and a left-eigenvector* $\mathbf{y}_j$ *corresponding to distinct eigenvalues* λ_i, λ_j, *are orthogonal.*

Proof: By definition,

$$\mathbf{A}\mathbf{x}_i = \lambda_i\mathbf{x}_i, \qquad \mathbf{A}^H\mathbf{y}_j = \bar{\lambda}_j\mathbf{y}_j. \tag{10.48}$$

Form the inner product of the first equation with y_j, and the second equation with $\mathbf{x}_i$,

$$(\mathbf{y}_j, \mathbf{A}\mathbf{x}_i) = \lambda_i(\mathbf{y}_j, \mathbf{x}_i), \qquad (\mathbf{x}_i, \mathbf{A}^H\mathbf{y}_j) = \bar{\lambda}_j(\mathbf{x}_i, \mathbf{y}_j). \tag{10.49}$$

This second relation gives

$$(\mathbf{y}_j, \mathbf{A}\mathbf{x}_i) = \lambda_j(\mathbf{y}_j, \mathbf{x}_i). \tag{10.50}$$

Subtract (10.50) from the first equation in (10.49),

$$(\lambda_i - \lambda_j)(\mathbf{y}_j, \mathbf{x}_i) = 0.$$

If $\lambda_i \neq \lambda_j$, this implies $(\mathbf{y}_j, \mathbf{x}_i) = 0$, which proves the theorem.

This leads to the following generalization of the idea of orthogonality.

DEFINITION **10.4**. Two sets of vectors $\mathbf{x}_1, \ldots, \mathbf{x}_n$, and $\mathbf{y}_1, \ldots, \mathbf{y}_n$ are said to be *biorthogonal* if, for $i, j = 1, \ldots, n$,

$$(\mathbf{y}_j, \mathbf{x}_i) = 0, \qquad i \neq j. \tag{10.51}$$

The following theorem is a basic result concerning the biorthogonality of right- and left-eigenvectors of a general matrix (compare Theorems 9.10, 9.12 for hermitian matrices).

THEOREM **10.17.** *If* $\mathbf{A}$ *has* n *independent right-eigenvectors* $\mathbf{x}_i$, *then to each* $\mathbf{x}_i$ *there corresponds a left-eigenvector* $\mathbf{y}_i$ *such that*

$$(\mathbf{y}_j, \mathbf{x}_i) = \begin{cases} 0, & i \neq j, \\ 1, & i = j. \end{cases} \tag{10.52}$$

Proof: Let $\mathbf{P} = [\mathbf{x}_1, \ldots, \mathbf{x}_n]$. Since the $\mathbf{x}_i$ are independent, $\mathbf{P}$ has an inverse. Introduce $\mathbf{Q}$ such that $\mathbf{Q}^H = \mathbf{P}^{-1}$. As in (9.50),

$$\mathbf{AP} = \mathbf{P\Lambda}.$$

Since $\mathbf{Q}^H\mathbf{P} = \mathbf{PQ}^H = \mathbf{I}$, this gives

$$\mathbf{Q}^H\mathbf{AP} = \mathbf{\Lambda}, \qquad \mathbf{Q}^H\mathbf{A} = \mathbf{\Lambda Q}^H, \qquad \mathbf{A}^H\mathbf{Q} = \mathbf{Q}\bar{\mathbf{\Lambda}}.$$

If the ith column of $\mathbf{Q}$ is denoted by $\mathbf{y}_i$, this means that $\mathbf{A}^H\mathbf{y}_i = \bar{\lambda}_i\mathbf{y}_i$, or $\mathbf{y}_i$ is a left-eigenvector of $\mathbf{A}$ corresponding to λ_i. Since $\mathbf{Q}^H\mathbf{P} = \mathbf{I}$, the result (10.52) follows.

In practice, we often normalize so that $\|\mathbf{x}_i\| = \|\mathbf{y}_i\| = 1$, in which case $(\mathbf{y}_i, \mathbf{x}_i)$ will not in general be equal to 1. The value of $(\mathbf{y}_i, \mathbf{x}_i)$ under these circumstances will be of considerable importance in Chapter 13. If $(\mathbf{y}_i, \mathbf{x}_i)$ is small compared with unity, this indicates that the eigenproblem is ill-conditioned numerically.

An important case when $\mathbf{A}$ has n independent eigenvectors occurs when the eigenvalues of $\mathbf{A}$ are distinct (Theorem 9.3).

The following theorem is implicit in the proof of Theorem 10.17 (compare Theorems 9.11, 9.12).

THEOREM **10.18.** *Using the conditions and notation of Theorem* 10.17, *let* $\mathbf{P}$, $\mathbf{Q}$ *denote the matrices whose ith columns are* $\mathbf{x}_i$, $\mathbf{y}_i$, *respectively.*

Then

(i) $$\mathbf{Q}^H\mathbf{P} = \mathbf{P}^H\mathbf{Q} = \mathbf{I}, \tag{10.53}$$

(ii) $$\mathbf{Q}^H\mathbf{A}\mathbf{P} = \mathbf{P}^{-1}\mathbf{A}\mathbf{P} = \mathbf{\Lambda}, \tag{10.54}$$

where $\mathbf{\Lambda}$ *is the diagonal matrix whose ith element is* λ_i.

Ex. 10.17. Verify Theorems 10.17, 10.18 using the numerical example

$$\mathbf{A} = \begin{bmatrix} 1 & 1 & 0 \\ 0 & 2 & 1 \\ 0 & 0 & 3 \end{bmatrix}. \tag{10.55}$$

Solution: The eigenvalues of $\mathbf{A}$ are $\lambda_1 = 1$, $\lambda_2 = 2$, $\lambda_3 = 3$. The corresponding eigenvectors of $\mathbf{A}$ and $\mathbf{A}^T$ are found to be

$$\mathbf{x}_1 = \begin{bmatrix} 1 \\ 0 \\ 0 \end{bmatrix}, \qquad \mathbf{x}_2 = \begin{bmatrix} 1 \\ 1 \\ 0 \end{bmatrix}, \qquad \mathbf{x}_3 = \begin{bmatrix} 1 \\ 2 \\ 2 \end{bmatrix},$$

$$\mathbf{y}_1 = \begin{bmatrix} 2 \\ -2 \\ 1 \end{bmatrix}, \qquad \mathbf{y}_2 = \begin{bmatrix} 0 \\ 1 \\ -1 \end{bmatrix}, \qquad \mathbf{y}_3 = \begin{bmatrix} 0 \\ 0 \\ 1 \end{bmatrix}.$$

The reader will readily check the biorthogonal character of these sets, and that $(\mathbf{y}_i, \mathbf{x}_i) \neq 0$ for $i = 1, 2, 3$. Neither the $\mathbf{x}_i$ nor the $\mathbf{y}_i$ are orthogonal.

Ex. 10.18. Verify that Theorem 10.17 is not true for

$$\mathbf{A} = \begin{bmatrix} 1 & 1 \\ 0 & 1 \end{bmatrix}.$$

(Note that this matrix has repeated eigenvalues.)

Ex. 10.19. Generalize Theorem 9.14 to show that if sets $\mathbf{x}_i$, $\mathbf{y}_i$, $(i = 1 \text{ to } n)$ are biorthogonal and $(\mathbf{x}_i, \mathbf{y}_i) \neq 0$, then if a vector $\mathbf{u}$ can be expressed as a linear combination of the $\mathbf{x}_i$, the coefficients in the expansion are given by

$$\alpha_i = \frac{(\mathbf{y}_i, \mathbf{u})}{(\mathbf{y}_i, \mathbf{x}_i)}.$$

10.8 Singular Values and Singular Vectors

The theory of orthogonal expansions considered so far is based on square matrices. When the matrices are nonsymmetric and the eigenvalues are complex, the numerical work may be formidable. The theory is not applicable without further extension (using, for example, ideas in Chapter 11) if the matrix of order n has less than n linearly independent eigenvectors. In this section we investigate a somewhat different type of theory that derives its simplicity from the fact that the eigenvalues of a hermitian matrix are real. *In this section* $\mathbf{A}$ *represents a general* $m \times n$ *matrix with complex elements.*

DEFINITION **10.5.** If $\mathbf{A}$ is a general $m \times n$ matrix, μ is a nonzero number, and $\mathbf{u}$, $\mathbf{v}$ are vectors such that

$$\mathbf{A}\mathbf{u} = \mu\mathbf{v}, \qquad \mathbf{A}^H\mathbf{v} = \mu\mathbf{u}, \tag{10.56}$$

then μ is called a *singular value* of $\mathbf{A}$ and $\mathbf{u}$, $\mathbf{v}$ are called a pair of *singular vectors* corresponding to $\mathbf{A}$.

Note that Equations (10.56) imply

$$\begin{bmatrix} \mathbf{0} & \mathbf{A} \\ \mathbf{A}^H & \mathbf{0} \end{bmatrix} \begin{bmatrix} \mathbf{v} \\ \mathbf{u} \end{bmatrix} = \mu \begin{bmatrix} \mathbf{v} \\ \mathbf{u} \end{bmatrix} \tag{10.57}$$

so that μ is an eigenvalue of a hermitian matrix, and therefore real. Also, if $\mathbf{u}$, $\mathbf{v}$ are singular vectors corresponding to μ, then $\mathbf{u}$, $-\mathbf{v}$ are singular vectors corresponding to $-\mu$. Hence, singular values occur in pairs $\pm\mu$ and *we need consider only singular values that are greater than or equal to zero*. From (10.56),

$$\mathbf{A}^H\mathbf{A}\mathbf{u} = \mu\mathbf{A}^H\mathbf{v} = \mu^2\mathbf{u}. \tag{10.58}$$

Hence, $\mathbf{u}$ is an eigenvector of $\mathbf{A}^H\mathbf{A}$ corresponding to the eigenvalue μ^2. Similarly, $\mathbf{v}$ is an eigenvector of $\mathbf{A}\mathbf{A}^H$ corresponding to the same eigenvalue μ^2. To check consistency we note that if we form the inner product of (10.58) with $\mathbf{u}$, we obtain

$$(\mathbf{u}, \mathbf{A}^H\mathbf{A}\mathbf{u}) = (\mathbf{A}\mathbf{u}, \mathbf{A}\mathbf{u}) = \mu^2(\mathbf{u}, \mathbf{u}), \tag{10.59}$$

so that μ^2 is real and nonnegative. The eigenvectors of the matrix in (10.57) corresponding to zero values of μ are given by the nonzero solutions of

$$\mathbf{A}\mathbf{u} = \mathbf{0} \tag{10.60}$$

$$\mathbf{A}^H\mathbf{v} = \mathbf{0}. \tag{10.61}$$

The ranks of $\mathbf{A}$ and $\mathbf{A}^H$ are the same. Suppose that this rank is k. Then equations (10.60) and (10.61) have $n - k$ and $m - k$ linearly independent solutions, respectively, and these give rise to $m + n - 2k$ eigenvectors of the matrix in (10.57) of one of the forms

$$\begin{bmatrix} \mathbf{v} \\ \mathbf{0} \end{bmatrix}, \qquad \begin{bmatrix} \mathbf{0} \\ \mathbf{u} \end{bmatrix}.$$

Theorem 10.10 tells us that the matrix in (10.57) must have $m + n$ linearly independent eigenvectors, so that exactly $2k$ of these must correspond to nonzero values of μ. We have seen that the singular values occur in pairs $\pm\mu$, so that $\mathbf{A}$ has precisely k positive singular values, where k is the rank of $\mathbf{A}$. Let these be denoted by $\mu_1, \ldots, \mu_k$. From Theorem 10.10, the matrix $\mathbf{A}^H\mathbf{A}$ will have exactly k linearly independent eigenvectors, say $\mathbf{u}_1, \ldots, \mathbf{u}_k$, corresponding to the nonzero eigenvalues $\mu_1^2, \ldots, \mu_k^2$. If $n - k$ linearly independent solutions of $\mathbf{Au} = \mathbf{0}$ [equation (10.60)] are denoted by $\mathbf{u}_{k+1}, \ldots, \mathbf{u}_n$, these are eigenfunctions of $\mathbf{A}^H\mathbf{A}$ corresponding to an eigenvalue zero. These are independent of $\mathbf{u}_1, \ldots, \mathbf{u}_k$ since they correspond to a different eigenvalue [Theorem 9.3(i)]. Hence, $\mathbf{u}_1, \ldots, \mathbf{u}_n$ constitute a set of n linearly independent eigenvectors of $\mathbf{A}^H\mathbf{A}$. We can assume that these form an orthonormal set since $\mathbf{A}^H\mathbf{A}$ is hermitian, so that eigenfunctions corresponding to distinct eigenvalues are orthogonal, and independent eigenfunctions corresponding to the same eigenvalue can be orthonormalized by Gram-Schmidt. Define

$$\mathbf{U} = [\mathbf{u}_1, \ldots, \mathbf{u}_n]. \tag{10.62}$$

The matrix $\mathbf{U}$ is unitary.

For clarity we interpose an intermediate theorem.

THEOREM **10.19.** *If* $\mathbf{u}_i$, $i = 1, \ldots, k$, *are an orthonormal set of eigenvectors of* $\mathbf{A}^H\mathbf{A}$ *corresponding to the nonzero eigenvalues* $\mu_1^2, \ldots, \mu_k^2$ *and we define*

$$\mathbf{v}_i = \mu_i^{-1}\mathbf{A}\mathbf{u}_i, \qquad i = 1, \ldots, k, \tag{10.63}$$

then:

(i) *The* $\mathbf{v}_i$ *are an orthonormal set of eigenvectors of* $\mathbf{AA}^H$ *corresponding to the nonzero eigenvalues* μ_i^2.

(ii) $\mathbf{u}_i$, $\mathbf{v}_i$ *are a pair of singular vectors corresponding to the singular value* μ_i.

Proof:

$$\mathbf{AA}^H\mathbf{v}_i = \mu_i^{-1}\mathbf{AA}^H\mathbf{A}\mathbf{u}_i = \mu_i\mathbf{A}\mathbf{u}_i = \mu_i^2\mathbf{v}_i.$$

$$(\mathbf{v}_i, \mathbf{v}_j) = (\mu_i\mu_j)^{-1}(\mathbf{A}\mathbf{u}_i, \mathbf{A}\mathbf{u}_j) = (\mu_i\mu_j)^{-1}(\mathbf{u}_i, \mathbf{A}^H\mathbf{A}\mathbf{u}_j)$$
$$= \left(\frac{\mu_j}{\mu_i}\right)(\mathbf{u}_i, \mathbf{u}_j) = \begin{cases} 0, & i \neq j, \\ 1, & i = j. \end{cases}$$

These formulae prove (i). From (10.63), $\mathbf{A}\mathbf{u}_i = \mu_i\mathbf{v}_i$, and $\mathbf{A}^H\mathbf{A}\mathbf{u}_i = \mu_i^2\mathbf{u}_i$ then gives $\mathbf{A}\mathbf{v}_i = \mu_i\mathbf{u}_i$, which proves (ii).

We now resume the main development of the theory. Let $\mathbf{v}_i = \mu_i^{-1}\mathbf{A}\mathbf{u}_i$, $i = 1, \ldots, k$, where the $\mathbf{u}_i$ are those that appear in (10.62). Let $\mathbf{v}_{k+1}, \ldots, \mathbf{v}_m$ denote $m - k$ linearly independent solutions of $\mathbf{A}^H\mathbf{v} = \mathbf{0}$ [equation (10.61)]. Then $\mathbf{v}_1, \ldots, \mathbf{v}_m$ constitute a set of linearly independent eigenvectors of $\mathbf{A}^H\mathbf{A}$. Also we can assume that the set is orthonormal since $\mathbf{v}_1, \ldots, \mathbf{v}_k$ are orthonormal by Theorem 10.19, and these are orthogonal to $\mathbf{v}_{k+1}, \ldots, \mathbf{v}_m$, which can be orthonormalized by Gram-Schmidt. Define

$$\mathbf{V} = [\mathbf{v}_1, \ldots, \mathbf{v}_m]. \tag{10.64}$$

The matrix $\mathbf{V}$ is unitary.

We summarize what we have proved so far.

THEOREM **10.20.** *Let* $\mathbf{A}$ *be a general* $m \times n$ *matrix of rank* k.

(i) $\mathbf{A}$ *has exactly* k *positive nonzero singular values, say* $\mu_1, \ldots, \mu_k$. *These are real.*

(ii) *Corresponding to each* μ_i *there is a pair of singular vectors* $\mathbf{u}_i, \mathbf{v}_i$. *These are eigenvectors of* $\mathbf{A}^H\mathbf{A}$ *and* $\mathbf{A}\mathbf{A}^H$, *respectively, corresponding to an eigenvalue* μ_i^2.

(iii) *The* k *sets* $\mathbf{u}_i, \mathbf{v}_i$ *in* (ii) *can be chosen so that* $\mathbf{U}$ *and* $\mathbf{V}$ *in* (10.62), (10.64) *are unitary, where* $\mathbf{u}_{k+1}, \ldots, \mathbf{u}_n$ *and* $\mathbf{v}_{k+1}, \ldots, \mathbf{v}_m$ *satisfy* $\mathbf{A}\mathbf{u}_i = \mathbf{0}$, $\mathbf{A}^H\mathbf{v}_i = \mathbf{0}$, *respectively.*

This immediately leads to the following.

THEOREM **10.21.** *Let* $\mathbf{A}$ *be a general* $m \times n$ *matrix of rank* k. *Then unitary matrices* $\mathbf{U}, \mathbf{V}$ *exist such that*

$$\mathbf{V}^H\mathbf{A}\mathbf{U} = \begin{bmatrix} \mathbf{\Lambda} & \mathbf{0} \\ \mathbf{0} & \mathbf{0} \end{bmatrix}, \tag{10.65}$$

where $\mathbf{\Lambda}$ *is a diagonal matrix of order* k *whose diagonal elements are the singular values of* $\mathbf{A}$.

Proof: Let $\mathbf{U}, \mathbf{V}$ be the matrices defined in (10.62), (10.64). We have

$$\begin{aligned} \mathbf{V}^H\mathbf{A}\mathbf{U} &= \mathbf{V}^H\mathbf{A}[\mathbf{u}_1, \ldots, \mathbf{u}_k, \mathbf{u}_{k+1}, \ldots, \mathbf{u}_n] \\ &= \begin{bmatrix} \mathbf{v}_1^H \\ \vdots \\ \mathbf{v}_k^H \\ \mathbf{v}_{k+1}^H \\ \vdots \\ \mathbf{v}_m^H \end{bmatrix} [\mu_1\mathbf{v}_1, \ldots, \mu_k\mathbf{v}_k, \mathbf{0}, \ldots, \mathbf{0}]. \end{aligned}$$

This gives (10.65), since the $\mathbf{v}_i$ are orthonormal.

As an application, consider:

THEOREM **10.22.** *A system* $\mathbf{A}\mathbf{x} = \mathbf{b}$ *of* m *equations in* n *unknowns is consistent if and only if* $(\mathbf{y}, \mathbf{b}) = 0$ *for every solution* $\mathbf{y}$ *of the homogeneous system* $\mathbf{A}^H\mathbf{y} = \mathbf{0}$. *An equivalent condition is that* $(\mathbf{v}_i, \mathbf{b}) = 0$, $i = k + 1, \ldots, m$, *where the* $\mathbf{v}_i$ *are the singular vectors in* (10.64). *If* $\mathbf{A}\mathbf{x} = \mathbf{b}$ *is consistent, the general solution is given by*

$$\mathbf{x} = \sum_{i=1}^{k} \frac{1}{\mu_i} (\mathbf{v}_i, \mathbf{b})\mathbf{u}_i + \sum_{i=k+1}^{n} \alpha_i\mathbf{u}_i, \tag{10.66}$$

where the α_i *are arbitrary constants.*

Proof: Let **U**, **V** denote the matrices (10.62), (10.64). The equation $\mathbf{Ax} = \mathbf{b}$ gives

$$(\mathbf{V}^H\mathbf{AU})(\mathbf{U}^H\mathbf{x}) = \mathbf{V}^H\mathbf{b}.$$

Introduce (10.65),

$$\begin{bmatrix} \mathbf{\Lambda} & \mathbf{0} \\ \mathbf{0} & \mathbf{0} \end{bmatrix}(\mathbf{U}^H\mathbf{x}) = \mathbf{V}^H\mathbf{b},$$

or

$$\begin{aligned} \mu_i(\mathbf{u}_i, \mathbf{x}) &= (\mathbf{v}_i, \mathbf{b}), \qquad i = 1, \ldots, k, \\ 0 &= (\mathbf{v}_i, \mathbf{b}), \qquad i = k+1, \ldots, m. \end{aligned} \tag{10.67}$$

Hence the equations are consistent if and only if $(\mathbf{v}_i, \mathbf{b}) = 0$ for $i = k + 1, \ldots, m$. This means that $(\mathbf{b}, \mathbf{y}) = 0$ where $\mathbf{y}$ is any linear combination of the $\mathbf{v}_i$. The $\mathbf{v}_i$ span the null space of $\mathbf{A}^H$. Hence, the equations are consistent if and only if $(\mathbf{b}, \mathbf{y}) = 0$ for any solution $\mathbf{y}$ of $\mathbf{A}^H\mathbf{y} = \mathbf{0}$. Also, the $\mathbf{u}_i$ form an orthonormal set so that we can always expand a solution $\mathbf{x}$ in the form

$$\mathbf{x} = \alpha_1\mathbf{u}_1 + \ldots + \alpha_n\mathbf{u}_n, \tag{10.68}$$

where, using (10.67),

$$\alpha_i = (\mathbf{u}_i, \mathbf{x}) = \mu_i^{-1}(\mathbf{v}_i, \mathbf{b}), \qquad i = 1, \ldots, k. \tag{10.69}$$

Equations (10.68), (10.69) give (10.66). As a cross-check, multiply (10.68) by **A**. Then

$$\mathbf{Ax} = \mathbf{b} = \alpha_1\mu_1\mathbf{v}_1 + \ldots + \alpha_k\mu_k\mathbf{v}_k.$$

Hence, we must have $(\mathbf{v}_i, \mathbf{b}) = \alpha_i\mu_i$ for $i = 1, \ldots, k$ and $(\mathbf{v}_i, \mathbf{b}) = 0$ for $i = k + 1, \ldots, m$.

The expansion (10.66) has several advantages over the orthodox eigenfunction expansion (Ex. 10.37):

$$\mathbf{x} = \sum_{i=1}^{k} \frac{(\mathbf{y}_i, \mathbf{b})\mathbf{x}_i}{\lambda_i(\mathbf{y}_i, \mathbf{x}_i)} + \sum_{i=k+1}^{n} \alpha_i\mathbf{x}_i \tag{10.70}$$

for the solution of $\mathbf{Ax} = \mathbf{b}$ where **A** is square and the $\mathbf{x}_i$, $\mathbf{y}_i$ correspond to right- and left-eigenvectors of **A**. The $\mathbf{x}_i$ correspond to eigenvalues $\lambda_i \neq 0$ for $i = 1, \ldots, k$, and $\mathbf{Ax}_i = \mathbf{0}$, $i = k + 1, \ldots, n$. It is assumed that **A** has n linearly independent right-eigenvectors. None of these restrictions hold for (10.66). Also the μ_i in (10.66) are real, whereas the λ_i in (10.70) may be complex.

Ex. 10.20. Compute the singular values and singular vectors for

$$\mathbf{A} = \begin{bmatrix} 1 & -1 \\ -1 & 1 \\ 2 & -2 \end{bmatrix}$$

and verify (10.65).

Ex. 10.21. Let **A** be an $m \times n$ matrix of rank k. Prove that the vector **x** that (a) minimizes $(\mathbf{b} - \mathbf{Ax}, \mathbf{b} - \mathbf{Ax})$, and (b) minimizes $(\mathbf{x}, \mathbf{x})$, is given by $\mathbf{x} = \mathbf{A}^+\mathbf{b}$, with

$$\mathbf{A}^+ = \mathbf{U}\begin{bmatrix} \mathbf{\Lambda}^{-1} & \mathbf{0} \\ \mathbf{0} & \mathbf{0} \end{bmatrix}\mathbf{V}^H,$$

where the notation is the same as in (10.65). Prove that $\mathbf{A}^+$ is the generalized inverse introduced in Section 5.6, Definition 5.3. Use this formula to compute the generalized inverse of the matrix in Ex. 10.20 and check that the result is the same as that obtained from Definition 5.3. Check that if **x** is given by (10.66), the minimum value of $(\mathbf{x}, \mathbf{x})$ is given by $\alpha_i = 0, i = k + 1, \ldots, n$, i.e., $\mathbf{x} = \mathbf{A}^+\mathbf{b}$.

Ex. 10.22. Why can we not generalize Theorem 9.15 to obtain a formula analogous to (9.56), (9.57) for the solutions of $(\mathbf{A} - \lambda\mathbf{I})\mathbf{x} = \mathbf{f}$ in terms of singular values and vectors?

Miscellaneous Exercises 10

Ex. 10.23. The eigenvalues of a hermitian matrix **A** are all equal if and only if **A** is a multiple of the unit matrix.

Ex. 10.24. If the columns of a square matrix constitute an orthonormal set, then so do the rows. If rows or columns of a unitary matrix are interchanged, then the resulting matrix is again unitary.

Ex. 10.25. If $\mathbf{x} = [\xi, \mathbf{y}]$, where $\|\mathbf{x}\| = 1$, ξ is a real scalar, and **y** is a $1 \times (n - 1)$ row vector, show that

$$\mathbf{Q} = \begin{bmatrix} \xi & \mathbf{y} \\ \mathbf{y}^H & -\mathbf{I} + (1 + \xi)^{-1}\mathbf{y}^H\mathbf{y} \end{bmatrix}$$

is both hermitian and unitary.

Ex. 10.26. Show that the matrix $\begin{bmatrix} 2i & 1 \\ 1 & 0 \end{bmatrix}$ has only one eigenvector. (The point of this example is that symmetric *complex* matrices do not have the nice property of symmetric real or hermitian matrices, of having n linearly independent eigenvectors.)

Ex. 10.27. Prove that two normal matrices are related by a unitary transformation if and only if they have the same eigenvalues.

Ex. 10.28. Prove that a matrix **A** is normal if and only if $\|\mathbf{Ax}\| = \|\mathbf{A}^H\mathbf{x}\|$ for all complex vectors **x**.

Ex. 10.29. Prove that a matrix **A** is hermitian if and only if $(\mathbf{Au}, \mathbf{v}) = (\mathbf{u}, \mathbf{Av})$ for all **u**, **v**.

Ex. 10.30. Prove that (a) A normal matrix is hermitian if and only if its eigenvalues are real.

(b) A normal matrix is unitary if and only if its eigenvalues have modulus unity.

Ex. 10.31. Deduce from one of the theorems in this chapter that a normal matrix has an orthonormal set of eigenvectors.

Ex. 10.32. Prove that a hermitian matrix **A** of order n has n orthogonal eigenvectors by the following argument:

(a) Suppose that there exists a subspace of $n \times 1$ column vectors, of dimension $p \geq 1$, such that, if **x** is in this subspace, then **Ax** is also in the subspace. Prove that **A** has an eigenvector in the subspace.

(b) Suppose that we have found $k < n$ orthogonal eigenvectors $\mathbf{x}_1, \ldots, \mathbf{x}_k$. Define W to be the space of all vectors orthogonal to the $\mathbf{x}_i$. Prove that this space is of dimension ≥ 1. Let **x** be a vector in W. Then

$$(\mathbf{Ax}, \mathbf{x}_i) = (\mathbf{x}, \mathbf{Ax}_i) = \lambda_i(\mathbf{x}, \mathbf{x}_i) = 0.$$

Hence **Ax** lies in W. From (a) this means that **A** has an eigenvector in W.

Complete the proof.

Ex. 10.33. For a general square matrix **A**, deduce from Theorem 10.6 that $\mathbf{A}^r \to \mathbf{0}$ as $r \to \infty$ if and only if all the eigenvalues of **A** have modulus less than unity.

Ex. 10.34. Show (using Householder transformations or otherwise) that any real $m \times n$ matrix **B** can be written in the form

$$\mathbf{B} = \mathbf{QU},$$

where **Q** is orthogonal and **U** is upper triangular.

Ex. 10.35. Use the result in Ex. 10.34 to show that the least squares solution of $\mathbf{Ax} = \mathbf{b}$ is given by solving

$$\mathbf{Ux} = \mathbf{Q}^T\mathbf{b},$$

where the notation is as in Ex. 10.34. (Provided that **Q** and **U** are computed by a stable method, this gives a way of avoiding ill-conditioning associated with the formation of $\mathbf{A}^T\mathbf{A}$ which occurs if we solve the least squares equations $\mathbf{A}^T\mathbf{Ax} = \mathbf{A}^T\mathbf{b}$ directly. An alternative method for improving conditioning was discussed in Section 8.8.)

Ex. 10.36. In Exs. 9.47, 9.48, compute $\mathbf{P}^{-1}$ by finding the left-eigenvectors of **A** instead of inverting **P** directly.

Ex. 10.37. Consider $(\mathbf{A} - \lambda\mathbf{I})\mathbf{x} = \mathbf{f}$, where **A** has n linearly independent right-eigenvectors $\mathbf{x}_i$. If $\mathbf{P} = [\mathbf{x}_1, \ldots, \mathbf{x}_n]$ and $\mathbf{y}_i$ denotes the ith row of $\mathbf{P}^{-1}$ (i.e., the corresponding left-eigenvectors of **A**), show that:

(a) If $\lambda \neq \lambda_i$ for any i,

$$\mathbf{x} = \sum_{i=1}^{n} \frac{(\mathbf{y}_i, \mathbf{f})\mathbf{x}_i}{(\lambda_i - \lambda)(\mathbf{y}_i, \mathbf{x}_i)}.$$

(b) If $\lambda = \lambda_j$ for some j, then no solution exists unless $(\mathbf{y}_j, \mathbf{f}) = 0$ (where this holds for all left-eigenvectors of **A** corresponding to λ_j). If this condition is satisfied, there is an infinity of solutions obtained by omitting from the above sum all the terms corresponding to λ_j, and adding arbitrary multiples of all the right-eigenvectors corresponding to λ_j.

Ex. 10.38. In order to illustrate the complications that can arise in the last exercise if **A** has less than n independent eigenvectors, consider

$$\mathbf{A} = \begin{bmatrix} \alpha & 1 & 0 \\ 0 & \alpha & 1 \\ 0 & 0 & \alpha \end{bmatrix}.$$

Then $(\mathbf{A} - \lambda\mathbf{I})\mathbf{x} = \mathbf{f}$ gives

$$\begin{aligned} (\alpha - \lambda)x_1 + x_2 \qquad &= f_1 \\ (\alpha - \lambda)x_2 + x_3 &= f_2 \\ (\alpha - \lambda)x_3 &= f_3. \end{aligned}$$

This implies

$$x_3 = \frac{f_3}{(\alpha - \lambda)}$$

$$x_2 = \frac{f_2}{(\alpha - \lambda)} - \frac{f_3}{(\alpha - \lambda)^2}$$

$$x_1 = \frac{f_1}{(\alpha - \lambda)} - \frac{f_2}{(\alpha - \lambda)^2} + \frac{f_3}{(\alpha - \lambda)^3}.$$

Ex. 10.39. If **A** is a real square matrix with real eigenvalues, prove that there exists an orthogonal matrix **P** such that $\mathbf{P}^T\mathbf{A}\mathbf{P}$ is triangular. Is this true if **A** has complex eigenvalues?

Ex. 10.40. Prove that if **A** is hermitian with orthonormal eigenvectors $\mathbf{x}_i$,

$$\mathbf{A} = \sum_{i=1}^{n} \lambda_i \mathbf{E}_i, \qquad \mathbf{E}_i = \mathbf{x}_i \mathbf{x}_i^H,$$

where the $\mathbf{x}_i$ are the eigenvectors of **A**. This is known as the *spectral decomposition* of **A**. Verify that

$$\mathbf{E}_i^2 = \mathbf{E}_i, \qquad \mathbf{E}_i\mathbf{E}_j = \mathbf{0} \quad (i \neq j),$$

$$\sum_{i=1}^{n} \mathbf{E}_i = \mathbf{I}, \qquad f(\mathbf{A}) = \sum_{i=1}^{n} f(\lambda_i)\mathbf{E}_i \quad (\text{polynomial } f).$$

Ex. 10.41. Prove that if **A** is a general matrix with n independent right-eigenvectors $\mathbf{x}_i$, and corresponding left-eigenvectors $\mathbf{y}_i$, the results in Ex. 10.40 are still true with $\mathbf{E}_i = (\mathbf{y}_i, \mathbf{x}_i)^{-1}\mathbf{x}_i\mathbf{y}_i^H$.

Ex. 10.42. Two hermitian matrices **A**, **B** of order n commute if and only if it is possible to find a set of n independent eigenvectors common to both **A** and **B**. Explain why this does *not* mean that an eigenvector of **A** must be an eigenvector of **B**. (Compare Exs. 11.31–11.32.)

Ex. 10.43. The complex eigenvalues of an orthogonal matrix **A** occur in pairs of the form $e^{+i\alpha}, e^{-i\alpha}$. If the order of **A** is odd and det **A** $= 1$, then 1 is an eigenvalue of **A**; if det **A** $= -1$, then -1 is an eigenvalue of **A**. If the order of **A** is even and det **A** $= -1$, then 1 and -1 are eigenvalues of **A**; if det **A** $= 1$, then **A** may have no real eigenvalues.

Ex. 10.44. Prove that the eigenvalues and eigenvectors of the hermitian matrix $\mathbf{A} + i\mathbf{B}$, where $\mathbf{A}$, $\mathbf{B}$ are real, can be deduced from those of the real symmetric matrix

$$\begin{bmatrix} \mathbf{A} & -\mathbf{B} \\ \mathbf{B} & \mathbf{A} \end{bmatrix}.$$

Ex. 10.45. Write an essay on possible difficulties in computing the eigenvalues and eigenvectors of tridiagonal matrices, based on, for example, [62], pp. 298–333, and [59], pp. 96–100.

Ex. 10.46. Write an essay on the computation of eigenvalues and eigenvectors in practice, using the Householder method. A convenient reference is the article by Ortega in [59].

Ex. 10.47. Write an essay on the so-called *LR* and *QR* algorithms for finding the eigenvalues and eigenvectors of a matrix. Possible references are Wilkinson [62], and the article by Parlett in [59].

Ex. 10.48. Let $\mathbf{A}$ be a real symmetric matrix and $\mathbf{u}_1$ an arbitrary real vector. Set

$$\mathbf{v}_1 = \mathbf{A}\mathbf{u}_1, \qquad \mathbf{u}_2 = \mathbf{v}_1 - \alpha_1\mathbf{u}_1,$$

where α_1 is determined so as to make $\mathbf{u}_2$ and $\mathbf{u}_1$ orthogonal, which gives $\alpha_1 = (\mathbf{u}_1, \mathbf{v}_1)/(\mathbf{u}_1, \mathbf{u}_1)$. Next, form

$$\mathbf{v}_2 = \mathbf{A}\mathbf{u}_2, \qquad \mathbf{u}_3 = \mathbf{v}_2 - \alpha_2\mathbf{u}_2 - \beta_1\mathbf{u}_1,$$

where α_2, β_1 are determined so that $\mathbf{u}_3$ is orthogonal to $\mathbf{u}_2$ and $\mathbf{u}_1$. This gives $\alpha_2 = (\mathbf{u}_2, \mathbf{v}_2)/(\mathbf{u}_2, \mathbf{u}_2)$, $\beta_1 = (\mathbf{u}_1, \mathbf{v}_2)/(\mathbf{u}_1, \mathbf{u}_1)$. Next, form

$$\mathbf{v}_3 = \mathbf{A}\mathbf{u}_3, \qquad \mathbf{u}_4 = \mathbf{v}_3 - \alpha_3\mathbf{u}_3 - \beta_2\mathbf{u}_2 - \gamma_1\mathbf{u}_1,$$

where α_3, β_2, γ_1 are determined so that $\mathbf{u}_4$ is orthogonal to $\mathbf{u}_3$, $\mathbf{u}_2$, $\mathbf{u}_1$. Prove that this gives $\gamma_1 = 0$. Show that at the general step we have

$$\mathbf{v}_r = \mathbf{A}\mathbf{u}_r, \qquad \mathbf{u}_{r+1} = \mathbf{v}_r - \alpha_r\mathbf{u}_r - \beta_{r-1}\mathbf{u}_{r-1},$$

where $\mathbf{u}_{r+1}$ is orthogonal to $\mathbf{u}_1, \ldots, \mathbf{u}_r$. Prove also that $\mathbf{u}_{n+1}$ must be identically zero. Let $\mathbf{x}$ be an eigenvector of $\mathbf{A}$ and set

$$\mathbf{x} = \alpha_1\mathbf{u}_1 + \ldots + \alpha_n\mathbf{u}_n.$$

Form $\mathbf{A}\mathbf{x}$ and express $\mathbf{A}\mathbf{u}_r = \mathbf{v}_r$ in terms of the $\mathbf{u}_s$ by the above formulae. Deduce that the eigenvalues of $\mathbf{A}$ are the same as the eigenvalues of the tridiagonal matrix

$$\begin{bmatrix} \alpha_1 & \beta_1 & 0 & \ldots & 0 \\ 1 & \alpha_2 & \beta_2 & \ldots & 0 \\ 0 & 1 & \alpha_3 & \ldots & 0 \\ & & \ldots & & \\ 0 & 0 & 0 & \ldots & \alpha_n \end{bmatrix}.$$

(The orthogonality conditions used to determine the α_i, β_i also minimize the $\|\mathbf{u}_i\|$. This is why the method, due to C. Lanczos, in also known as the method of *minimized iterations*.)

11 Similarity Transformations

11.1 Introduction

In the last chapter we were very much concerned with properties of eigenvectors connected with the idea of orthogonality. This led to the study of unitary transformations, in which the matrix **A** is transformed into a matrix **B** by means of the formula

$$\mathbf{B} = \mathbf{P}^H\mathbf{A}\mathbf{P}, \tag{11.1}$$

where **P** is a unitary matrix, i.e., $\mathbf{P}^{-1} = \mathbf{P}^H$. In this chapter we consider the more general type of transformation

$$\mathbf{B} = \mathbf{P}^{-1}\mathbf{A}\mathbf{P}. \tag{11.2}$$

Although (11.1) is a special case of (11.2), the theory of the two transformations develops along somewhat different lines. For this reason we have developed the theories associated with (11.1) and (11.2) independently, accepting a small amount of duplication in the interests of clarity.

DEFINITION **11.1.** If there exists a nonsingular matrix **P** such that $\mathbf{P}^{-1}\mathbf{A}\mathbf{P} = \mathbf{B}$, the matrix **B** is said to be *similar* to **A**, and we say that **B** is obtained from **A** by means of a *similarity transformation.*

This chapter is devoted to the study of similarity transformations. The first key result is Theorem 11.4, that a square matrix of order n can be reduced to diagonal form by a similarity transformation if and only if it has n linearly independent eigenvectors (Figure 11.1). One of the chief objectives is to throw light on what happens if a matrix has less than n independent eigenvectors. This case was not considered in Chapters 9 and 10. The key result is that every matrix can be reduced to the Jordan canonical form (Theorem 11.12). It is important

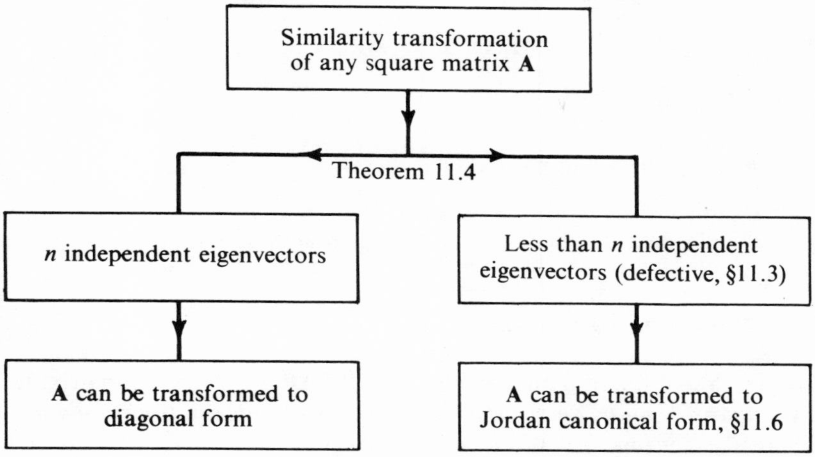

Figure 11.1 Similarity transformations.

for the reader to realize that although it takes a lot of painstaking analysis to establish this result theoretically, the practical procedure for carrying out the reduction, as outlined following (11.58), and used in Exs. 11.13, 11.14, is comparatively straightforward. The point of the theory is that it guarantees that the practical procedure will work, at least when rounding errors are absent.

We state some simple properties of similarity transformations.

THEOREM **11.1.** *Similarity is an equivalence relation, i.e.,* **A** *is similar to itself; if* **B** *is similar to* **A**, *then* **A** *is similar to* **B**; *and if* **C** *is similar to* **B** *and* **B** *to* **A**, *then* **C** *is similar to* **A**.

Proof: Using $\mathbf{P} = \mathbf{I}$, we see immediately that **A** is similar to **A**. If $\mathbf{P}^{-1}\mathbf{AP} = \mathbf{B}$ then $\mathbf{A} = \mathbf{PBP}^{-1} = \mathbf{Q}^{-1}\mathbf{BQ}$, where $\mathbf{Q} = \mathbf{P}^{-1}$, so that **A** is similar to **B**. If $\mathbf{C} = \mathbf{P}^{-1}\mathbf{BP}$, $\mathbf{B} = \mathbf{Q}^{-1}\mathbf{AQ}$, then $\mathbf{C} = (\mathbf{QP})^{-1}\mathbf{A}(\mathbf{QP})$, so that **C** is similar to **B**.

THEOREM **11.2.** (i) *Similar matrices have the same characteristic equation and the same eigenvalues.*

(ii) *If* $\mathbf{P}^{-1}\mathbf{AP} = \mathbf{B}$ *and* **x** *is an eigenvector of* **A**, *then* $\mathbf{P}^{-1}\mathbf{x}$ *is an eigenvector of* **B**.

Proof: Since $\det \mathbf{P}^{-1} \det \mathbf{P} = \det(\mathbf{P}^{-1}\mathbf{P}) = \det \mathbf{I} = 1$, we have

$$\det(\mathbf{B} - \lambda\mathbf{I}) = \det \mathbf{P}^{-1}(\mathbf{A} - \lambda\mathbf{I})\mathbf{P}$$
$$= \det \mathbf{P}^{-1} \det(\mathbf{A} - \lambda\mathbf{I}) \det \mathbf{P} = \det(\mathbf{A} - \lambda\mathbf{I}),$$

which proves (i). If $\mathbf{Ax} = \lambda\mathbf{x}$, we have

$$(\mathbf{P}^{-1}\mathbf{AP})(\mathbf{P}^{-1}\mathbf{x}) = \lambda(\mathbf{P}^{-1}\mathbf{x}), \tag{11.3}$$

or

$$\mathbf{B}(\mathbf{P}^{-1}\mathbf{x}) = \lambda(\mathbf{P}^{-1}\mathbf{x}),$$

which proves (ii), since $\mathbf{P}^{-1}\mathbf{x}$ cannot be zero.

Ex. 11.1. If **A** and **B** are similar, prove that det **A** = det **B**.

Ex. 11.2. If $\mathbf{P}^{-1}\mathbf{AP} = \mathbf{D}$, where **D** is a lower triangular matrix, prove that the diagonal elements of **D** are the eigenvalues of **A**.

11.2 Reduction to Diagonal Form

If it is possible to find a matrix **P** such that $\mathbf{P}^{-1}\mathbf{AP}$ is a diagonal matrix, we say that **P** *reduces* **A** *to diagonal form by means of a similarity transformation.* We have already met this type of reduction in Section 9.4, where we illustrated the usefulness of the reduction by showing how it could be used to find $\mathbf{A}^k$ for arbitrary positive integral k.

The basic theorem that we require for the present discussion is the following. (Compare Theorem 10.18. Strictly speaking, we should use the term "right-eigenvector" but we omit "right" when there is no risk of confusion.)

THEOREM **11.3.** *Corresponding to a given matrix* **A** *with n linearly independent eigenvectors, there exists a nonsingular matrix* **P** *such that*

$$\text{(i)} \qquad \mathbf{P}^{-1}\mathbf{AP} = \mathbf{\Lambda}, \tag{11.4}$$

$$\text{(ii)} \qquad \mathbf{A} = \mathbf{P\Lambda P}^{-1}, \tag{11.5}$$

where $\mathbf{\Lambda}$ *is a diagonal matrix whose diagonal elements are the eigenvalues of* **A**. *Conversely, if, for a given* **A**, *a matrix* **P** *and a diagonal matrix* $\mathbf{\Lambda}$ *exist such that* (11.4) *is true, then* **A** *has n linearly independent eigenvectors, which are the columns of* **P**, *and the diagonal elements of* $\mathbf{\Lambda}$ *are the eigenvalues of* **A**.

Proof: Suppose that **A** has n linearly independent eigenvectors $\mathbf{x}_1, \ldots, \mathbf{x}_n$. Set

$$\mathbf{P} = [\mathbf{x}_1, \ldots, \mathbf{x}_n]. \tag{11.6}$$

We have

$$\begin{aligned} \mathbf{AP} &= [\mathbf{Ax}_1, \ldots, \mathbf{Ax}_n] \\ &= [\lambda_1\mathbf{x}_1, \ldots, \lambda_n\mathbf{x}_n] = \mathbf{P\Lambda}, \end{aligned} \tag{11.7}$$

where $\mathbf{\Lambda}$ is a diagonal matrix whose eigenvalues are $\lambda_1, \ldots, \lambda_n$ (not necessarily distinct).

$$\mathbf{\Lambda} = \begin{bmatrix} \lambda_1 & 0 & \ldots & 0 \\ 0 & \lambda_2 & \ldots & 0 \\ & & \ldots & \\ 0 & 0 & \ldots & \lambda_n \end{bmatrix}. \tag{11.8}$$

Since the columns of **P** are linearly independent, **P** is nonsingular, and we can premultiply (11.7) by $\mathbf{P}^{-1}$, which gives (11.4). Conversely, suppose that a matrix **P** exists such that (11.4) is true. Multiplication by **P** gives

$$\mathbf{AP} = \mathbf{P\Lambda}.$$

If we denote the ith column of **P** by $\mathbf{x}_i$ so that **P** has the form (11.6), this means that

$$\mathbf{A}[\mathbf{x}_1, \ldots, \mathbf{x}_n] = [\mathbf{x}_1, \ldots, \mathbf{x}_n]\mathbf{\Lambda},$$

or

$$\mathbf{A}\mathbf{x}_i = \lambda_i \mathbf{x}_i.$$

Hence, the $\mathbf{x}_i$ are eigenvectors of **A** corresponding to eigenvalues which are the diagonal elements of $\mathbf{\Lambda}$. These eigenvectors must be linearly independent since **P** is invertible.

It is now easy to characterize the class of matrices that can be reduced to diagonal form by a similarity transformation. (Compare the analogous result for unitary transformations in Theorem 10.8).

THEOREM **11.4.** *A general square matrix* **A** *can be reduced to diagonal form by a similarity transformation if and only if* **A** *possesses n linearly independent eigenvectors.*

Proof: This theorem is simply a restatement of Theorem 11.3.

The situation with regard to similarity transformations is summarized in Figure 11.1, which should be compared with Figure 10.2 for unitary transformations.

Ex. 11.3. Illustrate Theorem 11.3 numerically, using

$$\mathbf{A} = \begin{bmatrix} 1 & 1 & 0 \\ 0 & 2 & 1 \\ 0 & 0 & 3 \end{bmatrix}. \tag{11.9}$$

Solution: The eigenvalues are the diagonal elements $\lambda_1 = 1$, $\lambda_2 = 2$, $\lambda_3 = 3$. The corresponding eigenvectors, written as the columns of a matrix, give

$$\mathbf{P} = \begin{bmatrix} 1 & 1 & 1 \\ 0 & 1 & 2 \\ 0 & 0 & 2 \end{bmatrix}.$$

A straightforward computation leads to

$$\mathbf{P}^{-1} = \tfrac{1}{2}\begin{bmatrix} 2 & -2 & 1 \\ 0 & 2 & -2 \\ 0 & 0 & 1 \end{bmatrix}.$$

The reader can check that

$$\mathbf{P}^{-1}\mathbf{A}\mathbf{P} = \begin{bmatrix} 1 & 0 & 0 \\ 0 & 2 & 0 \\ 0 & 0 & 3 \end{bmatrix}.$$

One of the reasons why the above theorem is extremely useful in practice is the following:

THEOREM **11.5.** *If a matrix* $\mathbf{P}$ *exists such that* $\mathbf{A} = \mathbf{P}\mathbf{\Lambda}\mathbf{P}^{-1}$, *where* $\mathbf{\Lambda}$ *is diagonal, then*

(i)
$$\mathbf{A}^k = \mathbf{P}\mathbf{\Lambda}^k\mathbf{P}^{-1} \tag{11.10}$$

for any positive integer k. If $\mathbf{A}$ *is nonsingular the result is true for any negative integer k. In particular,* $\mathbf{A}^{-1} = \mathbf{P}\mathbf{\Lambda}^{-1}\mathbf{P}^{-1}$.

(ii) *If* $f(x)$ *is a polynomial of degree m,*

$$f(x) = a_0x^m + a_1x^{m-1} + \ldots + a_m, \tag{11.11}$$

and by $f(\mathbf{A})$ *we mean*

$$f(\mathbf{A}) = a_0\mathbf{A}^m + a_1\mathbf{A}^{m-1} + \ldots + a_m\mathbf{I}, \tag{11.12}$$

then

$$f(\mathbf{A}) = \mathbf{P}\mathbf{D}\mathbf{P}^{-1}, \tag{11.13}$$

where $\mathbf{D}$ *is a diagonal matrix with diagonal elements* $f(\lambda_i)$.

Proof: For any positive integer k we have

$$\mathbf{A}^k = (\mathbf{P}\mathbf{\Lambda}\mathbf{P}^{-1})(\mathbf{P}\mathbf{\Lambda}\mathbf{P}^{-1})(\mathbf{P}\mathbf{\Lambda}\mathbf{P}^{-1}) \ldots$$

repeated k times. The associative law allows us to remove the parentheses. Since $\mathbf{P}^{-1}\mathbf{P} = \mathbf{I}$, the product collapses to give the required result immediately. If $k = -1$, we have

$$\mathbf{A}^{-1} = (\mathbf{P}\mathbf{\Lambda}\mathbf{P}^{-1})^{-1} = (\mathbf{P}^{-1})^{-1}\mathbf{\Lambda}^{-1}\mathbf{P}^{-1} = \mathbf{P}\mathbf{\Lambda}^{-1}\mathbf{P}^{-1},$$

so that the result is true for $k = -1$. The method used to prove the result for positive k can now be used to prove it for negative integer k. To prove (ii) we use part (i). From (11.10), (11.12),

$$\begin{aligned} f(\mathbf{A}) &= a_0\mathbf{P}\mathbf{\Lambda}^m\mathbf{P}^{-1} + a_1\mathbf{P}\mathbf{\Lambda}^{m-1}\mathbf{P}^{-1} + \ldots + a_m\mathbf{P}\mathbf{P}^{-1} \\ &= \mathbf{P}(a_0\mathbf{\Lambda}^m + a_1\mathbf{\Lambda}^{m-1} + \ldots + a_m\mathbf{I})\mathbf{P}^{-1}. \end{aligned}$$

Since $\mathbf{\Lambda}^r$ is a diagonal matrix with diagonal elements λ_i^r, this proves the required result.

Ex. 11.4. Find $\mathbf{A}^k$ for any integer k for the matrix $\mathbf{A}$ in (11.9).

Solution: Direct application of (11.10), using the matrix $\mathbf{P}$ found in Ex. 11.3, gives

$$\mathbf{A}^k = \tfrac{1}{2}\begin{bmatrix} 1 & 1 & 1 \\ 0 & 1 & 2 \\ 0 & 0 & 2 \end{bmatrix}\begin{bmatrix} 1 & 0 & 0 \\ 0 & 2^k & 0 \\ 0 & 0 & 3^k \end{bmatrix}\begin{bmatrix} 2 & -2 & 1 \\ 0 & 2 & -2 \\ 0 & 0 & 1 \end{bmatrix}$$

$$= \tfrac{1}{2}\begin{bmatrix} 2, & -2 + 2^{k+1}, & 1 - 2^{k+1} + 3^k \\ 0, & 2^{k+1}, & -2^{k+1} + 2 \cdot 3^k \\ 0, & 0, & 2 \cdot 3^k \end{bmatrix}.$$

This example shows the point of the developments in this section, in that we have produced a simple expression for the kth power of a matrix, for general k. It does not require much imagination to see that we could go on to consider functions of a matrix $\mathbf{A}$ that are more general than the polynomial (11.12). Since

$$e^x = 1 + x + \frac{1}{2!}x^2 + \frac{1}{3!}x^3 + \dots,$$

we could define

$$\exp \mathbf{A} = e^{\mathbf{A}} = \mathbf{I} + \mathbf{A} + \frac{1}{2!}\mathbf{A}^2 + \frac{1}{3!}\mathbf{A}^3 + \dots. \tag{11.14}$$

In the case where $\mathbf{A}$ has linearly independent eigenvectors this would lead to the following simple expression for $\exp \mathbf{A}$,

$$\exp \mathbf{A} = \mathbf{PDP}^{-1}, \tag{11.15}$$

where $\mathbf{P}$ is the matrix whose columns are the eigenvectors, as before, and $\mathbf{D}$ is a diagonal matrix whose elements are $\exp \lambda_i$. However, consideration of the convergence of infinite matrix series like (11.14) would take us outside the scope of the present discussion (see Ex. 13.40).

11.3 Defective Matrices

So far we have been concerned with matrices that have n linearly independent eigenvectors. It is easy to produce examples of matrices that have less than n linearly independent eigenvectors. Such matrices are said to be *defective*. We have already shown that a matrix with n distinct eigenvalues must have n linearly independent eigenvectors [Theorem 9.3(ii)]. Also, it follows directly from Theorem 11.4 that normal matrices have n independent eigenvectors. Hence, defective matrices must have repeated eigenvalues and they cannot be normal. However, if a matrix is not normal, or if it has repeated eigenvalues, this does not mean that it is defective.

We give examples to illustrate that a third-order matrix with one eigenvalue of multiplicity 3 may have 1, 2, or 3 independent eigenvectors.

Ex. 11.5. Show that

$$\mathbf{A} = \begin{bmatrix} \alpha & 0 & 0 \\ 0 & \alpha & 0 \\ 0 & 0 & \alpha \end{bmatrix}$$

has precisely three independent eigenvectors.

Solution: The matrix **A** has the eigenvalue $\lambda = \alpha$ of multiplicity 3. The equation for the eigenvectors is simply $\mathbf{0} \cdot \mathbf{x} = \mathbf{0}$, so that any 3×1 column vector is an eigenvector. The corresponding vector space spanned by these vectors is V_3, with dimension 3, so that **A** has exactly three linearly independent eigenvectors.

Ex. 11.6. Show that

$$\mathbf{A} = \begin{bmatrix} \alpha & 1 & 0 \\ 0 & \alpha & 0 \\ 0 & 0 & \alpha \end{bmatrix}$$

has precisely two independent eigenvectors.

Solution: **A** has the eigenvalue $\lambda = \alpha$ of multiplicity 3. The equation $(\mathbf{A} - \alpha\mathbf{I})\mathbf{x} = \mathbf{0}$ for the eigenvectors gives $x_2 = 0$, with x_1 and x_3 arbitrary. Hence, the general eigenvector has the form

$$\begin{bmatrix} x_1 \\ 0 \\ x_3 \end{bmatrix} = x_1 \begin{bmatrix} 1 \\ 0 \\ 0 \end{bmatrix} + x_3 \begin{bmatrix} 0 \\ 0 \\ 1 \end{bmatrix}.$$

This is a two-dimensional vector space, and **A** has exactly two linearly independent eigenvectors.

Ex. 11.7. Show that

$$\mathbf{A} = \begin{bmatrix} \alpha & 1 & 0 \\ 0 & \alpha & 1 \\ 0 & 0 & \alpha \end{bmatrix}$$

has precisely one linearly independent eigenvector.

Solution: **A** has the eigenvalue $\lambda = \alpha$ of multiplicity 3. The equation for the eigenvectors gives $x_2 = x_3 = 0$, so that the general eigenvector has the form

$$\begin{bmatrix} x_1 \\ 0 \\ 0 \end{bmatrix} = x_1 \begin{bmatrix} 1 \\ 0 \\ 0 \end{bmatrix},$$

which is a one-dimensional space, and there is only one linearly independent eigenvector.

Theorem 9.2 stated that eigenvectors corresponding to a given eigenvalue constitute a vector space, but the only thing we said about the dimension of this vector space was that it is at least 1. We now prove that this dimension cannot be greater than the multiplicity of the eigenvalue.

THEOREM **11.6.** *The number of linearly independent eigenvectors corresponding to a given eigenvalue is not greater than the multiplicity of the eigenvalue.*

Proof: Suppose that there are q independent eigenvectors $\mathbf{x}_1, \ldots, \mathbf{x}_q$ corresponding to an eigenvalue λ_1 of multiplicity k. Construct a nonsingular matrix with $\mathbf{x}_1, \ldots, \mathbf{x}_q$ as the first q columns. We denote this matrix by $\mathbf{Q}$ and write $\mathbf{Q}$ and $\mathbf{Q}^{-1}$ in partitioned matrix notation in the form

$$\mathbf{Q} = [\mathbf{U}, \mathbf{V}], \qquad \mathbf{Q}^{-1} = \begin{bmatrix} \mathbf{R} \\ \mathbf{S} \end{bmatrix}, \tag{11.16}$$

where $\mathbf{U}$ is $n \times q$ and $\mathbf{R}$ is $q \times n$. The columns of $\mathbf{U}$ are eigenvectors $\mathbf{x}_i$ of $\mathbf{A}$ corresponding to the eigenvalue λ_1, so that

$$\mathbf{AU} = \lambda_1 \mathbf{U}. \tag{11.17}$$

Also,

$$\mathbf{Q}^{-1}\mathbf{Q} = \begin{bmatrix} \mathbf{R} \\ \mathbf{S} \end{bmatrix} [\mathbf{U}, \mathbf{V}] = \begin{bmatrix} \mathbf{RU} & \mathbf{RV} \\ \mathbf{SU} & \mathbf{SV} \end{bmatrix} = \begin{bmatrix} \mathbf{I}_1 & \mathbf{0} \\ \mathbf{0} & \mathbf{I}_2 \end{bmatrix},$$

where $\mathbf{I}_1$ is a unit matrix of order q, so that

$$\mathbf{RU} = \mathbf{I}_1, \qquad \mathbf{RV} = \mathbf{0}, \qquad \mathbf{SU} = \mathbf{0}. \tag{11.18}$$

We have

$$\begin{aligned} \mathbf{Q}^{-1}\mathbf{AQ} &= \begin{bmatrix} \mathbf{R} \\ \mathbf{S} \end{bmatrix} \mathbf{A}[\mathbf{U} \quad \mathbf{V}] = \begin{bmatrix} \mathbf{RAU} & \mathbf{RAV} \\ \mathbf{SAU} & \mathbf{SAV} \end{bmatrix} \\ &= \begin{bmatrix} \lambda_1\mathbf{RU} & \mathbf{RAV} \\ \lambda_1\mathbf{SU} & \mathbf{SAV} \end{bmatrix} = \begin{bmatrix} \lambda_1\mathbf{I}_1 & \mathbf{RAV} \\ \mathbf{0} & \mathbf{SAV} \end{bmatrix}. \end{aligned}$$

Hence, by straightforward expansion,

$$\det(\mathbf{Q}^{-1}\mathbf{AQ} - \lambda\mathbf{I}) = (\lambda_1 - \lambda)^q \det(\mathbf{SAV} - \lambda\mathbf{I}). \tag{11.19}$$

This is the characteristic polynomial of $\mathbf{Q}^{-1}\mathbf{AQ}$ and we know that it is the same as the characteristic polynomial of $\mathbf{A}$. Since λ_1 is of multiplicity k, we know that the characteristic polynomial of $\mathbf{A}$ has the form

$$(\lambda_1 - \lambda)^k g(\lambda), \tag{11.20}$$

where $g(\lambda_1) \neq 0$. A comparison of (11.19) and (11.20) shows that $q \leq k$, which is the required result.

11.4 Reduction to Triangular Form

We know that defective matrices (i.e., matrices with less than n linearly independent eigenvectors) cannot be reduced to diagonal form by means of a similarity transformation, since matrices that can be reduced to diagonal form are not defective (Theorem 11.3). However, it is natural to ask: What is the simplest standard or canonical form to which a general matrix $\mathbf{A}$ can be reduced by means of a similarity transformation? A partial answer is given by the following theorem. As stated, the theorem is an immediate consequence of Theorem 10.6, but we give a proof from first principles, partly to show that there is considerable latitude in the choice of $\mathbf{P}$. There is no need for $\mathbf{P}$ to be unitary, as in the previous theorem.

THEOREM **11.7.** *If* $\mathbf{A}$ *is a general matrix with eigenvalues* $\lambda_1, \ldots, \lambda_n$ *(which need not be distinct), then there exists a nonsingular matrix* $\mathbf{P}$ *such that*

$$\mathbf{P}^{-1}\mathbf{A}\mathbf{P} = \mathbf{U}, \tag{11.21}$$

where $\mathbf{U}$ *is an upper triangular matrix with* $\lambda_1, \ldots, \lambda_n$ *along the diagonal.*

Proof: The eigenvalues of $\mathbf{U}$ are the diagonal elements so that, since similar matrices have the same eigenvalues [Theorem 11.2(i)], the eigenvalues of $\mathbf{A}$ are the diagonal elements of $\mathbf{U}$. Let $\mathbf{x}_1$ be an eigenvector of $\mathbf{A}$ corresponding to an eigenvalue λ_1. Let $\mathbf{Q}$ be *any* nonsingular matrix with $\mathbf{x}_1$ as its first column,

$$\mathbf{Q} = [\mathbf{x}_1, \mathbf{Q}'].$$

Then

$$\mathbf{A}\mathbf{Q} = [\lambda_1\mathbf{x}_1, \mathbf{A}\mathbf{Q}']. \tag{11.22}$$

If $\mathbf{e}_1$ denotes a unit column vector with first element unity and other elements zero, we have $\mathbf{x}_1 = \mathbf{Q}\mathbf{e}_1$, so that $\mathbf{Q}^{-1}\mathbf{x}_1 = \mathbf{Q}^{-1}\mathbf{Q}\mathbf{e}_1 = \mathbf{e}_1$. From (11.22) this means that

$$\mathbf{Q}^{-1}\mathbf{A}\mathbf{Q} = [\lambda_1\mathbf{e}_1, \mathbf{Q}^{-1}\mathbf{A}\mathbf{Q}'] = \begin{bmatrix} \lambda_1 & \boldsymbol{\alpha}_1 \\ \mathbf{0} & \mathbf{A}_1 \end{bmatrix}, \tag{11.23}$$

say, where $\boldsymbol{\alpha}_1$ is $1 \times (n-1)$ and $\mathbf{A}_1$ is $(n-1) \times (n-1)$. If $n = 2$, the theorem is proved. We now use induction. Suppose that the theorem is true for matrices of order $n - 1$. Since $\mathbf{A}_1$ is of order $n - 1$, there then exists a matrix $\mathbf{R}$, say, such that

$$\mathbf{R}^{-1}\mathbf{A}_i\mathbf{R} = \begin{bmatrix} \lambda_2 & v_{23} & \ldots & v_{2n} \\ 0 & \lambda_3 & \ldots & v_{3n} \\ & & \ldots & \\ 0 & 0 & \ldots & \lambda_n \end{bmatrix}. \tag{11.24}$$

The diagonal elements are $\lambda_2, \ldots, \lambda_n$, since the matrix on the right of (11.23) has the same eigenvalues as $\mathbf{A}$, namely $\lambda_1, \ldots, \lambda_n$, so that $\mathbf{A}_1$ must have eigenvalues $\lambda_2, \ldots, \lambda_n$, which means that the matrix on the right of (11.24) must have the same eigenvalues. Set

$$\mathbf{S} = \begin{bmatrix} 1 & \mathbf{0} \\ \mathbf{0} & \mathbf{R} \end{bmatrix}. \tag{11.25}$$

We have

$$(\mathbf{QS})^{-1}\mathbf{A}(\mathbf{QS}) = \mathbf{S}^{-1}\mathbf{Q}^{-1}\mathbf{AQS}$$

$$= \begin{bmatrix} 1 & \mathbf{0} \\ \mathbf{0} & \mathbf{R}^{-1} \end{bmatrix}\begin{bmatrix} \lambda_1 & \boldsymbol{\alpha}_1 \\ \mathbf{0} & \mathbf{A}_1 \end{bmatrix}\begin{bmatrix} 1 & \mathbf{0} \\ \mathbf{0} & \mathbf{R} \end{bmatrix} = \begin{bmatrix} \lambda_1 & \boldsymbol{\alpha}_1\mathbf{R} \\ \mathbf{0} & \mathbf{R}^{-1}\mathbf{A}_1\mathbf{R} \end{bmatrix} = \mathbf{U}, \tag{11.26}$$

where, in view of (11.24), $\mathbf{U}$ is an upper triangular matrix with $\lambda_1, \ldots, \lambda_n$ along the diagonal. This proves the required result (11.21).

It may help the reader if we give a numerical example using the same procedure as that used in the theorem, although we shall see later that a different method is usually more convenient in practice. (See Ex. 11.13.)

Ex. 11.8. Reduce the matrix

$$\mathbf{A} = \begin{bmatrix} 5 & 4 & 3 \\ -1 & 0 & -3 \\ 1 & -2 & 1 \end{bmatrix} \tag{11.27}$$

to upper triangular form by a similarity transformation.

Solution: The eigenvalues are found to be $\lambda_1 = -2$, $\lambda_2 = \lambda_3 = 4$, with two independent eigenvectors. We choose any eigenvector as the first column of a matrix, say $\mathbf{x}_1 = [1 \quad 0 \quad 1]^T$, corresponding to $\lambda_1 = -2$. We choose the second and third columns so that the resulting matrix $\mathbf{Q}$ is nonsingular. We can always choose these to be unit vectors, and we find, for instance,

$$\mathbf{Q} = \begin{bmatrix} 1 & 0 & 0 \\ -1 & 1 & 0 \\ -1 & 0 & 1 \end{bmatrix}, \qquad \mathbf{Q}^{-1} = \begin{bmatrix} 1 & 0 & 0 \\ 1 & 1 & 0 \\ 1 & 0 & 1 \end{bmatrix},$$

$$\mathbf{Q}^{-1}\mathbf{AQ} = \begin{bmatrix} -2 & 4 & 3 \\ 0 & 4 & 0 \\ 0 & 2 & 4 \end{bmatrix}.$$

The matrix

$$\begin{bmatrix} 4 & 0 \\ 2 & 4 \end{bmatrix}$$

has a repeated eigenvalue of 4, as it must have. There is only one corresponding eigenvector $\mathbf{z}_1 = [0, 1]^T$ which we use as the first column of a

2×2 matrix $\mathbf{R}$, picking any suitable second column that makes the matrix nonsingular. This is then used to form $\mathbf{S}$ defined in (11.25):

$$\mathbf{R} = \begin{bmatrix} 0 & 1 \\ 1 & 0 \end{bmatrix}, \qquad \mathbf{S} = \begin{bmatrix} 1 & 0 & 0 \\ 0 & 0 & 1 \\ 0 & 1 & 0 \end{bmatrix}, \qquad \mathbf{S}^{-1} = \begin{bmatrix} 1 & 0 & 0 \\ 0 & 0 & 1 \\ 0 & 1 & 0 \end{bmatrix},$$

$$\mathbf{S}^{-1}(\mathbf{Q}^{-1}\mathbf{A}\mathbf{Q})\mathbf{S} = \begin{bmatrix} -2 & 3 & 4 \\ 0 & 4 & 2 \\ 0 & 0 & 4 \end{bmatrix}. \tag{11.28}$$

This is upper triangular, as required.

The upper triangular form obtained in Theorem 11.7 can be simplified still further.

THEOREM **11.8.** *Suppose that an upper triangular matrix* $\mathbf{U}$ *has the following structure:*

$$\mathbf{U} = \begin{bmatrix} \mathbf{U}_{11} & \mathbf{U}_{12} & \dots & \mathbf{U}_{1s} \\ \mathbf{0} & \mathbf{U}_{22} & \dots & \mathbf{U}_{2s} \\ & & \dots & \\ \mathbf{0} & \mathbf{0} & \dots & \mathbf{U}_{ss} \end{bmatrix}, \tag{11.29}$$

where $\mathbf{U}_{ii}$ *is an upper triangular matrix, all of whose diagonal elements are equal to* λ_i. *Also,* $\lambda_1, \dots, \lambda_s$ *are distinct. Then there exists a nonsingular matrix* $\mathbf{P}$ *such that*

$$\mathbf{P}^{-1}\mathbf{U}\mathbf{P} = \begin{bmatrix} \mathbf{V}_1 & \mathbf{0} & \dots & \mathbf{0} \\ \mathbf{0} & \mathbf{V}_2 & \dots & \mathbf{0} \\ & & \dots & \\ \mathbf{0} & \mathbf{0} & \dots & \mathbf{V}_s \end{bmatrix}, \tag{11.30}$$

where $\mathbf{V}_i$ *is an upper triangular matrix, all of whose diagonal elements are equal to* λ_i.

Proof: Let $\mathbf{Q} = \mathbf{I} + \mathbf{K}$, where $\mathbf{K}$ is a matrix all of whose elements are zero except the (p, q)th element which is k, $p < q$. It is easily verified that $\mathbf{Q}^{-1} = \mathbf{I} - \mathbf{K}$. The similarity transformation $\mathbf{Q}^{-1}\mathbf{U}\mathbf{Q}$, where $\mathbf{U}$ is upper triangular, transforms u_{pq} $(p < q)$ into

$$u_{pq} - k(u_{qq} - u_{pp}), \tag{11.31}$$

and otherwise modifies only elements in $\mathbf{U}$ in the pth row to the right of u_{pq}, and in the qth column above u_{pq}. If $u_{pp} \neq u_{qq}$, we can choose $k = u_{pq}/(u_{qq} - u_{pp})$ and then (11.31) shows that the (p, q)th element in $\mathbf{Q}^{-1}\mathbf{U}\mathbf{Q}$ is zero. Returning to the notation (11.29), the elements u_{pq} such that the corresponding diagonal elements u_{pp}, u_{qq} are distinct lie in rectangular blocks. A sequence of similarity transformations of the above type can be carried out so as to reduce these u_{pq} to zero, row by row, starting at the left of the bottom row of the lowest rectangular block. This will give a matrix of the form (11.30).

Ex. 11.9. Reduce the upper triangular matrix (11.28) to the form (11.30) by means of a similarity transformation.

Solution: The proof of the theorem tells us that we first reduce the (1, 2) element to zero. Equation (11.31) gives $k = \frac{1}{2}$ and we find

$$\begin{bmatrix} 1 & -\frac{1}{2} & 0 \\ 0 & 1 & 0 \\ 0 & 0 & 1 \end{bmatrix}\begin{bmatrix} -2 & 3 & 4 \\ 0 & 4 & 2 \\ 0 & 0 & 4 \end{bmatrix}\begin{bmatrix} 1 & \frac{1}{2} & 0 \\ 0 & 1 & 0 \\ 0 & 0 & 1 \end{bmatrix} = \begin{bmatrix} -2 & 0 & 3 \\ 0 & 4 & 2 \\ 0 & 0 & 4 \end{bmatrix}.$$

The (1, 3) element is reduced to zero in a similar way. Details are left to the reader. However the (2, 3) element *cannot* be reduced to zero since the (2, 2) and (3, 3) diagonal elements are equal.

Note that Exs. 11.8, 11.9 have been included only to illustrate the theorems we have obtained. In practice, the matrix (11.27) would be reduced directly to the Jordan canonical form as in Ex. 11.13.

11.5 Nilpotent Matrices

In this section we consider the reduction of the submatrices that occur on the diagonal of (11.30) in Theorem 11.8. These are upper triangular, with equal diagonal elements:

$$\mathbf{V} = \begin{bmatrix} \lambda & v_{12} & \dots & v_{1q} \\ 0 & \lambda & \dots & v_{2q} \\ & & \dots & \\ 0 & 0 & \dots & \lambda \end{bmatrix}. \tag{11.32}$$

In order to deal with this matrix we first consider the reduction of a more general type of matrix.

DEFINITION **11.2.** A square matrix $\mathbf{B}$ such that $\mathbf{B}^p = \mathbf{0}$ and $\mathbf{B}^{p-1} \neq \mathbf{0}$ is said to be *nilpotent of index p* (or *grade p*).

Ex. 11.10. The matrix

$$\mathbf{H} = \begin{bmatrix} 0 & 1 & \dots & 0 \\ 0 & 0 & \dots & 0 \\ & & \dots & \\ 0 & 0 & \dots & 1 \\ 0 & 0 & \dots & 0 \end{bmatrix}, \tag{11.33}$$

with zeros everywhere except on the first superdiagonal, where the elements are unity, is nilpotent of index equal to the order of the matrix. (If $\mathbf{H}$ is of order unity, then $\mathbf{H} = [0]$.)

Solution: $\mathbf{H}^r$ is zero except for units in the rth superdiagonal. Hence, $\mathbf{H}^{n-1} \neq \mathbf{0}$, $\mathbf{H}^n = \mathbf{0}$, where n is the order of $\mathbf{H}$.

Ex. 11.11. The matrix $\mathbf{V} - \lambda\mathbf{I}$, where $\mathbf{V}$ is defined in (11.32), is nilpotent of index less than or equal to the order of $\mathbf{V}$.

THEOREM **11.9.** *If* $\mathbf{B}$ *is a nilpotent matrix of order* n *and index* p, *and* $\mathbf{u}$ *is an* $n \times 1$ *vector such that* $\mathbf{B}^{p-1}\mathbf{u} \neq \mathbf{0}$, *then*

(i) $\mathbf{u}, \mathbf{Bu}, \ldots, \mathbf{B}^{p-1}\mathbf{u}$ *are linearly independent,*

(ii) $p \leq n$.

Proof: If

$$\alpha_1\mathbf{u} + \alpha_2\mathbf{Bu} + \ldots + \alpha_{p-1}\mathbf{B}^{p-2}\mathbf{u} + \alpha_p\mathbf{B}^{p-1}\mathbf{u} = \mathbf{0}, \tag{11.34}$$

then successive multiplication by B gives

$$\begin{aligned} \alpha_1\mathbf{Bu} + \alpha_2 B^2\mathbf{u} \quad + \ldots + \alpha_{p-1}\mathbf{B}^{p-1}\mathbf{u} &= \mathbf{0} \\ \ldots \quad & \\ \alpha_1\mathbf{B}^{p-2}\mathbf{u} + \alpha_2\mathbf{B}^{p-1}\mathbf{u} \quad &= \mathbf{0} \\ \alpha_1\mathbf{B}^{p-1}\mathbf{u} \quad &= \mathbf{0}. \end{aligned}$$

Since $\mathbf{B}^{p-1}\mathbf{u} \neq \mathbf{0}$, these give in succession $\alpha_1 = \alpha_2 = \ldots = \alpha_p = 0$, so that the vectors are linearly independent. Part (ii) follows since more than n vectors are always linearly dependent so that there cannot be more than n vectors in the sequence in (i).

It is clear that a nonzero nilpotent matrix must be singular since otherwise $\mathbf{B}^p = \mathbf{0}$ would imply $\mathbf{B} = \mathbf{0}$.

Our main result concerning nilpotent matrices is:

THEOREM **11.10.** *If* $\mathbf{B}$ *is nilpotent of index* p, *then a similarity transformation exists such that*

$$\mathbf{P}^{-1}\mathbf{BP} = \begin{bmatrix} \mathbf{H}_1 & \mathbf{0} & \ldots & \mathbf{0} \\ \mathbf{0} & \mathbf{H}_2 & \ldots & \mathbf{0} \\ & & \ldots & \\ \mathbf{0} & \mathbf{0} & \ldots & \mathbf{H}_s \end{bmatrix}, \tag{11.35}$$

where the $\mathbf{H}_i$ *are square matrices with zeros everywhere except on the first superdiagonal where the elements are unity* [*see* (11.33)]. *The largest matrix* $\mathbf{H}_i$ *has order* p. *If the orders of the* $\mathbf{H}_i$ *are* $p, q, \ldots, r$, *then*

$$p + q + \ldots + r = n,$$

where n *is the order of* $\mathbf{B}$ *and* $p, q, \ldots, r$ *are uniquely determined by* $\mathbf{B}$. *There are* $N(\mathbf{B})$ *different numbers* $p, q, \ldots, r$, *where* $N(\mathbf{B})$ *is the dimension of the null space of* $\mathbf{B}$.

Proof: The proof is constructive and reasonably straightforward, but rather long. For clarity, we break it up into stages. (See also Ex. 11.12.)

(a) In order to see what we have to prove, we multiply (11.35) on the left by **P** and equate column vectors in the result. If $\mathbf{x}_i$ denotes the ith column of **P**, this gives

$$\begin{array}{llll} \mathbf{Bx}_1 = \mathbf{0} & \mathbf{Bx}_{p+1} = \mathbf{0} & \ldots & \mathbf{Bx}_{n-r+1} = \mathbf{0} \\ \mathbf{Bx}_2 = \mathbf{x}_1 & \mathbf{Bx}_{p+2} = \mathbf{x}_{p+1} & \ldots & \mathbf{Bx}_{n-r+2} = \mathbf{x}_{n-r+1} \\ & \ldots & & \\ \mathbf{Bx}_{p-1} = \mathbf{x}_{p-2} & \mathbf{Bx}_{p+q-1} = \mathbf{x}_{p+q-2} & \ldots & \mathbf{Bx}_{n-1} = \mathbf{x}_{n-2} \\ \mathbf{Bx}_p = \mathbf{x}_{p-1} & \mathbf{Bx}_{p+q} = \mathbf{x}_{p+q-1} & \ldots & \mathbf{Bx}_n = \mathbf{x}_{n-1}. \end{array} \tag{11.36}$$

The form in which we have written this array will be misleading unless we remember that there may be fewer entries in the columns as we proceed to the right. (We assume $p \geq q \geq \ldots \geq r$.) Thus if $r = 1$, the last column in (11.36) will consist of only one entry, namely $\mathbf{Bx}_n = \mathbf{0}$. If $r = 2$, there will be two entries, $\mathbf{Bx}_n = \mathbf{x}_{n-1}$ and $\mathbf{Bx}_{n-1} = \mathbf{0}$. It is only if $r = p$ that the number of entries in all of the columns will be the same. The array (11.36) can be rewritten in the following way. Matrices $\mathbf{X}_s$ are defined on the left, and the lines of (11.36) are written on the right. The $\mathbf{Z}_s$ are defined in the explanation that follows.

$$\begin{array}{ll} \mathbf{X}_1 = [\mathbf{x}_1, \mathbf{x}_{p+1}, \mathbf{x}_{p+q+1}, \ldots, \mathbf{x}_{n-r+1}] & \mathbf{BX}_1 = \mathbf{0} \\ \mathbf{X}_2 = [\mathbf{x}_2, \mathbf{x}_{p+2}, \ldots \quad] & \mathbf{BX}_2 = \mathbf{Z}_1 \\ \ldots & \\ \mathbf{X}_{p-1} = [\mathbf{x}_{p-1}, \mathbf{x}_{p+q-1}, \ldots] & \mathbf{BX}_{p-1} = \mathbf{Z}_{p-2} \\ \mathbf{X}_p = [\mathbf{x}_p, \mathbf{x}_{p+q}, \ldots] & \mathbf{BX}_p = \mathbf{Z}_{p-1}. \end{array} \tag{11.37}$$

If the matrix $\mathbf{X}_s$ has i_s columns, the assumption that $p \geq q \geq \ldots \geq r$ implies that

$$i_p \leq i_{p-1} \leq \ldots \leq i_2 \leq i_1.$$

The matrix $\mathbf{Z}_k$ consists of the first i_{k+1} columns of $\mathbf{X}_k$. We have $\mathbf{Z}_k = \mathbf{X}_k$ if and only if $i_{k+1} = i_k$. Since **P** is nonsingular, the $\mathbf{x}_i$ in (11.36), which are the columns of **P**, are a set of n linearly independent vectors. The vectors in (11.37) are simply a rearrangement of those in (11.36). What we have to prove is therefore that we can find n linearly independent vectors that can be arranged in the array (11.37), where i_s, the number of columns in $\mathbf{X}_s$, is independent of the way in which $\mathbf{X}_s$ is obtained, and $i_1 = N(\mathbf{B})$.

(b) Since the $\mathbf{Z}_s$ are part of the $\mathbf{X}_s$, we see that

$$\mathbf{B}^k\mathbf{x}_j = \mathbf{0}, \qquad j \leq k, \qquad k = 1, \ldots, p. \tag{11.38}$$

We prove that $[\mathbf{X}_1, \ldots, \mathbf{X}_k]$ constitutes a basis for the null space of $\mathbf{B}^k$. The columns of $[\mathbf{X}_1, \ldots, \mathbf{X}_p]$ span V_n so that a basis for the null space of $\mathbf{B}^k$ can be found by determining all vectors $\boldsymbol{\alpha}_i$, $i = 1, \ldots, p$ such that

$$\mathbf{B}^k[\mathbf{X}_1\boldsymbol{\alpha}_1 + \ldots + \mathbf{X}_p\boldsymbol{\alpha}_p] = \mathbf{0},$$

that is,

$$\mathbf{B}^k[\mathbf{X}_{k+1}\boldsymbol{\alpha}_{k+1} + \ldots + \mathbf{X}_p\boldsymbol{\alpha}_p] = \mathbf{0}. \tag{11.39}$$

If we multiply this equation by $\mathbf{B}^{p-k-1}$ we see that

$$\mathbf{B}^{p-1}\mathbf{X}_p\boldsymbol{\alpha}_p = \mathbf{0}. \tag{11.40}$$

The columns of $\mathbf{B}^{p-1}\mathbf{X}_p$ are contained in $\mathbf{X}_1$, so the columns of $\mathbf{B}^{p-1}\mathbf{X}_p$ are linearly independent. Hence $\boldsymbol{\alpha}_p = \mathbf{0}$. Multiplying the resulting form of (11.38) by $\mathbf{B}^{p-k-2}$ we can similarly prove that $\boldsymbol{\alpha}_{p-1} = \mathbf{0}$, then $\boldsymbol{\alpha}_{p-2} = \mathbf{0}$, and so on, down to $\boldsymbol{\alpha}_{k+1} = \mathbf{0}$. This proves that the null space of $\mathbf{B}^k$ is spanned by the columns of $[\mathbf{X}_1, \ldots, \mathbf{X}_k]$. These are linearly independent, so they constitute a basis for the null space of $\mathbf{B}^k$. If the dimension of the null space of $\mathbf{B}^k$ is denoted by j_k, we see that i_k, the number of columns in $\mathbf{X}_k$, is given by

$$i_k = j_k - j_{k-1}, \qquad j_0 = 0, \qquad j_p = n. \tag{11.41}$$

(c) This analysis suggests a method for the construction of the array (11.37). Suppose that

$$\mathbf{W}_1 = [\mathbf{w}_1, \ldots, \mathbf{w}_r], \qquad r = j_1 = N(\mathbf{B}), \tag{11.42}$$

constitutes a basis for the null space of $\mathbf{B}$. We have $\mathbf{B}^2\mathbf{w}_i = \mathbf{0}$, so that the vectors $\mathbf{w}_1, \ldots, \mathbf{w}_r$ are also in the null space of $\mathbf{B}^2$. Extend these vectors to form a basis for the null space of $\mathbf{B}^2$:

$$[\mathbf{w}_1, \ldots, \mathbf{w}_r, \mathbf{w}_{r+1}, \ldots, \mathbf{w}_s] = [\mathbf{W}_1 \quad \mathbf{W}_2], \qquad s = j_2. \tag{11.43}$$

The columns of $\mathbf{BW}_2$ are linearly independent. To prove this we note that otherwise $\mathbf{BW}_2\boldsymbol{\alpha} = \mathbf{0}$ for some nonzero $\boldsymbol{\alpha}$. The vector $\mathbf{W}_2\boldsymbol{\alpha}$ is nonzero since the columns of $\mathbf{W}_2$ are linearly independent. Also $\mathbf{B}(\mathbf{W}_2\boldsymbol{\alpha}) = \mathbf{0}$, so that $\mathbf{W}_2\boldsymbol{\alpha}$ is in the null space of $\mathbf{B}$, i.e.,

$$\mathbf{W}_2\boldsymbol{\alpha} - \mathbf{W}_1\boldsymbol{\beta} = \mathbf{0}. \tag{11.44}$$

The columns of $\mathbf{W}_1$ and $\mathbf{W}_2$ are linearly independent so that this implies $\boldsymbol{\alpha} = \mathbf{0}$, $\boldsymbol{\beta} = \mathbf{0}$, which gives the required result. Denote the columns of $\mathbf{BW}_2$ by

$$\mathbf{u}_1, \ldots, \mathbf{u}_s, \qquad s = j_2 - j_1.$$

These $\mathbf{u}_i$ are independent vectors in the null space of $\mathbf{B}$, since $\mathbf{B}^2\mathbf{W}_2 = \mathbf{0}$. Extend these to form a basis for the null space of $\mathbf{B}$, which we denote by

$$\mathbf{W}_1^{(1)} = [\mathbf{u}_1, \ldots, \mathbf{u}_s, \mathbf{u}_{s+1}, \ldots, \mathbf{u}_r] = [\mathbf{BW}_2 \quad \mathbf{U}_1^{(1)}] \tag{11.45}$$

say. The columns of

$$[\mathbf{W}_1^{(1)} \quad \mathbf{W}_2] \tag{11.46}$$

constitute a basis for the null space of $\mathbf{B}^2$. We continue the argument in abbreviated form. The columns of (11.46) are in the null space of $\mathbf{B}^3$. Extend these to form a basis for the null space of $\mathbf{B}^3$:

$$[\mathbf{W}_1^{(1)} \quad \mathbf{W}_2 \quad \mathbf{W}_3]. \tag{11.47}$$

Replace $\mathbf{W}_2$ and $\mathbf{W}_3$ by

$$\mathbf{W}_2^{(1)} = [\mathbf{BW}_3 \quad \mathbf{U}_2], \qquad \mathbf{W}_1^{(2)} = [\mathbf{B}^2\mathbf{W}_3 \quad \mathbf{BU}_2 \quad \mathbf{U}_1^{(2)}].$$

The arguments used above can be extended to show that

$$[\mathbf{W}_1^{(2)} \quad \mathbf{W}_2^{(1)} \quad \mathbf{W}_3] \tag{11.48}$$

constitute a basis for the null space of $\mathbf{B}^3$. Proceeding in this way we can construct the array (11.37). This constructed array can be rewritten in the form (11.36), which leads back to (11.35), with the properties stated in the theorem. This completes the proof.

To illustrate the proof, we work an example in detail. (A point that does not arise in this example is covered in Ex. 11.14.)

Ex. 11.12. Given that the following matrix is nilpotent, find its index, and reduce it to the canonical form of Theorem 11.10.

$$\mathbf{B} = \begin{bmatrix} 0 & 0 & 0 & 0 & 1 & 0 \\ 0 & 0 & 1 & 1 & 0 & -1 \\ 0 & 0 & 0 & 0 & 0 & 0 \\ 0 & 0 & 0 & 0 & 0 & 0 \\ 0 & 0 & 1 & 0 & 0 & -1 \\ 0 & 0 & 0 & 0 & 0 & 0 \end{bmatrix}. \tag{11.49}$$

Solution: Some details of the working are summarized in Table 11.1. We first reduce the matrix to row-echelon form. The original matrix and its row-echelon form are written to the left of the dotted lines in the upper and lower arrays, respectively. The row-echelon form enables us to find a basis for the null space of $\mathbf{B}$, which is three-dimensional. Suppose we choose

$$\mathbf{x}_1 = \begin{bmatrix} 1 \\ 0 \\ 0 \\ 0 \\ 0 \\ 0 \end{bmatrix}, \quad \mathbf{x}_2 = \begin{bmatrix} 0 \\ 1 \\ 0 \\ 0 \\ 0 \\ 0 \end{bmatrix}, \quad \mathbf{x}_3 = \begin{bmatrix} 0 \\ 0 \\ 1 \\ 0 \\ 0 \\ 1 \end{bmatrix}.$$

We now have to try to solve $\mathbf{Bx} = \mathbf{x}_i$ for $i = 1, 2, 3$, so (following the standard procedure described in Chapter 3) we write these as the columns numbered (1), (2), (3) in the top array in the table, and perform the same elementary row operations on these that were used to reduce the original matrix to row echelon form. This gives the columns numbered (4), (5), (6) in the second array, where we have performed one more elementary row operation to leave only one unit in the column numbered (6). The row-echelon form shows us that $\mathbf{Bx} = \mathbf{x}_3$ is contradictory, but we can find vectors

Table 11.1. WORKING FOR EX. 11.12.

Augmented matrices:

						$\mathbf{x}_1$ (1)	$\mathbf{x}_2$ (2)	$\mathbf{x}_3$ (3)	$\mathbf{x}_4$ (7)	$\mathbf{x}_5$ (8)	$\mathbf{x}_6$ (11)
0	0	0	0	1	0	1	0	0	0	0	0
0	0	1	1	0	−1	0	1	0	0	0	0
0	0	0	0	0	0	0	0	1	0	0	1
0	0	0	0	0	0	0	0	0	0	1	−1
0	0	1	0	0	−1	0	0	0	1	0	0
0	0	0	0	0	0	0	0	1	0	0	0

Row-echelon forms:

						(4)	(5)	(6)	(9)	(10)	(12)
0	0	1	0	0	−1	0	0	0	1	0	0
0	0	0	1	0	0	0	1	0	−1	0	0
0	0	0	0	1	0	1	0	0	0	0	0
0	0	0	0	0	0	0	0	1	0	0	0
0	0	0	0	0	0	0	0	0	0	1	0
0	0	0	0	0	0	0	0	0	0	0	1

such that $\mathbf{Bx} = \mathbf{x}_1$, $\mathbf{Bx} = \mathbf{x}_2$. By inspection of the row-echelon form, we see that suitable vectors are, respectively,

$$\mathbf{x}_4 = \begin{bmatrix} 0 \\ 0 \\ 0 \\ 0 \\ 1 \\ 0 \end{bmatrix}, \qquad \mathbf{x}_5 = \begin{bmatrix} 0 \\ 0 \\ 0 \\ 1 \\ 0 \\ 0 \end{bmatrix}.$$

We now have to try to solve $\mathbf{Bx} = \mathbf{x}_4$, $\mathbf{Bx} = \mathbf{x}_5$, so we insert $\mathbf{x}_4$ and $\mathbf{x}_5$ as columns (7), (8) in the first array in Table 11.1 and again reduce to row-echelon form which gives columns (9), (10). The result tells us that $\mathbf{Bx} = \mathbf{x}_5$ is contradictory, but $\mathbf{Bx} = \mathbf{x}_4$ can be solved, and a solution $\mathbf{x}_6$ to this equation is inserted as column (11) in the first array, which gives column (12) in the row-echelon form. The equation $\mathbf{Bx} = \mathbf{x}_6$ is contradictory as we should expect. To sum up, we have found $\mathbf{x}_1, \ldots, \mathbf{x}_6$ such that $\mathbf{Bx}_1 = \mathbf{Bx}_2 = \mathbf{Bx}_3 = \mathbf{0}$, and

$$\mathbf{Bx}_4 = \mathbf{x}_1, \qquad \mathbf{Bx}_6 = \mathbf{x}_4, \qquad \mathbf{Bx}_5 = \mathbf{x}_2. \tag{11.50}$$

We therefore assemble the vectors in the order

$$[\mathbf{x}_1 \quad \mathbf{x}_4 \quad \mathbf{x}_6 \quad \mathbf{x}_2 \quad \mathbf{x}_5 \quad \mathbf{x}_3] = \begin{bmatrix} 1 & 0 & 0 & 0 & 0 & 0 \\ 0 & 0 & 0 & 1 & 0 & 0 \\ 0 & 0 & 1 & 0 & 0 & 1 \\ 0 & 0 & -1 & 0 & 1 & 0 \\ 0 & 1 & 0 & 0 & 0 & 0 \\ 0 & 0 & 0 & 0 & 0 & 1 \end{bmatrix} = \mathbf{P},$$

say. From (11.50) we see that we should have $\mathbf{BP} = \mathbf{PH}$, where

$$\mathbf{H} = \left[\begin{array}{ccc|cc|c} 0 & 1 & 0 & 0 & 0 & 0 \\ 0 & 0 & 1 & 0 & 0 & 0 \\ 0 & 0 & 0 & 0 & 0 & 0 \\ \hline 0 & 0 & 0 & 0 & 1 & 0 \\ 0 & 0 & 0 & 0 & 0 & 0 \\ \hline 0 & 0 & 0 & 0 & 0 & 0 \end{array}\right], \tag{11.51}$$

and the reader can verify that this is correct. The index of $\mathbf{B}$ is the order of the largest block, namely 3. The number of different blocks is equal to the dimension of the null space of $\mathbf{B}$, which is also 3.

11.6 The Jordan Canonical Form

We are now in a position to specify a standard form known as the Jordan canonical form to which any matrix can be reduced by means of a similarity transformation.

DEFINITION **11.3.** A *Jordan block* is a square matrix whose elements are zero except for those on the principal diagonal, which are all equal, and those on the first superdiagonal, which are all equal to unity; thus,

$$\mathbf{J} = \begin{bmatrix} \lambda & 1 & 0 & \dots & 0 \\ 0 & \lambda & 1 & \dots & 0 \\ & & \dots & & \\ 0 & 0 & 0 & \dots & \lambda \end{bmatrix}. \tag{11.52}$$

The purpose of studying nilpotent matrices in the last section is to allow us to derive the following preliminary result.

THEOREM **11.11.** *If* $\mathbf{V}$ *is the upper triangular matrix defined in* (11.32), *then a nonsingular matrix* $\mathbf{T}$ *exists such that*

$$\mathbf{T}^{-1}\mathbf{V}\mathbf{T} = \begin{bmatrix} \mathbf{J}_1 & \mathbf{0} & \dots & \mathbf{0} \\ \mathbf{0} & \mathbf{J}_2 & \dots & \mathbf{0} \\ & & \dots & \\ \mathbf{0} & \mathbf{0} & \dots & \mathbf{J}_s \end{bmatrix}, \tag{11.53}$$

where the $\mathbf{J}_i$ *are Jordan blocks, all the diagonal elements being equal to the* λ *that appeared on the diagonal of* (11.32). *The number* s *is equal to the number of linearly independent eigenvectors of* $\mathbf{V}$. *The order of the largest submatrix* $\mathbf{J}_i$ *is equal to the index of the nilpotent matrix* $\mathbf{V} - \lambda\mathbf{I}$.

Proof: The matrix $\mathbf{V} - \lambda\mathbf{I}$ is nilpotent (Ex. 11.11), so we can apply Theorem 11.10. A matrix $\mathbf{P}$ exists such that

$$\mathbf{P}^{-1}(\mathbf{V} - \lambda\mathbf{I})\mathbf{P} = \mathbf{H},$$

where $\mathbf{H}$ is the matrix given on the right of (11.35). Hence,

$$\mathbf{P}^{-1}\mathbf{V}\mathbf{P} = \lambda\mathbf{I} + \mathbf{H}. \tag{11.54}$$

This is of the form stated in the theorem. The number of distinct blocks is equal to the dimension of the null space of $\mathbf{V} - \lambda\mathbf{I}$ which is equal to the number of linearly independent eigenvectors of $\mathbf{V}$.

The main theorem is:

THEOREM **11.12.** (*Jordan canonical form*). *If* $\mathbf{A}$ *is a general matrix of order* n, *a nonsingular matrix* $\mathbf{Q}$ *exists such that*

$$\mathbf{Q}^{-1}\mathbf{A}\mathbf{Q} = \begin{bmatrix} \mathbf{J}_1 & \mathbf{0} & \dots & \mathbf{0} \\ \mathbf{0} & \mathbf{J}_2 & \dots & \mathbf{0} \\ & & \dots & \\ \mathbf{0} & \mathbf{0} & \dots & \mathbf{J}_k \end{bmatrix}, \tag{11.55}$$

where the $\mathbf{J}_i$ *are Jordan blocks. The same eigenvalues may occur in different blocks but the number of distinct blocks corresponding to a given eigenvalue is equal to the number of independent eigenvectors corresponding to that eigenvalue.*

Proof: By combining Theorems 11.7, 11.8 we see that a matrix $\mathbf{R}$ exists such that

$$\mathbf{R}^{-1}\mathbf{A}\mathbf{R} = \begin{bmatrix} \mathbf{V}_1 & \dots & \mathbf{0} \\ & \dots & \\ \mathbf{0} & \dots & \mathbf{V}_s \end{bmatrix},$$

where the $\mathbf{V}_i$ are upper triangular matrices, and the diagonal elements of $\mathbf{V}_i$ are all equal to λ_i, $i = 1$ to s. If we set

$$\mathbf{B} = \begin{bmatrix} \mathbf{T}_1 & \dots & \mathbf{0} \\ & \dots & \\ \mathbf{0} & \dots & \mathbf{T}_s \end{bmatrix},$$

where $\mathbf{T}_i$ is a nonsingular square matrix of the same order as $\mathbf{V}_i$, we obtain

$$(\mathbf{RT})^{-1}\mathbf{A}(\mathbf{RT}) = \begin{bmatrix} \mathbf{T}_1^{-1}\mathbf{V}_1\mathbf{T}_1 & \dots & \mathbf{0} \\ & \dots & \\ \mathbf{0} & \dots & \mathbf{T}_s^{-1}\mathbf{V}_s\mathbf{T}_s \end{bmatrix}.$$

From Theorem 11.11 the $\mathbf{T}_i$ can be chosen so that each $\mathbf{T}_i^{-1}\mathbf{V}_i\mathbf{T}_i$ has the form (11.53). This proves the theorem.

Let $\mathbf{K}_r$ denote the submatrix of form (11.53) chosen from the Jordan form (11.55), consisting of all Jordan blocks corresponding to a given eigenvalue λ_r. Theorem 11.11 tells us that the order of the largest Jordan block in $\mathbf{K}_r$ is equal to the index of the nilpotent matrix $\mathbf{A} - \lambda_r\mathbf{I}$. In view of this it is convenient to introduce the following definition (compare Definition 11.2).

DEFINITION **11.4.** If the order of the largest Jordan block with a specific eigenvalue λ_i on its diagonal in the Jordan canonical form of $\mathbf{A}$ is denoted by p_i, we say that λ_i is an eigenvalue of *index* (or *grade*) p_i.

The key result is (11.55), namely that for every $\mathbf{A}$ we can find $\mathbf{Q}$ such that $\mathbf{Q}^{-1}\mathbf{AQ} = \mathbf{J}$, where $\mathbf{J}$ is the Jordan canonical form. On multiplying both sides by $\mathbf{Q}$, we obtain

$$\mathbf{AQ} = \mathbf{QJ}. \tag{11.56}$$

This replaces the equation $\mathbf{AP} = \mathbf{P\Lambda}$, which is the equation for diagonalization that we have met so often before. If the columns of $\mathbf{Q}$ are denoted by $\mathbf{q}_i$,

$$\mathbf{Q} = [\mathbf{q}_1, \ldots, \mathbf{q}_n],$$

the form of $\mathbf{J}$ tells us that (11.56) separates into equations of the form

$$\mathbf{Aq}_i = \lambda_i\mathbf{q}_i + \nu_i\mathbf{q}_{i-1}, \tag{11.57}$$

where ν_i may be either 0 or 1, depending on $\mathbf{J}$. This immediately suggests a practical procedure for finding the Jordan form.

To illustrate the point (and the previous theory) by a specific example, consider

$$\mathbf{B} = \mathbf{Q}^{-1}\mathbf{AQ} = \begin{bmatrix} \mathbf{J}_1 & \mathbf{0} & \mathbf{0} \\ \mathbf{0} & \mathbf{J}_2 & \mathbf{0} \\ \mathbf{0} & \mathbf{0} & \mathbf{J}_3 \end{bmatrix} = \mathbf{J}, \tag{11.58}$$

where

$$\mathbf{J}_1 = \begin{bmatrix} \alpha & 1 & 0 \\ 0 & \alpha & 1 \\ 0 & 0 & \alpha \end{bmatrix}, \qquad \mathbf{J}_2 = [\alpha], \qquad \mathbf{J}_3 = \begin{bmatrix} \beta & 1 \\ 0 & \beta \end{bmatrix}.$$

We first of all find the eigenvectors of $\mathbf{B}$. Suppose that $\mathbf{y}$ is an eigenvector corresponding to the eigenvalue α. We assume $\alpha \neq \beta$. Then

$$(\mathbf{B} - \alpha\mathbf{I})\mathbf{y} = \begin{bmatrix} 0 & 1 & 0 & 0 & 0 & 0 \\ 0 & 0 & 1 & 0 & 0 & 0 \\ 0 & 0 & 0 & 0 & 0 & 0 \\ 0 & 0 & 0 & 0 & 0 & 0 \\ 0 & 0 & 0 & 0 & \beta - \alpha & 1 \\ 0 & 0 & 0 & 0 & 0 & \beta - \alpha \end{bmatrix} \begin{bmatrix} y_1 \\ y_2 \\ y_3 \\ y_4 \\ y_5 \\ y_6 \end{bmatrix} = \mathbf{0}.$$

These equations have two independent solutions which can be taken to be the unit vectors $\mathbf{e}_1$ and $\mathbf{e}_4$. In a similar way, there is only one eigenvector corresponding to the second eigenvalue β, namely $\mathbf{e}_5$. Hence, $\mathbf{B}$ (and therefore $\mathbf{A}$) has precisely three independent eigenvectors.

The equations (11.57) for this example are

$$\begin{aligned}(\mathbf{A}-\alpha\mathbf{I})\mathbf{q}_1&=\mathbf{0}\\(\mathbf{A}-\alpha\mathbf{I})\mathbf{q}_2&=\mathbf{q}_1,\\(\mathbf{A}-\alpha\mathbf{I})\mathbf{q}_3&=\mathbf{q}_2\end{aligned}\qquad(\mathbf{A}-\alpha\mathbf{I})\mathbf{q}_4=\mathbf{0},\qquad\begin{aligned}(\mathbf{A}-\beta\mathbf{I})\mathbf{q}_5&=\mathbf{0}\\(\mathbf{A}-\beta\mathbf{I})\mathbf{q}_6&=\mathbf{q}_5.\end{aligned}$$

If $\mathbf{u}$ is an eigenvector of $\mathbf{J}$ corresponding to an eigenvalue λ, so that $\mathbf{Ju}=\lambda\mathbf{u}$, this means that

$$\mathbf{Q}^{-1}\mathbf{AQ}=\lambda\mathbf{u}\quad\text{or}\quad\mathbf{A}(\mathbf{Qu})=\lambda(\mathbf{Qu}).$$

Since $\mathbf{e}_1$, $\mathbf{e}_4$, $\mathbf{e}_5$ are eigenvectors of $\mathbf{J}$, this means that $\mathbf{q}_1$, $\mathbf{q}_4$, $\mathbf{q}_5$ are eigenvectors of $\mathbf{A}$. The other eigenvectors of $\mathbf{A}$, namely $\mathbf{q}_2$, $\mathbf{q}_3$, $\mathbf{q}_6$ are known as *generalized eigenvectors*.

Suppose now that we are given the matrix $\mathbf{A}$ in this example, and we know nothing beforehand about its eigenvalues and eigenvectors. If we compute its eigenvalues, we will find α of multiplicity 4 and β of multiplicity 2. If we compute the eigenvectors, we will find two eigenvectors $\mathbf{x}_1$, $\mathbf{x}_2$ corresponding to α, and one eigenvector $\mathbf{x}_3$ corresponding to β. If we try to solve

$$(\mathbf{A}-\beta\mathbf{I})\mathbf{x}=\mathbf{x}_3$$

we will find a solution, say $\mathbf{x}_4$, which is a generalized eigenvector. The multiplicity of β is 2, and we have found an eigenvector $\mathbf{x}_3$ and a generalized eigenvector $\mathbf{x}_4$, so we need not consider the eigenvalue β further. (The vectors $\mathbf{x}_3$, $\mathbf{x}_4$ correspond to $\mathbf{q}_5$, $\mathbf{q}_6$ in our previous notation.) To find the generalized eigenvectors corresponding to α, we try to solve

$$(\mathbf{A}-\alpha\mathbf{I})\mathbf{x}=a\mathbf{x}_1+b\mathbf{x}_2.$$

We will find that a solution exists for only one ratio of a to b. The corresponding vector $a\mathbf{x}_1+b\mathbf{x}_2$ is $\mathbf{q}_1$ in our previous notation. The solution $\mathbf{x}$ is $\mathbf{q}_2$. The vector $\mathbf{q}_4$ is any combination of $\mathbf{x}_1$ and $\mathbf{x}_2$ independent of $a\mathbf{x}_1+b\mathbf{x}_2=\mathbf{q}_1$. The multiplicity of α is 4 and we have found only two eigenvectors, and one generalized eigenvector. The remaining generalized eigenvector can only come from $(\mathbf{A}-\alpha\mathbf{I})\mathbf{x}=\mathbf{q}_2$.

The following examples should clarify the procedure. The point is that in order to carry out the reduction to the Jordan canonical form in practice we do not follow the sequence of steps outlined in the course of the theorems since it is much simpler to operate directly on the original matrix. The theorems tell us the kind of thing we are looking for, and we go after this directly.

Ex. 11.13. Reduce the following matrix to Jordan canonical form:

$$\mathbf{A}=\begin{bmatrix}5&4&3\\-1&0&-3\\1&-2&1\end{bmatrix}.\tag{11.59}$$

Solution: A straightforward calculation gives eigenvalues $\lambda_1 = -2$, $\lambda_2 = \lambda_3 = 4$, with only two independent eigenvectors,

$$\mathbf{x}_1 = \begin{bmatrix} 1 \\ -1 \\ -1 \end{bmatrix}, \qquad \mathbf{x}_2 = \begin{bmatrix} 1 \\ -1 \\ 1 \end{bmatrix}.$$

We obtain a third vector by solving $(\mathbf{A} - 4\mathbf{I})\mathbf{x}_3 = \mathbf{x}_2$. The solution of this equation is of course arbitrary to within a multiple of $\mathbf{x}_2$ and we obtain

$$\mathbf{x}_3 = \begin{bmatrix} 0 \\ 1 \\ -1 \end{bmatrix} + k\mathbf{x}_2,$$

where k is an arbitrary constant, the choice of which is not important for present purposes. If we take $k = 0$ and set

$$\mathbf{Q} = \begin{bmatrix} 1 & 1 & 0 \\ -1 & -1 & 1 \\ -1 & 1 & -1 \end{bmatrix}, \qquad \mathbf{Q}^{-1} = \frac{1}{2}\begin{bmatrix} 0 & -1 & -1 \\ 2 & 1 & 1 \\ 2 & 2 & 0 \end{bmatrix}, \tag{11.60}$$

we find

$$\mathbf{Q}^{-1}\mathbf{A}\mathbf{Q} = \begin{bmatrix} -2 & 0 & 0 \\ 0 & 4 & 1 \\ 0 & 0 & 4 \end{bmatrix}. \tag{11.61}$$

It is clear that the matrix $\mathbf{Q}$ is not unique.

Ex. 11.14. Reduce the following matrix to Jordan canonical form.

$$\mathbf{A} = \begin{bmatrix} 2 & 2 & -1 \\ -1 & -1 & 1 \\ -1 & -2 & 2 \end{bmatrix}. \tag{11.62}$$

Solution: We find $\lambda_1 = \lambda_2 = \lambda_3 = 1$, with two independent eigenvectors, say

$$\mathbf{x}_1' = \begin{bmatrix} 1 \\ 0 \\ 1 \end{bmatrix}, \qquad \mathbf{x}_2' = \begin{bmatrix} 0 \\ 1 \\ 2 \end{bmatrix}.$$

It is clear from the general theory that, since there are two independent eigenvectors, there are two Jordan canonical boxes $\mathbf{J}_1$ and $\mathbf{J}_2$. The third vector required to form $\mathbf{Q}$ is obtained by solving

$$(\mathbf{A} - \mathbf{I})\mathbf{x}_3' = \alpha\mathbf{x}_1' + \beta\mathbf{x}_2',$$

where α, β are constants chosen so that these equations have a nonzero solution. On trying to solve the equations we find that we must set $\beta = -\alpha$. A suitable solution is then $x_1 = \alpha$, $x_2 = x_3 = 0$. We must take one of the columns of $\mathbf{Q}$ to be $\alpha\mathbf{x}_1' + \beta\mathbf{x}_2'$. The value of α is arbitrary. If we take $\alpha = 1$, we might choose

$$\mathbf{Q} = [\mathbf{x}_1' - \mathbf{x}_2', \mathbf{x}_3', \mathbf{x}_1'] = \begin{bmatrix} 1 & 1 & 1 \\ -1 & 0 & 0 \\ -1 & 0 & 1 \end{bmatrix},$$

which gives

$$\mathbf{Q}^{-1}\mathbf{A}\mathbf{Q} = \begin{bmatrix} 1 & 1 & 0 \\ 0 & 1 & 0 \\ 0 & 0 & 1 \end{bmatrix}. \tag{11.63}$$

11.7 Systems of Differential Equations with Constant Coefficients

Systems of linear differential equations with constant coefficients can be solved by means of the results concerning the reduction of matrices to standard form by similarity transformations that we have developed in previous sections. We wish to consider

$$\begin{aligned} \dot{z}_1 &= \frac{dz_1}{dt} = a_{11}z_1 + a_{12}z_2 + \ldots + a_{1n}z_n + f_1(t) \\ \dot{z}_2 &= \frac{dz_2}{dt} = a_{21}z_1 + a_{22}z_2 + \ldots + a_{2n}z_n + f_2(t) \\ &\ldots \\ \dot{z}_n &= \frac{dz_n}{dt} = a_{n1}z_1 + a_{n2}z_2 + \ldots + a_{nn}z_n + f_n(t). \end{aligned} \tag{11.64}$$

We introduce the notation

$$\dot{\mathbf{z}} = \left[\frac{dz_i}{dt}\right], \qquad \mathbf{f}(t) = [f_i(t)],$$

in terms of which the above system can be written

$$\dot{\mathbf{z}} = \mathbf{A}\mathbf{z} + \mathbf{f}(t). \tag{11.65}$$

We note in passing that any differential equation with constant coefficients can be written in the above form. Thus consider

$$\dddot{x} + 4\ddot{x} + \dot{x} - 6x = f(t). \tag{11.66}$$

We introduce

$$z_1 = x, \qquad z_2 = \dot{x} = \dot{z}_1, \qquad z_3 = \ddot{x} = \dot{z}_2.$$

Then (11.66) can be written

$$\begin{bmatrix} \dot{z}_1 \\ \dot{z}_2 \\ \dot{z}_3 \end{bmatrix} = \begin{bmatrix} 0 & 1 & 0 \\ 0 & 0 & 1 \\ 6 & -1 & -4 \end{bmatrix} \begin{bmatrix} z_1 \\ z_2 \\ z_3 \end{bmatrix} + \begin{bmatrix} 0 \\ 0 \\ f(t) \end{bmatrix}. \tag{11.67}$$

For simplicity, we first deal with the case where $\mathbf{f}(t)$ in (11.65) is zero, so that we have to solve

$$\dot{\mathbf{z}} = \mathbf{A}\mathbf{z}. \tag{11.68}$$

If $\mathbf{A}$ can be reduced to diagonal form by a similarity transformation, then the solution of this equation is straightforward. Suppose that $\mathbf{P}$ exists such that

$\mathbf{P}^{-1}\mathbf{AP} = \mathbf{\Lambda}$ where $\mathbf{\Lambda}$ is a diagonal matrix, with diagonal elements equal to the eigenvalues of $\mathbf{A}$. We multiply (11.68) by $\mathbf{P}^{-1}$ and rearrange in the form

$$\frac{d}{dt}(\mathbf{P}^{-1}\mathbf{z}) = (\mathbf{P}^{-1}\mathbf{AP})\mathbf{P}^{-1}\mathbf{z}, \tag{11.69}$$

where, on the left-hand side, $\mathbf{P}^{-1}$ can be shifted through the differentiation sign because it is a matrix of constants. (If the reader is in doubt about this, he should write out everything in detail.) For simplicity, introduce

$$\mathbf{y} = \mathbf{P}^{-1}\mathbf{z}. \tag{11.70}$$

Since $\mathbf{P}^{-1}\mathbf{AP} = \mathbf{\Lambda}$ is diagonal, (11.69) can be written as the separate equations

$$\frac{dy_r}{dt} = \lambda_r y_r, \qquad r = 1, \ldots, n, \tag{11.71}$$

which can be integrated immediately to give

$$y_r = (y_r)_0 e^{\lambda_r t}, \tag{11.72}$$

where $(y_r)_0$ denotes the value of y_r at $t = 0$. If we denote the column vector consisting of these initial values by $\mathbf{y}_0$, equation (11.72) can be written

$$\mathbf{y} = \mathbf{L}\mathbf{y}_0, \tag{11.73}$$

where

$$\mathbf{L} = \begin{bmatrix} e^{\lambda_1 t} & 0 & \ldots & 0 \\ 0 & e^{\lambda_2 t} & \ldots & 0 \\ & & \ldots & \\ 0 & 0 & \ldots & e^{\lambda_n t} \end{bmatrix}.$$

From (11.70),

$$\mathbf{z} = \mathbf{Py}, \qquad \mathbf{y}_0 = \mathbf{P}^{-1}\mathbf{z}_0, \tag{11.74}$$

where $\mathbf{z}_0$ is the column vector consisting of the initial values of the z_r. Equation (11.73) gives the final solution

$$\mathbf{z} = \mathbf{PL}\mathbf{y}_0 = \mathbf{PLP}^{-1}\mathbf{z}_0. \tag{11.75}$$

It is instructive to write this solution in the form

$$\mathbf{z} = a_1\mathbf{p}_1 e^{\lambda_1 t} + a_2\mathbf{p}_2 e^{\lambda_2 t} + \ldots + a_n\mathbf{p}_n e^{\lambda_n t}, \tag{11.76}$$

where $a_i = (y_i)_0$, and $\mathbf{p}_i$ is the ith column of $\mathbf{P}$. The $\mathbf{p}_i$ are the n linearly independent eigenvectors of $\mathbf{A}$, and the a_i are arbitrary constants that are determined from the initial conditions.

Ex. 11.15. Solve (11.67) with $f(t) = 0$.

Solution: We find that the matrix $\mathbf{P}$ that reduces $\mathbf{A}$ to Jordan form is

$$\mathbf{P} = \begin{bmatrix} 1 & 1 & 1 \\ 1 & -2 & -3 \\ 1 & 4 & 9 \end{bmatrix}, \qquad \mathbf{P}^{-1} = \frac{1}{12}\begin{bmatrix} 6 & 5 & 1 \\ 12 & -8 & -4 \\ -6 & 3 & 3 \end{bmatrix}.$$

It is a straightforward matter to verify that $\mathbf{z} = \mathbf{PLy}_0$ [see(11.75)] gives

$$\begin{bmatrix} z_1 \\ z_2 \\ z_3 \end{bmatrix} = \begin{bmatrix} x \\ \dot{x} \\ \ddot{x} \end{bmatrix} = a_1 e^t \begin{bmatrix} 1 \\ 1 \\ 1 \end{bmatrix} + a_2 e^{-2t} \begin{bmatrix} 1 \\ -2 \\ 4 \end{bmatrix} + a_3 e^{-3t} \begin{bmatrix} 1 \\ -3 \\ 9 \end{bmatrix},$$

where y_0 is given, using (11.74), by

$$\begin{bmatrix} a_1 \\ a_2 \\ a_3 \end{bmatrix} = \mathbf{P}^{-1}\mathbf{z}_0 = \frac{1}{12}\begin{bmatrix} 6x_0 + 5\dot{x}_0 + \ddot{x}_0 \\ 12x_0 - 8\dot{x}_0 - 4\ddot{x}_0 \\ -6x_0 + 3\dot{x}_0 + 3\ddot{x}_0 \end{bmatrix},$$

and the suffix zero means the value at $t = 0$.

The situation is almost as simple when the matrix cannot be reduced to diagonal form, and we have to use the Jordan canonical form. If $\mathbf{Q}^{-1}\mathbf{AQ} = \mathbf{J}$, where $\mathbf{J}$ is the Jordan canonical form, the equation $\dot{\mathbf{z}} = \mathbf{Az}$ becomes, on introducing $\mathbf{Q}^{-1}\mathbf{z} = \mathbf{y}$ [compare (11.69)],

$$\dot{\mathbf{y}} = \mathbf{Jy}. \tag{11.77}$$

Suppose first that $\mathbf{J}$ is a single Jordan canonical block of the form given in equation (11.52). On writing out the separate equations in (11.77), we obtain

$$\begin{aligned} \frac{dy_1}{dt} &= \lambda y_1 + y_2, & \text{that is,} \quad & \frac{d(y_1 e^{-\lambda t})}{dt} = y_2 e^{-\lambda t} \\ &\dots & & \dots \\ \frac{dy_{n-1}}{dt} &= \lambda y_{n-1} + y_n, & \text{that is,} \quad & \frac{d(y_{n-1} e^{-\lambda t})}{dt} = y_n e^{-\lambda t} \\ \frac{dy_n}{dt} &= \lambda y_n, & \text{that is,} \quad & \frac{d(y_n e^{-\lambda t})}{dt} = 0. \end{aligned} \tag{11.78}$$

These can be solved in turn, starting from the last equation. It is left to the reader to show that $y_r e^{-\lambda t}$ can be expressed as a polynomial of degree $n - r$ in t, and that the final results can be written in the form

$$\mathbf{y} = \mathbf{Ky}_0, \tag{11.79}$$

where the rth element of $\mathbf{y}_0$ is the value of y_r at $t = 0$, and

$$\mathbf{K} = e^{\lambda t}\begin{bmatrix} 1 & t & \frac{1}{2}t^2 & \dots & \dfrac{t^{n-1}}{(n-1)!} \\ 0 & 1 & t & \dots & \dfrac{t^{n-2}}{(n-2)!} \\ & & & \dots & \\ 0 & 0 & 0 & \dots & 1 \end{bmatrix}. \tag{11.80}$$

In the general case, when $\mathbf{J}$ has the structure (11.55), we see that (11.77) and its solution involve

$$\mathbf{J} = \begin{bmatrix} \mathbf{J}_1 & \cdots & \mathbf{0} \\ & \cdots & \\ \mathbf{0} & \cdots & \mathbf{J}_k \end{bmatrix}, \qquad \mathbf{K} = \begin{bmatrix} \mathbf{K}_1 & \cdots & \mathbf{0} \\ & \cdots & \\ \mathbf{0} & \cdots & \mathbf{K}_k \end{bmatrix}, \tag{11.81}$$

where $\mathbf{K}_i$ is of the form (11.80) with λ_i in place of λ and k_i in place of n. To sum up the situation in this case: The solution of $\dot{\mathbf{z}} = \mathbf{Az}$ is given by

$$\mathbf{z} = \mathbf{Qy}, \qquad \text{where } \mathbf{y} = \mathbf{Ky}_0, \quad \text{and } \mathbf{y}_0 = \mathbf{Q}^{-1}\mathbf{z}_0. \tag{11.82}$$

In other words [compare (11.74), (11.75)],

$$\mathbf{z} = \mathbf{QKQ}^{-1}\mathbf{z}_0. \tag{11.83}$$

Ex. 11.16. Solve $\dot{\mathbf{z}} = \mathbf{Az}$ with $\mathbf{A}$ given by (11.59).

Solution: The reduction to Jordan canonical form was carried out in Ex. 11.13, with $\mathbf{Q}$ and $\mathbf{J}$ given in (11.60), (11.61). Hence, from (11.80), (11.81),

$$\mathbf{K} = \begin{bmatrix} e^{-2t} & 0 & 0 \\ 0 & e^{4t} & te^{4t} \\ 0 & 0 & e^{4t} \end{bmatrix}.$$

The solution then follows directly from (11.83).

So far we have confined our attention to the equation $\dot{\mathbf{z}} = \mathbf{Az}$. A slight extension of the method will take care of the more general equation (11.65), namely

$$\dot{\mathbf{z}} = \mathbf{Az} + \mathbf{f}(t). \tag{11.84}$$

Consider only the case where $\mathbf{A}$ can be reduced to diagonal form. If $\mathbf{P}^{-1}\mathbf{AP} = \mathbf{\Lambda}$ where $\mathbf{\Lambda}$ is diagonal, equation (11.84) can be written [compare (11.69)]

$$\frac{d}{dt}(\mathbf{P}^{-1}\mathbf{z}) = (\mathbf{P}^{-1}\mathbf{AP})\mathbf{P}^{-1}\mathbf{z} + \mathbf{P}^{-1}\mathbf{f}(t),$$

or

$$\dot{\mathbf{y}} = \mathbf{\Lambda y} + \mathbf{g}(t), \tag{11.85}$$

where we have introduced the notation $\mathbf{y} = \mathbf{P}^{-1}\mathbf{z}$, $\mathbf{g}(t) = \mathbf{P}^{-1}\mathbf{f}(t)$. The rth equation in (11.85) is

$$\frac{dy_r}{dt} = \lambda_r y_r + g_r(t), \tag{11.86}$$

or

$$\frac{d}{dt}(y_r e^{-\lambda_r t}) = g_r(t)e^{-\lambda_r t}$$

$$\left\{ y_r = e^{\lambda_r}(y_r)_0 + \int_0^t g_r(\tau)e^{-\lambda_r \tau}\, d\tau \right\}. \tag{11.87}$$

This equation generalizes (11.72). Instead of (11.73), we obtain

$$\mathbf{y} = \mathbf{L}\{\mathbf{y}_0 + \mathbf{w}(t)\},$$

where $\mathbf{L}$, $\mathbf{y}_0$ were defined in connection with (11.73), (11.74), and $\mathbf{w}(t)$ is a matrix whose rth element is given by the integral in (11.87). The solution is given by

$$\mathbf{z} = \mathbf{P}\mathbf{y} = \mathbf{P}\mathbf{L}\{\mathbf{y}_0 + \mathbf{w}(t)\}. \tag{11.88}$$

The case where $\mathbf{A}$ cannot be reduced to diagonal form can be solved in the same way, but instead of solving (11.86) we have to solve (11.78) with additional nonhomogeneous terms. Nothing new is introduced in principle, and we do not pursue the matter.

This concludes our discussion of the solution, by matrix methods, of systems of linear differential equations with constant coefficients.

11.8 Minimum Polynomials and the Cayley-Hamilton Theorem

To conclude this chapter we consider a topic that has close connections with the Jordan canonical form. The eigenvectors of a matrix are characterized by the fact that $(\mathbf{A} - \lambda\mathbf{I})\mathbf{x} = \mathbf{0}$. This means that if we define an ordinary linear polynomial in z, $f(z) = z - \lambda$, then a vector $\mathbf{x}$ exists such that

$$f(\mathbf{A})\mathbf{x} = \mathbf{0}, \tag{11.89}$$

where by $f(\mathbf{A})$ we understand the result of replacing z by $\mathbf{A}$ in $f(z)$, introducing a unit matrix in the constant term. The vector $\mathbf{x}$ in (11.89) must be the eigenvector of $\mathbf{A}$ corresponding to λ. Equation (11.89) is not true for arbitrary $\mathbf{x}$. However, if $\mathbf{x}$ is an arbitrary vector, and we consider the sequence $\mathbf{x}$, $\mathbf{A}\mathbf{x}$, $\mathbf{A}^2\mathbf{x}, \ldots, \mathbf{A}^r\mathbf{x}$, then there must be a minimum value p of r for which these vectors are dependent, and clearly $p \leq n$ if $\mathbf{x}$ is an $n \times 1$ vector. We may write the corresponding relation in the form

$$(\mathbf{A}^p + a_{p-1}\mathbf{A}^{p-1} + \ldots + a_0\mathbf{I})\mathbf{x} = \mathbf{0}, \tag{11.90}$$

where the a_i depend on $\mathbf{x}$.

DEFINITION **11.5.** If $f(z)$ is a polynomial in z of degree p, with coefficient of z^p unity, where $f(\mathbf{A})\mathbf{x} = \mathbf{0}$ for a specific vector $\mathbf{x}$, and p is the smallest integer for which such a polynomial exists, then $f(z)$ is called the *minimum polynomial of* $\mathbf{x}$ *with respect to* $\mathbf{A}$.

THEOREM **11.13.** (i) *If $g(z)$ is any other polynomial for which $g(\mathbf{A})\mathbf{x} = \mathbf{0}$, then the minimum polynomial $f(z)$ must divide $g(z)$.*

(ii) *The minimum polynomial is unique.*

Proof: By definition, the degree of $f(z)$ is less than or equal to the degree of $g(z)$. Hence,

$$f(z) = h(z)g(z) + k(z),$$

where the degree of $k(z)$ is less than p. We have

$$k(\mathbf{A})\mathbf{x} = f(\mathbf{A})\mathbf{x} - h(\mathbf{A})g(\mathbf{A})\mathbf{x} = \mathbf{0}.$$

By definition of the minimum polynomial we can have $k(\mathbf{A})\mathbf{x} = \mathbf{0}$ with the degree of k less than p only if $k(z)$ is identically zero. This proves (i). If $g(z)$ is a second minimum polynomial, its degree must be p from part (i), and

$$\{f(\mathbf{A}) - g(\mathbf{A})\}\mathbf{x} = \mathbf{0}.$$

But $f(z) - g(z)$ is of degree less than p, so that $f(z) - g(z)$ must be identically zero and this proves (ii).

Next consider the sequence of square matrices of order n given by $\mathbf{I}$, $\mathbf{A}$, $\mathbf{A}^2, \ldots$. These lie in the vector space of all $n \times n$ matrices, which has dimension n^2. Hence, $n^2 + 1$ of the matrices in the sequence will be linearly dependent. There will be a smallest integer s such that $\mathbf{I}, \mathbf{A}, \ldots, \mathbf{A}^s$ are linearly dependent, giving, say,

$$\mathbf{A}^s + \alpha_{s-1}\mathbf{A}^{s-1} + \ldots + \alpha_0\mathbf{I} = \mathbf{0}. \tag{11.91}$$

DEFINITION **11.6.** If $m(z)$ is a polynomial of degree s in z with coefficient of z^s unity, such that $m(\mathbf{A}) = \mathbf{0}$, and s is the smallest integer for which such a polynomial exists, then $m(z)$ is called the *minimum polynomial* of $\mathbf{A}$.

THEOREM **11.14.** (i) *If $l(z)$ is any other polynomial for which $l(\mathbf{A}) = \mathbf{0}$, then the minimum polynomial of $\mathbf{A}$ divides $l(\mathbf{A})$.*

(ii) *The minimum polynomial of $\mathbf{A}$ is unique.*

Proof: As for Theorem 11.13.

We now examine a connection between the minimum polynomial of a matrix and its Jordan canonical form.

THEOREM **11.15.** (i) *Similar matrices have the same minimum polynomial.*

(ii) *The minimum polynomial of the matrix* (11.53) *is given by $(z - \lambda)^p$ where p is the order of the largest submatrix $\mathbf{J}_i$.*

Proof: If $\mathbf{B} = \mathbf{P}^{-1}\mathbf{A}\mathbf{P}$ and

$$f(\mathbf{A}) = \mathbf{A}^r + \beta_{r-1}\mathbf{A}^{r-1} + \ldots + \beta_0\mathbf{I},$$

then it follows from the result $\mathbf{B}^i = \mathbf{P}^{-1}\mathbf{A}^i\mathbf{P}$ that

$$f(\mathbf{B}) = \mathbf{P}^{-1}f(\mathbf{A})\mathbf{P}. \tag{11.92}$$

Hence, $f(\mathbf{A}) = \mathbf{0}$ implies $f(\mathbf{B}) = \mathbf{0}$ and vice versa. The truth of (i) follows immediately. If the matrix (11.53) is denoted by $\mathbf{U}$, then $(\mathbf{U} - \lambda\mathbf{I})^p = \mathbf{0}$, $(\mathbf{U} - \lambda\mathbf{I})^{p-1} \neq \mathbf{0}$, where p is the order of the largest submatrix $\mathbf{J}_i$ (see Ex. 11.10). From Theorem 11.14(i), if $m(z)$ is the minimum polynomial of $\mathbf{U}$, then $m(z)$ must divide $(z - \lambda)^p$. Hence, $(z - \lambda)^p$ must be the minimum polynomial of $\mathbf{U}$.

THEOREM **11.16.** (i) *The minimum polynomial of a given matrix* $\mathbf{A}$ *is given by*

$$(z - \lambda_1)^{p_1} \dots (z - \lambda_s)^{p_s}, \tag{11.93}$$

where $\lambda_1, \dots, \lambda_s$ *are the distinct eigenvalues, and* λ_i *is of index* p_i.

(ii) (*The Cayley-Hamilton theorem.*) *Every matrix satisfies its characteristic equation, i.e., if* $f(\lambda)$ *is the characteristic polynomial of* $\mathbf{A}$, *then* $f(\mathbf{A}) = \mathbf{0}$.

Proof: From Theorem 11.15(i), the minimum polynomial of $\mathbf{A}$ is the same as the minimum polynomial of the Jordan canonical form of $\mathbf{A}$, which we denote by $\mathbf{B}$. Using for $\mathbf{B}$ the standard notation for the Jordan canonical form on the right of (11.55) we have, for any polynomial $p(z)$,

$$p(\mathbf{B}) = \begin{bmatrix} p(\mathbf{J}_1) & \dots & \mathbf{0} \\ & \dots & \\ \mathbf{0} & \dots & p(\mathbf{J}_k) \end{bmatrix}. \tag{11.94}$$

If the minimum polynomial of $\mathbf{B}$ is denoted by $m(z)$, we have $m(\mathbf{B}) = \mathbf{0}$ by definition, and (11.94) then tells us that $m(\mathbf{J}_i) = \mathbf{0}$ for all i. From Theorem 11.14(i) this means that the minimum polynomial $(z - \lambda_i)^{p_i}$ of $\mathbf{J}_i$ divides $m(z)$. Hence the polynomial (11.93) must divide $m(z)$. Conversely, if we substitute the polynomial in (11.93) for $p(z)$ in (11.94), Theorem 11.15(ii) tells us that $p(\mathbf{B}) = \mathbf{0}$. Theorem 11.14(i) then tells us that $m(z)$ must divide the polynomial (11.93). Hence (11.93) gives the minimum polynomial of $\mathbf{A}$. This proves (i). Part (ii) follows immediately since the characteristic polynomial of $\mathbf{A}$ is given by

$$(z - \lambda_1)^{q_1} \dots (z - \lambda_s)^{q_s},$$

where q_i is the number of times that λ_i occurs on the diagonal of the Jordan canonical form. Hence, $q_i \geq p_i$, and the minimum polynomial divides the characteristic polynomial.

Ex. 11.17. Show that if $\mathbf{A}$ can be diagonalized by a similarity transformation, the Cayley-Hamilton theorem is an immediate consequence of Theorem 11.5(ii).

Miscellaneous Exercises 11

Ex. 11.18. Show that two diagonal matrices are similar if and only if the diagonal elements of one are simply a rearrangement of the diagonal elements of the other.

Ex. 11.19. Prove that two matrices that can be diagonalized are similar to each other if and only if they have the same characteristic equation.

Ex. 11.20. Prove that a square matrix is similar to a diagonal matrix if and only if the multiplicity of any eigenvalue λ_i is equal to the dimension of the null space of $\mathbf{A} - \lambda_i\mathbf{I}$.

Ex. 11.21. Prove that $\mathbf{A}$ is nilpotent if and only if all its eigenvalues are zero.

Ex. 11.22. Prove from first principles that there are only two essentially different canonical forms for a 2×2 matrix, namely

$$\begin{bmatrix} \lambda_1 & 0 \\ 0 & \lambda_2 \end{bmatrix}, \quad \begin{bmatrix} \lambda_1 & 1 \\ 0 & \lambda_1 \end{bmatrix}.$$

(In the first form, the cases $\lambda_1 \neq \lambda_2$ and $\lambda_1 = \lambda_2$ are not regarded as essentially different.)

Ex. 11.23. How many essentially different Jordan canonical forms are there for a 4×4 matrix?

Ex. 11.24. If $\mathbf{A}$ is a real 2×2 matrix with complex conjugate eigenvalues, prove that a real nonsingular matrix $\mathbf{T}$ exists such that

$$\mathbf{T}^{-1}\mathbf{A}\mathbf{T} = \begin{bmatrix} \alpha & \beta \\ -\beta & \alpha \end{bmatrix}.$$

Ex. 11.25. Prove that $\mathbf{A}^r \to \mathbf{0}$ as $r \to \infty$, for general $\mathbf{A}$, if and only if the spectral radius of $\mathbf{A}$ is less than unity, $\rho(\mathbf{A}) < 1$. Show that the smaller $\rho(\mathbf{A})$, the more rapid the rate of convergence.

Ex. 11.26. Show that if $\mathbf{A}$ is nilpotent, the calculation of $e^{\mathbf{A}}$ can be reduced to evaluation of a polynomial in $\mathbf{A}$. If

$$\mathbf{A} = \begin{bmatrix} 0 & 1 \\ 0 & 0 \end{bmatrix}, \text{ prove that } e^{\mathbf{A}} = \begin{bmatrix} 1 & 1 \\ 0 & 1 \end{bmatrix}.$$

Ex. 11.27. If $\mathbf{A} = \mathbf{I} + \mathbf{N}$, where $\mathbf{N}$ is nilpotent, show how the formula $(1 + x)^{1/2} = 1 + \frac{1}{2}x - \frac{1}{8}x^2 + \ldots$ can be used to compute the square root of $\mathbf{I} + \mathbf{N}$ by evaluation of a polynomial in $\mathbf{A}$.

Ex. 11.28. Write an essay on applications of the Jordan canonical form to the solution of systems of ordinary differential equations with (a) constant coefficients, and (b) variable coefficients. Possible references are:

F. Brauer and J. Nohel, *Ordinary Differential Equations*, Benjamin (1967).

E. A. Coddington and N. Levinson, *Theory of Ordinary Differential Equations*, McGraw-Hill (1955).

Ex. 11.29. Some insight into the Jordan canonical form can be obtained from the following argument, which we present in a nonrigorous form. Suppose that

$$\mathbf{A}\mathbf{x}_1 = \lambda_1\mathbf{x}_1, \qquad \mathbf{A}\mathbf{x}_2 = \lambda_2\mathbf{x}_2, \qquad \lambda_1 \neq \lambda_2,$$

and that $\mathbf{A} = \mathbf{A}_0 + \varepsilon\mathbf{B}$, where $\mathbf{A}_0$ has a repeated eigenvalue λ_1. Suppose that, for small ε, $\lambda_2 \approx \lambda_1 + \varepsilon$, $\mathbf{x}_2 = \mathbf{x}_1 + \varepsilon\mathbf{z}$. Subtracting the two equations above, we find, neglecting second-order terms,

$$\mathbf{A}_0\mathbf{z} = \lambda_1\mathbf{z} + \mathbf{x}_1.$$

Hence, $\mathbf{z}$ corresponds to what we have called a generalized eigenvector. It appears when eigenvalues and eigenvectors coalesce.

Ex. 11.30. Prove the Cayley-Hamilton theorem by filling in the steps of the following argument. The adjoint adj $\mathbf{B}$ of any matrix $\mathbf{B}$ has the property that

$$\mathbf{B}\ \text{adj}\ \mathbf{B} = (\det \mathbf{B})\mathbf{I}. \tag{11.95}$$

Adj $(\mathbf{A} - \lambda\mathbf{I})$ is a matrix polynomial of degree $n - 1$ in λ, say

$$\text{adj}\ (\mathbf{A} - \lambda\mathbf{I}) = \mathbf{B}_{n-1}\lambda^{n-1} + \ldots + \mathbf{B}_0. \tag{11.96}$$

Substitute $\mathbf{A} - \lambda\mathbf{I}$ for $\mathbf{B}$ and (11.96) for adj $(\mathbf{A} - \lambda\mathbf{I})$ in (11.95) and deduce

$$\begin{aligned} \mathbf{B}_{n-1} \qquad\quad &= \mathbf{I} \\ \mathbf{B}_{n-2} - \mathbf{A}\mathbf{B}_{n-1} &= a_{n-1}\mathbf{I} \\ \ldots \quad & \\ -\mathbf{A}\mathbf{B}_0 &= a_0\mathbf{I}, \end{aligned}$$

where a_r is the coefficient of λ^r in the characteristic polynomial $f(\lambda)$. Multiply these equations by $\mathbf{A}^n, \mathbf{A}^{n-1}, \ldots, \mathbf{I}$ and deduce $f(\mathbf{A}) = \mathbf{0}$.

Ex. 11.31. Suppose that $\mathbf{A}$ and $\mathbf{B}$ commute, and each has n linearly independent eigenvectors. If $\mathbf{P}^{-1}\mathbf{B}\mathbf{P} = \mathbf{\Lambda}$, where $\mathbf{\Lambda}$ is diagonal, the distinct eigenvalues of $\mathbf{B}$ being $\lambda_1, \ldots, \lambda_s$ with multiplicities $m_1, \ldots, m_s$, then $\mathbf{P}^{-1}\mathbf{A}\mathbf{P}$ has a block-diagonal form,

$$\mathbf{P}^{-1}\mathbf{A}\mathbf{P} = \begin{bmatrix} \mathbf{C}_1 & \ldots & \mathbf{0} \\ & \ldots & \\ \mathbf{0} & \ldots & \mathbf{C}_s \end{bmatrix},$$

where $\mathbf{C}_i$ is $m_i \times m_i$.

Ex. 11.32. The result in the last exercise means that if we can find $\mathbf{B}$ such that $\mathbf{A}\mathbf{B} = \mathbf{B}\mathbf{A}$, where $\mathbf{B}$ has n eigenvectors (the columns of $\mathbf{P}$) that can be found easily, then it is often easy to find the eigenvectors of $\mathbf{A}$ by deducing them from those for $\mathbf{P}^{-1}\mathbf{A}\mathbf{P}$. A suitable form for $\mathbf{B}$ is often indicated on physical grounds when symmetry is present. As a simple example, consider the system of resistors and capacitors in Figure 11.2. If q_i is the charge on the ith capacitor, remembering that the voltage across a capacitor C containing charge q is

q/C, and the current through it is $i = dq/dt$, prove that the equations for the circuit are

$$RC\frac{d\mathbf{q}}{dt} = \mathbf{Aq}, \qquad \mathbf{A} = \begin{bmatrix} -2 & 1 & 1 \\ 1 & -2 & 1 \\ 1 & 1 & -2 \end{bmatrix}, \qquad \mathbf{q} = \begin{bmatrix} q_1 \\ q_2 \\ q_3 \end{bmatrix}.$$

Because of symmetry, the circuit is unchanged if capacitor 1 is called 2, 2 is called 3, and 3 is called 1. This suggests that we try the following permutation matrix for **B**. The eigenvectors of **B**, which give the columns of **P**, are easily found [$\omega = \frac{1}{2}(-1 + i\sqrt{3})$, $\omega^3 = 1$, $\omega^2 + \omega + 1 = 0$]:

$$\mathbf{B} = \begin{bmatrix} 0 & 1 & 0 \\ 0 & 0 & 1 \\ 1 & 0 & 0 \end{bmatrix}, \qquad \mathbf{P} = \begin{bmatrix} 1 & 1 & 1 \\ 1 & \omega & \omega^2 \\ 1 & \omega^2 & \omega \end{bmatrix}, \qquad \mathbf{P}^{-1} = \frac{1}{3}\begin{bmatrix} 1 & 1 & 1 \\ 1 & \omega^2 & \omega \\ 1 & \omega & \omega^2 \end{bmatrix}.$$

We readily find $\mathbf{AB} = \mathbf{BA}$ so that we can use the method in the last exercise. This gives

$$\mathbf{P}^{-1}\mathbf{AP} = \begin{bmatrix} 0 & 0 & 0 \\ 0 & -3 & 0 \\ 0 & 0 & -3 \end{bmatrix},$$

so that the eigenvalues of **A** are 0, -3, -3 and the eigenvectors are the columns of **P**.

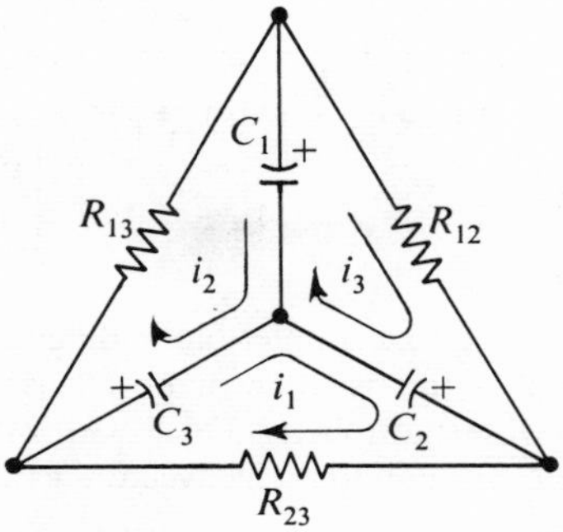

Figure 11.2 Resistor-capacitor network for Ex. 11.32.

Ex. 11.33. Use the method in the last exercise to solve the eigenproblem for the circulant matrix (Ex. 9.50).

Ex. 11.34. Show that the equations of motion for the ozone molecule in Figure 11.3 are given by

$$m\frac{d^2\mathbf{x}}{dt^2} = -k\mathbf{Ax}$$

where $\mathbf{x}$ is 6×1, m is the mass of each atom, k is the spring constant and, if $s = \sin(\pi/6)$, $c = \cos(\pi/6)$,

$$\mathbf{A} = \begin{bmatrix} \mathbf{Q} & \mathbf{R} \\ \mathbf{R}^T & \mathbf{S} \end{bmatrix},$$

where

$$\mathbf{Q} = c^2\begin{bmatrix} 2 & 1 & 1 \\ 1 & 2 & 1 \\ 1 & 1 & 2 \end{bmatrix}, \qquad \mathbf{R} = sc\begin{bmatrix} 0 & 1 & -1 \\ -1 & 0 & 1 \\ 1 & -1 & 0 \end{bmatrix},$$

$$\mathbf{S} = s^2\begin{bmatrix} 2 & -1 & -1 \\ -1 & 2 & -1 \\ -1 & -1 & 2 \end{bmatrix}.$$

The symmetry in 1, 2, 3 and 4, 5, 6 suggests that we try to see if the following matrix commutes with $\mathbf{A}$.

$$\mathbf{C} = \begin{bmatrix} \mathbf{B} & \mathbf{0} \\ \mathbf{0} & \mathbf{B} \end{bmatrix},$$

where $\mathbf{B}$ was defined in Exercise 11.32. It is left to the reader to check that $\mathbf{AC} = \mathbf{CA}$. We therefore form, using $\mathbf{P}$ defined in Exercise 11.32,

$$\begin{bmatrix} \mathbf{P}^{-1} & \mathbf{0} \\ \mathbf{0} & \mathbf{P}^{-1} \end{bmatrix}\begin{bmatrix} \mathbf{Q} & \mathbf{R} \\ \mathbf{R}^T & \mathbf{S} \end{bmatrix}\begin{bmatrix} \mathbf{P} & \mathbf{0} \\ \mathbf{0} & \mathbf{P} \end{bmatrix} = \frac{3}{4}\begin{bmatrix} 4 & 0 & 0 & 0 & 0 & 0 \\ 0 & 1 & 0 & 0 & i & 0 \\ 0 & 0 & 1 & 0 & 0 & -i \\ 0 & 0 & 0 & 0 & 0 & 0 \\ 0 & -i & 0 & 0 & 1 & 0 \\ 0 & 0 & i & 0 & 0 & 1 \end{bmatrix}.$$

This can be reduced to a simpler block-diagonal form by permuting rows and columns. Whether this is done or not, it is a simple matter to deduce the eigenvalues 0 with multiplicity 3, 1.5 with multiplicity 2, and 3 with multiplicity 1. The corresponding eigenvectors can be shown to be

$$\begin{bmatrix} 1 \\ -s \\ -s \\ 0 \\ -c \\ c \end{bmatrix}, \quad \begin{bmatrix} 0 \\ c \\ -c \\ 1 \\ -s \\ -s \end{bmatrix}, \quad \begin{bmatrix} 0 \\ 0 \\ 0 \\ 1 \\ 1 \\ 1 \end{bmatrix}, \quad \begin{bmatrix} 1 \\ -s \\ -s \\ 0 \\ c \\ -c \end{bmatrix}, \quad \begin{bmatrix} 0 \\ -c \\ c \\ 1 \\ -s \\ -s \end{bmatrix}, \quad \begin{bmatrix} 1 \\ 1 \\ 1 \\ 0 \\ 0 \\ 0 \end{bmatrix}.$$

The first three are rigid motions (two translations and a rotation). Only three nontrivial modes exist, of which the last is a dilatation.

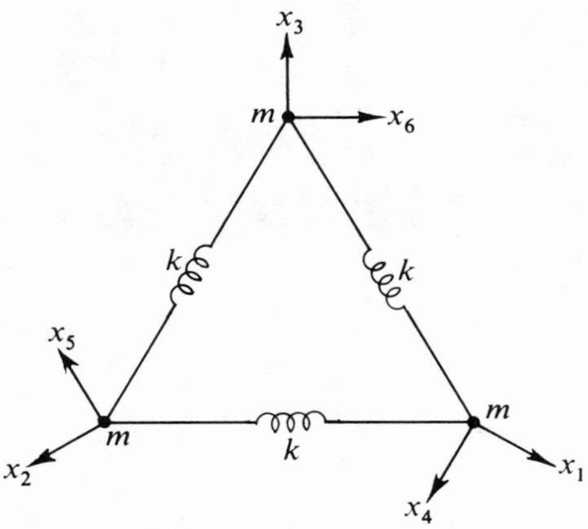

Figure 11.3 Ozone molecule for Ex. 11.34.

Ex. 11.35. A matrix **A** is called *stable* if the real parts of all its eigenvalues are less than zero. Prove that **A** is stable if and only if all the solutions of the differential equation

$$\frac{d\mathbf{x}(t)}{dt} = \mathbf{A}\mathbf{x}$$

tend to zero as t tends to infinity. (This result illustrates why it is important in electrical circuit theory, control theory, and other applications of mathematics to determine whether a given matrix is stable or not.) Write an essay on practical methods for determining whether a given matrix is stable or not without actually finding the eigenvalues (see, for instance, Franklin [37]).

12 Quadratic Forms and Variational Principles

12.1 A Geometrical Example Involving a Quadratic Form

We introduce the subject of quadratic forms by considering a simple geometrical example involving conic sections. We first of all solve the problem by elementary algebra, and then show that a matrix description leads naturally to eigenvalues and eigenvectors. The virtue of the eigenvector approach is that it provides a method for dealing with n-variable quadratic expressions that are generalizations of the equation for conics in two dimensions.

Consider the problem of discovering the nature of the curve represented by the equation

$$ax^2 + 2kxy + by^2 = c, \tag{12.1}$$

where a, k, b, c are given numbers. The clue to the analysis lies in transforming the equation to a new set of perpendicular axes X, Y, rotated through an angle θ with respect to the old x, y-axes, and such that the resulting equation has no cross-term in XY. In order to perform the rotation of axes algebraically, we set (Figure 12.1)

$$\begin{aligned} x &= X\cos\theta - Y\sin\theta, \\ y &= X\sin\theta + Y\cos\theta, \end{aligned} \tag{12.2}$$

where θ is an angle which is at our disposal. If we substitute (12.2) in (12.1), we obtain

$$\alpha X^2 + 2\kappa XY + \beta Y^2 = c, \tag{12.3a}$$

where

$$\left.\begin{aligned} \alpha &= a\cos^2\theta + 2k\sin\theta\cos\theta + b\sin^2\theta, \\ \kappa &= (b-a)\sin\theta\cos\theta + k(\cos^2\theta - \sin^2\theta), \\ \beta &= a\sin^2\theta - 2k\sin\theta\cos\theta + b\cos^2\theta. \end{aligned}\right\} \tag{12.3b}$$

$$OR = OQ \cos \theta - PQ \sin \theta$$
$$RP = OQ \sin \theta + PQ \cos \theta$$

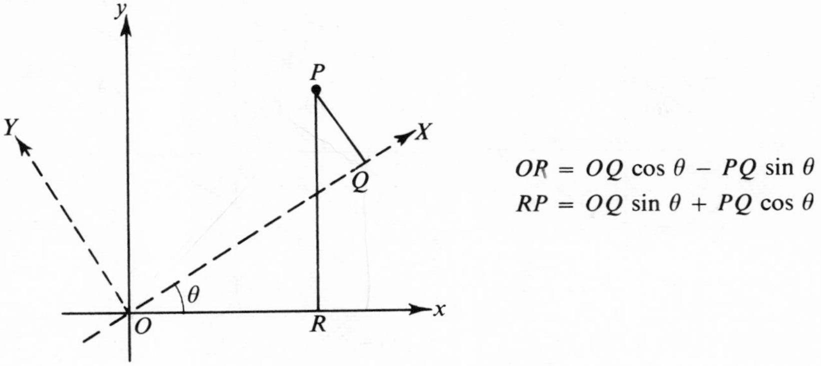

Figure 12.1 Rotation of axes.

The quantity κ vanishes if we choose θ so that

$$\tan 2\theta = \frac{2k}{(a - b)}. \tag{12.4}$$

We then have

$$\alpha X^2 + \beta Y^2 = c. \tag{12.5}$$

If θ satisfies (12.4), we find, after some laborious algebra, that $\alpha\beta = ab - k^2$. By inspection of (12.5) we see that there are three cases to consider:

(a) $k^2 < ab$ (α and β have the same sign). If α, β, c have the same sign, then (12.1) represents an ellipse [Figure 12.2(a)]. If the sign of c is opposite to that of α and β, then there are no points x, y that satisfy (12.1).

(b) $k^2 = ab$ (either α or β is zero). Apart from the trivial case $\alpha = \beta = 0$, (12.1) represents two parallel straight lines [Figure 12.2(b)].

(c) $k^2 > ab$ (α and β have opposite signs). If $c \neq 0$, then (12.1) represents a hyperbola [Figure 12.2(c)]. If $c = 0$, the equation represents two straight lines through the origin.

In matrix notation, the analysis leading from (12.1) to (12.5) can be rewritten in the following way. We introduce the matrices

$$\mathbf{x} = \begin{bmatrix} x \\ y \end{bmatrix}, \qquad \mathbf{A} = \begin{bmatrix} a & k \\ k & b \end{bmatrix}, \qquad \mathbf{c} = [c], \tag{12.6}$$

$$\mathbf{X} = \begin{bmatrix} X \\ Y \end{bmatrix}, \qquad \mathbf{S} = \begin{bmatrix} \cos \theta & -\sin \theta \\ \sin \theta & \cos \theta \end{bmatrix}, \qquad \mathbf{D} = \begin{bmatrix} \alpha & 0 \\ 0 & \beta \end{bmatrix}. \tag{12.7}$$

It is easy to verify that (12.1), (12.2), (12.3) are, respectively,

$$\mathbf{x}^T \mathbf{A} \mathbf{x} = \mathbf{c}, \tag{12.8}$$

$$\mathbf{x} = \mathbf{S} \mathbf{X}, \tag{12.9}$$

$$\mathbf{X}^T \mathbf{D} \mathbf{X} = \mathbf{c}. \tag{12.10}$$

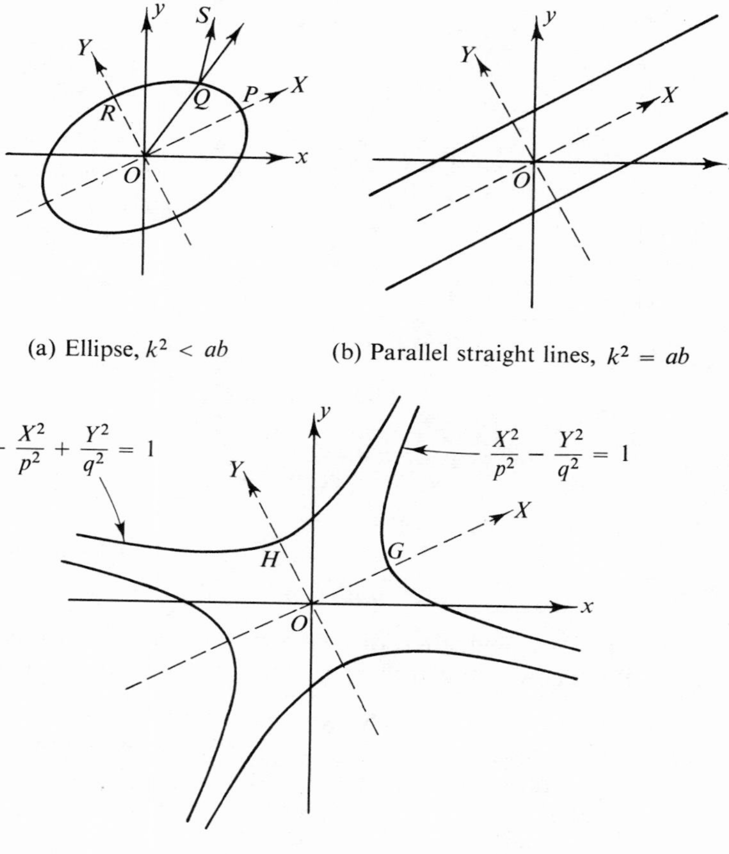

(a) Ellipse, $k^2 < ab$ (b) Parallel straight lines, $k^2 = ab$

(c) Hyperbola, $k^2 > ab$

Figure 12.2 Curves represented by (12.1).

On substituting the expression (12.9) for $\mathbf{x}$ in (12.8), we obtain

$$\mathbf{X}^T(\mathbf{S}^T\mathbf{A}\mathbf{S})\mathbf{X} = \mathbf{c}.$$

A comparison of this equation with (12.10) shows that, since these equations must be true for all $\mathbf{X}$, we must have

$$\mathbf{S}^T\mathbf{A}\mathbf{S} = \mathbf{D}, \tag{12.11}$$

i.e., $\mathbf{S}$ is a matrix that transforms $\mathbf{A}$ to diagonal form.

In matrix notation, the problem of simplifying the original equation (12.1) can therefore be posed as follows: Find a matrix $\mathbf{S}$ representing a rotation such that $\mathbf{S}^T\mathbf{A}\mathbf{S}$ is a diagonal matrix. One of the key phrases here is "representing a rotation." It turns out (see Ex. 12.48) that $\mathbf{S}$ must be an orthogonal matrix, i.e., $\mathbf{S}$ has the property

$$\mathbf{S}\mathbf{S}^T = \mathbf{S}^T\mathbf{S} = \mathbf{I}. \tag{12.12}$$

In the present case it is easy to verify that the matrix $\mathbf{S}$ introduced in (12.7) satisfies this condition. On premultiplying both sides of (12.11) by $\mathbf{S}$ and using (12.12), we see that

$$\mathbf{AS} = \mathbf{SD}. \tag{12.13}$$

If we set $\mathbf{S} = [\mathbf{s}_1, \mathbf{s}_2]$, this means, on introducing $\mathbf{D}$ from (12.7), that (12.13) gives

$$\mathbf{A}[\mathbf{s}_1, \mathbf{s}_2] = [\alpha\mathbf{s}_1, \beta\mathbf{s}_2],$$

i.e.,

$$\mathbf{A}\mathbf{s}_1 = \alpha\mathbf{s}_1, \qquad \mathbf{A}\mathbf{s}_2 = \beta\mathbf{s}_2.$$

Hence, α, β are the *eigenvalues* of $\mathbf{A}$ and $\mathbf{s}_1$, $\mathbf{s}_2$ are the corresponding *eigenvectors*.

From this point onwards we therefore replace equation (12.5), representing the conic section referred to the X, Y-axes, by the entirely equivalent equation:

$$\lambda_1 X^2 + \lambda_2 Y^2 = 1, \tag{12.14}$$

where we have also replaced c by 1. This choice of c means that instead of starting with (12.1) we are starting from

$$ax^2 + 2kxy + by^2 = 1. \tag{12.15}$$

Provided $c \neq 0$ (i.e., equation (12.1) does not represent two intersecting straight lines), there is no loss of generality in doing this, since it corresponds simply to dividing (12.1) throughout by a constant, which does not change the curves.

We can now give a geometrical interpretation of the eigenvalues by discussing the three cases listed above in connection with (12.5), but now using (12.14) as the basis for the discussion.

(a′) If λ_1 and λ_2 have the same (positive) sign, we compare (12.14) with the canonical equation for an ellipse whose major and minor axes coincide with the X, Y-axes [Figure 12.2(a)],

$$\frac{X^2}{p^2} + \frac{Y^2}{q^2} = 1,$$

where $p = OP$ and $q = OR$ are the lengths of the axes. A comparison of this equation with (12.14) yields

$$p^2 = OP^2 = \frac{1}{\lambda_1}, \qquad q^2 = OR^2 = \frac{1}{\lambda_2}. \tag{12.16}$$

Hence, the eigenvalues λ_1, λ_2 are inversely proportional to the squares of the lengths of the axes of the ellipse.

(b′) If one of the eigenvalues is zero, equation (12.14) shows immediately that this corresponds to the case of two parallel straight lines, and then the nonzero (positive) eigenvalue is proportional to the inverse of the square of the distance from the origin to either of the lines.

(c′) If λ_1 and λ_2 have opposite signs, we compare (12.14) with the canonical equation for a hyperbola

$$\pm\left\{\frac{X^2}{p^2} - \frac{Y^2}{q^2}\right\} = 1.$$

The situation is slightly different from that for an ellipse since we must include both signs on the left of this equation, in order to obtain a geometrical interpretation for both the eigenvalues λ_1 and λ_2. Suppose that $\lambda_1 > 0$ (i.e., $\lambda_2 < 0$). We first take the plus sign on the left. In this case, there is no real Y corresponding to $X = 0$, i.e., the curve does not cut the Y-axis. In Figure 12.2(c), the equation represents the curve that cuts the X-axis in G, and its reflection in the Y-axis. At G we have $Y = 0$, so that $OG^2 = p^2 = 1/\lambda_1$. If we take the minus sign on the left of the above equation, we find that we are dealing with the other hyperbola in Figure 12.2(c) which cuts the Y axis in H, where $X = 0$ so that $OH^2 = q^2$. Remembering that we are still assuming $\lambda_1 > 0$, $\lambda_2 < 0$, the equation for this conic is not (12.14) but

$$-\lambda_1 X^2 - \lambda_2 Y^2 = 1.$$

Hence, $OH^2 = q^2 = -\lambda_2$. Summing up, we have

$$OG^2 = p^2 = \frac{1}{\lambda_1}, \qquad OH^2 = q^2 = -\frac{1}{\lambda_2}. \tag{12.17}$$

This geometrical discussion has been a digression, and we return to the original problem, which was to discover the nature of the conic (12.1) by means of a change of variable corresponding to a rotation of axes. In view of the analysis in equations (12.8)–(12.14), we can now solve this problem by a method which is quite different from the elementary geometrical argument given at the beginning of this section. The end result of the analysis will be precisely the same as before, namely (12.5).

We start by solving the eigenvalue problem, i.e., we find the constants λ for which the following matrix equation has nonzero solutions:

$$\mathbf{A}\mathbf{x} = \lambda\mathbf{x},$$

where $\mathbf{A}$ is the matrix given in (12.6). The corresponding solutions $\mathbf{x}$ are the eigenvectors. On writing out this equation in detail, we obtain

$$\begin{bmatrix} a & k \\ k & b \end{bmatrix}\begin{bmatrix} x \\ y \end{bmatrix} = \lambda\begin{bmatrix} x \\ y \end{bmatrix},$$

that is,

$$\left.\begin{aligned} (a - \lambda)x + ky &= 0 \\ kx + (b - \lambda)y &= 0. \end{aligned}\right\} \tag{12.18}$$

This is a set of two homogeneous equations in two unknowns. From the theory of such systems we know that nonzero solutions exist only if the determinant of the coefficients is zero,

$$\begin{vmatrix} a-\lambda & k \\ k & b-\lambda \end{vmatrix} = 0, \tag{12.19}$$

or

$$\lambda^2 - (a+b)\lambda + (ab - k^2) = 0.$$

This is a quadratic in λ with two roots,

$$\tfrac{1}{2}(a+b) \pm \tfrac{1}{2}\{(a-b)^2 + 4k^2\}^{1/2}.$$

It is left to the reader to check that these are precisely the quantities α, β defined by (12.3b), as the above theory suggests. We can also find the eigenvectors corresponding to the two values of λ and check that these, when normalized, are the columns of **S** defined in (12.7).

Rather than carry through these algebraic verifications in detail, it is perhaps equally instructive to consider a numerical example.

Ex. 12.1. Investigate the nature of the curve

$$x^2 + 4xy - 2y^2 = c.$$

Solution: The matrix **A** is

$$\mathbf{A} = \begin{bmatrix} 1 & 2 \\ 2 & -2 \end{bmatrix}$$

and the eigenvalue problem is to solve (12.18),

$$\begin{aligned} (1-\lambda)x + 2y &= 0 \\ 2x - (2+\lambda)y &= 0. \end{aligned} \tag{12.20}$$

The eigenvalues are the roots of the quadratic

$$\lambda^2 + \lambda - 6 = 0,$$

i.e., $\lambda_1 = 2$, $\lambda_2 = -3$. Solution of the equations obtained by substituting these values in (12.20) gives the corresponding normalized eigenvectors,

$$\mathbf{x}_1 = \frac{1}{\sqrt{5}}\begin{bmatrix} 2 \\ 1 \end{bmatrix}, \qquad \mathbf{x}_2 = \frac{1}{\sqrt{5}}\begin{bmatrix} -1 \\ 2 \end{bmatrix}.$$

This gives

$$\mathbf{S} = \frac{1}{\sqrt{5}}\begin{bmatrix} 2 & -1 \\ 1 & 2 \end{bmatrix}, \tag{12.21}$$

and the reader will readily check that

$$\mathbf{S}^T\mathbf{S} = \mathbf{I}, \qquad \mathbf{S}^T\mathbf{A}\mathbf{S} = \begin{bmatrix} 2 & 0 \\ 0 & -3 \end{bmatrix}.$$

On comparing **S** defined in (12.7) with (12.21), we see that $\cos\theta = 2/\sqrt{5}$, $\sin\theta = 1/\sqrt{5}$, and it is easy to deduce that $\tan 2\theta$ is then $\frac{4}{3}$ which is the value that can be found independently from (12.4). The end result is that if the coordinates (x, y) are transformed into coordinates (X, Y) by means of (12.9), where **S** is given by (10.21), the conic becomes

$$2X^2 - 3Y^2 = c,$$

so that the conic is a hyperbola.

Another way of looking at the original problem depicted in Figure 12.2 is to reflect that the eigenvalues in Figures 12.2(a), (c) are related to the distances from the origin to the points P, R and G, H, respectively. At all of these points, the normal to the curve is in the same direction as the radius vector. This is not true at the general point, e.g., consider Q, at which OQ and QS are not in the same direction. The slope of the curve, dy/dx, is given by implicit differentiation of (12.1) with respect to x,

$$2ax + 2k\left(y + x\frac{dy}{dx}\right) + 2by\frac{dy}{dx} = 0.$$

The slope of the normal at a point (x, y) is therefore given by

$$-\frac{1}{(dy/dx)} = \frac{kx + by}{ax + ky}.$$

We wish this to be identical with the slope of the radius vector, i.e., we require

$$\frac{y}{x} = \frac{kx + by}{ax + ky},$$

or

$$ax + ky = \lambda x$$
$$kx + by = \lambda y,$$

where λ is a factor of proportionality. These are identical with (12.18). Suppose that these have solutions $\lambda = \lambda_1, \lambda_2$ with corresponding eigenvectors (x_i, y_i), $i = 1, 2$. If we substitute (x_i, y_i) for (x, y) in (12.1), we obtain

$$c = (ax_i + ky_i)x_i + (kx_i + by_i)y_i = \lambda_i(x_i^2 + y_i^2),$$

i.e., for the special points in which we are interested, the distance from the origin to the conic is inversely proportional to the square root of the corresponding eigenvalue. We have already obtained and discussed this result, from a slightly different point of view, in (a′), (b′) above. In addition, the eigenvectors specify y_i/x_i which are the slopes of the lines being considered, i.e., the eigenvectors give the directions of the radius vectors specifying the axes of the ellipse or hyperbola.

Ex. 12.2. Check that the eigenvalues given by (12.19) are the quantities α, β given in (12.3b), as suggested in the text. Deduce the result $\alpha\beta = ab - k^2$ [see the sentence following (12.5)] as an almost trivial consequence.

Ex. 12.3. Suppose that we translate coordinates by shifting the origin to x_0, y_0, so that the new coordinates ξ, η are related to the old by

$$x = \xi + x_0, \qquad y = \eta + y_0.$$

Show that the general quadratic curve

$$ax^2 + 2kxy + by^2 + 2cx + 2dy + e = 0$$

becomes

$$a\xi^2 + 2k\xi\eta + b\eta^2 + 2C\xi + 2D\eta + E = 0,$$

where

$$C = ax_0 + ky_0 + c, \qquad D = kx_0 + by_0 + d.$$

Show that if $ab - k^2 \neq 0$ or $ab - k^2 = 0$ and $ad = bc$, we can choose x_0, y_0 so that the equation for the curve becomes

$$a\xi^2 + 2k\xi\eta + b\eta^2 + E = 0,$$

which can be analyzed by the method used to deal with (12.1). However, if $ab = k^2$, $ad \neq bc$, there is no loss of generality in assuming $a \neq 0$ (since if $a = b = 0$, then $k = 0$, and we have no quadratic). We can then choose $y_0 = 0$, $x_0 = -c/a$, so that $C = 0$. The equation for the curve now becomes

$$a\xi^2 + 2k\xi\eta + b\eta^2 + 2D\eta + E = 0.$$

A rotation of axes to reduce the quadratic terms to the form (12.5) will give

$$\alpha X^2 + 2\gamma Y = c,$$

which is the equation for a parabola.

Ex. 12.4. Investigate the nature of the curves given by the following equations. Sketch the curves.

(a) $x^2 + 12xy + y^2 = 10$.
(b) $x^2 - 4xy + 4y^2 = 0$.
(c) $5x^2 + 8xy + 5y^2 = 10$.
(d) $5x^2 - 8xy + 5y^2 - 18x + 18y + 8 = 0$.
(e) $9x^2 - 12xy + 4y^2 - 42x - 2y + 7 = 0$.

12.2 Quadratic Forms

We generalize some of the ideas introduced in the last section. A *quadratic form* in n real variables $x_1, x_2, \ldots, x_n$ associated with a real matrix $\mathbf{A}$, is a scalar quantity consisting of a sum of multiples of the products and squares of the variables:

$$\begin{aligned} F &= \sum_{i=1}^{n}\sum_{j=1}^{n} a_{ij}x_i x_j \\ &= a_{11}x_1^2 + (a_{12} + a_{21})x_1x_2 + a_{22}x_2^2 + \cdots. \end{aligned} \tag{12.22}$$

If we introduce the matrices $\mathbf{x} = [x_i]$, $\mathbf{A} = [a_{ij}]$, the quadratic form can be written, using inner product notation, as

$$F = \sum_{i=1}^{n} x_i \sum_{j=1}^{n} a_{ij}x_j = \sum_{i=1}^{n} x_i(\mathbf{Ax})_i = (\mathbf{x}, \mathbf{Ax}). \tag{12.23}$$

According to the definition just given, we can associate a quadratic form with *any* matrix $\mathbf{A}$, but it is clear when the quadratic form is written out in detail, as in (12.22), that the terms involving a_{ij} and a_{ji} will give a contribution

$$(a_{ij} + a_{ji})x_i x_j, \tag{12.24}$$

i.e., the contribution depends on $a_{ij} + a_{ji}$ and not on a_{ij}, a_{ji} separately. This means that if we start with a general matrix $\mathbf{A}$ and obtain from it a second matrix $\mathbf{A}' = \frac{1}{2}(\mathbf{A} + \mathbf{A}^T)$, where (i, j)th and (j, i)th elements are both $\frac{1}{2}(a_{ij} + a_{ji})$, the quadratic forms $(\mathbf{x}, \mathbf{Ax})$ and $(\mathbf{x}, \mathbf{A}'\mathbf{x})$ are identical. Hence, without loss of generality we can assume that the quadratic form is associated with a symmetric matrix when the a_{ij} and x_i are real.

When we are dealing with complex elements, we recall from the discussion in Section 9.3 that there is a natural way to generalize the real inner product that occurs in (12.23) (see Definition 9.4), and then hermitian matrices play the same role as symmetric matrices in the real case. This suggests that the natural generalization of (12.23) is still $(\mathbf{x}, \mathbf{Ax})$ but now $\mathbf{A}$ is hermitian and $\mathbf{x}$ may have complex elements. We have already seen during the proof of Theorem 9.8 (see also Ex. 9.10) that $(\mathbf{x}, \mathbf{Ax})$ is real.

DEFINITION **12.1.** The *quadratic form* associated with the hermitian matrix $\mathbf{A}$ is the real quantity $(\mathbf{x}, \mathbf{Ax})$. When $\mathbf{A}$ is a real symmetric matrix, we refer to the *real quadratic form* $(\mathbf{x}, \mathbf{Ax})$.

It may be noted in passing that in many textbooks the quadratic form $(\mathbf{x}, \mathbf{Ax})$ is written as $\mathbf{x}^T\mathbf{Ax}$ in the real case, and $\bar{\mathbf{x}}^T\mathbf{Ax}$ in the complex case. Also, the theory for the real case is often worked out in detail, and the corresponding theory for the complex case is left as exercises. However, as we saw in Chapter 9, the inner product notation provides a convenient tool for dealing with the real and complex cases together, and this is the policy we shall adopt here.

We quote three of the many reasons why quadratic forms are important:

(a) In two dimensions, conics are the simplest curves after the straight line, and play a fundamental role in two-dimensional geometry. In n dimensions, quadratic forms give rise to the analogue of conics, so that quadratic forms play a fundamental role in n-dimensional geometry.

(b) If we expand a function of n variables in a Taylor series, performing the expansion around the origin for simplicity, we obtain

$$f(x_1, \ldots, x_n) = (f)_0 + \sum_{i=1}^{n} (f_i)_0 x_i + \sum_{i=1}^{n}\sum_{j=1}^{n} (f_{ij})_0 x_i x_j + \ldots, \tag{12.25}$$

where

$$f_i = \frac{\partial f}{\partial x_i}, \qquad f_{ij} = \frac{\partial^2 f}{\partial x_i \, \partial x_j},$$

and the notation $(\quad)_0$ means that quantities are evaluated at the origin. At a stationary value of the function, we have $\partial f/\partial x_i = 0$, and the nature of the behavior of the function near this stationary value will depend on the behavior of a quadratic form. This is a generalization of the theory of maxima and minima of functions of a single variable, $f(x)$, for which the nature of the extremum depends on d^2f/dx^2. These considerations apply in practical problems involving, for instance, the optimization of the response of a system involving several variables, where we are interested in the behavior near the optimum.

(c) In dynamics, physical quantities like kinetic energy, and potential energy in the neighborhood of equilibrium, can be expressed as quadratic forms. The theory of small vibrations in many-coordinate systems depends on the theory of quadratic forms.

As illustrated in the last section, the key to the study of quadratic forms is the idea of a change of variable from coordinates $\mathbf{x}$ to coordinates $\mathbf{y}$ by means of a transformation

$$\mathbf{x} = \mathbf{S}\mathbf{y},$$

where $\mathbf{S}$ is a nonsingular matrix. We restrict ourselves to nonsingular $\mathbf{S}$ since it is only in this case that we can write $\mathbf{y} = \mathbf{S}^{-1}\mathbf{x}$, so that a given $\mathbf{x}$ determines a unique $\mathbf{y}$, and a given $\mathbf{y}$ determines a unique $\mathbf{x}$. Substitution of $\mathbf{x} = \mathbf{S}\mathbf{y}$ into $F = (\mathbf{x}, \mathbf{A}\mathbf{x})$ gives

$$F = (\mathbf{S}\mathbf{y}, \mathbf{A}\mathbf{S}\mathbf{y}) = (\mathbf{y}, \mathbf{S}^H\mathbf{A}\mathbf{S}\mathbf{y}) = (\mathbf{y}, \mathbf{B}\mathbf{y}),$$

where

$$\mathbf{B} = \mathbf{S}^H\mathbf{A}\mathbf{S}. \tag{12.26}$$

If we can find $\mathbf{S}$ so that $\mathbf{B}$ is a diagonal matrix with diagonal elements β_i, then we have obtained a representation for F of the form

$$F = \beta_1\bar{y}_1y_1 + \cdots + \beta_n\bar{y}_ny_n,$$

and the form of F has been very considerably simplified. So far we have said nothing about $\mathbf{S}$ except that it must be nonsingular. In many applications of quadratic forms we wish to compare the sizes of various quantities that are involved, so that, if we change variables by a formula of the type $\mathbf{x} = \mathbf{S}\mathbf{y}$, it is important that lengths be preserved, i.e., that $(\mathbf{x}, \mathbf{x}) = (\mathbf{y}, \mathbf{y})$. Then $(\mathbf{x}, \mathbf{x}) = (\mathbf{S}\mathbf{y}, \mathbf{S}\mathbf{y}) = (\mathbf{y}, \mathbf{S}^H\mathbf{S}\mathbf{y}) = (\mathbf{y}, \mathbf{y})$ for all $\mathbf{x}$, so that $\mathbf{S}^H\mathbf{S} = \mathbf{I}$. This means that, in order to preserve distances, $\mathbf{S}$ must be unitary, and then (12.26) is a unitary transformation.

Our basic result on the simplification of quadratic forms is a direct result of Theorem 10.9: If $\mathbf{A}$ is hermitian, there exists a unitary matrix $\mathbf{P}$ such that $\mathbf{P}^H\mathbf{A}\mathbf{P}$ is a diagonal matrix whose diagonal elements are the eigenvalues of $\mathbf{A}$.

THEOREM **12.1.** *If* **A** *is a hermitian matrix of order n and* **P** *is a unitary matrix whose columns are the normalized eigenvectors of* **A**, *then*

$$(\mathbf{x}, \mathbf{Ax}) = \lambda_1 \bar{y}_1 y_1 + \lambda_2 \bar{y}_2 y_2 + \ldots + \lambda_n \bar{y}_n y_n \tag{12.27}$$

where $\mathbf{x} = \mathbf{Py}$ *and the* λ_i *are the eigenvalues of* **A**. *If* **A** *is real symmetric and* **P** *is an orthogonal matrix whose columns are normalized eigenvectors of* **A**, *then, if* $\mathbf{x} = \mathbf{Py}$,

$$(\mathbf{x}, \mathbf{Ax}) = \lambda_1 y_1^2 + \lambda_2 y_2^2 + \ldots + \lambda_n y_n^2. \tag{12.28}$$

Proof: From Theorem 10.9 we have $\mathbf{P}^H\mathbf{AP} = \mathbf{\Lambda}$, where $\mathbf{\Lambda}$ is a diagonal matrix whose diagonal elements are the eigenvalues of **A**. Hence, on setting $\mathbf{x} = \mathbf{Py}$,

$$(\mathbf{x}, \mathbf{Ax}) = (\mathbf{Py}, \mathbf{APy}) = (\mathbf{y}, \mathbf{P}^T\mathbf{APy}) = (\mathbf{y}, \mathbf{\Lambda y}),$$

and this is the required result. The last part is a special case of the first, and it is stated separately only because of its importance.

A quadratic form containing no cross-products is said to be in *diagonal form.* We say that the transformation $\mathbf{x} = \mathbf{Py}$ in the above theorem has *diagonalized* the form. The theorem shows that any quadratic form can be diagonalized by a unitary transformation.

Ex. 12.5. Diagonalize the following quadratic form.

$$F = 3x_1^2 + 2x_2^2 + 3x_3^3 - 2x_1x_2 - 2x_2x_3.$$

Solution: We see that $F = (\mathbf{x}, \mathbf{Ax})$, where

$$\mathbf{A} = \begin{bmatrix} 3 & -1 & 0 \\ -1 & 2 & -1 \\ 0 & -1 & 3 \end{bmatrix}.$$

The reduction of this matrix to diagonal form was investigated in Chapter 9, where the required orthogonal matrix **P** was found to be that given in (9.46). (See Ex. 9.18.) The corresponding eigenvalues of **A** are 1, 3, 4, and if we set $\mathbf{x} = \mathbf{Py}$ we find

$$F = y_1^2 + 3y_2^2 + 4y_3^2.$$

Ex. 12.6. As an example of an application of diagonalization, we consider the following optimization problem in chemical engineering. A chemical reaction involves the temperature T, the concentration c of one of the reactants, and the time t of the reaction. It is required to investigate how the yield η of the reaction varies when T, c, t are altered within certain limits. Preliminary experiments led to the levels $T = 167°c$, $c = 27.5\%$, $t = 6.5$ hr, and indicated that T could be varied by $\pm 5°C$, c by $\pm 2.5\%$, and t by ± 1.5 hr. We introduce the standardized variables

$$x_1 = \frac{(T - 167)}{5}, \qquad x_2 = \frac{(c - 27.5)}{2.5}, \qquad x_3 = \frac{(t - 6.5)}{1.5}, \tag{12.29}$$

where we are now interested in the range $-1 \leq x_i \leq +1$.

By measuring η for various values of the x_i around $x_i = 0$, it is possible to represent η approximately by a second degree surface in the neighborhood of $x_i = 0$, $i = 1, 2, 3$. The technical details of how this is done are irrelevant here. They can be found, for instance, in the book edited by O. L. Davies quoted in the bibliographical notes, where G. E. P. Box gives the original example on which the present discussion is based. The numbers have been changed slightly so that the arithmetic can be carried out by pencil and paper, but in practice the calculations would be performed on a digital computer.

Suppose that the following equation is found, relating the yield η to the independent variables $\mathbf{x}$, near $\mathbf{x} = \mathbf{0}$.

$$\begin{aligned}\eta = 57.79 &+ 1.78x_1 + 0.50\sqrt{3x_2} + 1.08\sqrt{3x_3} \\ &-1.4x_1^2 - 1.4x_3^2 - 1.4\sqrt{3x_1x_2} - 1.2\sqrt{3x_1x_3} - 1.2x_2x_3. \qquad (12.30)\end{aligned}$$

The value of η is stationary when $\partial\eta/\partial x_i = 0$, $i = 1, 2, 3$. This gives the following simultaneous linear equations for the determination of the stationary point.

$$\begin{aligned}2.8x_1 + 1.4\sqrt{3}x_2 + 1.2\sqrt{3}x_3 &= 1.78 \\ 1.4\sqrt{3}x_1 \qquad\qquad + \quad 1.2x_3 &= 0.5\sqrt{3} \\ 1.2\sqrt{3}x_1 + \quad 1.2x_3 + \quad 2.8x_3 &= 1.08\sqrt{3}.\end{aligned} \qquad (12.31)$$

The solution of these equations is given by $x_1 = 0.1$, $x_2 = 0.1\sqrt{3}$, $x_3 = 0.3\sqrt{3}$. We therefore make the following change of variables:

$$z_1 = x_1 - 0.1, \qquad z_2 = x_2 - 0.1\sqrt{3}, \qquad z_3 = x_3 - 0.3\sqrt{3}. \quad (12.32)$$

In terms of these variables, the expression for η becomes

$$\eta = 58.44 - 1.4z_1^2 - 1.4z_3^2 - 1.4\sqrt{3}z_1z_2 - 1.2\sqrt{3}z_1z_3 - 1.2z_2z_3. \quad (12.33)$$

In symbols, the analysis, so far, is a particular case of the following. If

$$\eta = (\mathbf{x}, \mathbf{Ax}) - 2(\mathbf{x}, \mathbf{b}) + c,$$

the stationary value is given by $\mathbf{x} = \mathbf{x}_0$, where $\mathbf{Ax}_0 = \mathbf{b}$. We make the change of variable $\mathbf{z} = \mathbf{x} - \mathbf{x}_0$, obtaining

$$\eta = (\mathbf{z}, \mathbf{Az}) + (\mathbf{c} - (\mathbf{x}_0, \mathbf{b})).$$

The point of the transformation is to eliminate the linear terms in η.

The next step is to diagonalize the quadratic form in (12.33) which, for convenience, we write as $\eta = 58.44 - (\mathbf{z}, \mathbf{Az})$, where

$$\mathbf{A} = \begin{bmatrix} 1.4 & 0.7\sqrt{3} & 0.6\sqrt{3} \\ 0.7\sqrt{3} & 0 & 0.6 \\ 0.6\sqrt{3} & 0.6 & 1.4 \end{bmatrix}. \quad (12.34)$$

The eigenvalues of this matrix are found to be $\lambda_1 = 3$, $\lambda_2 = 0.5$, $\lambda_3 = -0.7$, with corresponding normalized eigenvectors

$$\mathbf{z}_1 = \begin{bmatrix} 0.4\sqrt{3} \\ 0.4 \\ 0.6 \end{bmatrix}, \qquad \mathbf{z}_2 = \begin{bmatrix} 0.3\sqrt{3} \\ 0.3 \\ -0.8 \end{bmatrix}, \qquad \mathbf{z}_3 = \begin{bmatrix} 0.5 \\ -0.5\sqrt{3} \\ 0 \end{bmatrix}. \quad (12.35)$$

As described in Theorem 12.1 above, we now set $\mathbf{z} = \mathbf{P}\mathbf{y}$, where $\mathbf{P} = [\mathbf{z}_1, \mathbf{z}_2, \mathbf{z}_3]$. We then find that (12.33) gives

$$\eta = 58.44 - 3y_1^2 - 0.5y_2^2 + 0.7y_3^2.$$

In order to see what is happening, we investigate this result in the neighborhood of $\mathbf{y} = \mathbf{0}$, in which case the response is given approximately by

$$\eta = 58.44 - 3y_1^2.$$

The maximum response is then given by $y_1 = 0$. Since $\mathbf{y} = \mathbf{P}^T\mathbf{z}$, we see, on using (12.32), (12.35), that

$$y_1 = 0.4\sqrt{3}(x_1 - 0.1) + 0.4(x_2 - 0.1\sqrt{3}) + 0.6(x_3 - 0.3\sqrt{3}).$$

Expressing this in terms of the original variables by means of (12.29), we see that the relation $y_1 = 0$ is

$$\sqrt{3}(T - 167) + 2(c - 27.5) + 5(t - 6.5) = 3.25\sqrt{3}. \qquad (12.36)$$

The statement that the yield is a maximum when $y_1 = 0$ is equivalent to the statement that any combination of T, c, t on the plane (12.36) will maximize the yield.

The conclusion of this analysis is that the level surfaces are approximately planes in the region in which we are interested, as illustrated graphically in Figure 12.3, which shows the level surfaces corresponding to the maximum

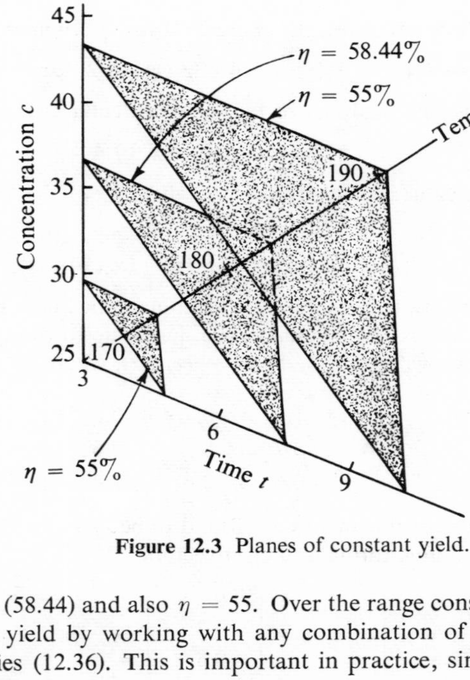

Figure 12.3 Planes of constant yield.

value of η (58.44) and also $\eta = 55$. Over the range considered we can obtain maximum yield by working with any combination of the variables T, c, t that satisfies (12.36). This is important in practice, since it means that the operating conditions can be chosen to satisfy criteria in addition to maximum yield.

One of the important consequences of Theorem 12.1 is that it enables us to make a fundamental classification of quadratic forms. We consider only the case where **A** is real symmetric and **x** is real. Then the orthogonal transformation used in Theorem 12.1 corresponds to a rigid rotation of the coordinate system, distances remaining unchanged.

DEFINITION **12.2.** The surface in n-dimensional space defined by the equation

$$(\mathbf{x}, \mathbf{Ax}) = 1,$$

where **A** is a real symmetric matrix of order n, is known as a *central quadric.* In the case $n = 2$ the word "surface" must be replaced by "curve."

Theorem 12.1 [equation (12.28)] states that, relative to the transformed axes, the equation of the quadric becomes

$$\lambda_1 y_1^2 + \lambda_2 y_2^2 + \ldots + \lambda_n y_n^2 = 1.$$

We have already examined the two-dimensional case in Section 12.1 (Figure 12.2),

$$\lambda_1 y_1^2 + \lambda_2 y_2^2 = 1.$$

There are then three possibilities:

(a) Ellipse: λ_1, λ_2 have the same sign.
(b) Hyperbola: λ_1, λ_2 have opposite signs.
(c) Two parallel straight lines: one zero eigenvalue.

In the three-variable case there are five possibilities. Consider the surface represented by

$$\lambda_1 x_1^2 + \lambda_2 x_2^2 + \lambda_3 x_3^2 = 1.$$

The following cases arise (the reader should visualize these surfaces in three-dimensional space):

(a) Ellipsoid: λ_1, λ_2, λ_3 positive. When two λ's are equal, the surface is a rotational ellipsoid. When three λ's are equal, we have a sphere.

(b) Hyperboloid with one sheet: λ_1, λ_2 positive, λ_3 negative. When the two positive λ's are equal, we have a rotational hyperboloid or "cooling tower."

(c) Hyperboloid with two sheets: λ_1 positive, λ_2, λ_3 negative. When the two negative λ's are equal, we have a rotational hyperboloid.

(d) Elliptic or hyperbolic cylinder: one of the λ_i is zero.

(e) Two parallel planes: two of the λ_i are zero.

We can carry out a similar classification when more than three variables are involved, though then, of course, the results no longer have a direct geometrical significance.

12.3 Definite Quadratic Forms

Some quadratic forms have the property that $(\mathbf{x}, \mathbf{Ax}) > 0$ for all $\mathbf{x} \neq \mathbf{0}$. A simple example is

$$F = x_1^2 + x_2^2 + 2x_3^2.$$

Another important type of quadratic form has the property that $(\mathbf{x}, \mathbf{Ax}) \geq 0$ for all $\mathbf{x}$, although for this class of form it is not true that $(\mathbf{x}, \mathbf{Ax}) = 0$ implies $\mathbf{x} = \mathbf{0}$. A simple example is

$$F = (x_1 - x_2)^2 + 2x_3^2,$$

which is zero for the nonzero vector given by $x_1 = k$, $x_2 = k$, $x_3 = 0$, for any k. In general, of course, a quadratic form can be either positive or negative. The special cases that are one-signed are important, and we introduce the following terminology.

DEFINITION **12.3.** The matrix $\mathbf{A}$ in this definition is always hermitian. (This means symmetric in the real case.) The quadratic form $(\mathbf{x}, \mathbf{Ax})$ is said to be *positive definite* if $(\mathbf{x}, \mathbf{Ax}) > 0$ for all $\mathbf{x} \neq \mathbf{0}$, and *positive semidefinite* if $(\mathbf{x}, \mathbf{Ax}) \geq 0$ for all $\mathbf{x}$. The matrix $\mathbf{A}$ is said to be *positive definite* or *semidefinite* if the corresponding quadratic form is positive definite or semidefinite. Negative forms and matrices are defined similarly. A quadratic form is said to be *indefinite* if it is positive for some $\mathbf{x}$, negative for others.

According to this definition, positive definite matrices are also positive semidefinite. If it is necessary to say that $(\mathbf{x}, \mathbf{Ax}) \geq 0$ and there exists a nonzero $\mathbf{x}$ such that $(\mathbf{x}, \mathbf{Ax}) = 0$, we shall say that $\mathbf{A}$ is positive semidefinite and singular (see Ex. 12.31).

In the last section we confined our attention to unitary transformations because we were interested in keeping lengths unchanged. When studying whether a quadratic form is positive definite or not it is convenient to relax this restriction and consider any transformation of the type $\mathbf{B} = \mathbf{S}^H\mathbf{AS}$, where $\mathbf{S}$ is nonsingular.

DEFINITION **12.4.** If there exists a nonsingular matrix $\mathbf{S}$ such that $\mathbf{S}^H\mathbf{AS} = \mathbf{B}$ we say that $\mathbf{B}$ is *hermitian-congruent* to $\mathbf{A}$, and that $\mathbf{B}$ is obtained from $\mathbf{A}$ by a *hermitian-congruence* transformation. When $\mathbf{A}$ and $\mathbf{S}$ are real we can omit the word hermitian. In this case, if $\mathbf{A}$, $\mathbf{B}$ are *congruent*, a real nonsingular matrix $\mathbf{S}$ exists such that $\mathbf{S}^T\mathbf{AS} = \mathbf{B}$.

It is important to note that the property of being positive definite is not affected by a congruence transformation.

THEOREM **12.2.** *If* $(\mathbf{x}, \mathbf{Ax})$ *is a positive definite quadratic form and* $\mathbf{B} = \mathbf{S}^H\mathbf{AS}$, *where* $\mathbf{S}$ *is a nonsingular square matrix, then* $(\mathbf{x}, \mathbf{Bx})$ *is also a positive definite quadratic form. Similarly for positive semidefinite forms, etc.*

Proof: We have

$$(\mathbf{x}, \mathbf{Bx}) = (\mathbf{x}, \mathbf{S}^H\mathbf{ASx}) = (\mathbf{Sx}, \mathbf{A}(\mathbf{Sx})).$$

Since $\mathbf{S}$ is nonsingular, $\mathbf{Sx} \neq \mathbf{0}$ if $\mathbf{x} \neq \mathbf{0}$ ($\mathbf{Sx} = \mathbf{0}$ implies $\mathbf{x} = \mathbf{0}$). But if $\mathbf{Sx} \neq \mathbf{0}$, we know from the definition of a positive definite form that $((\mathbf{Sx}), \mathbf{A}(\mathbf{Sx})) > 0$. Hence, if $\mathbf{x} \neq 0$, we have $(\mathbf{x}, \mathbf{Bx}) > 0$, and this form is positive definite. The other cases can be proved similarly.

If we know the eigenvalues of $\mathbf{A}$ we can immediately say whether $(\mathbf{x}, \mathbf{Ax})$ is definite or not.

THEOREM **12.3.** (i) $(\mathbf{x}, \mathbf{Ax})$ *is positive definite if and only if every eigenvalue of* $\mathbf{A}$ *is positive.*

(ii) $(\mathbf{x}, \mathbf{Ax})$ *is positive semidefinite if and only if all the eigenvalues of* $\mathbf{A}$ *are nonnegative.*

(iii) $(\mathbf{x}, \mathbf{Ax})$ *is indefinite if* $\mathbf{A}$ *has both positive and negative eigenvalues and conversely.*

Proof: From Theorem 12.1 we can introduce new variables $\mathbf{y}$ defined by $\mathbf{x} = \mathbf{Sy}$, where $\mathbf{S}$ is nonsingular, such that

$$(\mathbf{x}, \mathbf{Ax}) = \lambda_1\bar{y}_1y_1 + \lambda_2\bar{y}_2y_2 + \dots + \lambda_n\bar{y}_ny_n. \tag{12.37}$$

If every eigenvalue λ_i is positive, then the form on the right of this equation is positive definite so that, by Theorem 12.2, the form on the left, namely $(\mathbf{x}, \mathbf{Ax})$, is also positive definite. This proves (i). Parts (ii) and (iii) can be proved similarly.

The criterion for definiteness in Theorem 12.3, which depends on knowing the eigenvalues of $\mathbf{A}$, is not very convenient in practice, and we establish a simpler set of conditions for determining whether a matrix is positive definite. Before proving the main result (Theorem 12.6 below) we state some simple necessary conditions.

THEOREM **12.4.** *Necessary conditions for a hermitian matrix* $\mathbf{A}$ *to be positive definite are:*

(i) *The diagonal elements of* $\mathbf{A}$ *must be positive.*

(ii) $a_{ii}a_{jj} > |a_{ij}|^2, \qquad i \neq j.$

(iii) *The element of* **A** *of largest absolute value must lie on the diagonal.*

(iv) det **A** > 0. (**A** *is nonsingular.*)

Proof: In the quadratic form $(\mathbf{x}, \mathbf{Ax})$, choose all the x_j to be zero except x_i. Then $(\mathbf{x}, \mathbf{Ax}) = a_{ii}\,|x_i|^2$, and, since $x_i \neq 0$, we must have $a_{ii} > 0$. To prove (ii), choose all the x_j to be zero except x_i and x_k. Then

$$\begin{aligned}(\mathbf{x}, \mathbf{Ax}) &= a_{ii}\,|x_i|^2 + a_{ij}\bar{x}_i x_j + \bar{a}_{ij}x_i\bar{x}_j + a_{jj}\,|x_j|^2 \\ &= a_{ii}\left|\, x_i + \frac{a_{ij}x_j}{a_{ii}}\right|^2 + \frac{\{a_{ii}a_{jj} - |a_{ij}|^2\}\,|x_j|^2}{a_{ii}}. \end{aligned} \tag{12.38}$$

By choosing $x_i = -a_{ij}x_j/a_{ii}$ in this expression, we see that, since $a_{ii} > 0$, a necessary condition for $(\mathbf{x}, \mathbf{Ax})$ to be positive is that $a_{ii}a_{jj} - |a_{ij}|^2 > 0$. To prove (iii), suppose that for some i, j we have $|a_{ij}| \geq a_{ii}$, $|a_{ij}| \geq a_{jj}$, where, from (i), $a_{ii} > 0$, $a_{jj} > 0$. In this case, $|a_{ij}|^2 \geq a_{ii}a_{jj}$, which contradicts (ii). To prove (iv) we remind the reader that det **A** is precisely equal to the product of the eigenvalues. From Theorem 12.3, the eigenvalues of a positive definite matrix are all positive so that det $\mathbf{A} > 0$, which proves (iv).

To prove Theorem 12.6 we require the following preliminary result.

THEOREM **12.5.** *Let* **A** *be hermitian and let* $\mathbf{A}_k$ *denote the* $k \times k$ *matrix in the top left of* **A**. *If the* $\mathbf{A}_k$ *are all nonsingular* ($k = 1$ *to* n), *then* **A** *can be decomposed uniquely in the form*

$$\mathbf{A} = \mathbf{LDL}^H, \tag{12.39}$$

where **L** *is a lower triangular matrix with units on its principal diagonal, and* **D** *is a diagonal matrix with nonzero real diagonal elements which are the pivots obtained when* **A** *is reduced to row-echelon form by elementary row operations, working systematically along the main diagonal.*

Proof: From Theorem 7.12 we know that any square matrix **A** with nonsingular $\mathbf{A}_k$ can be expressed in the form

$$\mathbf{A} = \mathbf{LDB}, \tag{12.40}$$

where **L** and **B** are lower and upper triangular with units on the diagonal, and **D** is diagonal. Theorem 7.12(iii) tells us that the diagonal elements of **D** are the pivots in Gaussian elimination. Since det $\mathbf{A}_k$ is nonzero for $k = 1, \ldots, n$, and det $\mathbf{A}_k$ is given by the product of the first k diagonal elements of **D**, the diagonal elements of **D** are nonzero. We have therefore to prove that $\mathbf{B} = \mathbf{L}^H$ and that the elements of **D** are real. To do this, we note that the hermitian transpose of (12.40) gives, since **A** is hermitian,

$$\mathbf{A} = \mathbf{B}^H\mathbf{D}^H\mathbf{L}^H = \mathbf{LDB}.$$

Hence,

$$\mathbf{D}^H(\mathbf{L}^H\mathbf{B}^{-1}) = (\mathbf{L}^H\mathbf{B}^{-1})^H\mathbf{D}. \tag{12.41}$$

The matrix $\mathbf{L}^H\mathbf{B}^{-1}$ is upper triangular, so that the matrix on the left is upper triangular and the matrix on the right is lower triangular. Hence, both must be diagonal. Hence, $\mathbf{L}^H\mathbf{B}^{-1}$ must be diagonal. This is the product of two upper triangular matrices with units on their diagonal, so we must have $\mathbf{L}^H\mathbf{B}^{-1} = \mathbf{I}$ or $\mathbf{B} = \mathbf{L}^H$, as claimed. Equation (12.41) then gives $\mathbf{D}^H = \mathbf{D}$, i.e., the diagonal elements of $\mathbf{D}$ are real.

We can now prove our main result on positive-definite quadratic forms:

THEOREM **12.6.** *Either of the following sets of conditions is necessary and sufficient for* $(\mathbf{x}, \mathbf{Ax})$ *to be positive definite* ($\mathbf{A}$ *is hermitian*):

(i) *Reduce* $\mathbf{A}$ *to row-echelon form working systematically along the main diagonal. Then all the pivots are positive.*

(ii) *The principal minors consisting of the determinants of the* $k \times k$ *matrices in the top left-hand corner of* $\mathbf{A}$ ($k = 1$ *to* n) *are all positive:*

$$a_{11} > 0, \qquad \begin{vmatrix} a_{11} & a_{12} \\ a_{21} & a_{22} \end{vmatrix} > 0, \qquad \begin{vmatrix} a_{11} & a_{12} & a_{13} \\ a_{21} & a_{22} & a_{23} \\ a_{31} & a_{32} & a_{33} \end{vmatrix} > 0, \ldots. \tag{12.42}$$

Proof: Let $\mathbf{A}_k$ denote the $k \times k$ matrix in the top left of $\mathbf{A}$. If $\mathbf{A}$ is positive definite, then all the $\mathbf{A}_k$ are positive definite ($k = 1$ to n). Otherwise we could choose a $k \times 1$ vector $\mathbf{x}_k$ such that $(\mathbf{x}_k, \mathbf{A}_k\mathbf{x}_k)$ is nonpositive, and construct a vector $\mathbf{x}$ with its first k components equal to those of $\mathbf{x}_k$ and the remainder zero. For this choice of $\mathbf{x}$ we have $(\mathbf{x}, \mathbf{Ax}) = (\mathbf{x}_k, \mathbf{A}_k\mathbf{x}_k)$, which by supposition is nonpositive, and this is impossible. Hence, $\mathbf{A}_k$ is positive definite, which, by Theorem 12.4(iv) means that $\det \mathbf{A}_k > 0$, which proves that the condition in (ii) is necessary. Also $\det \mathbf{A}_k = p_1p_2 \ldots p_k$, where the p_i are the pivots found when reducing $\mathbf{A}$ to row-echelon form. Since $\det \mathbf{A}_k > 0$ for all k, all the p_i must be positive. This proves that the condition in (i) is necessary. Conversely, suppose that $\det \mathbf{A}_k > 0$ for all k. This is given if (ii) is assumed, and it is true if (i) is assumed since $\det \mathbf{A}_k = p_1p_2 \ldots p_k$. If $\det \mathbf{A}_k > 0$, then $\mathbf{A}_k$ is nonsingular and Theorem 12.5 then tells us that $\mathbf{A}$ can be written in the form (12.39) so that $\mathbf{A}$ is hermitian-congruent to a diagonal matrix $\mathbf{D}$ with real positive elements. Since $(\mathbf{x}, \mathbf{Dx})$ is positive definite, Theorem 12.2 tells us that $(\mathbf{x}, \mathbf{Ax})$ is positive definite. This shows that either condition (i) or (ii) is sufficient.

The point of this theorem is that we can find out whether a quadratic form is positive definite merely by reducing the corresponding matrix to row-echelon form, checking whether all the pivots are positive, as illustrated in the following example. We do not need to know anything about the eigenvalues or eigenvectors.

Ex. 12.7. Is the following quadratic form positive definite?

$$F = 2x_1^2 + x_2^2 + 6x_3^2 + 2x_1x_2 + x_1x_3 + 4x_2x_3.$$

Solution: We write down the matrix of the quadratic form, and reduce it to upper triangular form, *not* dividing the resulting rows by the pivots, so that the pivots appear on the diagonal of the final matrix,

$$A = \begin{bmatrix} 2 & 1 & \frac{1}{2} \\ 1 & 1 & 2 \\ \frac{1}{2} & 2 & 6 \end{bmatrix} \rightarrow \begin{bmatrix} 2 & 1 & \frac{1}{2} \\ 0 & \frac{1}{2} & 1\frac{3}{4} \\ 0 & 0 & -\frac{1}{4} \end{bmatrix}.$$

The pivots are 2, $\frac{1}{2}$, $-\frac{1}{4}$ and since one is negative, the quadratic form is *not* positive definite.

12.4 Simultaneous Diagonalization of Two Quadratic Forms

The analysis of certain problems in the applied sciences (for instance, in mechanics and economics) can be simplified considerably by reducing two real quadratic forms simultaneously to diagonal form by means of a (real) nonsingular congruence transformation. In order to be able to do this it is necessary that one of the quadratic forms be positive definite. We carry the theory through for hermitian matrices, with real symmetric matrices as a special case.

THEOREM **12.7.** *Let* **A**, **B** *be hermitian matrices, where* **B** *is positive definite.*

(i) *There exists a nonsingular matrix* **R** *such that*

$$\mathbf{R}^H\mathbf{A}\mathbf{R} = \boldsymbol{\Lambda}, \qquad \mathbf{R}^H\mathbf{B}\mathbf{R} = \mathbf{I} \tag{12.43}$$

where $\boldsymbol{\Lambda}$ *is a diagonal matrix with real diagonal elements.*

(ii) *The change of variable* $\mathbf{x} = \mathbf{R}\mathbf{y}$ *gives*

$$(\mathbf{x}, \mathbf{A}\mathbf{x}) = \lambda_1\bar{y}_1y_1 + \lambda_2\bar{y}_2y_2 + \ldots + \lambda_n\bar{y}_ny_n, \tag{12.44}$$

$$(\mathbf{x}, \mathbf{B}\mathbf{x}) = \bar{y}_1y_1 + \bar{y}_2y_2 + \ldots + \bar{y}_ny_n. \tag{12.45}$$

If **A**, **B**, **x** *are real, then* **R**, **y** *can be taken to be real.*

Proof: Since **B** is hermitian we know from Theorem 10.9 that a unitary matrix **P** exists such that

$$\mathbf{P}^H\mathbf{B}\mathbf{P} = \mathbf{K}, \tag{12.46}$$

where **K** is diagonal. Since **B** is positive definite, all the diagonal elements of **K** are positive, say k_i^2, so we can set

$$\mathbf{K} = \mathbf{D}^2, \tag{12.47}$$

where $\mathbf{D}$ is a diagonal matrix with real diagonal elements k_i. Introducing (12.47) into (12.46), we find, on setting $\mathbf{PD}^{-1} = \mathbf{Q}$, that

$$\mathbf{Q}^H\mathbf{BQ} = \mathbf{I}.$$

Consider $\mathbf{Q}^H\mathbf{AQ}$. This is hermitian, so by Theorem 10.9 a unitary transformation exists which reduces this to diagonal form, say

$$\mathbf{S}^H(\mathbf{Q}^H\mathbf{AQ})S = \mathbf{R}^H\mathbf{AR} = \mathbf{\Lambda}, \tag{12.48}$$

where $\mathbf{R} = \mathbf{QS}$ and $\mathbf{\Lambda}$ is diagonal. Since $\mathbf{A}$ is hermitian, $\mathbf{R}^H\mathbf{AR}$ is hermitian, and the diagonal elements of $\mathbf{\Lambda}$ are real. Also,

$$\mathbf{R}^H\mathbf{BR} = \mathbf{S}^H\mathbf{Q}^H\mathbf{BQS} = \mathbf{S}^H\mathbf{S} = \mathbf{I}, \tag{12.49}$$

and (12.48), (12.49) are the required result (12.43). This proves part (i), and the remainder of the theorem is immediate.

The theorem proves the existence of the matrices $\mathbf{R}$ and $\mathbf{\Lambda}$ in (12.43) but it does not give any insight into the significance of these matrices. This we now consider.

Since $\mathbf{R}$ is nonsingular, we can rewrite (12.43) as

$$\mathbf{AR} = (\mathbf{R}^H)^{-1}\mathbf{\Lambda}, \qquad \mathbf{BR} = (\mathbf{R}^H)^{-1}.$$

Hence,

$$\mathbf{AR} = \mathbf{BR\Lambda}. \tag{12.50}$$

Denote the diagonal elements of $\mathbf{\Lambda}$ by λ_i and the columns of $\mathbf{R}$ by $\mathbf{x}_i$. Then this equation gives

$$\mathbf{Ax}_i = \lambda_i\mathbf{Bx}_i.$$

The second equation in (12.43) gives, in this notation,

$$\begin{bmatrix} \mathbf{x}_1^H \\ \cdot \\ \cdot \\ \cdot \\ \mathbf{x}_n^H \end{bmatrix} \mathbf{B}[\mathbf{x}_1, \ldots, \mathbf{x}_n] = \mathbf{I}.$$

Multiplying out and equating individual elements, we see that

$$(\mathbf{x}_i, \mathbf{Bx}_j) = 0, \quad i \neq j; \qquad (\mathbf{x}_i, \mathbf{Bx}_i) = 1.$$

The λ_i are the roots of the equation

$$(\lambda_1 - \lambda) \ldots (\lambda_n - \lambda) = \det(\mathbf{\Lambda} - \lambda\mathbf{I}).$$

Since $\mathbf{R}$ is nonsingular, $\det(\mathbf{\Lambda} - \lambda\mathbf{I}) = 0$ if and only if

$$\det\{(\mathbf{R}^H)^{-1}(\mathbf{\Lambda} - \lambda\mathbf{I})\mathbf{R}^{-1}\} = \det(\mathbf{A} - \lambda\mathbf{B}) = 0. \tag{12.51}$$

We have proved:

THEOREM **12.8.** *Let* **A**, **B** *be hermitian matrices, where* **B** *is positive definite, and* λ_i, $i = 1, \ldots, n$, *denote the roots of the polynomial equation* $\det(\mathbf{A} - \lambda\mathbf{B}) = 0$.

(i) *There exists a set of n linearly independent vectors* $\mathbf{x}_i$ *such that*

$$\mathbf{A}\mathbf{x}_i = \lambda_i \mathbf{B}\mathbf{x}_i, \qquad i = 1, \ldots, n, \tag{12.52}$$

$$(\mathbf{x}_i, \mathbf{B}\mathbf{x}_j) = \begin{cases} 1, & i = j, \\ 0, & i \neq j. \end{cases} \tag{12.53}$$

(ii) *If* $\mathbf{R} = [\mathbf{x}_1, \ldots, \mathbf{x}_n]$, *then*

$$\mathbf{R}^H\mathbf{A}\mathbf{R} = \mathbf{\Lambda}, \qquad \mathbf{R}^H\mathbf{B}\mathbf{R} = \mathbf{I}. \tag{12.54}$$

It is convenient to introduce the following definition to describe the situation.

DEFINITION **12.5.** If $(\mathbf{u}, \mathbf{B}\mathbf{v}) = 0$, then the vectors **u**, **v** are said to be **B**-*orthogonal*. A set of vectors $\mathbf{x}_1, \ldots, \mathbf{x}_n$ such that $(\mathbf{x}_i, \mathbf{B}\mathbf{x}_j) = 0$ for $i \neq j$ is called a **B**-*orthogonal set*. If the magnitude of **u** is such that $(\mathbf{u}, \mathbf{B}\mathbf{u}) = 1$, we say that **u** is **B**-*normalized*. If the vectors $\mathbf{x}_i$ in a **B**-orthogonal set are also **B**-normalized, we say that the set is **B**-*orthonormal*.

Ex. 12.8. Reduce the following matrices simultaneously to diagonal form, using the method described in the proof of Theorem 12.7.

$$\mathbf{A} = \begin{bmatrix} 75 & 35 \\ 35 & -117 \end{bmatrix}, \qquad \mathbf{B} = \begin{bmatrix} 5 & -3 \\ -3 & 5 \end{bmatrix}. \tag{12.55}$$

Solution: We first find the eigenvalues of **B** which are 2, 8 and the corresponding eigenvectors. Then form **Q**, $\mathbf{Q}^T\mathbf{A}\mathbf{Q}$ and find **S**, **Λ**, **R** in turn.

$$\mathbf{P} = \frac{1}{\sqrt{2}}\begin{bmatrix} 1 & 1 \\ 1 & -1 \end{bmatrix}, \qquad \mathbf{Q} = \mathbf{P}\mathbf{D}^{-1} = \frac{1}{4}\begin{bmatrix} 2 & 1 \\ 2 & -1 \end{bmatrix},$$

$$\mathbf{Q}^T\mathbf{A}\mathbf{Q} = \begin{bmatrix} 7 & 24 \\ 24 & -7 \end{bmatrix}, \qquad \mathbf{S} = \frac{1}{5}\begin{bmatrix} 4 & -3 \\ 3 & 4 \end{bmatrix},$$

$$\mathbf{R} = \mathbf{Q}\mathbf{S} = \frac{1}{20}\begin{bmatrix} 11 & -2 \\ 5 & -10 \end{bmatrix}, \qquad \mathbf{\Lambda} = 25\begin{bmatrix} 1 & 0 \\ 0 & -1 \end{bmatrix}. \tag{12.56}$$

Ex. 12.9. Reduce the matrices (12.55) to diagonal form by the method described in the proof of Theorem 12.8.

Solution: The equation $\det(\mathbf{A} - \lambda\mathbf{B}) = 0$ gives $\lambda = \pm 25$. Corresponding to $\lambda = 25$ and $\lambda = -25$, the equations $(\mathbf{A} - \lambda\mathbf{B})\mathbf{z} = \mathbf{0}$ have the solutions

$$\mathbf{z}_1 = \begin{bmatrix} 11 \\ 5 \end{bmatrix}, \qquad \mathbf{z}_2 = \begin{bmatrix} 1 \\ 5 \end{bmatrix}.$$

We must now **B**-normalize these, which gives

$$\mathbf{R} = \frac{1}{20}\begin{bmatrix} 11 & 2 \\ 5 & 10 \end{bmatrix},$$

which agrees with (12.56) apart from an unimportant difference in sign.

Although the method in Ex. 12.9 may seem easier than that in Ex. 12.8, it may be more convenient to use the method of Ex. 12.8 on a digital computer even though it involves the solution of two eigenvalue problems, because the eigenvalue problems are of standard type for symmetric matrices.

We conclude this section by reminding the reader that the restriction that **B** is positive definite is essential. Peculiar things can happen if **B** is not positive definite, as illustrated in Ex. 12.11 below.

Ex. 12.10 Suppose that **A**, **B** are hermitian and **B** is positive definite. Show directly that:

(a) The roots of $\det(\mathbf{A} - \lambda\mathbf{B}) = 0$ are real.

(b) If $\mathbf{x}_i$ and $\mathbf{x}_j$ are solutions of $(\mathbf{A} - \lambda_i\mathbf{B})\mathbf{x}_i = \mathbf{0}$ and $(\mathbf{A} - \lambda_j\mathbf{B})\mathbf{x}_j = \mathbf{0}$ for two distinct roots λ_i, λ_j, of $\det(\mathbf{A} - \lambda\mathbf{B}) = 0$, show that $\mathbf{x}_i$ and $\mathbf{x}_j$ are **B**-orthogonal.

Ex. 12.11. Find the roots of $\det(\mathbf{A} - \lambda\mathbf{B}) = 0$ for the real symmetric matrices

$$\mathbf{A} = \begin{bmatrix} a & 0 \\ 0 & b \end{bmatrix}, \qquad \mathbf{B} = \begin{bmatrix} 0 & 1 \\ 1 & 0 \end{bmatrix},$$

and show that these are imaginary if $ab < 0$. (Note that in this case neither **A** nor **B** is positive definite.) If **A**, **B** are hermitian matrices of order n but neither is positive definite, and **x** is a solution of $(\mathbf{A} - \lambda\mathbf{B})\mathbf{x} = \mathbf{0}$ corresponding to a complex root $\lambda = \alpha + i\beta$, $\beta \neq 0$, prove that $(\mathbf{x}, \mathbf{A}\mathbf{x}) = (\mathbf{x}, B\mathbf{x}) = 0$. Check that this is true for the above example.

12.5 Descent Methods for Solving Simultaneous Linear Equations

In this section we discuss methods for solving the linear system $\mathbf{A}\mathbf{x} = \mathbf{b}$ based on properties of the quadratic form

$$Q(\mathbf{x}) = \tfrac{1}{2}(\mathbf{x}, \mathbf{A}\mathbf{x}) - (\mathbf{x}, \mathbf{b}).$$

The matrix **A** is assumed to be real symmetric and positive definite. The main reason for including this material is to give the reader further insight into the geometrical properties of positive definite quadratic forms.

Consider the level surfaces given by

$$Q(\mathbf{x}) = \tfrac{1}{2}(\mathbf{x}, \mathbf{A}\mathbf{x}) - (\mathbf{x}, \mathbf{b}) = k, \tag{12.57}$$

where k is a constant. We can rearrange this equation in the following form, valid for any $\boldsymbol{\xi}$.

$$Q(\mathbf{x}) = \tfrac{1}{2}((\mathbf{x} - \boldsymbol{\xi}), \mathbf{A}(\mathbf{x} - \boldsymbol{\xi})) + (\mathbf{x}, \mathbf{A}\boldsymbol{\xi} - \mathbf{b}) - \tfrac{1}{2}(\boldsymbol{\xi}, \mathbf{A}\boldsymbol{\xi}) = k. \quad (12.58)$$

Let us choose $\boldsymbol{\xi}$ to satisfy the linear equations $\mathbf{A}\boldsymbol{\xi} = \mathbf{b}$. Since $\mathbf{A}$ is positive definite, we know that det $\mathbf{A} > 0$, so that these equations have a unique solution. Equation (12.58) then becomes

$$Q(\mathbf{x}) = \tfrac{1}{2}((\mathbf{x} - \boldsymbol{\xi}), \mathbf{A}(\mathbf{x} - \boldsymbol{\xi})) - \tfrac{1}{2}(\boldsymbol{\xi}, \mathbf{A}\boldsymbol{\xi}) = k. \quad (12.59)$$

The vector $\boldsymbol{\xi}$ is unique and fixed. Since $\mathbf{A}$ is positive definite, we have $((\mathbf{x} - \boldsymbol{\xi}), \mathbf{A}(\mathbf{x} - \boldsymbol{\xi})) \geq 0$, with equality only if $\mathbf{x} - \boldsymbol{\xi} = \mathbf{0}$. Hence, from (12.59), if we vary $\mathbf{x}$, the minimum value of $Q(\mathbf{x})$ is given by $\mathbf{x} = \boldsymbol{\xi}$, and this minimum value is $Q(\boldsymbol{\xi}) = -\tfrac{1}{2}(\boldsymbol{\xi}, \mathbf{A}\boldsymbol{\xi})$. We have proved the following theorem.

THEOREM **12.9.** *If* $\mathbf{A}$ *is a symmetric positive definite matrix, the quadratic form*

$$Q(\mathbf{x}) = \tfrac{1}{2}(\mathbf{x}, \mathbf{A}\mathbf{x}) - (\mathbf{x}, \mathbf{b}) \quad (12.60)$$

has an absolute minimum for $\mathbf{x} = \boldsymbol{\xi}$, *where* $\mathbf{A}\boldsymbol{\xi} = \mathbf{b}$.

It is instructive to visualize this theorem geometrically in the two-variable case. If we set $\mathbf{x} - \boldsymbol{\xi} = \mathbf{y}$ in (12.59), this equation gives $(\mathbf{y}, \mathbf{A}\mathbf{y}) =$ constant, which is the equation for a central quadric with principal axes rotated with reference to the coordinate axes. This means that (12.59) is a quadric centered at the point $\mathbf{x} = \boldsymbol{\xi}$, given by $\mathbf{y} = \mathbf{0}$. In the two-dimensional case, the level surfaces given by (12.59), $Q(\mathbf{x}) = k$, for various values of the constant k, are ellipses in the x_1, x_2 plane, with a common center $\boldsymbol{\xi}$, as illustrated in Figure 12.4. If we form a three-dimensional picture by introducing a z-axis perpendicular to the plane of the paper in Figure 12.4, treating $Q(\mathbf{x}) = z$ as a function of the three variables x_1, x_2, z, the equation $Q(\mathbf{x}) = z$ gives a bowl-shaped surface,

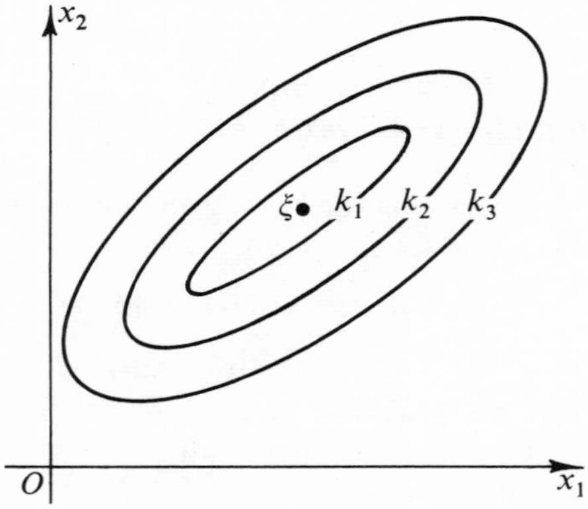

Figure 12.4 Level-curves for $Q(\mathbf{x}) =$ constant.

the minimum value of z corresponding to x_1, x_2 given by $\mathbf{x} = \boldsymbol{\xi}$. This geometrical description suggests that if we know an approximation $\mathbf{x}_0$ to the minimum point $\boldsymbol{\xi}$, we can improve this approximation in the following way. Suppose that the bowl represents a valley, the z-axis being vertical. In order to reach the minimum point $\boldsymbol{\xi}$, a walker standing at the point $\mathbf{x}_0$ need only walk downhill. Eventually he will reach the point $\boldsymbol{\xi}$.

Computationally it is convenient to proceed along straight lines. The argument then goes as follows. We wish to produce a sequence of approximations $\mathbf{x}_0, \mathbf{x}_1, \mathbf{x}_2, \ldots$ to $\boldsymbol{\xi}$. In order to obtain an improved estimate $\mathbf{x}_{i+1}$ from $\mathbf{x}_i$, we travel along a line whose direction is given by a known vector $\mathbf{p}_i$ so that

$$\mathbf{x}_{i+1} = \mathbf{x}_i + \alpha_i \mathbf{p}_i, \tag{12.61}$$

where α_i is a constant which we wish to determine by the condition that $Q(\mathbf{x}_{i+1})$ is a minimum. (Geometrically it is clear in Figure 12.4 that, as long as $\mathbf{p}_i$ is not horizontal, we can move along the direction $\mathbf{p}_1$ in a downward direction until we reach a minimum, beyond which Q will increase.)

THEOREM **12.10.** *If $\mathbf{x}_i$ is a given approximation to the solution $\boldsymbol{\xi}$ of the equations $\mathbf{A}\boldsymbol{\xi} = \mathbf{b}$ ($\mathbf{A}$ symmetric and positive definite), and if we set $\mathbf{x}_{i+1} = \mathbf{x}_i + \alpha_i \mathbf{p}_i$, where $\mathbf{p}_i$ is a known vector, then the value of α_i that minimizes $Q(\mathbf{x}_{i+1})$ is given by*

$$\alpha_i = \frac{(\mathbf{p}_i, \mathbf{r}_i)}{(\mathbf{p}_i, \mathbf{A}\mathbf{p}_i)} \tag{12.62}$$

where $\mathbf{r}_i = \mathbf{b} - \mathbf{A}\mathbf{x}_i$. For this value of α_i we have

$$(\mathbf{p}_i, \mathbf{r}_{i+1}) = 0 \tag{12.63}$$

$$Q(\mathbf{x}_{i+1}) = Q(\mathbf{x}_i) - \frac{1}{2}\frac{(\mathbf{p}_i, \mathbf{r}_i)^2}{(\mathbf{p}_i, \mathbf{A}\mathbf{p}_i)}. \tag{12.64}$$

Proof: We have

$$Q(\mathbf{x}_{i+1}) = \tfrac{1}{2}((\mathbf{x}_i + \alpha_i \mathbf{p}_i), \mathbf{A}(\mathbf{x}_i + \alpha_i \mathbf{p}_i)) - ((\mathbf{x}_i + \alpha_i \mathbf{p}_i), \mathbf{b})$$

$$\frac{\partial Q(\mathbf{x}_{i+1})}{\partial \alpha_i} = (\mathbf{p}_i, \mathbf{A}(\mathbf{x}_i + \alpha_i \mathbf{p}_i)) - (\mathbf{p}_i, \mathbf{b}) = -(\mathbf{p}_i, \mathbf{r}_i) + (\alpha_i \mathbf{p}_i, \mathbf{A}\mathbf{p}_i).$$

The optimum value of α_i is obtained by setting this expression equal to zero, which immediately gives (12.62). Also, on using the definition of $\mathbf{x}_{i+1}$ and the value we have just obtained for α_i,

$$(\mathbf{p}_i, \mathbf{r}_{i+1}) = (\mathbf{p}_i\,(\mathbf{b} - \mathbf{A}\mathbf{x}_{i+1})) = (\mathbf{p}_i\,(\mathbf{r}_i - \alpha_i \mathbf{A}\mathbf{p}_i)) = 0.$$

Finally,

$$\begin{aligned} Q(\mathbf{x}_{i+1}) &= Q(\mathbf{x}_i) + \alpha_i(\mathbf{p}_i, \mathbf{A}\mathbf{x}_i) + \tfrac{1}{2}\alpha_i^2(\mathbf{p}_i, \mathbf{A}\mathbf{p}_i) - \alpha_i(\mathbf{p}_i, \mathbf{b}) \\ &= Q(\mathbf{x}_i) - \alpha_i(\mathbf{p}_i, \mathbf{r}_i) + \tfrac{1}{2}\alpha_i^2(\mathbf{p}_i, \mathbf{A}\mathbf{p}_i), \end{aligned}$$

and substitution of the above value for α_i gives (12.64).

So far we have said nothing about the choice of the $\mathbf{p}_i$. Pursuing the analogy with a walker trying to find the bottom of a valley, introduced above in connection with Figure 12.4, if the walker has only local knowledge of his surroundings, he will tend to choose a path that takes him downhill as rapidly as possible, i.e., he will choose the path of steepest descent. Mathematically, we wish to investigate the direction in which $Q(\mathbf{x})$ decreases most rapidly. If we are at a point $\mathbf{x}_i$, this is given by a direction $\mathbf{u}$ determined by the condition that the modulus of the rate of descent at this point, namely,

$$\frac{dQ(\mathbf{x}_i + \alpha\mathbf{u})}{d\alpha} \quad \text{at} \quad \alpha = 0,$$

should be as large as possible, where we assume that $(\mathbf{u}, \mathbf{u})$ is a constant, e.g., $\mathbf{u}$ is a unit vector. From the definition (12.57) of Q, we see that

$$\frac{dQ(\mathbf{x}_i + \alpha\mathbf{u})}{d\alpha} = (\mathbf{u}, \mathbf{A}(\mathbf{x}_i + \alpha\mathbf{u})) - (\mathbf{u}, \mathbf{b}),$$

and the value of this at $\alpha = 0$ is given by

$$\left\{\frac{dQ(\mathbf{x}_i + \alpha\mathbf{u})}{d\alpha}\right\}_{\alpha=0} = -(\mathbf{u}, \mathbf{r}_i), \tag{12.65}$$

where $\mathbf{r}_i = \mathbf{b} - \mathbf{A}\mathbf{x}_i$, the residual corresponding to $\mathbf{x}_i$. If $\mathbf{u}$ is a unit vector, then $(\mathbf{u}, \mathbf{r}_i)$ is simply the magnitude of $\mathbf{r}_i$ times the cosine of the angle between $\mathbf{u}$ and $\mathbf{r}_i$ [see (9.29)] and this is a maximum when $\mathbf{u}$ and $\mathbf{r}_i$ lie in the same direction. Hence, the path of steepest descent lies in the same direction as $\mathbf{r}_i$.

Returning to the problem of the choice of $\mathbf{p}_i$, this means that if we wish to choose $\mathbf{p}_i$ to lie along the line of steepest descent, we simply take $\mathbf{p}_i = \mathbf{r}_i$.

We have now proved the following theorem. [The last sentence in the theorem is a direct result of (12.63).]

THEOREM **12.11.** *The method of steepest descent is an iterative procedure for determining the solution of a linear system* $\mathbf{A}\mathbf{x} = \mathbf{b}$, *where* $\mathbf{A}$ *is symmetric and positive definite, in which we start from a given initial approximation* $\mathbf{x}_0$ *and determine in succession*

$$\mathbf{x}_{i+1} = \mathbf{x}_i + \alpha_i\mathbf{r}_i, \qquad i = 0, 1, 2, \ldots,$$

where

$$\mathbf{r}_i = \mathbf{b} - A\mathbf{x}_i, \qquad \alpha_i = \frac{(\mathbf{r}_i, \mathbf{r}_i)}{(\mathbf{r}_i, \mathbf{A}\mathbf{r}_i)}.$$

Successive residuals are orthogonal:

$$(\mathbf{r}_{i+1}, \mathbf{r}_i) = 0. \tag{12.66}$$

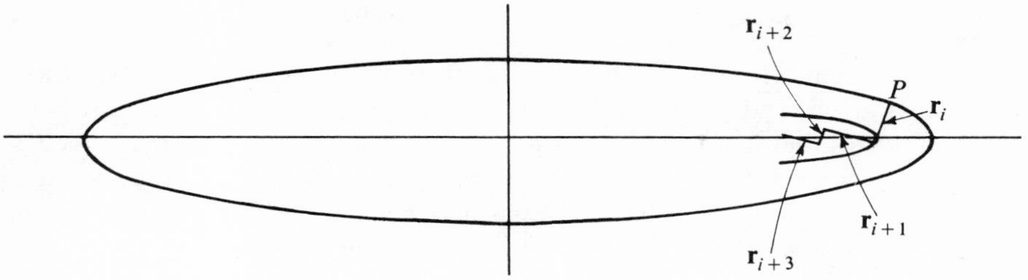

(a) The method of steepest descent

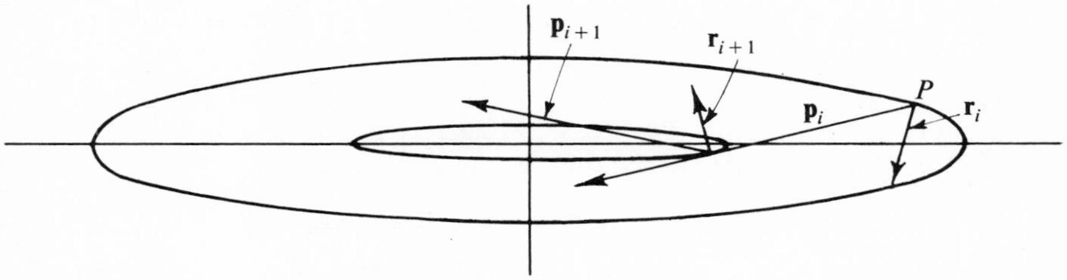

(b) The method of conjugate gradients (diagrammatic)

Figure 12.5 Descent methods when ellipses are elongated.

The method of steepest descent often converges extremely slowly in practice. The reason for this can be seen qualitatively from Figure 12.5(a). We consider the two-variable case $\mathbf{x} = [x_1, x_2]^T$, for which the level-curves $Q(\mathbf{x}) = z_k$ for various constants z_k, $k = 1, 2, \ldots$ are given by ellipses. For simplicity, the common center of these ellipses is taken to be the origin in Figure 12.5(a), and the major and minor axes are oriented along the x_1, x_2-axes. The surface $Q(\mathbf{x}) = z$, where z is a third variable, plotted vertically, is in the shape of a bowl, with minimum at the origin of coordinates. The purpose of descent methods is to start at a point $\mathbf{x}_0$ and move successively along straight lines to points $\mathbf{x}_1, \mathbf{x}_2, \ldots$ which approach the minimum point as rapidly as possible. If, as in Figure 12.5(a), the ellipses are elongated and we start at a point P near the end of the major axis, the line of steepest descent may go nowhere near the origin. The rate of convergence may then be extremely slow. In the general n-variable case, the rate of convergence depends on the ratio of the largest to the smallest eigenvalues. If this is large, the ellipsoids are elongated, and the rate of convergence is usually very slow. Steepest descent methods are not an efficient means of solving the linear system $\mathbf{Ax} = \mathbf{b}$, even when devices are used to accelerate the convergence. [We comment in passing that if we change the scales on the x_1, x_2-axes in Figure 12.5(a) so that the ellipses become circles, then of course the method of steepest descent will lead directly to the minimum point in one step. The snag is of course to know the correct changes of scale to make. The object of the method is to solve $\mathbf{Ax} = \mathbf{b}$, and determination of the correct change of scale is more difficult than the direct solution of $\mathbf{Ax} = \mathbf{b}$.]

We recall that steepest descent was a special case of a more general method discussed in connection with Theorem 12.10 in which we set $\mathbf{x}_{i+1} = \mathbf{x}_i + \alpha_i \mathbf{p}_i$ where $\mathbf{x}_0$ is given, and $\mathbf{p}_1, \mathbf{p}_2, \ldots$ are arbitrary. The discussion in the last paragraph indicates that if we choose the $\mathbf{p}_i$ so as to move along the line of steepest descent at each step, the resulting method converges very slowly in many cases. The next logical step would be to discuss better ways in which the $\mathbf{p}_i$ could be chosen. One method is to arrange that $\mathbf{p}_i$ and $\mathbf{p}_{i+1}$ are *conjugate* (or **A**-orthogonal in the terminology of Definition 12.5), i.e.,

$$(\mathbf{p}_i, \mathbf{A}\mathbf{p}_{i+1}) = 0.$$

This is illustrated in Figure 12.5(b). However, further discussion would take us too far afield.

Ex. 12.12. If in the method of Theorem 12.10 we choose

$$\mathbf{x}_{i+1} = \mathbf{x}_i + \alpha_{i,i}\mathbf{r}_i + \alpha_{i,i-1}\mathbf{r}_{i-1} + \ldots + \alpha_{i,0}\mathbf{r}_0,$$

show that

(a) $(\mathbf{r}_i, \mathbf{r}_j) = 0, \quad i \neq j,$

(b) the vector $\mathbf{x}_j$ will give the *exact* solution of $\mathbf{Ax} = \mathbf{b}$ for some $j \leq n$.

(We say that we are dealing with an n-step method.)

Ex. 12.13. If $R(\mathbf{x}) = (\mathbf{r}, \mathbf{Sr})$ where $\mathbf{r} = \mathbf{b} - \mathbf{Ax}$ and $\mathbf{S}$ is positive definite, show that the value of the constant α required to minimize $R(\mathbf{x} + \alpha\mathbf{p})$ for given $\mathbf{x}$, $\mathbf{p}$ is

$$\frac{(\mathbf{r}, \mathbf{SAp})}{(\mathbf{Ap}, \mathbf{SAp})}.$$

(Note that if $\mathbf{A}$ is positive definite, we can choose $\mathbf{S} = \mathbf{A}^{-1}$ and recover (12.62). A different procedure is given by choosing $\mathbf{S} = \mathbf{I}$, and this procedure will apply for arbitrary $\mathbf{A}$.)

12.6 A Geometrical Introduction to Rayleigh's Principle

We shall motivate the developments in the remainder of this chapter by going back to the discussion of Figure 12.2 in Section 12.1. The equation of the conic sections in the figure is (12.15),

$$ax^2 + 2kxy + by^2 = 1. \tag{12.67}$$

Suppose that the eigenvalues of

$$\begin{bmatrix} a & k \\ k & b \end{bmatrix} \tag{12.68}$$

are denoted by λ_1, λ_2. Consider first the case of the ellipse, for which $\lambda_1 > 0$, $\lambda_2 > 0$. In (12.16) we found that the eigenvalues are inversely proportional to the squares of the major axes. Using the notation in Figure 12.2(a), and (12.16),

$$\lambda_1 = \frac{1}{OP^2}, \qquad \lambda_2 = \frac{1}{OR^2}. \tag{12.69}$$

From the figure it is clear that we can characterize OP as the direction in which the general radius vector OQ is a maximum and OR as the direction in which it is a minimum. At the end of Section 12.1, we saw that the directions of OP and OQ give the eigenvectors corresponding to λ_1 and λ_2. Putting all of the above information together, this indicates that algebraically, for the case of the ellipse, the eigenvalues of the matrix **A** in (12.68) can be characterized as follows:

$$\lambda_1 = \min \frac{1}{x^2 + y^2}, \qquad \lambda_2 = \max \frac{1}{x^2 + y^2}, \tag{12.70}$$

where the minimum and the maximum are taken over all x, y subject to the restriction (12.67). The eigenvectors corresponding to λ_1, λ_2 are the vectors **x**, **y** that give the appropriate minimum or maximum.

Equations (12.67), (12.70) immediately suggest that in the case of a general hermitian matrix in n variables we should consider the *stationary* or *variational* character of the expression

$$(\mathbf{x}, \mathbf{x}) \quad \text{subject to} \quad (\mathbf{x}, \mathbf{Ax}) = 1. \tag{12.71}$$

We expect that these stationary values will be connected with the eigenvalues of **A**, and that the **x** that gives the stationary values will be connected with the eigenvectors of **A**. This will be investigated in the next section. We first show that (12.71) can be formulated in two other ways that are more convenient.

THEOREM **12.12.** *The following three problems are equivalent* (**A** *is a hermitian matrix*)*:*

(i) *Maximize* $1/(\mathbf{x}, \mathbf{x})$ *subject to* $(\mathbf{x}, \mathbf{Ax}) = 1$.
(ii) *Maximize* $(\mathbf{x}, \mathbf{Ax})/(\mathbf{x}, \mathbf{x})$ *for any* $\mathbf{x} \neq \mathbf{0}$.
(iii) *Maximize* $(\mathbf{x}, \mathbf{Ax})$ *subject to* $(\mathbf{x}, \mathbf{x}) = 1$.

Proof: Let ξ, η, ζ be the three maximum values in (i), (ii), (iii) and suppose that these are given by $\mathbf{x} = \mathbf{u}_0, \mathbf{v}_0, \mathbf{w}_0$, respectively. The definition of $\mathbf{u}_0$ gives, for any other vector **u** such that $(\mathbf{u}, \mathbf{Au}) = 1$,

$$F = \frac{1}{(\mathbf{u}_0, \mathbf{u}_0)} \geq \frac{1}{(\mathbf{u}, \mathbf{u})}, \qquad \text{with} \quad (\mathbf{u}_0, \mathbf{Au}_0) = (\mathbf{u}, \mathbf{Au}) = 1. \tag{12.72}$$

Set $\mathbf{z} = p\mathbf{u}_0$, $\mathbf{u} = q\mathbf{v}$ for any $p, q \neq 0$. Then

$$\xi = \frac{\bar{p}p}{(\mathbf{z}, \mathbf{z})} \geq \frac{\bar{q}q}{(\mathbf{v}, \mathbf{v})}, \qquad \text{with} \quad (\mathbf{z}, \mathbf{Az}) = \bar{p}p, \qquad (\mathbf{v}, \mathbf{Av}) = \bar{q}q.$$

Hence,

$$\xi \geq \frac{(\mathbf{v}, \mathbf{Av})}{(\mathbf{v}, \mathbf{v})}. \tag{12.73}$$

This is true for any $\mathbf{v} \neq \mathbf{0}$, and, in particular, for $\mathbf{v} = \mathbf{v}_0$. Hence,

$$\xi \geq \eta. \tag{12.74}$$

We reverse the argument. The definition of $\mathbf{v}_0$ gives, for any other vector $\mathbf{v} \neq \mathbf{0}$,

$$\eta = \frac{(\mathbf{v}_0, \mathbf{A}\mathbf{v}_0)}{(\mathbf{v}_0, \mathbf{v}_0)} \geq \frac{(\mathbf{v}, \mathbf{A}\mathbf{v})}{(\mathbf{v}, \mathbf{v})}. \tag{12.75}$$

Set $\mathbf{y} = \mathbf{v}_0/\|\mathbf{v}\|$, $\mathbf{u} = \mathbf{v}/\|\mathbf{v}\|$. Then (12.75) gives

$$\eta = (\mathbf{y}, \mathbf{A}\mathbf{y}) \geq (\mathbf{u}, \mathbf{A}\mathbf{u}), \qquad \text{where } (\mathbf{y}, \mathbf{y}) = (\mathbf{u}, \mathbf{u}) = 1.$$

This is true for any $\mathbf{u}$ such that $(\mathbf{u}, \mathbf{u}) = 1$, and, in particular, for $\mathbf{u} = \mathbf{u}_0$, which gives $\eta \geq \xi$. Combining this result with (12.74) we obtain $\xi = \eta$, as required. The equivalence of (ii) and (iii) is proved similarly.

From this theorem we see that equation (12.70) can be written

$$\lambda_1 = \min_{\mathbf{x} \neq \mathbf{0}} \frac{(\mathbf{x}, \mathbf{A}\mathbf{x})}{(\mathbf{x}, \mathbf{x})}, \qquad \lambda_2 = \max_{\mathbf{x} \neq \mathbf{0}} \frac{(\mathbf{x}, \mathbf{A}\mathbf{x})}{(\mathbf{x}, \mathbf{x})}. \tag{12.76}$$

At this point, the geometrical picture has merely suggested that these results are true. The situation is investigated analytically in the next section.

Ex. 12.14. Examine the hyperbola in Figure 12.2(c) from the same point of view as the ellipse has been examined in this section, and show that the geometrical picture suggests that (12.76) is also true for the hyperbola.

Solution: From (12.14), (12.17) we see that, for any $\lambda_1 > 0$, $\lambda_2 < 0$,

$$OG^2 = \frac{1}{\lambda_1}, \qquad \lambda_1 X^2 + \lambda_2 Y^2 = 1,$$

$$OH^2 = \frac{-1}{\lambda_2}, \qquad -(\lambda_1 X^2 + \lambda_2 Y^2) = 1,$$

and the figure suggests that, therefore,

$$\lambda_1 = \max \frac{1}{(\mathbf{x}, \mathbf{x})}, \qquad \text{subject to } (\mathbf{x}, \mathbf{A}\mathbf{x}) = 1,$$

$$\lambda_2 = -\max \frac{1}{(\mathbf{x}, \mathbf{x})}, \qquad \text{subject to } -(\mathbf{x}, \mathbf{A}\mathbf{x}) = 1.$$

From Theorem 12.12(i), (ii), with $-\mathbf{A}$ in place of $\mathbf{A}$, this second equation can be written

$$\lambda_2 = -\max_{\mathbf{x} \neq \mathbf{0}} \left\{ -\frac{(\mathbf{x}, \mathbf{A}\mathbf{x})}{(\mathbf{x}, \mathbf{x})} \right\} = \min_{\mathbf{x} \neq \mathbf{0}} \frac{(\mathbf{x}, \mathbf{A}\mathbf{x})}{(\mathbf{x}, \mathbf{x})}.$$

These results for λ_1, λ_2 are exactly those in (12.76).

12.7 Rayleigh's Principle

DEFINITION **12.6.** The *Rayleigh quotient* corresponding to a hermitian matrix **A** is the expression

$$\rho = \rho(\mathbf{x}) = \frac{(\mathbf{x}, \mathbf{Ax})}{(\mathbf{x}, \mathbf{x})}. \tag{12.77}$$

THEOREM **12.13.** *If* **A** *is hermitian with eigenvalues* $\lambda_1 \le \lambda_2 \le \ldots \le \lambda_n$, *then*

$$\lambda_1 \le \rho \le \lambda_n,$$

where ρ *is the Rayleigh quotient for any* $\mathbf{x} \ne \mathbf{0}$, *and*

$$\lambda_1 = \min_{\mathbf{x}\ne\mathbf{0}} \frac{(\mathbf{x}, \mathbf{Ax})}{(\mathbf{x}, \mathbf{x})}, \qquad \lambda_n = \max_{\mathbf{x}\ne\mathbf{0}} \frac{(\mathbf{x}, \mathbf{Ax})}{(\mathbf{x}, \mathbf{x})}. \tag{12.78}$$

Proof: If **A** is hermitian, an orthonormal set of eigenvectors exist, say $\mathbf{x}_1, \ldots,$ $\mathbf{x}_n$, where $\mathbf{x}_i$ corresponds to λ_i. Suppose that the expansion of an arbitrary vector in terms of the $\mathbf{x}_i$ is

$$\mathbf{x} = \sum_{i=1}^{n} \alpha_i \mathbf{x}_i. \tag{12.79}$$

Then

$$\mathbf{Ax} = \sum_{i=1}^{n} \alpha_i \lambda_i \mathbf{x}_i,$$

$$\rho = \frac{(\mathbf{x}, \mathbf{Ax})}{(\mathbf{x}, \mathbf{x})} = \frac{\lambda_1\bar{\alpha}_1\alpha_1 + \lambda_2\bar{\alpha}_2\alpha_2 + \ldots + \lambda_n\bar{\alpha}_n\alpha_n}{\bar{\alpha}_1\alpha_1 + \bar{\alpha}_2\alpha_2 + \ldots + \bar{\alpha}_n\alpha_n}. \tag{12.80}$$

We have

$$\rho - \lambda_1 = \frac{(\lambda_2 - \lambda_1)\bar{\alpha}_2\alpha_2 + \ldots + (\lambda_n - \lambda_1)\bar{\alpha}_n\alpha_n}{\bar{\alpha}_1\alpha_1 + \bar{\alpha}_2\alpha_2 + \ldots + \bar{\alpha}_n\alpha_n}. \tag{12.81}$$

Since $\lambda_i - \lambda_1 \ge 0$ for all i, we have $\rho \ge \lambda_1$. Also, if we choose $\mathbf{x} = \mathbf{x}_1$ this gives $\rho = \lambda_1$, which proves the first statement in (12.78). The remainder of the theorem is proved similarly by considering $\rho - \lambda_n$.

THEOREM **12.14.** *If* $\mathbf{x}_i$ *is an eigenvector of a hermitian matrix* **A** *corresponding to an eigenvalue* λ_i, *and if* $\mathbf{x} = \mathbf{x}_i + \varepsilon\mathbf{z}$, *then*

$$\rho(\mathbf{x}) = \lambda_i + \{\rho(\mathbf{z}) - \lambda_i\} \frac{(\mathbf{z}, \mathbf{z})}{(\mathbf{x}, \mathbf{x})} \bar{\varepsilon}\varepsilon. \tag{12.82}$$

Proof: We have

$$\begin{aligned}(\mathbf{x}, \mathbf{Ax}) &= (\mathbf{x}_i + \varepsilon\mathbf{z}, \mathbf{A}(\mathbf{x}_i + \varepsilon\mathbf{z}))\\ &= \lambda_i(\mathbf{x}_i, \mathbf{x}_i) + \bar{\varepsilon}\lambda_i(\mathbf{z}, \mathbf{x}_i) + \varepsilon\lambda_i(\mathbf{x}_i, \mathbf{z}) + \bar{\varepsilon}\varepsilon(\mathbf{z}, \mathbf{Az}),\end{aligned}$$

where we have used the fact that λ_i is real and $(\mathbf{x}_i, \mathbf{Az}) = (\mathbf{Ax}_i, \mathbf{z})$ since $\mathbf{A}$ is hermitian. Simple algebra then gives

$$\rho(\mathbf{x}) - \lambda_i = \frac{\bar{\varepsilon}\varepsilon[(\mathbf{z}, \mathbf{Az}) - \lambda_i(\mathbf{z}, \mathbf{z})]}{(\mathbf{x}, \mathbf{x})},$$

which is (12.82).

One of the reasons why Theorems 12.13 and 12.14 are important is that they give a method for finding the eigenvalues approximately. Theorem 12.14 tells us that if we know an approximation $\mathbf{x}$ to the eigenvector $\mathbf{x}_i$ that is accurate to first order in a small parameter ε, then the Rayleigh quotient $\rho(\mathbf{x})$ will give an approximation to λ_i that is accurate to *second* order in ε [since the error term in (12.82) is of order $\bar{\varepsilon}\varepsilon$]. This is not very useful for the intermediate eigenvalues $\lambda_2, \ldots, \lambda_{n-1}$, since for these eigenvalues the sign of the error term in (12.82) is unknown $(\lambda_1 \leq \rho \leq \lambda_n)$. However, if we are trying to estimate λ_1, we know that $\rho(\mathbf{z}) - \lambda_1 \geq 0$ for any z, so that the estimate $\rho(\mathbf{x})$ will always be an *upper bound* for λ_1. Similarly, $\rho(\mathbf{x})$ will always be a *lower bound* for λ_n. In vibration problems we can often guess the shape of the mode of vibration corresponding to the lowest frequency of vibration, and use the Rayleigh quotient to give an accurate upper bound for this lowest frequency of vibration. It is usually much more difficult to use the Rayleigh quotient to estimate the largest eigenvalue since it is difficult in general to make a good guess at the shape of the largest eigenvector.

Note that when we refer to the *largest* and *smallest* eigenvalues in the context of the Rayleigh quotient we mean that if the eigenvalues are ordered $\lambda_1 \leq \lambda_2 \leq \ldots \leq \lambda_n$ then λ_1 is the smallest eigenvalue and λ_n the largest. There is no implication concerning the absolute values of λ_1 and λ_n.

Ex. 12.15. Estimate the smallest eigenvalue of the following matrix by means of the Rayleigh quotient, given that it arises in a vibration problem similar to that discussed in Section 9.1.

$$\mathbf{A} = \begin{bmatrix} 1.7 & -1 & 0 \\ -1 & 2 & -1 \\ 0 & -1 & 2 \end{bmatrix}.$$

Solution: The Rayleigh quotient is

$$\rho = \frac{1.7x_1^2 + 2x_2^2 + 2x_3^2 - 2x_1x_2 - 2x_2x_3}{x_1^2 + x_2^2 + x_3^2}. \tag{12.83}$$

From the physics of the problem we know that the eigenvector corresponding to the lowest eigenvalue will have elements that are all of the same sign. If we try $\mathbf{x}_1 \approx [1, 1, 1]^T$ and $[1, 2, 1]^T$, we find $\rho = 0.57$ and 0.62, to two decimals. We know that these estimates are upper bounds, so the best estimate we have obtained is 0.57 corresponding to a trial eigenvector $[1, 1, 1]^T$. The exact eigenvalue is 0.5, corresponding to an eigenvector $[1, 1.2, 0.8]^T$.

Ex. 12.16. Use the Rayleigh quotient to obtain information concerning the eigenvalues of

$$\begin{bmatrix} 0 & -1 & 0 \\ -1 & -1 & 1 \\ 0 & 1 & 0 \end{bmatrix}. \tag{12.84}$$

Solution: The Rayleigh quotient is

$$\rho = \frac{-x_2^2 - 2x_1x_2 + 2x_2x_3}{x_1^2 + x_2^2 + x_3^2}.$$

We have no additional information in this case, and all we can do is try various forms for $\mathbf{x}$. For example, if we try $[1, 1, 1]^T$, $[1, 0, 0]^T$, $[0, 1, 0]^T$, $[1, 1, 0]^T$, $[1, 1, -1]^T$, we obtain $\rho = -\frac{1}{3}, 0, -1, -\frac{5}{3}$, so that the smallest eigenvalue is not greater than $-\frac{5}{3}$ and the largest one is not less than 0. (The smallest and largest eigenvalues are -2 and $+1$ with corresponding eigenvectors $[1, 2, -1]^T$, $[1, -1, -1]$.) Note that the results are much less satisfactory than in the previous example, and the knowledge that the Rayleigh quotient gives an upper bound for λ_1 and a lower bound for λ_3 is essential in deciding which of our trial functions gives the best estimates.

Ex. 12.17. Given that the eigenvector corresponding to the lowest eigenvalue of

$$\begin{bmatrix} 3 & -1 & 0 \\ -1 & 2 & -1 \\ 0 & -1 & 3 \end{bmatrix} \tag{12.85}$$

is of the form $[1, k, 1]^T$, find the exact value of k by forming the Rayleigh quotient ρ and setting $d\rho/dk = 0$.

Ex. 12.18. Given that a good approximation to the eigenvector corresponding to the lowest eigenvalue of a real symmetric matrix $\mathbf{A}$ is of the form $\alpha_1\mathbf{z}_1 + \alpha_2\mathbf{z}_2$, where $\mathbf{z}_1$ and $\mathbf{z}_2$ are given real vectors, but α_1, α_2 are unknown, show how to find optimum values for α_1, α_2 by forming the Rayleigh quotient ρ with $\mathbf{x} = \alpha_1\mathbf{z}_1 + \alpha_2\mathbf{z}_2$, setting $\partial\rho/\partial\alpha_1 = \partial\rho/\partial\alpha_2 = 0$, then solving a 2×2 eigenvalue problem. Generalize to the situation where the trial vector is $\alpha_1\mathbf{z}_1 + \ldots + \alpha_s\mathbf{z}_s$, $s < n$.

Returning to the general theory, we recall that so far we have considered only the smallest and largest eigenvalues. Geometrically we have been using the principle that the eigenvector $\mathbf{x}_1$ corresponding to the smallest eigenvalue can be found by looking for the largest radius vector from the origin to any point on an ellipsoid. This geometrical way of thinking about things suggests that the eigenvector corresponding to the second smallest eigenvalue can be found by looking for the largest radius vector from the origin to any point on an ellipsoid, among all those radius vectors that are perpendicular to $\mathbf{x}_1$, i.e.,

$$\lambda_2 = \min_{\substack{\mathbf{x} \neq \mathbf{0} \\ (\mathbf{x}, \mathbf{x}_1) = 0}} \frac{(\mathbf{x}, \mathbf{A}\mathbf{x})}{(\mathbf{x}, \mathbf{x})}.$$

Generalizing this geometrical argument leads to the following theorem.

THEOREM **12.15.** *If* **A** *is hermitian with eigenvalues* $\lambda_1, \ldots, \lambda_n$ *and corresponding eigenvectors* $\mathbf{x}_1, \ldots, \mathbf{x}_n$, *and* $\mathbf{x}$ *is a nonzero vector such that*

$$(\mathbf{x}, \mathbf{x}_1) = \ldots = (\mathbf{x}, \mathbf{x}_{j-1}) = 0, \tag{12.86}$$

then

$$\lambda_j = \min_{\mathbf{x}} \frac{(\mathbf{x}, \mathbf{A}\mathbf{x})}{(\mathbf{x}, \mathbf{x})}, \tag{12.87}$$

and

$$\lambda_j \leq \frac{(\mathbf{x}, \mathbf{A}\mathbf{x})}{(\mathbf{x}, \mathbf{x})} \leq \lambda_n. \tag{12.88}$$

Proof: Following the same lines of proof as in Theorem 12.13, if we represent **x** in the form (12.79), then (12.86) tells us that

$$\mathbf{x} = \sum_{i=j}^{n} \alpha_i \mathbf{x}_i.$$

Hence, (12.80) is replaced by

$$\frac{(\mathbf{x}, \mathbf{A}\mathbf{x})}{(\mathbf{x}, \mathbf{x})} = \frac{\lambda_j \alpha_j \bar{\alpha}_j + \ldots + \lambda_n \bar{\alpha}_n \alpha_n}{\bar{\alpha}_1 \alpha_1 + \ldots + \bar{\alpha}_n \alpha_n} \tag{12.89}$$

and

$$\rho - \lambda_j = \frac{(\lambda_{j+1} - \lambda_j)\bar{\alpha}_j \alpha_j + \ldots + (\lambda_n - \lambda_j)\bar{\alpha}_n \alpha_n}{\bar{\alpha}_1 \alpha_1 + \ldots + \bar{\alpha}_n \alpha_n}.$$

Hence, $\rho \geq \lambda_j$. If we choose $\mathbf{x} = \mathbf{x}_j$, this gives $\rho = \lambda_j$, which proves (12.87), and the left inequality in (12.88). The right inequality follows similarly by considering $\rho - \lambda_n$.

It is unfortunate that Theorem 12.15 is not very useful for the approximate determination of λ_j since it requires knowledge of the exact eigenvectors $\mathbf{x}_1, \ldots, \mathbf{x}_{j-1}$. More useful theorems are given in the next two sections.

Ex. 12.19. By considering the Rayleigh quotient for

$$\begin{bmatrix} a & b \\ 0 & d \end{bmatrix},$$

show that it is essential in Theorem 12.13 that **A** be hermitian.

Ex. 12.20. Extend Theorem 12.13 to the equation $\mathbf{A}\mathbf{x} = \lambda \mathbf{B}\mathbf{x}$, where **A**, **B** are hermitian and **B** is positive definite, by considering

$$\rho = \frac{(\mathbf{x}, \mathbf{A}\mathbf{x})}{(\mathbf{x}, \mathbf{B}\mathbf{x})}.$$

What happens if **B** is not positive definite?

Ex. 12.21. Show that the constant μ that minimizes $\|\mathbf{Ax} - \mu\mathbf{x}\|$ for a general square matrix **A** and any given **x** is

$$\mu = \frac{1}{2}\frac{(\mathbf{x}, (\mathbf{A}^H + \mathbf{A})\mathbf{x})}{(\mathbf{x}, \mathbf{x})}.$$

(Note that this is the Rayleigh quotient if **A** is hermitian.)

12.8 The Temple-Kato Brackets for Eigenvalues

Consider the expression

$$T = (\mathbf{Ax} - \mu\mathbf{x}, \mathbf{Ax} - \nu\mathbf{x}) \tag{12.90}$$

for a hermitian matrix **A** and any given real constants μ, ν. As in the proof of Theorem 12.13 we expand **x** in the eigenvector series (12.79), and we find

$$\mathbf{Ax} - \mu\mathbf{x} = \sum_{i=1}^{n} (\lambda_i - \mu)\mathbf{x}_i$$

with a similar expression for $\mathbf{Ax} - \nu\mathbf{x}$. Substitution in (12.90) yields

$$T = \sum_{i=1}^{n} (\lambda_i - \mu)(\lambda_i - \nu)\bar{\alpha}_i\alpha_i.$$

If no eigenvalue of **A** lies between μ and ν, then $\lambda_i - \mu$ and $\lambda_i - \nu$ always have the same sign, for all eigenvalues λ_i. Hence, $T \geq 0$ and this leads to

$$(\mathbf{Ax} - \mu\mathbf{x}, \mathbf{Ax} - \nu\mathbf{x}) \geq 0. \tag{12.91}$$

Definition 12.6 (12.77) of the Rayleigh quotient gives

$$(\mathbf{Ax} - \rho\mathbf{x}, \mathbf{x}) = 0. \tag{12.92}$$

We rewrite (12.91) in the form

$$((\mathbf{Ax} - \rho\mathbf{x}) + (\rho - \mu)\mathbf{x}, (\mathbf{Ax} - \rho\mathbf{x}) + (\rho - \nu)\mathbf{x}) \geq 0.$$

Using (12.92) we see that this implies

$$\|\mathbf{Ax} - \rho\mathbf{x}\|^2 + (\rho - \mu)(\rho - \nu)\|\mathbf{x}\|^2 \geq 0. \tag{12.93}$$

We introduce the notation

$$\varepsilon^2 = \frac{\|\mathbf{Ax} - \rho\mathbf{x}\|^2}{\|\mathbf{x}\|^2} = \frac{\|\mathbf{Ax}\|^2}{\|\mathbf{x}\|^2} - \rho^2, \tag{12.94}$$

where ε^2 is a known quantity for given **A**, **x**, and (12.93) becomes

$$(\rho - \mu)(\nu - \rho) \leq \varepsilon^2. \tag{12.95}$$

In this result ρ is the Rayleigh quotient and there is no eigenvalue between μ and ν. This basic inequality allows us to prove the following.

THEOREM **12.16.** *If α, β are any numbers such that $\lambda_{r-1} \le \alpha \le \lambda_r$ and $\lambda_r \le \beta \le \lambda_{r+1}$ and $\alpha < \rho < \beta$ where ρ is the Rayleigh quotient, then*

$$\rho - \frac{\varepsilon^2}{\beta - \rho} \le \lambda_r \le \rho + \frac{\varepsilon^2}{\rho - \alpha}, \qquad r = 2, 3, \ldots, \tag{12.96}$$

where ε^2 was defined in (12.94). *For the lowest eigenvalue, we have, for $-\infty < \rho < \beta \le \lambda_2$,*

$$\rho - \frac{\varepsilon^2}{\beta - \rho} \le \lambda_1 \le \rho. \tag{12.97}$$

Proof: The result (12.95) is true for $\mu = \lambda_r$ and $\nu = \beta$, where β has the properties specified in the theorem, since then there is no eigenvalue between μ and ν. This gives

$$(\rho - \lambda_r)(\beta - \rho) \le \varepsilon^2.$$

Since $\rho > \beta$, this implies $\rho - \lambda_r \le \varepsilon^2/(\beta - \rho)$, which gives the left inequalities in (12.96) and (12.97). Next in (12.95) choose $\nu = \lambda_r$, $r \ge 2$ and $\mu = \alpha$, where α has the properties specified in the theorem. Then

$$(\rho - \alpha)(\lambda_r - \rho) \le \varepsilon^2.$$

Since $\rho > \alpha$, this implies the right inequality in (12.96). For $r = 1$ we choose $\nu = \lambda_1$ and $\mu = \alpha$ where $\alpha < \lambda_1$ and $\alpha < \rho$. The right-hand inequality in (12.96) is still true. It is permissible to let α tend to $-\infty$. This gives $\lambda_1 - \rho \le 0$, which is the right inequality in (12.97). Of course, this is simply Rayleigh's principle.

Ex. 12.22. Find a lower bound for λ_1 in Ex. 12.15, given that $\lambda_2 > 1.8$.

Solution: This means that we can take $\beta = 1.8$ in the left inequality in (12.97). For $\mathbf{x} = [1, 1, 1]^T$ we find $\rho = 0.57$, $\varepsilon^2 = 0.176$, and $\lambda_1 \ge 0.57 - (0.176/1.23) \approx 0.43$. (The difficulty in the method is of course to know in the first place that $\lambda_2 > 1.8$. This is the bound found in Ex. 12.23 below.)

12.9 The Minimax Characterization of Eigenvalues

We know from Rayleigh's principle that for any $\mathbf{x} \ne \mathbf{0}$,

$$\rho = \frac{(\mathbf{x}, \mathbf{A}\mathbf{x})}{(\mathbf{x}, \mathbf{x})} \ge \lambda_1. \tag{12.98}$$

Suppose that we impose an additional restriction $(\mathbf{p}, \mathbf{x}) = 0$ for some given vector $\mathbf{p}$, and find the minimum of the Rayleigh quotient (12.98) over all $\mathbf{x} \ne \mathbf{0}$.

We wish to visualize the situation geometrically, so we replace the above problem by the equivalent (Theorem 12.12):

$$\begin{aligned} &\text{maximize} && (\mathbf{x}, \mathbf{x}) \\ &\text{subject to} && (\mathbf{x}, \mathbf{A}\mathbf{x}) = 1, \qquad (\mathbf{p}, \mathbf{x}) = 0. \end{aligned} \tag{12.99}$$

Suppose that the quadric $(\mathbf{x}, \mathbf{A}\mathbf{x}) = 1$ is an ellipsoid (all $\lambda_i > 0$) in three dimensions. The restriction $(\mathbf{p}, \mathbf{x}) = 0$ means that the point $\mathbf{x}$ lies on a plane through the origin perpendicular to the given vector $\mathbf{p}$, i.e., the maximum $(\mathbf{x}, \mathbf{x})$ satisfying the conditions in (12.99) is the square of the major axis of the ellipse given by the intersection of the ellipsoid $(\mathbf{x}, \mathbf{A}\mathbf{x}) = 1$ and the plane $(\mathbf{p}, \mathbf{x}) = 0$. Consider now the *minimum value of all such* $(\mathbf{x}, \mathbf{x})$ *for all possible vectors* $\mathbf{p}$. The reader should be able to visualize that this is the square of the *second largest* axis of the ellipsoid. We have already seen, in the paragraph preceding Theorem 12.15, that this characterizes the *second smallest* eigenvalue of $\mathbf{A}$. Remembering that when we revert to the Rayleigh quotient notation in (12.98) we have to interchange the roles of maximum and minimum (maximizing $(\mathbf{x}, \mathbf{x})$ corresponds to minimizing ρ, see Theorem 12.12), this argument indicates that

$$\lambda_2 = \max_{(\text{all } \mathbf{p})} \left\{ \min_{\text{fixed } \mathbf{p}} \frac{(\mathbf{x}, \mathbf{A}\mathbf{x})}{(\mathbf{x}, \mathbf{x})} \right\}, \qquad \mathbf{x} \neq \mathbf{0}, \qquad (\mathbf{p}, \mathbf{x}) = 0. \tag{12.100}$$

Figure 12.6 may help the reader to visualize what is happening. The length of the radius vector in the plane perpendicular to $\mathbf{p}$ is plotted as a function of the

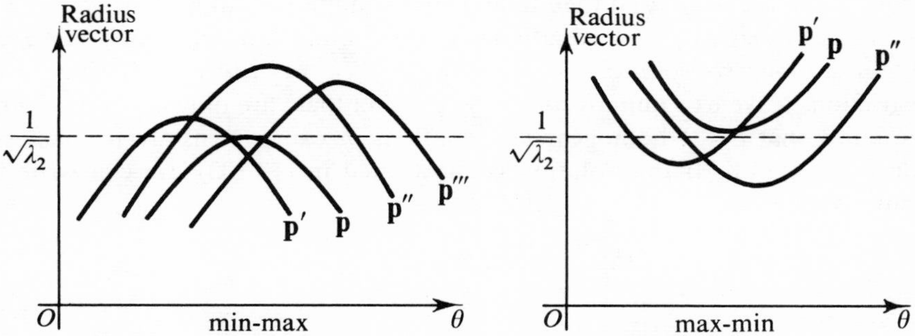

Figure 12.6 Max-min principle. θ = angle of rotation of radius vector in plane perpendicular to p. $\theta = 0$ is chosen arbitrarily in each case.

angle of rotation in this plane (in each case measured from an arbitrary origin), for various $\mathbf{p}$. We first find the maximum for each $\mathbf{p}$, and then the minimum over all $\mathbf{p}$. This gives $1/\sqrt{\lambda_2}$.

The important thing is that (12.100) characterizes λ_2 quite independently of the other eigenvalues.

We now give an algebraic proof of a generalization of this result.

THEOREM **12.17.** *If* $\mathbf{A}$ *is hermitian,*

$$\lambda_r = \max\left\{\min \frac{(\mathbf{x}, \mathbf{A}\mathbf{x})}{(\mathbf{x}, \mathbf{x})}\right\}, \tag{12.101}$$

where we first take the minimum over $\mathbf{x}$ *subject to* $(\mathbf{p}_i, \mathbf{x}) = 0$, $i = 1, 2, \ldots, r - 1$, *where the* $\mathbf{p}_i$ *are regarded as fixed vectors, and then we take the maximum over all possible* $\mathbf{p}_i$. *Also,*

$$\lambda_r = \min\left\{\max \frac{(\mathbf{x}, \mathbf{A}\mathbf{x})}{(\mathbf{x}, \mathbf{x})}\right\}, \tag{12.102}$$

where, in this second characterization, the maximum over $\mathbf{x}$ *is taken first, subject to* $(\mathbf{p}_i, \mathbf{x}) = 0$, $i = r + 1, \ldots, n$ *for fixed* $\mathbf{p}_i$, *and then the minimum is taken over all possible* $\mathbf{p}_i$.

Proof: Suppose that $\mathbf{A}$ is diagonalized by $\mathbf{P}$, $\mathbf{P}^H\mathbf{A}\mathbf{P} = \mathbf{\Lambda}$, where the diagonal elements of $\mathbf{\Lambda}$ are the eigenvalues of $\mathbf{A}$, and $\mathbf{P}$ is unitary.

$$(\mathbf{x}, \mathbf{A}\mathbf{x}) = (\mathbf{y}, \mathbf{\Lambda}\mathbf{y}), \qquad (\mathbf{x}, \mathbf{x}) = (\mathbf{y}, \mathbf{y}), \qquad (\mathbf{p}_i, \mathbf{x}) = (\mathbf{q}_i, \mathbf{y}),$$

where $\mathbf{x} = \mathbf{P}\mathbf{y}$, $\mathbf{q}_i = \mathbf{P}^H\mathbf{p}_i$. Hence, the right-hand side of (12.101), which we denote by L, can be replaced by

$$L = \max\left\{\min \frac{\lambda_1 y_1^2 + \ldots + \lambda_n y_n^2}{y_1^2 + \ldots + y_n^2}\right\}, \tag{12.103}$$

where we first take the minimum over $\mathbf{y}$ subject to $(\mathbf{q}_i, \mathbf{y}) = 0$, $i = 1, \ldots, r - 1$, where the $\mathbf{q}_i$ are fixed, and then take the maximum over all $\mathbf{q}_i$. The $(\mathbf{q}_i, \mathbf{y}) = 0$ can be regarded as $r - 1$ equations in the n unknowns $y_1, \ldots, y_n$. We can obtain a nonzero solution of these with $y_{r+1} = \ldots = y_n = 0$ since these restrictions leave us r unknowns $y_1, \ldots, y_r$ and there are only $r - 1$ equations. We know that $r - 1$ homogeneous equations in r unknowns always possess a nonzero solution. If this solution is substituted in (12.103), we can write the result as

$$\begin{aligned} L &= \max\left\{\min \frac{\lambda_1 y_1^2 + \ldots + \lambda_r y_r^2}{y_1^2 + \ldots + y_r^2}\right\} \\ &= \max\left\{\min\left[\lambda_r - \frac{(\lambda_r - \lambda_1)y_1^2 + \ldots + (\lambda_r - \lambda_{r-1})y_{r-1}^2}{y_1^2 + \ldots + y_r^2}\right]\right\}. \end{aligned} \tag{12.104}$$

Since $\lambda_1 \leq \lambda_2 \leq \ldots \leq \lambda_r$, this gives

$$L \leq \lambda_r. \tag{12.105}$$

The result (12.104) is true for any given $\mathbf{x}$, i.e., $\mathbf{y}$, and we must now consider what happens when we take the maximum over all possible choices of $\mathbf{x}$. If we choose $\mathbf{p}_i = \mathbf{P}\mathbf{e}_i$, where the $\mathbf{e}_i$ are the unit vectors, then $\mathbf{q}_i = \mathbf{e}_i$ and $(\mathbf{q}_i, \mathbf{y}) = 0$ implies $y_i = 0$ for $i = 1, \ldots, r - 1$. In this case the right-hand side of (12.104) reduces to λ_r, so that we have shown that there is a choice of $\mathbf{x}$ such that $L = \lambda_r$. This, in conjunction with (12.105), proves (12.101). The result (12.102) can be proved similarly.

Ex. 12.23. Find a lower bound for λ_2 for the matrix given in Ex. 12.15.

Solution: The first step is to minimize the Rayleigh quotient (12.83) with a linear constraint. It is clear from the proof of (12.87) that to obtain the exact result, the constraint we should apply is $(\mathbf{p}, \mathbf{x}) = 0$ where $\mathbf{p}$ is the eigenvector corresponding to the smallest eigenvalue. We do not know $\mathbf{p}$ exactly, but we do know an approximation to $\mathbf{p}$, namely $[1, 1, 1]^T$, so we impose the constraint $x_1 + x_2 + x_3 = 0$. If we set $x_1 = -x_2 - x_3$ in (12.83), we find that we now have to minimize

$$R = \frac{5.7x_2^2 + 3.4x_2x_3 + 3.7x_3^2}{2(x_2^2 + x_2x_3 + x_3^2)}.$$

This involves only two variables and minimization involves the solution of a quadratic equation. The minimum is found to be 1.81, and this is a lower bound for λ_2. We could try other vectors for $\mathbf{p}$. The largest resulting lower bound for λ_2 will be the best.

In order to show the power of the minimax principle, we prove the following theorem.

THEOREM **12.18.** *The eigenvalues $\lambda_1', \ldots, \lambda_{n-1}'$ of the matrix obtained by omitting the last row and column of a hermitian matrix $\mathbf{A}$ separate the eigenvalues $\lambda_1, \ldots, \lambda_n$ of $\mathbf{A}$.*

Proof: Let $\mathbf{A}_{n-1}$ denote the matrix obtained by omitting the last row and column of $\mathbf{A}$. Let $\mathbf{x}'$ and $\mathbf{p}_i'$ denote $(n - 1) \times 1$ column vectors and set

$$\mathbf{y} = \begin{bmatrix} \mathbf{x}' \\ 0 \end{bmatrix}, \qquad \mathbf{q}_i = \begin{bmatrix} \mathbf{p}_i' \\ 0 \end{bmatrix}. \tag{12.106}$$

Define

$$\rho(\mathbf{x}) = \frac{(\mathbf{x}, \mathbf{A}\mathbf{x})}{(\mathbf{x}, \mathbf{x})}, \qquad \rho_{n-1}(\mathbf{x}') = \frac{(\mathbf{x}', \mathbf{A}_{n-1}\mathbf{x}')}{(\mathbf{x}', \mathbf{x}')}.$$

We have

$$\rho(\mathbf{y}) = \rho_{n-1}(\mathbf{x}').$$

Hence, using (12.101),

$$\lambda_r' = \max\,\{\min \rho_{n-1}(\mathbf{x}')\} = \max\,\{\min \rho(\mathbf{y})\},$$

where in the first relation the minimum is taken subject to $r - 1$ relations of the form $(\mathbf{p}_i', \mathbf{x}') = 0$, and in the second relation the minimum is therefore subject to $r - 1$ relations of the form $(\mathbf{q}_i, \mathbf{y}) = 0$, where $\mathbf{q}_i$, $\mathbf{y}$ were defined in (12.106).

We deduce that

$$\lambda_r' = \max \{\min \rho(\mathbf{x})\},$$

where $\mathbf{x}$ is now subject to the r relations $(\mathbf{p}_i, \mathbf{x}) = 0$, $i = 1, \ldots, r$, where we take $\mathbf{p}_r = \mathbf{e}_n$, the unit vector with nth element unity, and the $\mathbf{p}_i$ are arbitrary $n \times 1$ column vectors for $i = 1, \ldots, r - 1$. However, the minimum of $\rho(\mathbf{x})$ for $\mathbf{x}$ subject to r relations $(\mathbf{p}_i, \mathbf{x}) = 0$ for *any* $\mathbf{p}_i$ may be greater than the minimum of $\rho(\mathbf{x})$ for the restrictions we have just described, i.e.,

$$\max \{\min \rho(\mathbf{x})\} \geq \lambda_r',$$

where $\mathbf{x}$ is subject to r relations $(\mathbf{p}_i, \mathbf{x}) = 0$ for any $\mathbf{p}_i$ and we maximize over all possible $\mathbf{p}_i$. The quantity on the left is λ_{r+1} by (12.101), so we have proved

$$\lambda_{r+1} \geq \lambda_r'.$$

The proof that

$$\lambda_r \leq \lambda_r' \tag{12.107}$$

goes similarly, using (12.102) instead of (12.101).

Ex. 12.24. Extend Theorem 12.18 to show that the eigenvalues of the matrix obtained by omitting *any* row and the corresponding column of a hermitian matrix $\mathbf{A}$ separate the eigenvalues of $\mathbf{A}$.

Ex. 12.25. Prove (12.107).

Ex. 12.26. Verify Theorem 12.18 and Ex. 12.24 for

$$\mathbf{A} = \begin{bmatrix} 3 & -1 & 0 \\ -1 & 2 & -1 \\ 0 & -1 & 3 \end{bmatrix}.$$

Miscellaneous Exercises 12

Ex. 12.27. Prove that if $\mathbf{A}$ is positive definite, then $\mathbf{A}^{-1}$ is also positive definite.

Ex. 12.28. Prove that if $\mathbf{A}$ is a positive definite matrix of order m and $\mathbf{B}$ is $m \times n$, then $\mathbf{B}^H\mathbf{A}\mathbf{B}$ is positive semidefinite. Prove that if the rank of $\mathbf{B}$ is n, then $\mathbf{B}^H\mathbf{A}\mathbf{B}$ is positive definite; if the rank of $\mathbf{B}$ is less than n, $\mathbf{B}^H\mathbf{A}\mathbf{B}$ is positive semidefinite and singular.

Ex. 12.29. If $\mathbf{A}$ is positive definite, so is any principal submatrix. (The diagonal elements of a principal submatrix of $\mathbf{A}$ are diagonal elements of $\mathbf{A}$.)

Ex. 12.30. If det $(\mathbf{A} + \lambda\mathbf{B} + \lambda^2\mathbf{C}) = 0$, where $\mathbf{A}$, $\mathbf{B}$, $\mathbf{C}$ are positive definite, prove that the real part of λ is less than zero. If $\mathbf{C}$ is only hermitian, prove that the real part of any complex λ is less than zero. [The reader might be interested to compare the brevity of the treatment using matrix notation with the longhand version of this problem, and other matters, in A. G. Webster, *The Dynamics of Particles*, etc., Hafner (1949), pp. 157–166, and appendices.]

Ex. 12.31. If $\mathbf{A}$ is positive semidefinite, prove that a nonzero $\mathbf{x}$ exists such that $(\mathbf{x}, \mathbf{Ax}) = 0$ if and only if $\mathbf{A}$ is singular.

Ex. 12.32. If $\mathbf{A}$ is positive semidefinite, prove that

(a) $\lambda_i \geq 0$.

(b) $\mathbf{B}^H\mathbf{AB}$ is also positive semidefinite, where $\mathbf{A}$ is $m \times m$, and $\mathbf{B}$ is $m \times n$.

(c) The determinant of any principal submatrix of $\mathbf{A}$ is greater than or equal to zero. In particular, $a_{ii} \geq 0$, $a_{ii}a_{jj} - |a_{ij}|^2 \geq 0$.

Ex. 12.33. Prove that a positive definite matrix $\mathbf{B}$ can be decomposed in the form $\mathbf{B} = \mathbf{LL}^H$, where $\mathbf{L}$ is lower triangular. Show that if $\mathbf{A}$ is hermitian and $\mathbf{B}$ is positive definite, the eigenvalues for $(\mathbf{A} - \lambda\mathbf{B})\mathbf{x} = \mathbf{0}$ are the same as the eigenvalues for the hermitian matrix $\mathbf{L}^{-1}\mathbf{A}(\mathbf{L}^H)^{-1}$, and the eigenvectors for one problem can be deduced from those for the other.

Ex. 12.34. If $\mathbf{A} = \mathbf{B} + \mathbf{C}$, where $\mathbf{B}$ is positive definite and $\mathbf{C}$ is positive semidefinite show that

(a) $\mathbf{A}$ is positive definite.

(b) $\det \mathbf{B} \leq \det \mathbf{A}$.

(c) $\mathbf{B}^{-1} - \mathbf{A}^{-1}$ is positive semidefinite.

Ex. 12.35. Prove that if $\mathbf{B}$ is positive definite and $\mathbf{A}$ is hermitian, the eigenvalues of $\mathbf{BA}$ are real.

Ex. 12.36. Reduce the following quadratic forms to a sum of multiples of squares by an orthogonal transformation.

(a) $5x_1^2 + 6x_2^2 + 7x_3^2 - 4x_1x_2 - 4x_2x_3$.

(b) $3x_1^2 + 2x_2^2 + 2x_3^2 + 2x_1x_2 + 4x_2x_3 + 2x_3x_1$.

(c) $x_1 + x_2^2 + x_3^2 + 4x_1x_2 + 4x_2x_3 + 4x_3x_1$.

Sketch, relative to their principal axes, the surfaces given by setting these quadratic forms equal to a positive constant.

Ex. 12.37. If $\mathbf{A}$ is positive definite, prove that

$$\det \mathbf{A} \leq a_{11}a_{22} \dots a_{nn}.$$

Deduce that, if $\mathbf{B}$ is an arbitrary square matrix,

$$|\det \mathbf{B}|^2 \leq \prod_{i=1}^{n} \left(\sum_{j=1}^{n} |b_{ij}|^2 \right).$$

This is known as *Hadamard's inequality*. The absolute value of the determinant of a matrix can be interpreted as the volume in n-dimensional space of the solid whose sides are defined by the rows (or columns) of the matrix. Hadamard's inequality then says that this volume is less than or equal to that of the n-dimensional solid whose sides have the same lengths. Verify this for $n = 2$, 3 from your knowledge of the geometry of parallelograms and parallelepipeds in two and three dimensions. Under what conditions is equality attained in Hadamard's inequality? Give an independent proof of the equality in this case. Show that if $a = \max |a_{ij}|$ then

$$|\det \mathbf{A}| \leq a^n n^{n/2}.$$

Ex. 12.38. If $d\mathbf{x}/dt = -\mathbf{A}\mathbf{x}$, where $\mathbf{A}$ is positive definite, prove that $\mathbf{x} \to \mathbf{0}$ as $t \to \infty$.

Ex. 12.39. If $\mathbf{A}\, d^2\mathbf{x}/dt^2 + \mathbf{B}\mathbf{x} = \mathbf{0}$, where $\mathbf{A}$, $\mathbf{B}$ are positive definite matrices with constant elements, prove that the elements of $\mathbf{x}$ are sums of pure oscillations.

Ex. 12.40. Prove that congruence is an equivalence relation (Definition 3.9). Prove that $\mathbf{A}$ is hermitian-congruent to a real diagonal matrix if and only if $\mathbf{A}$ is hermitian.

Ex. 12.41. A matrix is said to be *idempotent* if $\mathbf{A}^2 = \mathbf{A}$. Prove:

(a) The eigenvalues of an idempotent matrix are either 0 or 1.

(b) The only nonsingular idempotent matrix is the identity matrix.

(c) A necessary and sufficient condition that a *hermitian* matrix of order n be idempotent is that k of its eigenvalues are equal to 1, and the remaining $n - k$ are equal to zero, where k is the rank of the matrix.

(d) The trace of a hermitian idempotent matrix is equal to its rank.

(e) A singular 2×2 matrix with $a_{11} + a_{22} = 1$ is idempotent.

(f) If $\mathbf{AGA} = \mathbf{A}$, then $\mathbf{GA}$ is idempotent.

(g) If $\mathbf{A}$ is idempotent and $\mathbf{P}$ is unitary, $\mathbf{P}^H\mathbf{AP}$ is idempotent.

(h) $\mathbf{A} = \mathbf{U}(\mathbf{VU})^{-1}\mathbf{V}$ is idempotent.

Ex. 12.42. Suppose that n measurements are represented by a vector $\mathbf{x} = [x_1, \ldots, x_n]^T$. The mean and variance of the measurements are given by

$$\bar{x} = \frac{1}{n}\sum_{i=1}^{n} x_i, \qquad s^2 = \frac{1}{n}\sum_{i=1}^{n} (x_i - \bar{x})^2.$$

Show that

$$s^2 = \left(\mathbf{x}, \left(\mathbf{I} - \frac{1}{n}\mathbf{J}\right)\mathbf{x}\right),$$

where $\mathbf{J}$ is a square matrix, all of whose elements are unity. Prove that $\mathbf{I} - n^{-1}\mathbf{J}$ is idempotent. (Applications of idempotent matrices occur in statistics and regression theory. See, for instance, Graybill [78].)

Ex. 12.43. Show that, for any hermitian matrix $\mathbf{A}$, a hermitian-congruence transformation $\mathbf{S}$ exists such that

$$\mathbf{S}^H\mathbf{AS} = \begin{bmatrix} \mathbf{I}_r & \mathbf{0} & \mathbf{0} \\ \mathbf{0} & -\mathbf{I}_s & \mathbf{0} \\ \mathbf{0} & \mathbf{0} & \mathbf{0} \end{bmatrix},$$

where $\mathbf{I}_r$, $\mathbf{I}_s$ are unit matrices of orders r and s, and the integers r, s are always the same for a given $\mathbf{A}$, independent of $\mathbf{S}$, which is not unique. If the quadratic form $(\mathbf{x}, \mathbf{Ax})$ is reduced to a sum of squares $(\mathbf{y}, \mathbf{Dy})$, where $\mathbf{D}$ is diagonal, by a nonsingular transformation $\mathbf{x} = \mathbf{Py}$, prove that the number of positive, negative, and zero diagonal elements of $\mathbf{D}$ is always the same, independent of the transformation. (The diagonal elements of $\mathbf{D}$ must, of course, be real.) This is known as *Sylvester's law of inertia.*

Ex. 12.44. Verify the steps in the following reduction of $(\mathbf{x}, \mathbf{Ax})$ to a sum of squares by the elementary procedure of "completing the square." $\mathbf{A}$ is assumed to be real, symmetric, and nonsingular. The matrices that occur are those that appear in Gaussian elimination or triangular decomposition when solving $\mathbf{Ax} = \mathbf{b}$. The procedure gives a method for finding a congruence transformation that reduces $\mathbf{A}$ to diagonal form. Prove that, in a notation explained below,

$$(\mathbf{x}, \mathbf{Ax}) = a_{11}y_1^2 + (\mathbf{x}_2, \mathbf{A}^{(2)}\mathbf{x}_2) = a_{11}y_1^2 + a_{22}^{(2)}y_2^2 + (\mathbf{x}_3, \mathbf{A}^{(3)}\mathbf{x}_3),$$

and so on, until finally

$$(\mathbf{x}, \mathbf{Ax}) = a_{11}y_1^2 + a_{22}^{(2)}y_2^2 + \dots a_{nn}^{(n)}y_n^2, \tag{12.108}$$

where

$$\begin{bmatrix} y_1 \\ y_2 \\ \\ y_n \end{bmatrix} = \begin{bmatrix} 1 & m_{21} & m_{31} & \dots & m_{n1} \\ 0 & 1 & m_{32} & \dots & m_{n2} \\ & & \dots & & \\ 0 & 0 & 0 & \dots & 1 \end{bmatrix} \begin{bmatrix} x_1 \\ x_2 \\ \\ x_n \end{bmatrix}, \tag{12.109}$$

$$\mathbf{A}^{(k)} = \begin{bmatrix} a_{kk}^{(k)} & \dots & a_{kn}^{(k)} \\ & \dots & \\ a_{nk}^{(k)} & \dots & a_{nn}^{(k)} \end{bmatrix}.$$

The notation is that in Section 7.6, except that $\mathbf{A}^{(k)}$ now stands for the square matrix of order $n - k + 1$ in the bottom right of $\mathbf{A}$. In matrix notation, if (12.109) is $\mathbf{y} = \mathbf{Mx}$, equation (12.108) gives

$$(\mathbf{x}, \mathbf{Ax}) = (\mathbf{y}, \mathbf{Dy}) = (\mathbf{Mx}, \mathbf{DMx}) = (\mathbf{x}, \mathbf{M}^T\mathbf{DMx}),$$

where $\mathbf{D}$ is a diagonal matrix whose ith diagonal element is $a_{ii}^{(i)}$. Since this is true for any $\mathbf{x}$, deduce that $\mathbf{A} = \mathbf{M}^T\mathbf{DM}$. (This gives an independent proof of Theorem 12.5 for real $\mathbf{A}$.) What happens if the rank of $\mathbf{A}$ is less than its order?

Ex. 12.45. Show that, when reducing a real symmetric square matrix $\mathbf{A}$ to row-echelon form, the numbers of positive, negative, and zero pivots are equal to the numbers of positive, negative, and zero eigenvalues.

Ex. 12.46. If $\mathbf{A}$ is a positive definite hermitian matrix, there exists a unique positive definite hermitian matrix $\mathbf{B}$ such that $\mathbf{A} = \mathbf{B}^2$. If $\mathbf{A}$ is semidefinite, $\mathbf{B}$ is semidefinite. $\mathbf{B}$ is called the *square root* of $\mathbf{A}$.

Ex. 12.47. Prove:

(a) If $\mathbf{A}$ is hermitian, then $\mathbf{U} = e^{i\mathbf{A}}$ is unitary. Conversely, any unitary matrix $\mathbf{U}$ can be expressed in the form $\mathbf{U} = e^{i\mathbf{A}}$, where $\mathbf{A}$ is hermitian.

(b) If $\mathbf{A}$ is any square matrix, there exist positive definite or semidefinite hermitian matrices $\mathbf{M}$ and $\mathbf{N}$, and unitary matrices $\mathbf{U}$ and $\mathbf{V}$ such that $\mathbf{A} = \mathbf{UM} = \mathbf{NV}$. This is known as the *polar* representation of $\mathbf{A}$, by analogy with the representation $a + ib = re^{i\theta}$ for any complex number. The matrices $\mathbf{M}$, $\mathbf{N}$ are unique. If $\mathbf{A}$ is nonsingular, $\mathbf{U} = \mathbf{V}$ and this matrix is unique.

Ex. 12.48. An orthogonal matrix $\mathbf{A}$ is called *proper* if $\det \mathbf{A} = 1$ and *improper* if $\det \mathbf{A} = -1$. Prove that all proper and improper 2×2 matrices can be written in the following forms, respectively, where $0 \le \alpha < 2\pi$:

$$\mathbf{L} = \begin{bmatrix} \cos\alpha & -\sin\alpha \\ \sin\alpha & \cos\alpha \end{bmatrix} \quad \text{and} \quad \begin{bmatrix} \cos\alpha & \sin\alpha \\ \sin\alpha & -\cos\alpha \end{bmatrix}.$$

In (12.2) we have shown that if axes are rotated in a plane, the coordinates $\mathbf{x} = [x, y]^T$ with respect to the old axes, and $\mathbf{x}' = [X, Y]^T$ with respect to the new axes are related by the equation $\mathbf{x} = \mathbf{L}\mathbf{x}'$, or, equivalently, $\mathbf{x}' = \mathbf{L}^T\mathbf{x}$ where $\mathbf{L}$ is the first matrix given above. Prove conversely that any proper 2×2 matrix represents a unique rotation; also that any improper 2×2 matrix represents rotation followed (or preceded) by a reflection in a line through the origin.

Ex. 12.49. In Figure 12.7, a sequence of rotations is outlined by means of which a set of axes (x, y, z) is transferred to a set (x''', y''', z''') by three two-dimensional rotations involving angles ψ, θ, ϕ, which are called the *Eulerian*

(1) Positive rotation about z-axis by angle ψ, new axes $x'y'z'$
(2) Positive rotation about x'-axis by angle θ, new axes $x''y''z''$
(3) Positive rotation about z''-axis by angle φ, new axes $x'''y'''z'''$
The dotted circle lies in the xy-plane. The solid circle lies in the $x'''y'''$-plane (perpendicular to z''').

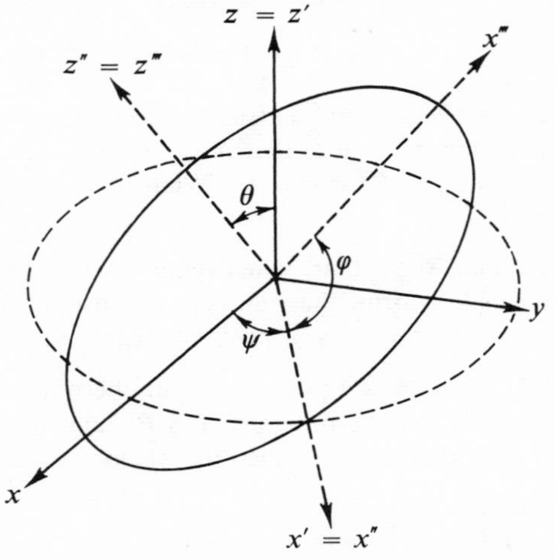

Figure 12.7 Eulerian angles.

angles. Show that

$$\begin{bmatrix} x''' \\ y''' \\ z''' \end{bmatrix} = \begin{bmatrix} \cos\phi & \sin\phi & 0 \\ -\sin\phi & \cos\phi & 0 \\ 0 & 0 & 1 \end{bmatrix} \begin{bmatrix} 1 & 0 & 0 \\ 0 & \cos\theta & \sin\theta \\ 0 & -\sin\theta & \cos\theta \end{bmatrix}$$

$$\times \begin{bmatrix} \cos\psi & \sin\psi & 0 \\ -\sin\psi & \cos\psi & 0 \\ 0 & 0 & 1 \end{bmatrix} \begin{bmatrix} x \\ y \\ z \end{bmatrix} = \mathbf{A} \begin{bmatrix} x \\ y \\ z \end{bmatrix},$$

where

$$\mathbf{A} = \begin{bmatrix} \cos\phi\cos\psi & \cos\phi\sin\psi & \sin\phi\sin\theta \\ \quad -\sin\phi\cos\theta\sin\psi, & \quad +\sin\phi\cos\theta\cos\psi, & \\ -\sin\phi\cos\psi & -\sin\phi\sin\psi & \cos\phi\sin\theta \\ \quad -\cos\phi\cos\theta\sin\psi, & \quad +\cos\phi\cos\theta\cos\psi, & \\ \sin\theta\sin\psi, & -\sin\theta\cos\psi, & \cos\theta \end{bmatrix}.$$

Show (without forming $\mathbf{A}^H\mathbf{A}$ or $\mathbf{A}\mathbf{A}^H$ directly) that $\mathbf{A}$ is orthogonal.

Ex. 12.50. Show that any proper 3×3 orthogonal matrix represents a rotation by filling in the details of the following argument. Define θ by $\cos\theta = a_{33}$, where $0 \le \theta < \pi$. Then $a_{13}^2 + a_{23}^2 = \sin^2\theta$, and we can define ϕ uniquely in $0 \le \phi < 2\pi$ by $a_{13} = \sin\theta\sin\phi$, $a_{23} = \sin\theta\cos\phi$. Similarly, define ψ uniquely in $0 \le \psi < 2\pi$ by $a_{31} = \sin\theta\sin\psi$, $a_{32} = -\sin\theta\cos\psi$. We have $a_{11}^2 + a_{12}^2 = 1 - \sin^2\phi\sin^2\theta$, and, from orthogonality of the first and third rows, $a_{11}\sin\psi - a_{12}\cos\psi = -\sin\phi\cos\theta$. Solve, to find a_{11} and a_{12},

$$a_{11} = -\sin\phi\cos\theta\sin\psi \pm \cos\phi\cos\psi,$$
$$a_{12} = \cos\phi\cos\theta\cos\psi \pm \cos\phi\sin\psi,$$

where upper and lower signs go together. Find similar expressions for a_{21}, a_{22}. Show that if and only if $\det\mathbf{A} = +1$ (not -1), the matrix can be written in the same form as $\mathbf{A}$ in Ex. 12.49, which represents a rotation.

Ex. 12.51. Consider a finite rotation of a body by an angle α about an axis OA as in Figure 12.8. Suppose that the vector $\mathbf{x} = \overrightarrow{OP}$ making an angle β with OA moves to $\mathbf{y} = \overrightarrow{OQ}$. If PR, QR are perpendicular to OA, and QS is a line perpendicular to PR in the plane PRQ, as shown, we have

$$\overrightarrow{OQ} = \overrightarrow{OP} + \overrightarrow{PS} + \overrightarrow{SQ}.$$

Let $\mathbf{n}$ be a unit vector along OA. Show that

$$\mathbf{y} = \mathbf{x} - (1 - \cos\alpha)\{\mathbf{x} - (\mathbf{x}, \mathbf{n})\mathbf{n}\} + \sin\alpha\mathbf{N}\mathbf{x}$$
$$= \{\cos\alpha\mathbf{I} + (1 - \cos\alpha)\mathbf{n}\mathbf{n}^T + \sin\alpha\mathbf{N}\}\mathbf{x} = \mathbf{R}\mathbf{x},$$

where this defines $\mathbf{R}$, and

$$\mathbf{n} = \begin{bmatrix} n_1 \\ n_2 \\ n_3 \end{bmatrix}, \qquad \mathbf{N} = \begin{bmatrix} 0 & -n_3 & n_2 \\ n_3 & 0 & -n_1 \\ -n_2 & n_1 & 0 \end{bmatrix}.$$

Verify that $\mathbf{R}$ is orthogonal. (See also the last sentence in Ex. 12.56.)

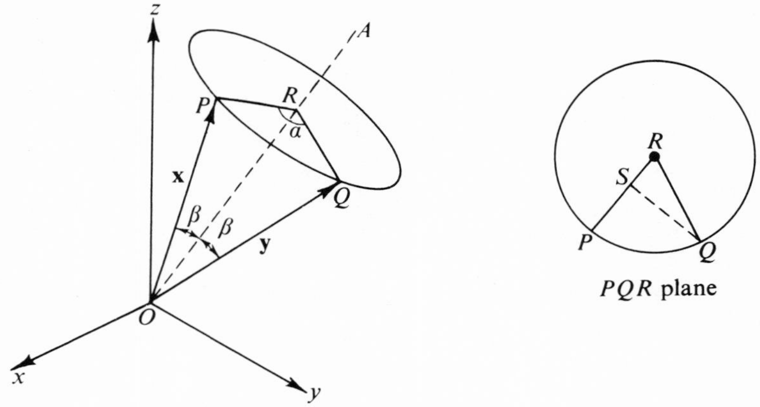

Figure 12.8 Rotation around axis OA. Vector $\mathbf{x} = \overrightarrow{OP}$ moves to $\mathbf{y} = \overrightarrow{OQ}$.

Ex. 12.52. Prove that a proper real 3×3 orthogonal matrix $\mathbf{A}$ has eigenvalues $1, e^{i\alpha}, e^{-i\alpha}$, where

$$\cos \alpha = \tfrac{1}{2}(a_{11} + a_{22} + a_{33} - 1).$$

Prove that the eigenvector corresponding to the eigenvalue 1 has components

$$n_1 : n_2 : n_3 = a_{23} + a_{32} : a_{31} + a_{13} : a_{12} + a_{21}.$$

Ex. 12.53. Prove that if

$$\mathbf{N} = \begin{bmatrix} 0 & -n_3 & n_2 \\ n_3 & 0 & -n_1 \\ -n_2 & n_1 & 0 \end{bmatrix},$$

where $n_1^2 + n_2^2 + n_3^2 = 1$, then, setting $\mathbf{n} = [n_1, n_2, n_3]^T$,

$$e^{\alpha\mathbf{N}} = \cos \alpha\mathbf{I} + (1 - \cos \alpha)\mathbf{n}\mathbf{n}^T + \sin \alpha\mathbf{N}.$$

Prove conversely that any 3×3 real orthogonal matrix $\mathbf{A}$ can be written in this form, where α and the n_i are the same as in Ex. 12.52.

Ex. 12.54. Prove that any 3×3 real orthogonal matrix represents a rotation around the axis $\mathbf{n} = [n_1, n_2, n_3]^T$ by an angle α, where the notation is as in Ex. 12.52.

Ex. 12.55. Suppose that x_1, x_2, x_3 and x_1', x_2', x_3' are two sets of axes with a common origin, as in Figure 12.9. Let l_{ij} denote the cosine of the angle between the x_i'-and x_j-axes. Let any vector $\overrightarrow{OP}$ have coordinates $\mathbf{x}$ and $\mathbf{x}'$ with respect to the two sets of axes. Prove that

$$\mathbf{x}' = \mathbf{L}\mathbf{x}, \tag{12.110}$$

where $\mathbf{L} = [l_{ij}]$ is orthogonal.

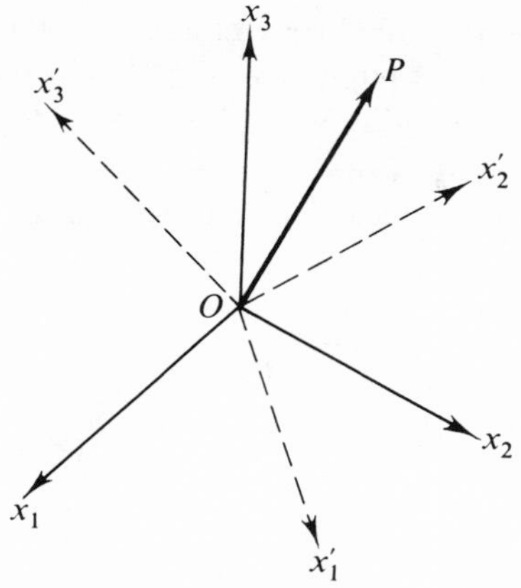

Figure 12.9 Two sets of axes.

Ex. 12.56. Suppose that, given a set of coordinate axes in space, a physical quantity can be specified by determining (by measurement or otherwise) its components along the three axes. Thus we might consider the components of a force or a velocity. Let $\mathbf{u}$ and $\mathbf{u}'$ denote 3×1 column vectors consisting of components for the same physical quantity specified with respect to two different sets of coordinate axes with a common origin (Figure 12.9). We say that the quantity represented by $\mathbf{u}$ and $\mathbf{u}'$ is a *physical vector* or *Cartesian tensor of order one* if

$$\mathbf{u}' = \mathbf{L}\mathbf{u},$$

where $\mathbf{L}$ is the orthogonal matrix defined in the last exercise. On taking the first and second derivatives of (12.110) with respect to time we see immediately, since $\mathbf{L}$ is a constant vector, that velocity and acceleration are physical vectors. Force is also a physical vector, since force equals mass times acceleration.

A *Cartesian tensor of order two* is defined as a 3×3 matrix $\mathbf{A}$ associated with a set of coordinate axes in space, that obeys the transformation law

$$\mathbf{A}' = \mathbf{L}\mathbf{A}\mathbf{L}^T,$$

where $\mathbf{A}$, $\mathbf{A}'$ are the matrices representing the tensor referred to the two coordinate systems, with the same $\mathbf{L}$ as before. Prove that, if $\mathbf{u}$ is a tensor of order one,

$$\mathbf{U} = \begin{bmatrix} 0 & -u_3 & u_2 \\ u_3 & 0 & -u_1 \\ -u_2 & u_1 & 0 \end{bmatrix}$$

is a tensor of order two. Conversely, if $\mathbf{U}$ is a tensor of order two, show that the corresponding $\mathbf{u}$ is a tensor of order one. Prove that if $\mathbf{A}$, $\mathbf{v}$ are tensors of order two and one, $\mathbf{A}\mathbf{v}$ is a tensor of order one. If $\mathbf{u}$, $\mathbf{v}$ are tensors of order one, then

$$\mathbf{w} = \begin{bmatrix} u_2v_3 - u_3v_2 \\ u_3v_1 - u_1v_3 \\ u_1v_2 - u_2v_1 \end{bmatrix}$$

is a tensor of order one. (In vector language, this last statement says that the vector product is a physical vector.) Verify that the matrix **R** introduced at the end of Ex. 12.51 is a Cartesian tensor of order two.

Ex. 12.57. The moments of inertia of a system of particles of masses m_i at positions (x_i, y_i, z_i) are defined by the matrix

$$\mathbf{J} = \sum m_i \begin{bmatrix} y_i^2 + z_i^2 & -x_iy_i & -z_ix_i \\ -x_iy_i & z_i^2 + x_i^2 & -y_iz_i \\ -z_ix_i & -y_iz_i & x_i^2 + y_i^2 \end{bmatrix}.$$

Show that

$$\mathbf{J} = -\sum m_i\mathbf{R}_i^2,$$

where

$$\mathbf{R}_i = \begin{bmatrix} 0 & -z_i & y_i \\ z_i & 0 & -x_i \\ -y_i & x_i & 0 \end{bmatrix}.$$

Deduce that **J** is a Cartesian tensor of order two. If the body is continuous, the sums are replaced by integrals. Prove that the diagonal elements of the inertia tensor for a cube are all equal, and the off-diagonal elements are all zero, irrespective of the orientation of the coordinate axes with respect to the cube. (This is a good example of the way in which a result that would be difficult to find directly is almost obvious if we use more powerful tools.)

Ex. 12.58. Write an essay on applications of matrix versions of the theory of Cartesian tensors. Possible references are Braae [36], Heading [41], and

(a) R. Aris, *Vectors, Tensors, and the Basic Equations of Fluid Mechanics*, Prentice-Hall (1962).

(b) G. Temple, *Cartesian Tensors*, Methuen (1960).

Ex. 12.59. Write an essay on applications of quadratic forms in one of the following:

(a) Mechanics and/or small vibrations (see, for instance, Braae [36], Goldstein [77], Heading [41]).

(b) Optimization (see reference in bibliographical notes, in connection with Ex. 12.6, to an article by G. E. P. Box).

(c) Regression analysis and statistics (see Graybill [78], Rao [95], and Searle [47]).

13 Norms and Error Estimates

13.1 Vector Norms

In Chapter 9, equation (9.33), we defined the *length* or *norm* of an $n \times 1$ column vector $\|\mathbf{x}\|$ to be

$$\|\mathbf{x}\| = (|x_1|^2 + |x_2|^2 + \ldots + |x_n|^2)^{1/2}.$$

Thus $\|\mathbf{x}\|$ is a single number that gives an overall estimate of the size of the elements in $\mathbf{x}$. If $\|\mathbf{x}\|$ is large, at least one of the elements in $\mathbf{x}$ is large, and vice versa. There are various other numbers that have this property. In this chapter, we shall apply the word "norm" to any number associated with $\mathbf{x}$ that has certain of the useful properties of the length of a physical vector. More precisely, we widen the use of the word norm to include *any* number $\|\mathbf{x}\|$ associated with $\mathbf{x}$ that has the following properties.

DEFINITION **13.1.** The *vector norm* of $\mathbf{x}$ is a nonnegative number denoted by $\|\mathbf{x}\|$, associated with $\mathbf{x}$, satisfying:

(a) $\|\mathbf{x}\| > 0$ for $\mathbf{x} \neq \mathbf{0}$, $\|\mathbf{x}\| = 0$ implies $\mathbf{x} = \mathbf{0}$.

(b) $\|k\mathbf{x}\| = |k|\ \|\mathbf{x}\|$ for any scalar k.

(c) $\|\mathbf{x} + \mathbf{y}\| \leq \|\mathbf{x}\| + \|\mathbf{y}\|$ (the triangle inequality).

The third condition is called the triangle inequality because it is a generalization of the fact that the length of any side of a triangle is less than the sum of the lengths of the other two sides.

Anticipating Theorem 13.2, we state that each of the following quantities defines a vector norm.

$$\|\mathbf{x}\|_1 = |x_1| + |x_2| + \ldots + |x_n|, \tag{13.1}$$

$$\|\mathbf{x}\|_2 = (|x_1|^2 + |x_2|^2 + \ldots + |x_n|^2)^{1/2}, \tag{13.2}$$

$$\|\mathbf{x}\|_\infty = \max_i |x_i|. \tag{13.3}$$

We call these the 1, 2, and ∞ norms. The reason for the terminology is that these are special cases of the norm

$$\|\mathbf{x}\|_p = (|x_1|^p + |x_2|^p + \ldots + |x_n|^p)^{1/p}.$$

We first prove that $\|\mathbf{x}\|_2$ satisfies the triangle inequality. We remind the reader of the Definition 9.4 of an inner product,

$$(\mathbf{x}, \mathbf{y}) = \bar{x}_1 y_1 + \bar{x}_2 y_2 + \ldots + \bar{x}_n y_n,$$

so that $\|\mathbf{x}\|_2^2 = (\mathbf{x}, \mathbf{x})$.

THEOREM **13.1.** (i) $|(\mathbf{x}, \mathbf{y})| \leq \|\mathbf{x}\|_2 \|\mathbf{y}\|_2$ *(the Schwarz inequality).*
(ii) $\|\mathbf{x} + \mathbf{y}\|_2 \leq \|\mathbf{x}\|_2 + \|\mathbf{y}\|_2$ *(the triangle inequality).*

Proof: We have

$$\begin{aligned} 0 \leq \|\mathbf{x} + \alpha\mathbf{y}\|_2^2 &= (\mathbf{x}, \mathbf{x}) + (\mathbf{x}, \alpha\mathbf{y}) + (\alpha\mathbf{y}, \mathbf{x}) + (\alpha\mathbf{y}, \alpha\mathbf{y}) \\ &= \|\mathbf{x}\|_2^2 + \alpha(\mathbf{x}, \mathbf{y}) + \bar{\alpha}(\overline{\mathbf{x}, \mathbf{y}}) + \bar{\alpha}\alpha \, \|\mathbf{y}\|_2^2. \end{aligned} \tag{13.4}$$

Schwarz's inequality is identically true if $(\mathbf{x}, \mathbf{y}) = 0$. When $(\mathbf{x}, \mathbf{y}) \neq 0$, we choose $\alpha = - \|\mathbf{x}\|_2^2/(\mathbf{x}, \mathbf{y})$. Equation (13.4) then gives

$$-\|\mathbf{x}\|_2^2 + \frac{\|\mathbf{x}\|_2^4 \, \|\mathbf{y}\|_2^2}{|(\mathbf{x}, \mathbf{y})|^2} \geq 0, \tag{13.5}$$

from which the Schwarz inequality follows. To prove the triangle inequality, we have, using the fact that the real part of a complex number has a magnitude less than or equal to its modulus,

$$\begin{aligned} \|\mathbf{x} + \mathbf{y}\|_2^2 &= \|\mathbf{x}\|_2^2 + (\mathbf{x}, \mathbf{y}) + (\mathbf{y}, \mathbf{x}) + \|\mathbf{y}\|_2^2 \\ &= \|\mathbf{x}\|_2^2 + 2 \operatorname{Re} (\mathbf{x}, \mathbf{y}) + \|\mathbf{y}\|_2^2 \\ &\leq \|\mathbf{x}\|_2^2 + 2 \, |(\mathbf{x}, \mathbf{y})| + \|\mathbf{y}\|_2^2 \\ &\leq \|\mathbf{x}\|_2^2 + 2 \, \|\mathbf{x}\|_2 \, \|\mathbf{y}\|_2 + \|\mathbf{y}\|_2^2 \\ &= (\|\mathbf{x}\|_2 + \|\mathbf{y}\|_2)^2. \end{aligned} \tag{13.6}$$

THEOREM **13.2.** *The numbers* $\|\mathbf{x}\|_1$, $\|\mathbf{x}\|_2$, $\|\mathbf{x}\|_\infty$ *defined by* (13.1)–(13.3) *are norms, i.e., they possess the properties required by Definition* 13.1.

Proof: The proof is left to the reader, with the hint that we require the preliminary result that if a and b are complex numbers, then

$$|a + b| \leq |a| + |b|.$$

We note that

$$\begin{aligned} \|\mathbf{x}\|_\infty &\leq \|\mathbf{x}\|_1 \leq n\|\mathbf{x}\|_\infty \\ \|\mathbf{x}\|_\infty &\leq \|\mathbf{x}\|_2 \leq \sqrt{n}\|\mathbf{x}\|_\infty. \end{aligned} \tag{13.7}$$

From the Schwarz inequality applied to vectors with elements $|x_i|$ and 1 respectively, we see that $\|\mathbf{x}\|_1 \leq \sqrt{n}\,\|\mathbf{x}\|_2$. Also, by inspection, $\|\mathbf{x}\|_2^2 \leq \|\mathbf{x}\|_1^2$. Hence

$$\frac{1}{\sqrt{n}}\,\|\mathbf{x}\|_2 \leq \|\mathbf{x}\|_\infty \leq \|\mathbf{x}\|_2, \qquad \|\mathbf{x}\|_2 \leq \|\mathbf{x}\|_1 \leq \sqrt{n}\,\|\mathbf{x}\|_2,$$

$$\frac{1}{n}\,\|\mathbf{x}\|_1 \leq \|\mathbf{x}\|_\infty \leq \|\mathbf{x}\|_1, \qquad \frac{1}{\sqrt{n}}\,\|\mathbf{x}\|_1 \leq \|\mathbf{x}\|_2 \leq \|\mathbf{x}\|_1.$$

In a sense, therefore, the 1, 2, and ∞ norms are equivalent.

Ex. 13.1. Prove Theorem 13.2.

Ex. 13.2. Prove that $\big|\,\|\mathbf{x}\| - \|\mathbf{y}\|\,\big| \leq \|\mathbf{x} - \mathbf{y}\|$.

13.2 Matrix Norms

We could try to define norms for matrices in exactly the same way as for vectors. For instance, we might define a norm for a matrix $\mathbf{A} = [a_{ij}]$ to be the maximum $|a_{ij}|$ over all i, j. However, matrices usually occur in conjunction with vectors and it is convenient to define matrix norms $\|\mathbf{A}\|$ in such a way that they are *compatible* with a vector norm in the sense that

$$\|\mathbf{A}\mathbf{x}\| \leq \|\mathbf{A}\|\,\|\mathbf{x}\|. \tag{13.8}$$

It is also desirable that a matrix norm possess the property

$$\|\mathbf{A}\mathbf{B}\| \leq \|\mathbf{A}\|\,\|\mathbf{B}\|. \tag{13.9}$$

DEFINITION **13.2.** The *matrix norm* of a square matrix $\mathbf{A}$ is a nonnegative number denoted by $\|\mathbf{A}\|$, associated with $\mathbf{A}$, such that:

(a) $\|\mathbf{A}\| > 0$ for $\mathbf{A} \neq \mathbf{0}$, $\|\mathbf{A}\| = 0$ implies $\mathbf{A} = \mathbf{0}$.
(b) $\|k\mathbf{A}\| = |k|\,\|\mathbf{A}\|$ for any scalar k.
(c) $\|\mathbf{A} + \mathbf{B}\| \leq \|\mathbf{A}\| + \|\mathbf{B}\|$.
(d) $\|\mathbf{A}\mathbf{B}\| \leq \|\mathbf{A}\|\,\|\mathbf{B}\|$.

A matrix norm is said to be *compatible* with a vector norm $\|\mathbf{x}\|$ if

(e) $\|\mathbf{A}\mathbf{x}\| \leq \|\mathbf{A}\|\,\|\mathbf{x}\|$.

(See also the note following Definition 13.3.)

We now show how to derive, from a given vector norm, a matrix norm that is compatible with the vector norm. Since we must have $\|\mathbf{A}\mathbf{x}\| \leq \|\mathbf{A}\|\,\|\mathbf{x}\|$, this suggests that we define

$$\|\mathbf{A}\| = \sup_{\mathbf{x}\neq\mathbf{0}} \frac{\|\mathbf{A}\mathbf{x}\|}{\|\mathbf{x}\|}, \tag{13.10}$$

where sup denotes the *least upper bound* for all $\mathbf{x} \neq \mathbf{0}$. If we introduce $\mathbf{z} = \mathbf{x}/\|\mathbf{x}\|$, we see that $\|\mathbf{z}\| = 1$ and $\|\mathbf{Ax}\|/\|\mathbf{x}\| = \|\mathbf{Az}\|$, so that (13.10) is equivalent to

$$\|\mathbf{A}\| = \sup_{\|\mathbf{z}\|=1} \|\mathbf{Az}\|. \tag{13.11}$$

We shall show in the course of the proof of Theorem 13.4 that a $\mathbf{z}$ exists such that the upper limit is attained for each of the 1, 2, and ∞ vector norms. (It is not difficult to prove that such a $\mathbf{z}$ must exist for *any* vector norm, but this would be an unnecessary distraction from our main objective which is to find the matrix norms compatible with the 1, 2, ∞ vector norms.) Since we make the hypothesis in the following theorem that the maximum is attained, we replace "sup" in (13.11) by "max" in the statement of the theorem.

THEOREM **13.3.** *If a vector* $\mathbf{z}$ *exists such that the maximum is attained in the formula*

$$\|\mathbf{A}\| = \max_{\|\mathbf{z}\|=1} \|\mathbf{Az}\|,$$

then $\|\mathbf{A}\|$ *is a matrix norm.*

Proof: We have to show that $\|\mathbf{A}\|$ satisfies conditions (a)–(d) in Definition 13.2.

(a) If $\mathbf{A} \neq \mathbf{0}$, then a vector $\mathbf{z}$ with $\|\mathbf{z}\| = 1$ can always be found such that $\mathbf{Az} \neq \mathbf{0}$, so that $\|\mathbf{A}\| > 0$. If $\|\mathbf{A}\| = 0$, this implies that $\|\mathbf{Az}\| = 0$ for all $\mathbf{z}$ such that $\|\mathbf{z}\| = 1$. If we choose $\mathbf{z}$ to be the unit vectors, in turn, the corresponding $\mathbf{Az}$ are the columns of $\mathbf{A}$, so that the norms of the columns of $\mathbf{A}$ are zero. Hence, the columns of $\mathbf{A}$ are zero, i.e., $\mathbf{A} = \mathbf{0}$.

(b) We have

$$\|c\mathbf{A}\| = \max_{\|\mathbf{z}\|=1} \|c\mathbf{Az}\| = |c| \max_{\|\mathbf{z}\|=1} \|\mathbf{Az}\| = |c|\,\|\mathbf{A}\|.$$

(c) Let $\mathbf{z}_0$ be a vector such that $\|(\mathbf{A}+\mathbf{B})\mathbf{z}_0\| = \|\mathbf{A}+\mathbf{B}\|$, $\|\mathbf{z}_0\| = 1$. (The point of the hypothesis in the theorem is that such a $\mathbf{z}_0$ exists.) Then

$$\begin{aligned}\|\mathbf{A}+\mathbf{B}\| &= \|(\mathbf{A}+\mathbf{B})\mathbf{z}_0\| \le \|\mathbf{Az}_0\| + \|\mathbf{Bz}_0\| \\ &\le \|\mathbf{A}\|\,\|\mathbf{z}_0\| + \|\mathbf{B}\|\,\|\mathbf{z}_0\| = \|\mathbf{A}\| + \|\mathbf{B}\|.\end{aligned}$$

(d) Let $\mathbf{z}_0$ be a vector such that $\|\mathbf{ABz}_0\| = \|\mathbf{AB}\|$, $\|\mathbf{z}_0\| = 1$. Then

$$\begin{aligned}\|\mathbf{AB}\| &= \|\mathbf{ABz}_0\| = \|\mathbf{A}(\mathbf{Bz}_0)\| \le \|\mathbf{A}\|\,\|\mathbf{Bz}_0\| \\ &\le \|\mathbf{A}\|\,\|\mathbf{B}\|\,\|\mathbf{z}_0\| = \|\mathbf{A}\|\,\|\mathbf{B}\|.\end{aligned}$$

DEFINITION **13.3.** A matrix norm constructed by means of (13.11) is said to be the *natural norm* associated with the vector norm. We also say that the matrix norm is *subordinate to*, or *induced by*, the vector norm.

From now on we assume that all the matrix norms we use are natural norms.

THEOREM **13.4.** *The natural norms associated with the* 1, 2, *and* ∞ *vector norms are*

$$\|\mathbf{A}\|_1 = \max_j \sum_{i=1}^{n} |a_{ij}| \quad (\textit{maximum absolute column sum}), \tag{13.12}$$

$$\|\mathbf{A}\|_2 = \{\textit{maximum eigenvalue of } \mathbf{A}^H\mathbf{A}\}^{1/2}, \tag{13.13}$$

$$\|\mathbf{A}\|_\infty = \max_i \sum_{j=1}^{n} |a_{ij}| \quad (\textit{maximum absolute row sum}). \tag{13.14}$$

Proof: We first consider the 1 norm. If $\|\mathbf{z}\|_1 = 1$, we have

$$\sum_{j=1}^{n} |z_j| = 1.$$

Also,

$$\begin{aligned} \|\mathbf{A}\mathbf{z}\|_1 &= \sum_{i=1}^{n} \left| \sum_{j=1}^{n} a_{ij} z_j \right| \le \sum_{i=1}^{n} \sum_{j=1}^{n} |a_{ij}|\,|z_j| = \sum_{j=1}^{n} |z_j| \sum_{i=1}^{n} |a_{ij}| \\ &\le \left(\max_j \sum_{i=1}^{n} |a_{ij}|\right)\left(\sum_{j=1}^{n} |z_j|\right) = \max_j \sum_{i=1}^{n} |a_{ij}|. \end{aligned} \tag{13.15}$$

Hence,

$$\|\mathbf{A}\|_1 = \max_{\|\mathbf{z}\|=1} \|\mathbf{A}\mathbf{z}\|_1 \le \max_j \sum_{i=1}^{n} |a_{ij}|. \tag{13.16}$$

Suppose that the value of j for which the maximum is attained is $j = k$. Choose $\mathbf{z}$ so that

$$z_i = 1 (i = k), \qquad 0 (i \neq k).$$

For this $\mathbf{z}$,

$$\|\mathbf{A}\mathbf{z}\|_1 = \sum_{i=1}^{n} |a_{ik}|.$$

Hence, for this $\mathbf{z}$, equality is attained in (13.16). This means that the hypothesis of Theorem 13.3 is satisfied and (13.12) gives a natural 1-matrix-norm. We next consider the ∞ norm. If $\|\mathbf{z}\|_\infty = 1$, this means that

$$\max_j |z_j| = 1.$$

In this case,

$$\|\mathbf{A}\mathbf{z}\|_\infty = \max_i \left| \sum_{j=1}^{n} a_{ij} z_j \right| \le \max_i \sum_{j=1}^{n} |a_{ij}|\,|z_j| \le \max_i \sum_{j=1}^{n} |a_{ij}|.$$

Hence,

$$\|\mathbf{A}\|_\infty = \max_{\|\mathbf{z}\|=1} \|\mathbf{A}\mathbf{z}\|_\infty \le \max_i \sum_{j=1}^{n} |a_{ij}|. \tag{13.17}$$

Suppose that the value of i that gives the maximum sum on the right is $i = k$. Construct a vector $\mathbf{z}$ with

$$z_j = +1 \quad \text{if} \quad a_{kj} \ge 0, \qquad z_j = -1 \quad \text{if} \quad a_{kj} < 0.$$

For this $\mathbf{z}$,

$$\|\mathbf{Az}\|_\infty = \sum_{j=1}^{n} |a_{kj}|.$$

Hence, equality is attained in (13.14) for this $\mathbf{z}$, the hypothesis in Theorem 13.3 is satisfied, and (13.14) gives a natural ∞-matrix-norm. Finally, consider the 2 norm. If $\|\mathbf{z}\|_2 = 1$, this means, using inner-product notation,

$$(\mathbf{z}, \mathbf{z}) = 1.$$

We have [remembering (9.34)]

$$\|\mathbf{Az}\|_2 = (\mathbf{Az}, \mathbf{Az})^{1/2} = (\mathbf{z}, \mathbf{A}^H\mathbf{Az})^{1/2} \tag{13.18}$$

or

$$\|\mathbf{A}\|_2^2 = \max_{(\mathbf{z},\mathbf{z})=1} (\mathbf{z}, \mathbf{A}^H\mathbf{Az}).$$

Rayleigh's principle (Section 12.7) states that this maximum value is the largest eigenvalue of $\mathbf{A}^H\mathbf{A}$ and that a $\mathbf{z}$ exists such that the maximum is attained. (This is, in fact, the eigenvector of $\mathbf{A}^H\mathbf{A}$ corresponding to the maximum eigenvalue.) Hence, the hypothesis in Theorem 13.3 is satisfied, and (13.13) gives a natural 2-matrix-norm.

$\|\mathbf{A}\|_2$ is sometimes called the *spectral norm* of $\mathbf{A}$ and this should be distinguished from the *spectral radius* of $\mathbf{A}$, $\rho(\mathbf{A})$, which is the maximum value of $|\lambda_i|$, where the λ_i are the eigenvalues of $\mathbf{A}$. (See Section 9.7, Definition 9.10.) As an example, consider, for real k,

$$\mathbf{A} = \begin{bmatrix} 1 & k \\ 0 & 1 \end{bmatrix}, \qquad \mathbf{A}^H\mathbf{A} = \begin{bmatrix} 1 & k \\ k & 1 + k^2 \end{bmatrix}. \tag{13.19}$$

It is easy to show that

$$\rho(\mathbf{A}) = 1, \qquad \|\mathbf{A}\|_2 = \{\tfrac{1}{2}k^2 + 1 + \tfrac{1}{2}k(k^2 + 4)^{1/2}\}^{1/2}. \tag{13.20}$$

For large k, the 2-matrix-norm is large even though the spectral radius is unity.

THEOREM **13.5.** *For any natural norm* $\|\mathbf{A}\|$,

$$\rho(\mathbf{A}) \le \|\mathbf{A}\|.$$

Proof: Let $\mathbf{x}_i$ be any normalized eigenvector corresponding to an eigenvalue λ_i

$$\|\mathbf{A}\| = \max_{\|\mathbf{z}\|=1} \|\mathbf{Az}\| \ge \|\mathbf{Ax}_i\| = \|\lambda_i\mathbf{x}_i\| = |\lambda_i|\,\|\mathbf{x}_i\| = |\lambda_i|.$$

This holds for any eigenvalue, so the theorem follows.

This is a very useful theorem since it holds for *any* natural norm and the 1 and ∞ norms are easily calculated. This means that we have an easily calculable bound for the spectral radius. Thus, in the example (13.19) we have

$$\rho(\mathbf{A}) \le \|\mathbf{A}\|_1 = \|\mathbf{A}\|_\infty = 1 + |k|. \tag{13.21}$$

On the other hand, this is not a very useful result if $|k|$ is large, since then we have a very crude estimate of the true spectral radius $\rho(\mathbf{A}) = 1$. This illustrates one of the characteristic features of analysis using norms. We obtain rigorous bounds but the results may sometimes not be very useful if we are looking for *realistic* bounds for any particular example.

Ex. 13.3. Prove that

$$\|\mathbf{A}\|_2^2 \leq \|\mathbf{A}\|_1 \, \|\mathbf{A}\|_\infty.$$

Ex. 13.4. Prove that for a diagonal matrix the 1, 2, and ∞ norms are the same.

Ex. 13.5. Verify the expression for $\|\mathbf{A}\|_2$ in (13.20).

Ex. 13.6. Show that for any natural norm $\|\mathbf{I}\| = 1$.

13.3 Computable Error Bounds for Linear Systems

The following theorem is basic, when using norms to obtain error bounds for linear systems. The main point of the theorem is that, if a simple criterion is satisfied, the existence of the inverse of a certain matrix is guaranteed.

THEOREM **13.6.** *If* $\|\mathbf{S}\| < 1$ *where the norm is such that* $\|\mathbf{I}\| = 1$, *then* $\mathbf{I} + \mathbf{S}$ *is nonsingular and*

$$\frac{1}{1 + \|\mathbf{S}\|} \leq \|(\mathbf{I} + \mathbf{S})^{-1}\| \leq \frac{1}{1 - \|\mathbf{S}\|}. \tag{13.22}$$

Proof: If the eigenvalues of $\mathbf{S}$ are λ_i, then, from Theorem 13.5, $|\lambda_i| < 1$. The eigenvalues of $\mathbf{I} + \mathbf{S}$ are $1 + \lambda_i$ and therefore the eigenvalues of $\mathbf{I} + \mathbf{S}$ are nonzero. Hence, $\mathbf{I} + \mathbf{S}$ is nonsingular. We have

$$(\mathbf{I} + \mathbf{S})(\mathbf{I} + \mathbf{S})^{-1} = \mathbf{I}. \tag{13.23}$$

Since we are assuming that $\|\mathbf{I}\| = 1$, this gives

$$1 \leq \|\mathbf{I} + \mathbf{S}\| \, \|(\mathbf{I} + \mathbf{S})^{-1}\| \leq (1 + \|\mathbf{S}\|) \, \|(\mathbf{I} + \mathbf{S})^{-1}\|,$$

which is the left-hand inequality in (13.22). A rearrangement of (13.23) gives

$$(\mathbf{I} + \mathbf{S})^{-1} = \mathbf{I} - \mathbf{S}(\mathbf{I} + \mathbf{S})^{-1}, \tag{13.24}$$

which yields

$$\|(\mathbf{I} + \mathbf{S})^{-1}\| \leq 1 + \|\mathbf{S}(\mathbf{I} + \mathbf{S})^{-1}\| \leq 1 + \|\mathbf{S}\| \, \|(\mathbf{I} + \mathbf{S})^{-1}\|,$$

which is the right-hand inequality in (13.22).

If we have computed an estimate $\hat{\mathbf{x}}$ for the exact solution $\mathbf{x}$ of the system $\mathbf{Ax} = \mathbf{b}$, it is natural to ask how we can check the accuracy of $\hat{\mathbf{x}}$. We have already pointed out in Section 8.7 that the residual $\mathbf{r} = \mathbf{b} - \mathbf{A}\hat{\mathbf{x}}$ tells us nothing about the accuracy of $\hat{\mathbf{x}}$ unless we also know an estimate for $\mathbf{A}^{-1}$. We give a brief discussion of some relevant error estimates.

Let $\mathbf{C}$ be an approximate inverse of $\mathbf{A}$ and define the residual matrix by either of the following.

$$\mathbf{R} = \mathbf{I} - \mathbf{CA} \quad \text{or} \quad \mathbf{R} = \mathbf{I} - \mathbf{AC}. \tag{13.25}$$

THEOREM 13.7. *If* $\|\mathbf{R}\| < 1$, *then:*

(i) $\mathbf{A}$ *and* $\mathbf{C}$ *are nonsingular.*

(ii) $\|\mathbf{A}^{-1}\| \leq \|\mathbf{C}\|/(1 - \|\mathbf{R}\|)$. (13.26)

(iii) $\|\mathbf{C} - \mathbf{A}^{-1}\| \leq \|\mathbf{C}\| \, \|\mathbf{R}\|/(1 - \|\mathbf{R}\|)$. (13.27)

Proof: Consider the case when $\mathbf{R} = \mathbf{I} - \mathbf{AC}$. (The situation when $\mathbf{R} = \mathbf{I} - \mathbf{CA}$ can be dealt with similarly.)

$$\mathbf{AC} = \mathbf{I} - \mathbf{R}. \tag{13.28}$$

Using Theorem 13.6, since $\|\mathbf{R}\| < 1$, $\mathbf{I} - \mathbf{R}$ and hence $\mathbf{AC}$ is nonsingular. This means that $\mathbf{A}$ and $\mathbf{C}$ are each nonsingular, which is (i). Rewrite (13.28) in the form

$$\mathbf{A}^{-1} = \mathbf{C}(\mathbf{I} - \mathbf{R})^{-1}.$$

Part (ii) follows directly on taking norms and using (13.22), Theorem 13.6. Multiplication of (13.28) by $\mathbf{A}^{-1}$ gives

$$\mathbf{C} - \mathbf{A}^{-1} = -\mathbf{A}^{-1}\mathbf{R}.$$

Taking norms,

$$\|\mathbf{C} - \mathbf{A}^{-1}\| \leq \|\mathbf{A}^{-1}\| \, \|\mathbf{R}\|.$$

Part (iii) follows on using part (ii).

Note that the bounds on the right of (13.26), (13.27) are computable.

Part (i) of this theorem is important if we are not sure whether $\mathbf{A}$ is singular or not. If $\mathbf{A}$ is known exactly, and we can find an approximate inverse $\mathbf{C}$ such that either $\|\mathbf{I} - \mathbf{AC}\|$ or $\|\mathbf{I} - \mathbf{CA}\|$ is less than unity, this guarantees that $\mathbf{A}$ is nonsingular. Of course, this may not be directly relevant if we are considering the more subtle situation where $\mathbf{A}$ is "nearly singular" (Section 8.4). The inverse of $\mathbf{A}$ can exist and yet be meaningless.

THEOREM 13.8. *If* $\hat{\mathbf{x}}$ *is an approximate solution of* $\mathbf{Ax} = \mathbf{b}$ *and* $\mathbf{r} = \mathbf{b} - \mathbf{A}\hat{\mathbf{x}}$, *then, if* $\mathbf{C}$ *is an approximate inverse of* $\mathbf{A}$ *satisfying either* $\|\mathbf{R}\| = \|\mathbf{I} - \mathbf{AC}\| < 1$ *or* $\|\mathbf{R}\| = \|\mathbf{I} - \mathbf{CA}\| < 1$, *a solution* $\mathbf{x}$ *of* $\mathbf{Ax} = \mathbf{b}$ *exists, and*

$$\|\mathbf{x} - \hat{\mathbf{x}}\| \leq \frac{\|\mathbf{r}\| \, \|\mathbf{C}\|}{1 - \|\mathbf{R}\|}. \tag{13.29}$$

Proof: Since $\mathbf{Ax} = \mathbf{b}$ and $\mathbf{A\hat{x}} = \mathbf{b} - \mathbf{r}$, we have $\mathbf{A}(\mathbf{x} - \mathbf{\hat{x}}) = \mathbf{r}$. From Theorem 13.7(i), $\mathbf{A}$ is nonsingular, so that

$$\mathbf{x} - \mathbf{\hat{x}} = \mathbf{A}^{-1}\mathbf{r}.$$

Taking norms,

$$\|\mathbf{x} - \mathbf{\hat{x}}\| \le \|\mathbf{A}^{-1}\|\ \|\mathbf{r}\|$$

and (13.29) follows from Theorem 13.7(ii).

Ex. 13.7. Prove that if a matrix is strictly row-diagonally-dominant, i.e.,

$$\sum_{j=1}^{n}{}' |a_{ij}| < |a_{ii}|, \qquad i = 1, \ldots, n,$$

where the prime indicates that the term $i = j$ in the sum is omitted, then the matrix is nonsingular.

Ex. 13.8. Apply (13.26), (13.27) to the matrices $\mathbf{A}$, $\mathbf{C}$ given in (8.82), using (8.83), to deduce that $\|\mathbf{A}^{-1}\|_\infty < 212$, $\|\mathbf{C} - \mathbf{A}^{-1}\|_\infty < 22$. Verify that these results are correct by computing the exact $\mathbf{A}^{-1}$.

Ex. 13.9. If $x_1 + x_2 = 2$, $x_1 + 0.99x_2 = 1.99$, use (13.29), with $\mathbf{C}$ given by (8.82), to deduce the following bounds for the errors in the corresponding approximate solutions.

(a) If $\hat{x}_1 = 2$, $\hat{x}_2 = 0$, then $|\mathbf{x} - \mathbf{\hat{x}}\|_\infty \le 2.2$.
(b) If $\hat{x}_1 = \hat{x}_2 = 1.1$, then $\|\mathbf{x} - \mathbf{\hat{x}}\|_\infty \le 43$.

[The exact value of $\|\mathbf{x} - \mathbf{\hat{x}}\|_\infty$ is 2 in (a) and 0.2 in (b). The point of this example is that (13.29) gives a rigorous *bound* but *not* an *estimate.* It is *not* true that the smaller the bound, the better the answer.]

13.4 Norms and the Condition of Linear Equations

We recall from Chapter 8 that a set of simultaneous linear equations is said to be ill-conditioned if "small" changes in the coefficients produce "large" changes in the solution. We can use norms to produce a *condition number* which, under some circumstances, can serve as a measure of condition. Our main result is the following.

THEOREM **13.9.** *Consider the equations* $\mathbf{Ax} = \mathbf{b}$. *Suppose that changes from* $\mathbf{A}$ *to* $\mathbf{A} + \delta\mathbf{A}$ *and* $\mathbf{b}$ *to* $\mathbf{b} + \delta\mathbf{b}$, *where* $\|\delta\mathbf{A}\|\ \|\mathbf{A}^{-1}\| < 1$, *produce a change in the solution from* $\mathbf{x}$ *to* $\mathbf{x} + \delta\mathbf{x}$. *Then*

$$\frac{\|\delta\mathbf{x}\|}{\|\mathbf{x}\|} \le CM(\mathbf{A})\left\{\frac{\|\delta\mathbf{b}\|}{\|\mathbf{b}\|} + \frac{\|\delta\mathbf{A}\|}{\|\mathbf{A}\|}\right\}, \tag{13.30}$$

where

$$M(\mathbf{A}) = \|\mathbf{A}\|\ \|\mathbf{A}^{-1}\|, \tag{13.31}$$

$$C = (1 - \|\delta\mathbf{A}\|\ \|\mathbf{A}^{-1}\|)^{-1}. \tag{13.32}$$

Proof: We have

$$(\mathbf{A} + \delta\mathbf{A})(\mathbf{x} + \delta\mathbf{x}) = \mathbf{b} + \delta\mathbf{b},$$

that is,

$$(\mathbf{A} + \delta\mathbf{A})\,\delta\mathbf{x} = \delta\mathbf{b} - \delta\mathbf{A}\,\mathbf{x}$$

or

$$\delta\mathbf{x} = \mathbf{A}^{-1}(\mathbf{I} + \mathbf{A}^{-1}\delta\mathbf{A})^{-1}(\delta\mathbf{b} - \delta\mathbf{A}\,\mathbf{x}).$$

Hence,

$$\begin{aligned}\|\delta\mathbf{x}\| &\le \|\mathbf{A}^{-1}\|\ \|\mathbf{I} + \mathbf{A}^{-1}\delta\mathbf{A}\|(\|\delta\mathbf{b}\| + \|\delta\mathbf{A}\|\ \|\mathbf{x}\|)\\ &\le C\|\mathbf{A}^{-1}\|(\|\delta\mathbf{b}\| + \|\delta\mathbf{A}\|\ \|\mathbf{x}\|),\end{aligned}$$

where we have used the right-hand inequality in (13.22), which leads to the value of C given in (13.32). Hence,

$$\frac{\|\delta\mathbf{x}\|}{\|\mathbf{x}\|} \le C\ \|\mathbf{A}\|\ \|\mathbf{A}^{-1}\| \left\{\frac{\|\delta\mathbf{b}\|}{\|\mathbf{A}\|\ \|\mathbf{x}\|} + \frac{\|\delta\mathbf{A}\|}{\|\mathbf{A}\|}\right\}. \tag{13.33}$$

Since $\mathbf{Ax} = \mathbf{b}$, we have $\|\mathbf{A}\|\ \|\mathbf{x}\| \ge \|\mathbf{b}\|$ and use of this result in (13.33) leads to (13.30).

If the perturbation $\delta\mathbf{A}$ in $\mathbf{A}$ is small enough, the constant C defined in (13.32) is close to unity. Inspection of (13.30) then shows that the overall relative change $\|\delta\mathbf{x}\|/\|\mathbf{x}\|$ in the unknowns due to small changes in $\mathbf{A}$ and $\mathbf{b}$ will be small if $M(\mathbf{A}) = \|\mathbf{A}\|\ \|\mathbf{A}^{-1}\|$ is small. This means that a small $M(\mathbf{A})$ implies that the equations are well-conditioned in the sense specified in the last sentence (though we note in passing that this does *not* mean that each individual unknown is well-conditioned—see, for instance, Ex. 8.13). However, *the converse is not true;* A large $M(\mathbf{A}) = \|\mathbf{A}\|\ \|\mathbf{A}^{-1}\|$ does *not* imply that the equations are ill-conditioned. The reason for this is that (13.30) gives only an upper bound for $\|\delta\mathbf{x}\|/\|\mathbf{x}\|$, and this upper bound is not necessarily a realistic estimate.

The point can be illustrated by the matrix (13.19) considered earlier. Suppose that

$$\begin{aligned}x_1 + kx_2 &= 1\\ x_2 &= -1,\end{aligned} \tag{13.34}$$

where $k > 0$. It is easily checked by the methods of Section 8.2 that this set of equations is extremely well-conditioned with respect to relative variations of the elements on the right, for all $k > 0$. However, if we apply (13.30) with $\delta\mathbf{A} = \mathbf{0}$, we see that

$$\frac{\|\delta\mathbf{x}\|}{\|\mathbf{x}\|} \le M(\mathbf{A})\frac{\|\delta\mathbf{b}\|}{\|\mathbf{b}\|}, \tag{13.35}$$

where, for either the 1 or the ∞ norm, and $k > 0$,

$$M(\mathbf{A}) = \|\mathbf{A}\|\ \|\mathbf{A}^{-1}\| = (1 + k)^2.$$

Although $M(\mathbf{A})$ is large for large k, equations (13.34) are well-conditioned for large k. It is wrong to think that large $M(\mathbf{A})$ indicates ill-conditioning. The bound (13.35) is correct but unrealistic for large k, since the multiplying constant $M(\mathbf{A})$ is far larger than necessary.

The factor we have not mentioned so far is that the relative condition of (13.34) is independent of scaling (Theorem 8.2), but if we rescale the equations to obtain a new matrix $\mathbf{A}'$, say, the corresponding $M(\mathbf{A}')$ will not be the same as $M(\mathbf{A})$, in general. This suggests that we should scale so as to minimize $M(\mathbf{A}')$. A convenient way of doing this in the present example is to set $x_1 = \alpha x_1'$ in (13.34) and multiply the second equation by β so that

$$\mathbf{A}' = \begin{bmatrix} \alpha & k \\ 0 & \beta \end{bmatrix}, \qquad (\mathbf{A}')^{-1} = \frac{1}{\alpha\beta}\begin{bmatrix} \beta & -k \\ 0 & \alpha \end{bmatrix},$$

and, for either the 1 or ∞ norm, assuming $\alpha > 0$, $\beta > 0$,

$$M(\mathbf{A}') = \left\{\max\left(1, \frac{\alpha + k}{\beta}\right)\right\}\left\{\max\left(1, \frac{\beta + k}{\alpha}\right)\right\}. \tag{13.36}$$

We can make $M(\mathbf{A}')$ as close to 1 as we please by choosing $\alpha = \beta =$ some large number. The fact that we have been able to rescale so as to obtain a small value of $M(\mathbf{A}')$, together with the fact that the relative condition is independent of scaling, indicates that the original equations are well-conditioned.

Although we have been considering only the *condition* of the equations $\mathbf{Ax} = \mathbf{b}$, which is defined in terms of *exact* calculations, our discussion has a very important bearing on the effects of rounding error when solving $\mathbf{Ax} = \mathbf{b}$ numerically. The detailed analysis of rounding error is outside the scope of this book, but we sketched the basic idea behind "backward error analysis" in Ex. 8.25. It can be proved that, if we use complete pivoting, the rounding errors introduced by Gaussian elimination are such that the computed solution $\hat{\mathbf{x}}$ can be obtained by *exact* calculation from a set of equations $(\mathbf{A} + \delta\mathbf{A})\hat{\mathbf{x}} = \mathbf{b} + \delta\mathbf{b}$ where the relative errors

$$\frac{\|\delta\mathbf{A}\|}{\|\mathbf{A}\|}, \qquad \frac{\|\delta\mathbf{b}\|}{\|\mathbf{b}\|}$$

are *small* in some sense [see, for example, (8.97)–(8.99)]. From (13.33) this means that the relative errors in the computed solution, $\|\hat{\mathbf{x}} - \mathbf{x}\|/\|\mathbf{x}\|$ will be small if $M(\mathbf{A})$ is small. [Note that the converse is not true. Even if $M(\mathbf{A})$ is large the effects of rounding error may be small.] What the above result tells us is that if we can rescale $\mathbf{A}$ to obtain equations $\mathbf{A}'\mathbf{x}' = \mathbf{b}'$ such that $M(\mathbf{A}')$ is small, and we solve $\mathbf{A}'\mathbf{x}' = \mathbf{b}'$ by Gaussian elimination with complete pivoting, the relative error in the computed solution $\mathbf{x}'$ will be small, even though the error in the computed solution $\mathbf{x}$ of the original set $\mathbf{Ax} = \mathbf{b}$, using complete pivoting, may be large. The essential effect of scaling is that it *changes the choice of pivots* if pivoting is used. (Remember that if we are working in floating point, scaling will not affect the relative errors in the computed solution if the choice of pivots is not changed. See Theorem 8.7.) This argument indicates that *if we scale so as to minimize $M(\mathbf{A})$ then we will optimize the choice of pivots.* No direct proof linking the optimization of the choice of pivots to the scaling exists at the present stage of the subject. [An instructive example will be considered later. Neither partial nor complete pivoting will lead to a satsfactory choice of pivots for the matrix **A** given in (13.68), which has a large $M(\mathbf{A})$. The scaled form $\mathbf{A}_4$ in (13.73), which has a small $M(\mathbf{A})$, *does* lead to a satisfactory choice of pivots. See also Ex. 8.14. Note also (13.42) which is the optimally scaled form of any 2×2 matrix and is suitable for partial or complete pivoting.]

The train of thought in the last few paragraphs leads to:

DEFINITION **13.4.** The *minimum condition number* $K(\mathbf{A})$ of a matrix **A** with respect to relative changes is defined by

$$K(\mathbf{A}) = \min \|\mathbf{PAQ}\| \, \|\mathbf{Q}^{-1}\mathbf{A}^{-1}\mathbf{P}^{-1}\|, \tag{13.37}$$

where the minimum is taken over all diagonal scaling matrices **P**, **Q**.

Since $\mathbf{BB}^{-1} = \mathbf{I}$, we see that $\|\mathbf{B}\| \, \|\mathbf{B}^{-1}\| \geq 1$, so that the minimum possible value of $K(\mathbf{A})$ is unity. If $K(\mathbf{A}) = 1$, we have the best possible conditioning in the present sense. If $K(\mathbf{A})$ is comparable with unity (say 10 or 100), we say that the equations are well-conditioned. If $K(\mathbf{A})$ is much larger than unity, say 10^4 or 10^6, we say that the equations are ill-conditioned. The number $K(\mathbf{A})$ gives an *overall* condition number, compared with the individual condition numbers introduced in Section 8.2, Definition 8.1, and Theorem 8.1.

Ex. 13.10. If the diagonal elements of **P**, **Q** in (13.37) are denoted by p_i, q_i, show that, without loss of generality, one of the p_i and one of the q_i can be taken equal to unity.

Ex. 13.11. Find $K(\mathbf{A})$ for the general 2×2 matrix, for the ∞ norm.

Solution: We wish to determine $p > 0$, $q > 0$ so that $\|\mathbf{A}'\|_\infty \|(\mathbf{A}')^{-1}\|_\infty$ is as small as possible, with

$$\mathbf{A}' = \begin{bmatrix} a_{11} & qa_{12} \\ pa_{21} & pqa_{22} \end{bmatrix}, \qquad (\mathbf{A}')^{-1} = \begin{bmatrix} \alpha_{11} & \dfrac{\alpha_{12}}{p} \\ \dfrac{\alpha_{21}}{q} & \dfrac{\alpha_{22}}{pq} \end{bmatrix}, \tag{13.38}$$

where α_{ij} is the (i, j)th element of $\mathbf{A}^{-1}$. Define

$$f = |a_{11}| + q\,|a_{12}|, \qquad g = p(|a_{21}| + q\,|a_{22}|),$$

$$\xi = |\alpha_{11}| + \frac{1}{p}\,|\alpha_{12}|, \qquad \eta = \frac{1}{q}\left(|\alpha_{21}| + \frac{1}{p}\,|\alpha_{22}|\right).$$

We then have

$$M(\mathbf{A}') = \|\mathbf{A}'\|_\infty \|(\mathbf{A}')^{-1}\|_\infty = \max(f, g) \times \max(\xi, \eta) = \max(f\xi, f\eta, g\xi, g\eta).$$

We wish to find the p and q that minimize $M(\mathbf{A}')$. Suppose that $f > g$, i.e.,

$$|a_{11}| + q\,|a_{12}| \geq p(|a_{21}| + q\,|a_{22}|). \tag{13.39}$$

Then

$$M(\mathbf{A}') = (|a_{11}| + q\,|a_{12}|) \times \max\left[\left(|\alpha_{11}| + \frac{1}{p}|\alpha_{12}|\right), \frac{1}{q}\left(|\alpha_{21}| + \frac{1}{p}|\alpha_{22}|\right)\right]. \tag{13.40}$$

Inspection of this equation shows that $M(\mathbf{A}')$ can be decreased if we increase p until we have equality in (13.39). A further increase would mean that $f < g$ and (13.40) would have to be replaced by

$$M(\mathbf{A}') = (|a_{21}| + q\,|a_{22}|) \times \max\left[(p\,|\alpha_{11}| + |\alpha_{12}|), \frac{1}{q}(p\,|\alpha_{21}| + |\alpha_{22}|)\right].$$

In this case, $M(\mathbf{A}')$ is minimized when p is as *small* as possible and this again leads to equality in (13.39). A similar argument shows that $M(\mathbf{A}')$ is minimized when $\xi = \eta$. Summing up, the minimum $M(\mathbf{A}')$ is obtained when we arrange that the absolute row sums of $\mathbf{A}'$ are the same. Similarly for $(\mathbf{A}')^{-1}$,

$$|a_{11}| + q\,|a_{12}| = p(|a_{21}| + q\,|a_{22}|), \qquad |a_{11}| + p\,|a_{21}| = q(|a_{12}| + p\,|a_{22}|), \tag{13.41}$$

where in $\xi = \eta$ we have inserted explicit expressions for the α_{ij}. Subtraction yields

$$p\,|a_{21}| = q\,|a_{12}|, \qquad |a_{11}| = pq\,|a_{22}|.$$

It is left to the reader to complete the details and show that the resulting p, q can be chosen so that

$$\mathbf{A}' = a_{11}\begin{bmatrix} 1 & \alpha \\ \pm\alpha & 1 \end{bmatrix}, \tag{13.42}$$

where $\alpha = |a_{12}a_{21}/a_{11}a_{22}|^{1/2}$; we have also multiplied rows and columns by ± 1 if necessary, and the $-$ sign holds if $a_{12}a_{21}$ and $a_{11}a_{22}$ have opposite signs, otherwise it is a $+$ sign. In either case, the condition number of $\mathbf{A}$, namely $K(\mathbf{A})$, which is the minimum value of $M(\mathbf{A}')$, is given by

$$K(\mathbf{A}) = \frac{(|a_{11}a_{22}|^{1/2} + |a_{12}a_{21}|^{1/2})^2}{|a_{11}a_{22} - a_{12}a_{21}|}. \tag{13.43}$$

This is an interesting result because it shows that the condition number is always large if the determinant of coefficients is small compared with $|a_{11}a_{22}|$ and $|a_{12}a_{21}|$, i.e., if severe cancellation occurs when forming the determinant.

Ex. 13.12. Show that exactly the same results (13.42), (13.43) are obtained in Ex. 13.11 if we use the 1 norm instead of the ∞ norm.

13.5 Scaling to Minimize $\|\mathbf{PAQ}\|\ \|\mathbf{Q}^{-1}\mathbf{A}^{-1}\mathbf{P}^{-1}\|$

In this section we consider the problem of finding the scaling of an arbitrary real matrix $\mathbf{A}$ that will lead to the condition number $K(\mathbf{A})$ defined in (13.37), Definition 13.4, i.e., we wish to find diagonal matrices $\mathbf{P}$, $\mathbf{Q}$, such that

$$\|\mathbf{PAQ}\|\ \|\mathbf{Q}^{-1}\mathbf{A}^{-1}\mathbf{P}^{-1}\| \tag{13.44}$$

is as small as possible. Without loss of generality, we can assume that the diagonal elements of $\mathbf{P}$, $\mathbf{Q}$ are greater than zero.

Suppose that $\mathbf{A}$ is a given real matrix, and that we use the ∞ norm. Let S_i and T_i denote the absolute row sums of $\mathbf{PAQ}$ and $\mathbf{Q}^{-1}\mathbf{A}^{-1}\mathbf{P}^{-1}$,

$$S_i = p_i \sum_{j=1}^{n} |a_{ij}|\, q_j, \qquad T_i = \frac{1}{q_i} \sum_{j=1}^{n} \frac{|\alpha_{ij}|}{p_i}, \tag{13.45}$$

where $\mathbf{A} = [a_{ij}]$, $\mathbf{A}^{-1} = [\alpha_{ij}]$, and p_i, q_i are the diagonal elements of $\mathbf{P}$, $\mathbf{Q}$, respectively (i.e., the scale factors). Then

$$\|\mathbf{PAQ}\|_\infty\ \|\mathbf{Q}^{-1}\mathbf{A}^{-1}\mathbf{P}^{-1}\|_\infty = \left\{\max_i S_i\right\}\left\{\max_i T_i\right\}. \tag{13.46}$$

If we set

$$\xi = \|\mathbf{PAQ}\|_\infty, \qquad \eta = \|\mathbf{Q}^{-1}\mathbf{A}^{-1}\mathbf{P}^{-1}\|_\infty, \tag{13.47}$$

this means that

$$S_i \le \xi, \qquad T_i \le \eta, \qquad i = 1, \ldots, n, \tag{13.48}$$

or, from (13.45),

$$\sum_{j=1}^{n} |a_{ij}|\, q_j \le \frac{\xi}{p_i}, \qquad \sum_{j=1}^{n} \frac{|\alpha_{ij}|}{p_j} \le \eta q_i, \qquad i = 1, \ldots, n. \tag{13.49}$$

We introduce the $n \times 1$ column vectors

$$\mathbf{p} = \left[\frac{1}{p_i}\right], \qquad \mathbf{q} = [q_i], \tag{13.50}$$

and the notation

$$\mathbf{A}_+ = [|a_{ij}|], \qquad \mathbf{A}_+^{-1} = [|\alpha_{ij}|], \tag{13.51}$$

i.e., the subscript $+$ means that we replace each element in the original matrix by its absolute value. (The notation $|\mathbf{A}|$ is often used for $\mathbf{A}_+$ in the literature. Note that $\mathbf{A}_+^{-1}$ is *not* the inverse of $\mathbf{A}_+$.) In this notation, (13.49) states that

$$\mathbf{A}_+\mathbf{q} \le \xi\mathbf{p}, \qquad \mathbf{A}_+^{-1}\mathbf{p} \le \eta\mathbf{q}. \tag{13.52}$$

Elimination of $\mathbf{p}$ and $\mathbf{q}$ in turn gives

$$\mathbf{A}_+\mathbf{A}_+^{-1}\mathbf{p} \le \mu\mathbf{p}, \tag{13.53}$$

$$\mathbf{A}_+^{-1}\mathbf{A}_+\mathbf{q} \le \mu\mathbf{q}, \tag{13.54}$$

where $\mu = \xi\eta$. From the definition of ξ and η in (13.47) we see that μ is precisely the expression in (13.44), so that our objective is to minimize μ, for all possible choices of p and q.

This objective can be achieved for the special case $\mathbf{A}_+\mathbf{A}_+^{-1} > \mathbf{0}$, or $\mathbf{A}_+^{-1}\mathbf{A}_+ > \mathbf{0}$, by means of the following theorem. The results are also of interest in their own right. (The proof requires an argument that is more sophisticated than the other proofs in this book.)

THEOREM **13.10.** *Let* $\mathbf{C}$ *be a positive matrix,* $c_{ij} > 0$ *for all* i, j.

(i) *For any given* $\mathbf{x}$, $\mathbf{x} \geq \mathbf{0}$, $\mathbf{x} \neq \mathbf{0}$, *define a constant* $\mu(\mathbf{x})$ *to be the smallest number such that*

$$\mathbf{Cx} \leq \mu(\mathbf{x})\mathbf{x}. \tag{13.55}$$

Then a vector $\mathbf{x}_0 > \mathbf{0}$ *exists such that, for all* $\mathbf{x} \geq \mathbf{0}$, $\mathbf{x} \neq \mathbf{0}$,

$$\mu = \mu(\mathbf{x}_0) \leq \mu(\mathbf{x}). \tag{13.56}$$

(ii) μ *is a positive, real, simple eigenvalue of* $\mathbf{C}$, *and it is equal to the spectral radius* $\rho(\mathbf{C})$, *i.e., it is the eigenvalue of maximum modulus.*

(iii) *If the maximum absolute row sum of* $\mathbf{C}$ *is* S, *and the minimum absolute row sum is* s, *then*

$$s \leq \mu \leq S. \tag{13.57}$$

Proof: Consider a definition of $\mu(\mathbf{x})$ equivalent to (13.55),

$$\mu(\mathbf{x}) = \max_i \left\{\frac{(\mathbf{Cx})_i}{x_i}\right\}, \qquad (\mathbf{Cx})_i = \sum_{j=1}^{n} c_{ij}x_j, \tag{13.58}$$

where, if $x_i = 0$ for any i, we take $\mu(\mathbf{x}) = \infty$. Since $(\mathbf{Cx})_i > 0$ for all i, and $\mathbf{x} \geq \mathbf{0}$, $\mathbf{x} \neq \mathbf{0}$, $\mu(\mathbf{x})$ is a positive number or infinity, and we can consider the greatest lower bound (infimum) of $\mu(\mathbf{x})$ over all $\mathbf{x} \geq \mathbf{0}$, $\mathbf{x} \neq \mathbf{0}$. Define

$$\mu = \inf_{\mathbf{x}} \{\mu(\mathbf{x})\}, \qquad \mathbf{x} \geq \mathbf{0}, \quad \mathbf{x} \neq \mathbf{0}. \tag{13.59}$$

In order to show that this lower bound is attained, we use Weierstrass's theorem on extrema: *Suppose that the variables* $z_1, \ldots, z_n$ *are restricted to a finite closed domain, and that* $f(\mathbf{z})$ *is a continuous function of the* z_i. *Then there exist values of* $\mathbf{z}$ *for which* $f(\mathbf{z})$ *assumes its maximum and minimum values either in the interior or on the boundary of the domain.* Since $\mu(\mathbf{x})$ and $\mu(\alpha\mathbf{x})$ have the same value for any scalar α, we need consider only the set of all $\mathbf{x}$ such that $\|\mathbf{x}\| = 1$. This set is finite and closed, but unfortunately $\mu(\mathbf{x})$ is not continuous on this set since $\mu(\mathbf{x}) = \infty$ when $x_i = 0$. In order to exclude zero x_i, and yet keep the set closed, consider the set of $\mathbf{z}$ such that

$$\mathbf{z} = \mathbf{Cx}, \qquad \|\mathbf{x}\| = 1, \qquad \mathbf{x} \geq \mathbf{0}. \tag{13.60}$$

Since $c_{ij} > 0$ for all i, j and $x_i > 0$ for some i, we have $\mathbf{z} > \mathbf{0}$. The set of $\mathbf{z}$ must be closed, since any sequence $\mathbf{z}_1, \mathbf{z}_2, \ldots$ with a limit point $\mathbf{z}^*$ must have come from a sequence $\mathbf{x}_1, \mathbf{x}_2, \ldots$ with a limit point $\mathbf{x}^*$; also, $\mathbf{z}^* = \mathbf{Cx}^*$ and $\mathbf{x}^*$ is in the original set of $\mathbf{x}$ since this is closed. Hence, $\mathbf{z}^*$ must be in the set (13.60).

The next point is that, multiplying (13.55) by $\mathbf{C}$ (remembering that without loss of generality we can normalize $\mathbf{x}$ so that $\|\mathbf{x}\| = 1$),

$$\mathbf{Cz} \leq \mu(\mathbf{x})\mathbf{z}, \qquad \mathbf{z} = \mathbf{Cx},\ \|\mathbf{x}\| = 1, \qquad \mathbf{x} \geq \mathbf{0}. \tag{13.61}$$

We now define $\eta(\mathbf{z})$, for a given $\mathbf{x}$ to be the smallest number such that

$$\mathbf{Cz} \leq \eta(\mathbf{z})\mathbf{z}, \qquad \mathbf{z} = \mathbf{Cx}, \qquad \|\mathbf{x}\| = 1, \qquad \mathbf{x} \geq \mathbf{0}. \tag{13.62}$$

Clearly $\eta(\mathbf{z}) \leq \mu(\mathbf{x})$. Also, if we define

$$\eta = \inf_{\mathbf{z}} \{\eta(\mathbf{z})\}, \qquad \mathbf{z} = \mathbf{Cx}, \qquad \|\mathbf{x}\| = 1, \quad \mathbf{x} \geq \mathbf{0}, \tag{13.63}$$

we have $\eta \leq \mu$. The infimum in this last formula is taken over $\mathbf{z}$ lying in a finite closed domain. The Weierstrass theorem applies, and a $\mathbf{z}_0$ exists such that the limit is attained. Suppose now that, for this η, $\mathbf{z}_0$,

$$\eta\mathbf{z}_0 - \mathbf{Cz}_0 \geq \mathbf{0}, \qquad \eta\mathbf{z}_0 - \mathbf{Cz}_0 \neq \mathbf{0}. \tag{13.64}$$

Multiply by $\mathbf{C}$ and use the same argument that led to the conclusion that $\mathbf{z} > \mathbf{0}$ in (13.60). Then

$$\eta\,\mathbf{w} - \mathbf{Cw} > \mathbf{0}, \qquad \mathbf{w} = \mathbf{Cz}_0.$$

Hence, we can find $\varepsilon > 0$ such that

$$(\eta - \varepsilon)\mathbf{w} - \mathbf{Cw} \geq \mathbf{0},$$

which contradicts the definition of η in (13.63). The assumption that must be wrong is the second equation in (13.64). We must have $\mathbf{Cz}_0 = \eta\mathbf{z}_0$, so that η is an eigenvalue of $\mathbf{C}$. Equation (13.55) now shows that $\eta = \mu(\mathbf{z}_0)$, and since $\eta \leq \mu$, where μ was defined in (13.59), this means that $\eta = \mu$. This completes the proof of part (i). In the course of the proof we have shown that $\mu = \eta$ is a positive real eigenvalue of $\mathbf{C}$. The remainder of the proof of part (ii) is left for Exs. 13.15, 13.16. To prove part (iii), we see that

$$\sum_{j=1}^{n} c_{ij}x_j \geq s x_q, \qquad i = 1, \ldots, n,$$

where x_j is the jth element of the eigenvector, and we assume that x_q is the smallest of these elements. But

$$\sum_{j=1}^{n} c_{qj}x_j = \mu x_q,$$

so that $\mu \geq s$. We can similarly prove that $\mu \leq S$.

This theorem enables us to answer the scaling problem for a certain class of matrices.

THEOREM **13.11.** *If* $\mathbf{A}_+\mathbf{A}_+^{-1} > \mathbf{0}$, $\mathbf{A}_+^{-1}\mathbf{A}_+ > \mathbf{0}$, *then the condition number*

$$K(\mathbf{A}) = \min_{\mathbf{P},\mathbf{Q}} \|\mathbf{PAQ}\|_\infty \|\mathbf{Q}^{-1}\mathbf{A}^{-1}\mathbf{P}^{-1}\|_\infty \qquad (13.65)$$

is equal to μ, *the maximum eigenvalue of* $\mathbf{A}_+\mathbf{A}_+^{-1}$ (*or* $\mathbf{A}_+^{-1}\mathbf{A}_+$). *The diagonal elements* p_i, q_i *of the corresponding scaling matrices* $\mathbf{P}$, $\mathbf{Q}$ *are given by* $\mathbf{p} = [1/p_i]$, $\mathbf{q} = [q_i]$, *where* $\mathbf{p}$, $\mathbf{q}$ *are given by*

$$\mathbf{A}_+\mathbf{A}_+^{-1}\mathbf{p} = \mu\mathbf{p}, \qquad \mathbf{A}_+^{-1}\mathbf{A}_+\mathbf{q} = \mu\mathbf{q}. \qquad (13.66)$$

These scaling matrices are such that the absolute row sums of $\mathbf{PAQ}$ *are the same, and similarly for* $\mathbf{Q}^{-1}\mathbf{A}^{-1}\mathbf{P}^{-1}$.

Proof: At the beginning of this section we showed that the problem of finding $\mathbf{P}$, $\mathbf{Q}$ to minimize (13.44) was equivalent to finding $\mathbf{p}$ and $\mathbf{q}$ such that μ in (13.53), (13.54) was as small as possible. Theorem 13.10 proved that these problems are solved by unique positive eigenvectors $\mathbf{p}$, $\mathbf{q}$ such that

$$\mathbf{A}_+\mathbf{A}_+^{-1}\mathbf{p} = \mu_1\mathbf{p}, \qquad \mathbf{A}_+^{-1}\mathbf{A}_+\mathbf{q} = \mu_2\mathbf{q}.$$

On multiplying the first equation by $\mathbf{A}_+^{-1}$, we see that $\mathbf{A}_+^{-1}\mathbf{p}$ is a positive eigenvector of $\mathbf{A}_+^{-1}\mathbf{A}_+$ corresponding to an eigenvalue μ_1. But $\mathbf{A}_+^{-1}\mathbf{A}_+$ can have only one positive eigenvector so that $\mathbf{A}_+^{-1}\mathbf{p}$ is a multiple of $\mathbf{q}$ and $\mu_1 = \mu_2$. Without loss of generality, we can set

$$\mathbf{A}_+^{-1}\mathbf{p} = \mathbf{q}, \qquad \mathbf{A}_+\mathbf{q} = \mu\mathbf{p}$$

from which, on recalling that $\mathbf{p} = \mathbf{P}^{-1}\mathbf{e}$, $\mathbf{q} = \mathbf{Qe}$, where $\mathbf{e}$ is a column vector whose elements are all unity,

$$\mathbf{Q}^{-1}\mathbf{A}_+^{-1}\mathbf{P}^{-1}\mathbf{e} = \mathbf{e}, \qquad \mathbf{PA}_+\mathbf{Qe} = \mu\mathbf{e},$$

which proves the last statement in the theorem.

THEOREM **13.12.** *If* s *and* S *are the minimum and maximum row-sums of* $\mathbf{A}_+\mathbf{A}_+^{-1}$, *respectively* (*or* $\mathbf{A}_+^{-1}\mathbf{A}_+$), *then bounds on the minimum condition number* $K(\mathbf{A})$ *are given by*

$$s \le K(\mathbf{A}) \le S. \qquad (13.67)$$

Proof: Theorem 13.11 tells us that $K(\mathbf{A})$ is given by the spectral radius of $\mathbf{A}_+\mathbf{A}_+^{-1}$ or $\mathbf{A}_+^{-1}\mathbf{A}_+$, and Theorem 13.10(iii) immediately gives the bounds stated.

This theorem gives easily computable upper and lower bounds for the condition number. The closer these bounds, the more satisfactory the scaling of the matrices. We say, somewhat loosely, that a matrix $\mathbf{A}$ is "properly scaled with respect to the ∞ norm" if the bounds s and S are close together (alternatively, if the absolute row-sums of $\mathbf{A}$ are approximately equal, and also those of $\mathbf{A}^{-1}$).

Ex. 13.13. Show that the following matrix (for which an approximate inverse is quoted) is *not* properly scaled if $|\varepsilon| \ll 1$.

$$\mathbf{A} = \begin{bmatrix} 2 & 1 & 1 \\ 1 & \varepsilon & \varepsilon \\ 1 & \varepsilon & -\varepsilon \end{bmatrix}, \qquad \mathbf{A}^{-1} \approx \begin{bmatrix} -\varepsilon & 1 & 0 \\ 1 & -\dfrac{1}{2\varepsilon} & \dfrac{1}{2\varepsilon} \\ 0 & \dfrac{1}{2\varepsilon} & -\dfrac{1}{2\varepsilon} \end{bmatrix}. \tag{13.68}$$

At this point, in order to scale a matrix **A**, it is necessary to compute $\mathbf{A}^{-1}$ and then to estimate the eigenvalue μ and eigenvectors **p**, **q** in (13.66). The following theorem suggests an easier procedure.

THEOREM **13.13.** (i) (*Row scaling*). *A diagonal matrix* **P** *that minimizes* $\|\mathbf{PA}\|_\infty \, \|\mathbf{A}^{-1}\mathbf{P}^{-1}\|_\infty$ *is given by choosing* $p_{ii} = 1/S_i$, *where the* S_i *are the absolute row-sums of* **A**. *The absolute row-sums of* **PA** *are then all equal.*

(ii) (*Column scaling*). *A diagonal matrix* **Q** *that minimizes* $\|\mathbf{AQ}\|_\infty \, \|\mathbf{Q}^{-1}\mathbf{A}^{-1}\|_\infty$ *is given by choosing* $q_{ii} = T_i$, *where the* T_i *are the absolute row-sums of* $\mathbf{A}^{-1}$. *The absolute row-sums of* $\mathbf{Q}^{-1}\mathbf{A}^{-1}$ *are all equal.*

Proof: In part (i) we are considering the special case of (13.44) in which **Q** is the unit matrix. The analysis leading to (13.53)–(13.54) still holds with $\mathbf{Q} = \mathbf{I}$. Instead of **q** we must take a column matrix **e**, all of whose elements are unity. Equation (13.54) then gives

$$\mathbf{A}_+^{-1}\mathbf{A}_+\mathbf{e} \le \mu\mathbf{e}. \tag{13.69}$$

This means that a lower bound for μ is given by

$$\mu \ge \max_i \sum_{j=1}^{n} |\alpha_{ij}| \left\{ \sum_{k=1}^{n} |a_{jk}| \right\} = \max_i \sum_{j=1}^{n} S_j \, |\alpha_{ij}|. \tag{13.70}$$

Also,

$$\mu = \|\mathbf{PA}\|_\infty \, \|\mathbf{A}^{-1}\mathbf{P}^{-1}\|_\infty = \left\{ \max_i p_{ii} S_i \right\} \left\{ \max_i \sum_{j=1}^{n} \frac{1}{p_{jj}} |\alpha_{ij}| \right\}, \tag{13.71}$$

where S_i is the ith absolute row sum of **A**,

$$S_i = \sum_{j=1}^{n} |a_{ij}|.$$

A comparison of (13.70) and (13.71) shows that the lower bound in (13.70) is attained if we choose $p_{ii} = 1/S_i$. Clearly, the absolute row-sums of $\mathbf{A}' = \mathbf{PA}$ are then all equal to unity. This proves part (i). Part (ii) is proved similarly by setting $\mathbf{p} = \mathbf{e}$ in (13.53).

This theorem suggests the following iterative procedure for the two-sided scaling of a matrix. Compute, for $r = 1, 2, \ldots$ in succession,

$$\mathbf{A}_{2r} = \mathbf{P}_r\mathbf{A}_{2r-1}, \qquad \mathbf{A}_{2r+1} = \mathbf{A}_{2r}\mathbf{Q}_r, \qquad (\mathbf{A}_1 = \mathbf{A}), \tag{13.72}$$

where $\mathbf{P}_r$, $\mathbf{Q}_r$ are chosen so as to make the absolute row-sums of $\mathbf{A}_{2r}$ and $\mathbf{A}_{2r+1}^{-1}$ nearly equal, respectively. In practice, it is not necessary to scale exactly. The nearest power of 10 is usually sufficient. The procedure is illustrated in the following example.

Ex. 13.14. Scale the matrix **A** given in (13.68), Ex. 13.13, in such a way that $\|\mathbf{A}'\|_\infty \, \|(\mathbf{A}')^{-1}\|_\infty$ for the resulting matrix $\mathbf{A}'$ is close to the condition number of **A**.

Solution: We are interested only in an approximation to the scaling that gives the exact condition number, so we can work with the approximation to the inverse given in (13.68). For this reason also, it is good enough to take $\mathbf{P}_1$ in (13.72) to be simply the unit matrix, so that $\mathbf{A}_2 = \mathbf{A}$. The absolute row-sums of $\mathbf{A}_2^{-1}$ are approximately $1, 1/|\varepsilon|, 1/|\varepsilon|$, which give the factors T_i for $\mathbf{Q}_1$ (see Theorem 13.13), so that, omitting absolute values which are not important,

$$\mathbf{A}_3 = \mathbf{A}_2\mathbf{Q}_1 = \begin{bmatrix} 2 & \dfrac{1}{\varepsilon} & \dfrac{1}{\varepsilon} \\ 1 & 1 & 1 \\ 1 & 1 & -1 \end{bmatrix}.$$

The absolute row-sums are now approximately $2/|\varepsilon|, 3, 3$ which give the factors S_i for $\mathbf{P}_2$ (see Theorem 13.13), so that, making the factors $1/\varepsilon, 1, 1$ for convenience, we can take the diagonal elements of $\mathbf{P}_2$ to be $\varepsilon, 1, 1$, and

$$\mathbf{A}_4 = \mathbf{P}_2\mathbf{A}_3 = \begin{bmatrix} 2\varepsilon & 1 & 1 \\ 1 & 1 & 1 \\ 1 & 1 & -1 \end{bmatrix}, \qquad \mathbf{A}_4^{-1} \approx \begin{bmatrix} -1 & 1 & 0 \\ 1 & -\frac{1}{2} & \frac{1}{2} \\ 0 & \frac{1}{2} & -\frac{1}{2} \end{bmatrix}. \tag{13.73}$$

The absolute row-sums of $\mathbf{A}_4$ are approximately equal, and the same is true for $\mathbf{A}_4^{-1}$, so that $\mathbf{A}_4$ is a suitably scaled form of **A**, with $K(\mathbf{A}_4) = 3.2 = 6$. To scale $\mathbf{A}_4$ perfectly, we could solve the eigenvalue problems (13.66) involving

$$(\mathbf{A}_4)_+(\mathbf{A}_4)_+^{-1} \approx \begin{bmatrix} 1 & 1 & 1 \\ 2 & 2 & 1 \\ 2 & 2 & 1 \end{bmatrix}, \qquad (\mathbf{A}_4)_+^{-1}(\mathbf{A}_4)_+ \approx \begin{bmatrix} 1 & 2 & 2 \\ 1 & 2 & 2 \\ 1 & 1 & 1 \end{bmatrix}. \tag{13.74}$$

From (13.67) we see that the exact condition number $K(\mathbf{A})$ must therefore lie between 3 and 5. Since (13.73) gives a condition number 6, this means that the scaling in (13.73) is good enough for practical purposes.

In Theorem 13.11 we imposed the conditions $\mathbf{A}_+\mathbf{A}_+^{-1} > \mathbf{0}$ and $\mathbf{A}_+^{-1}\mathbf{A}_+ > \mathbf{0}$. To see what may happen if these conditions are not satisfied, consider the matrix in (13.34), where $k > 0$:

$$\mathbf{A} = \begin{bmatrix} 1 & k \\ 0 & 1 \end{bmatrix}, \qquad \mathbf{A}^{-1} = \begin{bmatrix} 1 & -k \\ 0 & 1 \end{bmatrix},$$
$$\mathbf{A}_+\mathbf{A}_+^{-1} = \begin{bmatrix} 1 & 2k \\ 0 & 1 \end{bmatrix}, \tag{13.75}$$

so that we do not have $\mathbf{A}_+\mathbf{A}_+^{-1} > \mathbf{0}$. The spectral radius is 1 and the corresponding eigenvector $\mathbf{p}$ that should give the scale factors is $\mathbf{p} = [1\ 0]^T$. Hence, the required scale factors do not exist, except in some limiting sense, as in the discussion of (13.36). The assumptions $\mathbf{A}_+\mathbf{A}_+^{-1} > \mathbf{0}$ and $\mathbf{A}_+^{-1}\mathbf{A}_+ > \mathbf{0}$ have been made to simplify the theory.

Ex. 13.15. Prove that in Theorem 13.10:
(a) There is only one eigenvector corresponding to μ.
(b) $\mathbf{C}$ has only the one nonnegative eigenvector.

Ex. 13.16. Prove that if, for $\mathbf{C}, \mathbf{x} \geq \mathbf{0}, \mathbf{x} \neq \mathbf{0}$, we define

$$\nu(\mathbf{x}) = \min_i \left\{\frac{(\mathbf{Cx})_i}{x_i}\right\}, \qquad \nu = \sup_{\mathbf{x}} \{\nu(\mathbf{x})\},$$

then a vector $\mathbf{x}_0 > \mathbf{0}$ exists such that the least upper bound (supremum) is attained, and the corresponding value of ν is identical with μ defined in Theorem 13.10. Deduce that μ is the spectral radius $\rho(\mathbf{C})$ of $\mathbf{C}$.

Ex. 13.17. Develop results corresponding to Theorems 13.11, 13.12 for the 1 norm instead of the ∞ norm. In particular, show that when the condition number is minimized, the absolute column sums of $\mathbf{PAQ}$ are the same, and similarly for $\mathbf{Q}^{-1}\mathbf{A}^{-1}\mathbf{P}^{-1}$.

13.6 Computable Error Bounds for Eigenvalues

In the remainder of this chapter we make some brief remarks in connection with the computation of eigenvalues and eigenvectors. This is a vast and technical subject. Many of the more obvious methods are computationally unstable and/or inefficient. For example, determination of the characteristic polynomial and calculation of its roots suffers from both of these disadvantages. Using an efficient stable method, a digital computer can produce a complete system of eigenvalues and eigenvectors for a matrix of order 50 in less than a minute, but it is easy to invent examples for which the results are very inaccurate.

A useful analogy can be drawn with the situation when solving a system of n linear equations in n unknowns. If the elements of the augmented matrix are exact, and all calculations are performed exactly, it is easy to decide whether the system has zero, one, or an infinity of solutions. However, if rounding errors are present, difficulties occur if the matrix of coefficients is "nearly-singular" (Section 8.4). In a somewhat similar way, if the elements of a square matrix are exact, and calculations can be performed exactly, it is a straightforward matter to reduce the matrix to Jordan canonical form. However, although the various possible Jordan forms are clearly differentiated mathematically (Theorem 11.12), this is not true computationally. Thus, the 2×2 unit matrix has a repeated eigenvalue $\lambda = 1$, and two linearly independent eigenvectors, e.g., the unit vectors $\mathbf{e}_1$, $\mathbf{e}_2$. The matrix

$$\begin{bmatrix} 1 & \varepsilon \\ 0 & 1 \end{bmatrix}, \tag{13.76}$$

for any finite ε, no matter how small, has a repeated eigenvalue $\lambda = 1$, but only one eigenvector $\mathbf{e}_1$. This example illustrates that uncertainty in the coefficients and rounding errors means that matrices can be "nearly-defective." The scaling problem also rears its ugly head. We can scale without changing the eigenvalues by using a similarity transformation $\mathbf{P}^{-1}\mathbf{A}\mathbf{P}$ with $\mathbf{P}$ diagonal. Thus, for (13.76) we might consider

$$\begin{bmatrix} 1 & 0 \\ 0 & \varepsilon \end{bmatrix}\begin{bmatrix} 1 & \varepsilon \\ 0 & 1 \end{bmatrix}\begin{bmatrix} 1 & 0 \\ 0 & \varepsilon^{-1} \end{bmatrix} = \begin{bmatrix} 1 & 1 \\ 0 & 1 \end{bmatrix} \tag{13.77}$$

and there would seem to be no doubt that the matrix on the right should be considered defective, whereas the original matrix (13.76) might be regarded as close to the unit matrix, which is not defective.

Because of the specialist nature of the general case, we confine our attention to the situation where a matrix $\mathbf{A}$ has a set of n linearly independent right-eigenvectors $\mathbf{x}_i$, and n independent left-eigenvectors $\mathbf{y}_i$, corresponding to eigenvalues λ_i. Suppose that an approximate system of eigenvalues λ_i' and right-eigenvectors $\mathbf{x}_i'$ has been computed for a matrix $\mathbf{A}$, and that $\mathbf{P}'$ denotes the square matrix whose ith column is $\mathbf{x}_i'$. Define the residual matrix $\mathbf{R}$ by the equation

$$\mathbf{AP}' = \mathbf{P}'\mathbf{\Lambda}' + \mathbf{R}, \tag{13.78}$$

where $\mathbf{\Lambda}'$ is a diagonal matrix whose ith diagonal element is λ_i'. In the usual way, $\mathbf{AP}' - \mathbf{P}'\mathbf{\Lambda}'$ should be computed in double precision. We assume that the $\mathbf{x}_i'$ are linearly independent (since otherwise they are not reasonable approximations to the $\mathbf{x}_i$). The matrix $\mathbf{P}'$ is then nonsingular and we can multiply (13.78) by $(\mathbf{P}')^{-1}$,

$$(\mathbf{P}')^{-1}\mathbf{AP}' = \mathbf{\Lambda}' + \mathbf{S}, \qquad \mathbf{S} = (\mathbf{P}')^{-1}\mathbf{R}. \tag{13.79}$$

It is reasonable to assume that $\mathbf{S}$ is in some sense small compared with $\mathbf{\Lambda}'$, since otherwise λ_i' and $\mathbf{x}_i'$ can hardly be regarded as approximations to λ_i and $\mathbf{x}_i$. Since (13.79) represents a similarity transformation on $\mathbf{A}$, the eigenvalues of $\mathbf{A}$ are given by the eigenvalues of $\mathbf{\Lambda}' + \mathbf{S}$, where we are assuming that $\mathbf{S}$ is small in some sense, compared with $\mathbf{\Lambda}'$.

Bounds on the eigenvalues can now be obtained using *Gerschgorin's circle theorem* which states the following.

THEOREM **13.14.** *Each eigenvalue of a matrix* **B** *satisfies at least one of the inequalities*

$$|\lambda - b_{ii}| \leq r_i, \qquad r_i = \sum_{j=1}^{n}{}' |b_{ij}|, \qquad i = 1, \ldots, n, \tag{13.80}$$

where the prime indicates that the term $i = j$ in the sum is omitted. In words, every eigenvalue of **B** *lies in at least one of the circles with center b_{ii} and radius r_i in the complex λ-plane.*

Proof: If λ is an eigenvalue of **B**, and **x** the corresponding eigenvector, then $\mathbf{Bx} = \lambda\mathbf{x}$, which implies

$$(\lambda - b_{ii})x_i = \sum_{j=1}^{n}{}' b_{ij}x_j, \qquad i = 1, \ldots, n, \tag{13.81}$$

where the prime indicates that the term $i = j$ in the sum has been omitted. Suppose that x_k is the largest element of **x**. Then $|x_j/x_k| \leq 1$ for all j, and

$$|\lambda - b_{kk}| \leq \sum_{j=1}^{n}{}' |b_{kj}| \left|\frac{x_j}{x_k}\right| \leq \sum_{j=1}^{n}{}' |b_{kj}|.$$

Since this is true for *any* eigenvalue, this proves the theorem.

In practice, we often wish to use Gerschgorin's theorem to estimate the eigenvalues of a matrix $\mathbf{C} = [c_{ij}]$ where the off-diagonal elements of **C** are much smaller than the diagonal elements. [This is the case for (13.79), which led to the present discussion.] Instead of applying Gerschgorin's theorem directly to **C**, much more accurate bounds can often be found by first applying a simple similarity transformation $\mathbf{Q}^{-1}\mathbf{CQ}$, where **Q** is diagonal. We illustrate the procedure in the 3×3 case. If **Q** is the matrix obtained by multiplying the first row of the unit matrix by k, we have

$$\mathbf{Q}^{-1}\mathbf{CQ} = \begin{bmatrix} c_{11} & \dfrac{c_{12}}{k} & \dfrac{c_{13}}{k} \\ kc_{21} & c_{22} & c_{23} \\ kc_{31} & c_{32} & c_{33} \end{bmatrix}. \tag{13.82}$$

The Gerschgorin circles are given by:

Centers:	c_{11}	c_{22}	c_{33}
Radii:	$\dfrac{|c_{12}| + |c_{13}|}{k}$	$k\,|c_{21}| + |c_{23}|$	$k\,|c_{31}| + |c_{33}|$

Suppose that for $k = 1$ the three circles are disjoint. As k increases, the radius of the first circle will decrease, whereas the radii of the other two circles will increase. Clearly there will be an optimum value of k for which the radius of the first circle will be as small as possible, while still being disjoint from the others.

Ex. 13.18. Estimate the eigenvalues of

$$\mathbf{C} = \begin{bmatrix} 1 & -10^{-5} & 2 \cdot 10^{-5} \\ 4 \cdot 10^{-5} & 0.5 & -3 \cdot 10^{-5} \\ -10^{-5} & 3 \cdot 10^{-5} & 0.1 \end{bmatrix}. \tag{13.83}$$

Solution: Direct application of the Gerschgorin theorem shows that the eigenvalues λ_i of $\mathbf{C}$ satisfy

$$|1 - \lambda_1| \leq 3 \cdot 10^{-5}, \qquad |0.5 - \lambda_2| \leq 7 \cdot 10^{-5}, \qquad |0.1 - \lambda_3| \leq 4 \cdot 10^{-5}.$$

However, a much better bound on λ_1 can be obtained by taking $k = 10^4$ in (13.82), which is the largest power of 10 such that the Gerschgorin circle for λ_1 is disjoint from the other two. (The nearest power of 10 is chosen for convenience.) This gives

$$\mathbf{Q}^{-1}\mathbf{C}\mathbf{Q} = \begin{bmatrix} 1 & 10^{-9} & 2 \cdot 10^{-9} \\ 4 \cdot 10^{-1} & 0.5 & -3 \cdot 10^{-5} \\ -10^{-1} & 3 \cdot 10^{-5} & 0.1 \end{bmatrix}, \tag{13.84}$$

so that

$$|1 - \lambda_1| \leq 3 \cdot 10^{-9}.$$

Ex. 13.19. Extend Ex. 13.18 to obtain accurate estimates of λ_2 and λ_3 for the matrix in (13.83).

Returning to the question that started this discussion, namely the estimation of the accuracy of computed estimates λ_i' for the eigenvalues of a matrix $\mathbf{A}$, we note that the exact eigenvalues λ_i of $\mathbf{A}$ are also the exact eigenvalues of $\mathbf{\Lambda}' + \mathbf{S}$ in (13.79). We have already said that we are interested in cases where $\mathbf{S}$ is in some sense small compared with $\mathbf{\Lambda}'$, and this is precisely the situation to which the Gerschgorin theorem applies. Having obtained accurate eigenvalues using the procedure in Ex. 13.18, we can easily compute more accurate eigenvectors of $\mathbf{\Lambda}' + \mathbf{S}$, since this is almost diagonal. Hence, we can recover more accurate eigenvectors of $\mathbf{A}$. We can also compute bounds on the accuracy of the eigenvectors, but the details lie outside the scope of this book.

13.7 Error Bounds for Eigenvalues and Eigenvectors (continued)

So far we have assumed that we have estimates for the complete system of eigenvalues and eigenvectors. It is instructive to consider what we can say if we know estimates for only one single eigenvalue, say μ, and the corresponding eigenvector, say $\mathbf{v}$.

THEOREM 13.15. *Suppose that a matrix* $\mathbf{A}$ *has a set of n linearly independent eigenvectors* $\mathbf{x}_i$ *corresponding to eigenvalues* λ_i, *and that, for some* μ, $\mathbf{v}$,

$$\mathbf{A}\mathbf{v} - \mu\mathbf{v} = \boldsymbol{\eta}, \qquad \|\mathbf{v}\| = 1. \tag{13.85}$$

Then, for the 1, 2, *and* ∞ *norms,*

$$\min_i |\lambda_i - \mu| \leq \|\boldsymbol{\eta}\|\ \|\mathbf{P}\|\ \|\mathbf{P}^{-1}\|, \tag{13.86}$$

where $\mathbf{P}$ *is the matrix whose kth column is* $\mathbf{x}_k$. *If* $\mathbf{A}$ *is normal (in particular, symmetric or hermitian), then*

$$\min_i |\lambda_i - \mu| \leq \|\boldsymbol{\eta}\|_2. \tag{13.87}$$

Proof: We have $\mathbf{AP} = \mathbf{P\Lambda}$, or $\mathbf{A} = \mathbf{P\Lambda P}^{-1}$, where $\mathbf{\Lambda}$ is a diagonal matrix whose ith diagonal element is λ_i. Hence, (13.85) can be rewritten

$$\mathbf{P}(\mathbf{\Lambda} - \mu\mathbf{I})\mathbf{P}^{-1}\mathbf{v} = \boldsymbol{\eta} \tag{13.88}$$

or, assuming that μ is not an eigenvalue [in which case (13.86) is trivial],

$$\mathbf{v} = \mathbf{P}(\mathbf{\Lambda} - \mu\mathbf{I})^{-1}\mathbf{P}^{-1}\boldsymbol{\eta}.$$

Taking norms, remembering that $\|\mathbf{v}\| = 1$,

$$1 \leq \|\mathbf{P}\|\ \|(\mathbf{\Lambda} - \mu\mathbf{I})^{-1}\|\ \|\mathbf{P}^{-1}\|\ \|\boldsymbol{\eta}\|.$$

For the 1, 2, or ∞ norms, we have

$$\|(\mathbf{\Lambda} - \mu\mathbf{I})^{-1}\| = \max_i \frac{1}{|\lambda_i - \mu|}.$$

Hence, (13.86) follows. If $\mathbf{A}$ is normal, the matrix $\mathbf{P}$ can be chosen to be unitary, and then $\|\mathbf{P}\|_2 = \|\mathbf{P}^{-1}\|_2 = 1$ (Ex. 13.25). Equation (13.87) follows immediately from (13.86).

The result (13.87) is remarkable because it says that if $\mathbf{A}$ is symmetric or hermitian and $\boldsymbol{\eta}$ is small, then μ is always a good approximation to some eigenvalue of $\mathbf{A}$. This is quite different from the type of result that holds for simultaneous linear equations, where a small residual gives no guarantee that the solution is accurate. However (13.87) holds for only a restricted class of matrices.

In order to illuminate the general situation, suppose that the right-eigenvectors of $\mathbf{A}$ are normalized so that $\|\mathbf{x}_k\|_2 = (\mathbf{x}_k, \mathbf{x}_k)^{1/2} = 1$. Denote the left-eigenvectors of $\mathbf{A}$ by $\mathbf{y}_k$, also normalized so that $\|\mathbf{y}_k\|_2 = 1$. Then

$$\mathbf{P} = [\mathbf{x}_1, \ldots, \mathbf{x}_n], \qquad \mathbf{P}^{-1} = \left[\frac{\mathbf{y}_1}{(\mathbf{y}_1, \mathbf{x}_1)}, \ldots, \frac{\mathbf{y}_n}{(\mathbf{y}_n, \mathbf{x}_n)}\right]^H. \tag{13.89}$$

If we multiply (13.88) by $\mathbf{P}^{-1}$, the ith equation in the result gives

$$(\lambda_i - \mu)(\mathbf{y}_i, \mathbf{v}) = (\mathbf{y}_i, \boldsymbol{\eta}).$$

If $\mathbf{v}$ is an approximation to $\mathbf{x}_k$, we should expect that $(\mathbf{y}_k, \mathbf{v}) \approx (\mathbf{y}_k, \mathbf{x}_k)$ and

$$\lambda_k - \mu \approx \frac{(\mathbf{y}_k, \boldsymbol{\eta})}{(\mathbf{y}_k, \mathbf{x}_k)}. \tag{13.90}$$

We recall that $\|\mathbf{y}_k\|_2 = 1$, so that if $(\mathbf{y}_k, \mathbf{x}_k)$ is of order unity, μ will be close to λ_k if $\boldsymbol{\eta}$ is small. However, for defective matrices, $(\mathbf{y}_k, \mathbf{x}_k)$ may be zero and there is no guarantee that μ will be close to λ_k even if $\boldsymbol{\eta}$ is small. Obviously, also, there is likely to be trouble if $\mathbf{A}$ is "nearly" defective. This is indicated also by (13.86), since $\|\mathbf{P}^{-1}\|$ is large when any of the $(\mathbf{y}_i, \mathbf{x}_i)$ are small.

We next consider error bounds for a known approximate eigenvector. A simple example shows that even for a symmetric matrix, a small residual vector $\boldsymbol{\eta} = \mathbf{A}\mathbf{v} - \lambda\mathbf{v}$, $\|\mathbf{v}\| = 1$, does not guarantee an accurate eigenvector. Consider

$$\mathbf{A} = \begin{bmatrix} a & \varepsilon \\ \varepsilon & a \end{bmatrix}, \qquad \mu = a, \qquad \mathbf{v} = \begin{bmatrix} 1 \\ 0 \end{bmatrix},$$
$$\mathbf{A}\mathbf{v} - \mu\mathbf{v} = \begin{bmatrix} 0 \\ \varepsilon \end{bmatrix} = \boldsymbol{\eta}, \qquad \|\boldsymbol{\eta}\|_2 = \varepsilon. \tag{13.91}$$

Theorem 13.14, (13.87), tells us that μ does not differ from an eigenvalue of $\mathbf{A}$ by more than ε. In fact, $\mathbf{A}$ has eigenvalues $\lambda_1 = a + \varepsilon$, $\lambda_2 = a - \varepsilon$. However, the corresponding eigenvectors are

$$\mathbf{x}_1 = \begin{bmatrix} 1 \\ 1 \end{bmatrix}, \qquad \mathbf{x}_2 = \begin{bmatrix} 1 \\ -1 \end{bmatrix}, \tag{13.92}$$

and $\mathbf{v}$ is in no sense a good approximation to either of these, no matter how small ε is. We need some additional information. What is happening is that the two eigenvalues are so close together that $\mathbf{A}\mathbf{x}_1 - \lambda_2\mathbf{x}_1$ and $\mathbf{A}\mathbf{x}_2 - \lambda_1\mathbf{x}_2$ are both small vectors, so that since μ is nearly equal to λ_1 and λ_2, any vector of the form $\mathbf{u} = \alpha\mathbf{x}_1 + \beta\mathbf{x}_2$ will give a small value for $\mathbf{A}\mathbf{u} - \mu\mathbf{u}$. This indicates that we should look for some additional information that separates the eigenvalues that are close to μ from those that are far away from μ. This line of thought leads to the following theorem.

THEOREM **13.16.** *If* $\mathbf{A}$ *is hermitian and* μ, $\mathbf{v}$, λ_i, $\mathbf{x}_i$, $\boldsymbol{\eta}$ *are defined as in Theorem* 13.15; *also,* $|\lambda_i - \mu| \le \|\boldsymbol{\eta}\|_2$ *for* $i = 1, \ldots, r$, *and* $|\lambda_i - \mu| \ge d$ *for* $i = r + 1, \ldots, n$; *then there exists a vector* $\mathbf{x}$ *of the form*

$$\mathbf{x} = a_1\mathbf{x}_1 + \ldots + a_r\mathbf{x}_r \tag{13.93}$$

such that

$$\|\mathbf{v} - \mathbf{x}\|_2 \le \frac{\|\boldsymbol{\eta}\|_2}{d}. \tag{13.94}$$

Proof: Since **A** is hermitian, we can assume that the $\mathbf{x}_i$ form an orthonormal set, and $\mathbf{v}$ can be expanded in the form

$$\mathbf{v} = \sum_{i=1}^{n} a_i \mathbf{x}_i. \tag{13.95}$$

We choose the a_i in (13.93) to be precisely the a_i determined by (13.95), so that

$$\|\mathbf{v} - \mathbf{x}\|_2 = \left\| \sum_{i=r+1}^{n} a_i \mathbf{x}_i \right\|_2 = \left\{ \sum_{i=r+1}^{n} |a_i|^2 \right\}^{1/2}. \tag{13.96}$$

From (13.95),

$$\|\boldsymbol{\eta}\|_2 = \|\mathbf{A}\mathbf{v} - \mu\mathbf{v}\|_2 = \left\| \sum_{i=1}^{n} a_i(\lambda_i - \mu)\mathbf{x}_i \right\|_2$$

$$= \left\{ \sum_{i=1}^{n} |a_i|^2 (\lambda_i - \mu)^2 \right\}^{1/2} \geq d \left\{ \sum_{i=r+1}^{n} |a_i|^2 \right\}^{1/2}. \tag{13.97}$$

Combining (13.96), (13.97), we deduce (13.94).

Ex. 13.20. Prove (13.87) directly by the following argument. If **A** is normal, it has n linearly independent eigenvectors $\mathbf{x}_i$ corresponding to eigenvalues λ_i. Hence, we can write

$$\mathbf{v} = \sum_{i=1}^{n} \alpha_i \mathbf{x}_i, \qquad \boldsymbol{\eta} = \mathbf{A}\mathbf{v} - \lambda\mathbf{v} = \sum_{i=1}^{n} (\lambda_i - \lambda)\alpha_i \mathbf{x}_i.$$

Deduce (13.87) by considering $\|\boldsymbol{\eta}\|_2$ and $\|\mathbf{v}\|_2$.

Ex. 13.21. For a given approximate eigenvector $\mathbf{v}$, prove that the bound (13.87) for an approximate eigenvalue μ is minimized if we choose

$$\mu = \frac{1}{2} \frac{\{(\mathbf{v}, \mathbf{A}\mathbf{v}) + (\mathbf{A}\mathbf{v}, \mathbf{v})\}}{(\mathbf{v}, \mathbf{v})}.$$

If **A** is hermitian, this reduces to the Rayleigh quotient.

13.8 The Condition of Eigenvalues and Eigenvectors

We are interested in the changes in the eigenvalues and eigenvectors produced by small changes in a matrix **A** for several reasons. If the elements of **A** are not known exactly, we usually wish to know how large the corresponding uncertainties will be in the eigenvalues and eigenvectors. If the eigenvalues and eigenvectors are very sensitive to small changes in **A** (*ill-conditioned*), they will be difficult to compute accurately, due to the effects of rounding errors, which are equivalent to changes in **A**. The analysis will again illustrate the value of the theory of unitary and similarity transformations. By means of this theory we can gain considerable insight into the conditions under which the eigenproblem is well- or ill-conditioned.

THEOREM 13.17. (i) *If* $\mathbf{A}$ *has* n *linearly independent eigenvectors* $\mathbf{x}_i$ *corresponding to eigenvalues* λ_i, *and* λ *is an eigenvalue of* $\mathbf{A} + \mathbf{E}$, *then, for the* 1, 2, *or* ∞ *norm*,

$$\min_i |\lambda_i - \lambda| \leq \|\mathbf{E}\| \, \|\mathbf{P}\| \, \|\mathbf{P}^{-1}\|, \tag{13.98}$$

where $\mathbf{P}$ *is the matrix whose columns are* $\mathbf{x}_i$.

(ii) *If* $\mathbf{A}$ *is normal* (*which includes symmetric and hermitian*),

$$\min_i |\lambda_i - \lambda| \leq \|\mathbf{E}\|_2. \tag{13.99}$$

Proof: Let $\mathbf{x}$ be the eigenvector of $\mathbf{A} + \mathbf{E}$ corresponding to λ. Then

$$(\mathbf{A} - \lambda\mathbf{I})\mathbf{x} = -\mathbf{E}\mathbf{x}. \tag{13.100}$$

As in the derivation of (13.88), this can be rewritten as

$$\mathbf{P}(\mathbf{\Lambda} - \lambda\mathbf{I})\mathbf{P}^{-1}\mathbf{x} = -(\mathbf{E}\mathbf{P})(\mathbf{P}^{-1}\mathbf{x}),$$

where $\mathbf{\Lambda}$ is a diagonal matrix with diagonal elements λ_i. Hence, if λ is not an eigenvalue of $\mathbf{A}$ [in which case (13.98) is trivial],

$$\mathbf{P}^{-1}\mathbf{x} = -(\mathbf{\Lambda} - \lambda\mathbf{I})^{-1}(\mathbf{P}^{-1}\mathbf{E}\mathbf{P})(\mathbf{P}^{-1}\mathbf{x}).$$

For the 1, 2, or ∞ norm,

$$\|\mathbf{P}^{-1}\mathbf{x}\| \leq \|(\mathbf{\Lambda} - \lambda\mathbf{I})^{-1}\| \, \|\mathbf{P}^{-1}\| \, \|\mathbf{E}\| \, \|\mathbf{P}\| \, \|\mathbf{P}^{-1}\mathbf{x}\|,$$

$$\|(\mathbf{\Lambda} - \lambda\mathbf{I})^{-1}\| = \max_i |\lambda_i - \lambda|^{-1},$$

and (13.98) follows. A normal matrix $\mathbf{P}$ can be taken to be unitary, for which $\|\mathbf{P}\|_2 = \|\mathbf{P}^{-1}\|_2 = 1$, so that (13.98) reduces to (13.99).

The result (13.99) is simple and important. It means that for hermitian matrices, small changes in the elements of the matrix produce small changes in all of the eigenvalues of the matrix, i.e., *all of the eigenvalues of a hermitian matrix are well-conditioned.*

It is well known that if the roots of a polynomial equation are close together, the roots will be sensitive to small changes in the coefficient of the polynomial (Ex. 13.38). However, the result that we have just proved shows that the roots of the characteristic equation of a hermitian matrix are never sensitive to small changes in the elements of the matrix. This is an illustration of the general statement that evaluation of the characteristic polynomial and determination of its zeros is a very *bad* way to determine eigenvalues.

The simplest and perhaps the most useful result in connection with the condition of a specific eigenvalue is the following.

THEOREM **13.18.** *Under the conditions of Theorem* 13.17, *if* $\mathbf{E} = \varepsilon\mathbf{B}$, *where* ε *is small, and the minimum in* (13.98) *occurs for* $i = k$ *where* λ_k *is a simple eigenvalue, then, for sufficiently small* ε,

$$\lambda = \lambda_k + \varepsilon \frac{(\mathbf{y}_k, \mathbf{B}\mathbf{x}_k)}{(\mathbf{y}_k, \mathbf{x}_k)} + \delta, \qquad |\delta| \le C\varepsilon^2, \tag{13.101}$$

where C *is a constant,* $\mathbf{y}_k$ *is the left-eigenvector of* $\mathbf{A}$ *corresponding to* λ_k, *and* $\|\mathbf{x}_k\|_2 = \|\mathbf{y}_k\|_2 = 1$.

Proof: The eigenvalues of $\mathbf{A} + \varepsilon\mathbf{B}$ are the same as those of

$$\mathbf{P}^{-1}\mathbf{A}\mathbf{P} = \mathbf{\Lambda} + \varepsilon\mathbf{P}^{-1}\mathbf{B}\mathbf{P}.$$

If we set $\mathbf{C} = [c_{ij}] = \mathbf{P}^{-1}\mathbf{B}\mathbf{P}$ and use the notation (13.89), we see that

$$c_{ij} = \frac{(\mathbf{y}_i, \mathbf{B}\mathbf{x}_j)}{(\mathbf{y}_i, \mathbf{x}_j)}.$$

We now use the Gerschgorin circle theorem to localize the kth eigenvalue of $\mathbf{\Lambda} + \varepsilon\mathbf{C}$. As previously explained, we first carry out a similarity transformation, replacing $\mathbf{\Lambda} + \varepsilon\mathbf{C}$ by $\mathbf{\Lambda} + \varepsilon\mathbf{S}^{-1}\mathbf{C}\mathbf{S}$, where $\mathbf{S}$ is given by dividing the kth row of the unit matrix by $c\varepsilon$, where c is a constant to be determined. Gerschgorin's theorem then gives

$$|\lambda - \lambda_k - \varepsilon c_{kk}| \le c\varepsilon^2 {\sum_{j=1}^{n}}' |c_{kj}|,$$

$$|\lambda - \lambda_i - \varepsilon c_{ii}| \le \frac{1}{c} |c_{ik}| + \varepsilon {\sum_{j=1}^{n}}'' |c_{ij}|, \qquad i \ne k,$$

where the prime means that the term $j = k$ is omitted, and the double prime means that the two terms $j = i, k$ are omitted. We may choose c so that $|c_{ik}| < c\,|\lambda_k - \lambda_i|$ for all $i \ne k$, and then for sufficiently small ε the circle with center $\lambda_k + \varepsilon c_{kk}$ is isolated from the others, and the required result follows.

The result is *not* true if $\mathbf{A}$ does not have n linearly independent eigenvectors. Thus,

$$\begin{bmatrix} a & 1 \\ 0 & a \end{bmatrix} \tag{13.102}$$

has the repeated eigenvalue $\lambda = a$ and only one eigenvector, while the matrix

$$\begin{bmatrix} a & 1 \\ \varepsilon & a \end{bmatrix} = \begin{bmatrix} a & 1 \\ 0 & a \end{bmatrix} + \varepsilon \begin{bmatrix} 0 & 0 \\ 1 & 0 \end{bmatrix}$$

has the eigenvalues $a \pm \varepsilon^{1/2}$. A small change in the elements of $\mathbf{A}$ defined in (13.102) can produce comparatively large changes in the eigenvalues. The eigenvalues of this matrix are badly conditioned.

To conclude this chapter, we outline (nonrigorously) the corresponding theory for the perturbation of an *eigenvector* caused by changing a matrix $\mathbf{A}$ with n independent eigenvectors to $\mathbf{A} + \varepsilon\mathbf{B}$ where ε is small. Let λ_1, $\mathbf{x}_1$ be an eigenvalue and eigenvector of $\mathbf{A}$, and $\lambda_1(\varepsilon)$, $\mathbf{x}_1(\varepsilon)$, the corresponding quantities for $\mathbf{A} + \varepsilon\mathbf{B}$. We have

$$(\mathbf{A} + \varepsilon\mathbf{B})\mathbf{x}_1(\varepsilon) = \lambda_1(\varepsilon)\mathbf{x}_1(\varepsilon). \tag{13.103}$$

It can be proved that, since $\mathbf{A}$ has n independent eigenvectors, $\lambda_1(\varepsilon)$ and $\mathbf{x}_1(\varepsilon)$ can both be expanded in power series in ε:

$$\lambda_1(\varepsilon) = \lambda_1 + \varepsilon\eta + O(\varepsilon^2), \qquad \mathbf{x}_1(\varepsilon) = \mathbf{x}_1 + \varepsilon\mathbf{z} + O(\varepsilon^2). \tag{13.104}$$

Inserting these in (13.102) and neglecting second-order terms, we obtain

$$\mathbf{A}\mathbf{z} + \mathbf{B}\mathbf{x}_1 = \lambda_1\mathbf{z} + \eta\mathbf{x}_1. \tag{13.105}$$

The vector $\mathbf{z}$ can be expanded in terms of the right-eigenvectors $\mathbf{x}_i$ of $\mathbf{A}$, but no term in $\mathbf{x}_1$ is required since the dominant term in (13.104) is $\mathbf{x}_1$, and eigenvectors are arbitrary to within a constant multiplying factor:

$$\mathbf{z} = \alpha_2\mathbf{x}_2 + \ldots + \alpha_n\mathbf{x}_n. \tag{13.106}$$

Substituting in (13.105), we obtain

$$(\mathbf{B} - \eta\mathbf{I})\mathbf{x}_1 + \sum_{j=2}^{n}(\lambda_j - \lambda_1)\alpha_j\mathbf{x}_j = \mathbf{0}.$$

Form the inner product with each of the left-eigenvectors $\mathbf{y}_i$ in turn, remembering that $(\mathbf{y}_i, \mathbf{x}_j) = 0$, $i \neq j$. This gives

$$\eta = \frac{(\mathbf{y}_1, \mathbf{B}\mathbf{x}_1)}{(\mathbf{y}_1, \mathbf{x}_1)}, \qquad \alpha_i = \frac{(\mathbf{y}_i, \mathbf{B}\mathbf{x}_1)}{(\lambda_1 - \lambda_i)(\mathbf{y}_i, \mathbf{x}_i)}$$

if $\lambda_j \neq \lambda_1$ $(j = 2, \ldots, n)$. The first part of this result agrees with (13.101) and the second gives, from (13.104), (13.106),

$$\mathbf{x}_1(\varepsilon) = \mathbf{x}_1 + \varepsilon\left\{\sum_{i=2}^{n}\frac{(\mathbf{y}_i, \mathbf{B}\mathbf{x}_1)}{(\lambda_1 - \lambda_i)(\mathbf{y}_i, \mathbf{x}_i)}\right\} + O(\varepsilon^2). \tag{13.107}$$

This is the basic result concerning the perturbation in an eigenvector resulting from a perturbation in $\mathbf{A}$, if $\mathbf{A}$ has n independent eigenvectors and λ_1 is distinct from the other eigenvalues. The eigenvector $\mathbf{x}_1$ will be ill-conditioned if λ_1 is *near* any of the other eigenvalues. We should expect this since, if λ_1 is a repeated eigenvalue, there will be two or more eigenvectors corresponding to λ_1. If λ_1 is close to another eigenvalue, computational procedures will tend to produce a vector in the space common to the two eigenvectors, even though the two eigenvectors correspond to distinct eigenvalues. (See the paragraph preceding Theorem 13.16.) The occurrence of $(\mathbf{y}_i, \mathbf{x}_i)$ in the denominators in (13.107) can be misleading in that small values of these quantities do not necessarily imply that the eigenvector is ill-conditioned, since cancellation may occur (see

Ex. 13.22). An eigenvector is certainly well-conditioned if the corresponding eigenvalue is well separated from the others, and none of the quantities $(\mathbf{y}_i, \mathbf{x}_i)$ is small.

We have said enough to indicate that the situation for a matrix with a general Jordan canonical form will be very complicated. Fortunately, the important thing from our point of view is to realize the conditions under which trouble is likely to arise, and we need not pursue this matter further.

Ex. 13.22. If

$$\mathbf{A} = \begin{bmatrix} 2 & 0 & 0 \\ 0 & 1 & 1 \\ 0 & 0 & 1+\varepsilon \end{bmatrix},$$

show that

$$(\mathbf{y}_1, \mathbf{x}_1) = 1, \qquad (\mathbf{y}_2, \mathbf{x}_2) = -\frac{\varepsilon}{(1+\varepsilon^2)^{1/2}}, \qquad (\mathbf{y}_3, \mathbf{x}_3) = \frac{\varepsilon}{(1+\varepsilon^2)^{1/2}}.$$

Show, however, that the vector $\mathbf{x}_1$ corresponding to $\lambda_1 = 2$ is *not* sensitive to perturbations in the matrix, in spite of the fact that individual terms in the series in (13.107) are large.

Miscellaneous Exercises 13

Ex. 13.23. If the elements of a 2×2 matrix $\mathbf{A}$ are all zero except for a_{21}, show that the 1, 2, and ∞ norms of $\mathbf{A}$ are equal to $|a_{21}|$.

Ex. 13.24. Prove that $\|\mathbf{A}^{-1} - \mathbf{B}^{-1}\| \leq \|\mathbf{A}^{-1}\|\, \|\mathbf{B}^{-1}\|\, \|\mathbf{A} - \mathbf{B}\|$.

Ex. 13.25. If $\mathbf{P}$ is unitary, prove that $\|\mathbf{P}\|_2 = 1$, $\|\mathbf{PA}\|_2 = \|\mathbf{A}\|_2$.

Ex. 13.26. Prove that for a (complex) nonsingular 2×2 matrix $\mathbf{A}$ such that

$$\mathbf{A}^H\mathbf{A} = \begin{bmatrix} a & b \\ \bar{b} & d \end{bmatrix},$$

we have

$$\|\mathbf{A}\|_2\, \|\mathbf{A}^{-1}\|_2 = \frac{|\lambda_2|^2}{|\lambda_1\lambda_2|},$$

where

$$\lambda_1\lambda_2 = ad - |b|^2, \qquad |\lambda_2| = \tfrac{1}{2}\{|a+d| + [(a-d)^2 + 4\,|b|^2]^{1/2}\}.$$

Deduce (or prove otherwise) that

$$\|\mathbf{A}\|_2\|\mathbf{A}^{-1}\|_2 = \sigma + (\sigma^2 - 1)^{1/2},$$

where

$$\sigma = \frac{1}{2}\left\{\frac{(|a_{11}|^2 + |a_{12}|^2 + |a_{21}|^2 + |a_{22}|^2)}{|a_{11}a_{22} - a_{12}a_{21}|}\right\}.$$

Deduce that if $\mathbf{A}$ is scaled so as to minimize $\|\mathbf{A}\|_2\|\mathbf{A}^{-1}\|_2$, we arrive back at precisely the scaled matrix (13.42) and the condition number (13.43) for the ∞ norm found in Ex. 13.11.

Ex. 13.27. The *euclidean norm* $\|\mathbf{A}\|_E$ of a matrix is defined by

$$\|\mathbf{A}\|_E = \left\{\sum_{i=1}^{n}\sum_{j=1}^{n} |a_{ij}|^2\right\}^{1/2}.$$

Prove that:

(a) $\|\mathbf{A}\|_E^2 = \text{tr}(\mathbf{A}^H\mathbf{A})$.

(b) $\|\mathbf{A}\|_2 \le \|\mathbf{A}\|_E \le n^{1/2}\|\mathbf{A}\|_2$.

(c) $\|\mathbf{A}\|_E$ satisfies conditions (a)–(d) of Definition 13.2.

(d) $\|\mathbf{I}\|_E = n^{1/2}$. (From Ex. 13.6 this means that the euclidean norm cannot be a natural norm. We could try to insert a factor of $n^{-1/2}$ in the definition to make the norm of **I** unity, but it does not seem to be possible to find a vector norm with reference to which this type of matrix norm is both compatible and natural.)

(e) For a diagonal matrix **D**, the euclidean norm is $\{\sum |d_{ii}|^2\}^{1/2}$, whereas the 1, 2, and ∞ norms are all $\{\max |d_{ii}|\}$.

(f) For a unitary matrix **P**, $\|\mathbf{P}\|_E = n^{1/2}$ and $\|\mathbf{PA}\|_E = \|\mathbf{A}\|_E$.

Ex. 13.28. Prove that the following results are true for 1, 2, or ∞ norms. Consider a sequence $\mathbf{A}_1, \mathbf{A}_2, \ldots$ of square matrices.

(a) $\mathbf{A}_r \to \mathbf{A}$ as $r \to \infty$ if and only if $\|\mathbf{A}_r - \mathbf{A}\| \to 0$. If $\mathbf{A}_r \to \mathbf{A}$ then $\|\mathbf{A}_r\| \to \|\mathbf{A}\|$.

(b) The three following statements are equivalent:

(i) $\mathbf{A}^r \to \mathbf{0}$ as $r \to \infty$.

(ii) $\|\mathbf{A}^r\| \to 0$ as $r \to \infty$.

(iii) $\rho(\mathbf{A}) < 1$.

(c) $\mathbf{A}^r \to \mathbf{0}$ as $r \to \infty$ if $\|\mathbf{A}\| < 1$.

(d) The geometric series $\mathbf{I} + \mathbf{A} + \mathbf{A}^2 + \ldots$ is convergent if and only if $\mathbf{A}^r \to \mathbf{0}$ as $r \to \infty$.

(e) If $\mathbf{A}^r \to \mathbf{0}$ as $r \to \infty$, then $\mathbf{I} - \mathbf{A}$ is nonsingular and $(\mathbf{I} - \mathbf{A})^{-1} = \mathbf{I} + \mathbf{A} + \mathbf{A}^2 + \ldots$. Deduce Theorem 13.6.

Ex. 13.29. Prove that the Jacobi and Gauss-Seidel iterative methods for the solution of $\mathbf{Ax} = \mathbf{b}$ (Section 9.7) converge if **A** is strictly diagonally dominant. (This term is defined in Ex. 13.7.)

Ex. 13.30. If approximate lower and upper triangular factors **L**, **U** of a matrix **A** are known such that $\mathbf{LU} = \mathbf{A} + \mathbf{E}$, where $\|\mathbf{E}\|\,\|\mathbf{A}^{-1}\| < \frac{1}{2}$, prove that the iterative procedure

$$\mathbf{LUz}_i = \mathbf{r}_i = \mathbf{b} - \mathbf{Ax}_i, \qquad \mathbf{x}_{i+1} = \mathbf{x}_i + \mathbf{z}_i, \qquad \mathbf{x}_0 = \mathbf{0},$$

will converge to the solution **x** of $\mathbf{Ax} = \mathbf{b}$.

Ex. 13.31. Deduce the result in Ex. 13.7 by a direct application of Gerschgorin's theorem.

Ex. 13.32. Prove that every eigenvalue of a matrix **B** satisfies at least one of the inequalities

$$|\lambda - b_{jj}| \le s_j, \qquad s_j = \sum_{i=1}^{n}{}' |b_{ij}|, \qquad j = 1, \ldots, n.$$

Ex. 13.33. Assuming that the zeros of a polynomial are continuous functions of the coefficients of a polynomial, prove that the eigenvalues of a matrix are continuous functions of the elements of the matrix.

Ex. 13.34. Using the result in the last exercise, prove that if k of the Gerschgorin circles in Theorem 13.14 form a connected region disjoint from the remaining disks, then precisely k eigenvalues lie in this region. Deduce that an isolated Gerschgorin circle contains exactly one eigenvalue. Deduce also that if all the Gerschgorin circles of a real matrix are disconnected, then all the eigenvalues of the matrix are real.

Ex. 13.35. Suppose that $\mathbf{C}$ is a matrix whose off-diagonal elements are much smaller than its diagonal elements, and that we wish to find a Gerschgorin circle for the eigenvalue near a_{ii} by applying Theorem 13.14 to $\mathbf{Q}^{-1}\mathbf{C}\mathbf{Q}$, where $\mathbf{Q}$ is the matrix obtained by multiplying the ith row of the unit matrix by k. Show that a good estimate for the value of k that will minimize the radius of the Gerschgorin circle is given by

$$k \approx \min_j \left\{ \frac{|a_{ii} - a_{jj}|}{|a_{ji}|} \right\}.$$

Ex. 13.36. Prove by applying the Gerschgorin argument to (13.79) that a reasonable estimate to use for λ_i' is $\mathbf{y}_i'\mathbf{A}\mathbf{x}_i'$, where $\mathbf{x}_i'$ and $\mathbf{y}_i'$ are the ith column of $\mathbf{P}'$ and the ith row of $(\mathbf{P}')^{-1}$, respectively.

Ex. 13.37. Consider the upper triangular matrix $\mathbf{A}$ with diagonal elements $a_{ii} = 21 - i$, the elements just above the diagonal $a_{i,i+1}$ all equal to 20, and all other elements zero. If $\mathbf{x}_i$ is normalized so that $x_1 = 1$, and $\mathbf{y}_i$ is normalized so that $y_{20} = 1$, show that

$$s_i = (\mathbf{y}_i, \mathbf{x}_i) = \frac{(20 - i)!\,(i - 1)!}{20^{19}}, \qquad s_{10} = s_{11} \approx \frac{1}{4 \cdot 10^{12}}.$$

(This is an example of a matrix with apparently reasonably well separated eigenvalues for which the eigenproblem is badly conditioned.)

Ex. 13.38. Prove that if the equation $f(x) = 0$ has a double root at $x = z$, then the equation $f(x) + \varepsilon g(x) = 0$, for small ε, has two roots near $x = z$ such that

$$z_1 = z + k\varepsilon^{1/2} + O(\varepsilon), \qquad z_2 = z - k\varepsilon^{1/2} + O(\varepsilon).$$

Assume that f, g can be expanded in Taylor series around $x = z$, and $g(z) \neq 0$, $f''(z) \neq 0$. [The point of this result is that a small perturbation of order ε will produce much larger alterations of order $\varepsilon^{1/2}$ in the repeated root.]

Ex. 13.39. Prove that if $\mathbf{A} + \Delta\mathbf{A}$ is singular, $(\mathbf{A} + \Delta\mathbf{A})\mathbf{x} = \mathbf{0}$, $\mathbf{x} \neq \mathbf{0}$,

$$\|\mathbf{x}\| = \|\mathbf{A}^{-1}\mathbf{A}\mathbf{x}\| \leq \|\mathbf{A}^{-1}\|\,\|\mathbf{A}\mathbf{x}\| = \|\mathbf{A}^{-1}\|\,\|(\Delta\mathbf{A})\mathbf{x}\| \leq \|\mathbf{A}^{-1}\|\,\|\Delta\mathbf{A}\|\,\|\mathbf{x}\|.$$

Deduce that all $\Delta\mathbf{A}$ such that $\mathbf{A} + \Delta\mathbf{A}$ are singular are such that

$$\|\Delta\mathbf{A}\| \geq \frac{1}{\|\mathbf{A}^{-1}\|}. \tag{13.108}$$

Prove that in the ∞ norm, the matrix $\Delta\mathbf{A}$ of the smallest norm that makes $\mathbf{A}$ singular is given by $\Delta\mathbf{A} = -\mathbf{u}\mathbf{v}^T/\|\mathbf{A}^{-1}\|_\infty$, where, if the maximum absolute row-sum of $\mathbf{A}^{-1} = [\alpha_{ij}]$ occurs for the pth row, we take $u_j = +1$ for $\alpha_{pj} \geq 0$, $u_j = -1$ for $\alpha_{pj} < 0$; also $v_p = 1$, $v_i = 0$ $(i \neq p)$. (If $\|\mathbf{A}\|\ \|\mathbf{A}^{-1}\|$ is large, this example says that we can find a $\Delta\mathbf{A}$ with $\|\Delta\mathbf{A}\|/\|\mathbf{A}\|$ small, such that $\mathbf{A} + \Delta\mathbf{A}$ is singular. This gives a connection between "large condition number" and "nearly-singular matrix.")

Ex. 13.40. Prove that the exponential matrix exp **A**, already mentioned in Section 11.2, exists, using the following argument. Define

$$\mathbf{S}_k = \sum_{r=1}^{k} \frac{1}{r!}\,\mathbf{A}^r. \tag{13.109}$$

For all i, j we have $\max |a_{ij}| \leq \|\mathbf{A}\|$. Hence

$$\max |(\mathbf{A}^r)_{ij}| \leq \|\mathbf{A}^r\| \leq \|\mathbf{A}\|^r. \tag{13.110}$$

The series

$$\sum_{r=1}^{\infty} \frac{1}{r!}\,\|\mathbf{A}\|^r$$

is convergent. From (13.110), the terms of this series dominate the (i, j) elements of the corresponding matrices in the series (13.109), which is therefore also convergent when $r \to \infty$. Note that in practice exp **A** is usually evaluated by using a similarity transformation to reduce **A** to Jordan form. If **A** can be reduced to diagonal form, the end-result is (11.15).

Ex. 13.41. Prove that

$$\mathbf{A} = \begin{bmatrix} 0 & 1 & 0 \\ 1 & 0 & 0 \\ 0 & 0 & 1 \end{bmatrix} \quad \text{implies} \quad e^{\alpha\mathbf{A}} = \begin{bmatrix} \cosh\alpha & \sinh\alpha & 0 \\ \sinh\alpha & \cosh\alpha & 0 \\ 0 & 0 & e^{\alpha} \end{bmatrix}.$$

Ex. 13.42. Under what conditions is $e^{\mathbf{A}}e^{\mathbf{B}} = e^{\mathbf{A}+\mathbf{B}}$? Deduce that $e^{\alpha\mathbf{C}}e^{\beta\mathbf{C}} = e^{(\alpha+\beta)\mathbf{C}}$.

Ex. 13.43. If **D** is a diagonal matrix with elements $d_{ii} = e^{\lambda_i}$, prove that $\mathbf{D} = e^{\mathbf{\Lambda}}$, where $\mathbf{\Lambda}$ is a diagonal matrix with diagonal elements λ_i.

Ex. 13.44. If $\mathbf{A} = \exp \mathbf{K}$, then $\mathbf{P}^{-1}\mathbf{A}\mathbf{P} = \exp \mathbf{P}^{-1}\mathbf{K}\mathbf{P}$.

Ex. 13.45. Theorem 13.10 and the results in Ex. 13.15 enable us to state some general results which are relevant to certain problems in probability theory. (See for instance the Markov chain example in Section 2.5.) A square matrix **A** of order n is called a *stochastic matrix* if

$$\text{(a)}\ a_{ij} \geq 0, \qquad \text{all } i, j \qquad\qquad \text{(b)}\ \sum_{i=1}^{n} a_{ij} = 1, \qquad j = 1, \ldots, n.$$

(Note that in the literature the term stochastic usually refers to a matrix whose *transpose* has the properties stated.) An $n \times 1$ column vector is said to be a (*probability*) *distribution* if

$$\text{(a)}\ x_i \geq 0, \qquad i = 1, \ldots, n \qquad\qquad \text{(b)}\ \sum_{i=1}^{n} x_i = 1.$$

Prove:

(a) A nonnegative matrix $\mathbf{A}$ is stochastic if and only if $\mathbf{e}^T\mathbf{A} = \mathbf{e}^T$, where $\mathbf{e}$ is a column vector all of whose elements are unity.

(b) If $\mathbf{A}$ is stochastic, $\mathbf{A}^k$ is stochastic, $k = 2, 3, \ldots$.

(c) A nonnegative vector $\mathbf{x}$ is a distribution if and only if $\mathbf{e}^T\mathbf{x} = 1$.

(d) If $\mathbf{x}$ is a distribution and $\mathbf{A}$ is stochastic, then $\mathbf{A}^k\mathbf{x}$ is a distribution, $k = 2, 3, \ldots$.

(e) If $\mathbf{A}$ is a positive stochastic matrix (i.e., $\mathbf{A} > \mathbf{0}$) then the eigenvalue of largest modulus of $\mathbf{A}$ is unity, and this eigenvalue is simple. All other eigenvalues are less than unity in modulus.

(f) If the eigenvector of $\mathbf{A}$ that corresponds to the eigenvalue 1 is denoted by $\mathbf{z}$ then $\mathbf{z} > \mathbf{0}$. The corresponding eigenvector of $\mathbf{A}^T$ is $\mathbf{e}$.

(g) If $\mathbf{A}$ is positive stochastic and $\mathbf{x}_0$ is any distribution,

$$\lim_{r\to\infty} \mathbf{A}^r = \mathbf{z}\mathbf{e}^T,$$

$$\lim_{r\to\infty} \mathbf{A}^r\mathbf{x}_0 = \mathbf{z}.$$

(h) Verify the results in (e)–(g) for the matrix used in Section 2.5, which was examined from an eigenvalue point of view in Ex. 9.47.

14 Abstract Vector Spaces and Linear Transformations

14.1 Abstract Vector Spaces

One of the important features of matrix algebra is that the subject provides an introduction to a much more general tool, namely the theory of linear spaces, which is a branch of functional analysis. It turns out that many of the concepts that we have been developing in connection with matrices can also be usefully applied to other mathematical objects, for example, functions of a real or complex variable.

So far we have developed the theory of vector spaces in terms of row and column vectors. The basic property of vectors from our present point of view is that we can form linear combinations of vectors. There are various other mathematical entities or objects such that we wish to consider linear combinations of these entities. We have already met the example of geometrical vectors in two- and three-dimensional space, where vectors are defined as directed line-segments. At first sight it might seem that geometrical vectors in three-dimensional space and 3×1 column matrices are mathematical objects of completely different kinds, and that the operations of addition and multiplication by scalars, when performed on these objects, have nothing in common except the words used. However, we have already indicated in Section 4.1 that this is not the case, since the operations obey the same laws for geometrical vectors and column matrices. If $\vec{u}$, $\vec{v}$ and $\mathbf{u}$, $\mathbf{v}$ are geometrical vectors and column matrices, respectively, then

$$\vec{u} + \vec{v} = \vec{v} + \vec{u}, \qquad \mathbf{u} + \mathbf{v} = \mathbf{v} + \mathbf{u},$$
$$\alpha(\beta\vec{u}) = (\alpha\beta)\vec{u}, \qquad \alpha(\beta\mathbf{u}) = (\alpha\beta)\mathbf{u},$$

and so on.

We shall assume that we are dealing with a collection or set of mathematical entities in connection with which certain operations called "addition" and "multiplication by a scalar" are defined. We shall not define the precise nature of these entities, so that we shall not specify how these operations are actually carried out. However, we shall specify axioms or rules that the operations must obey. In this way, we can isolate the fundamental assumptions without considering the concrete details of particular cases. The advantage of this procedure is that we can work out the consequences of the assumptions once and for all. If a particular set is known to obey the fundamental axioms, then we can immediately say that all the theorems in the general theory apply. The point of what we are trying to do is that we can simplify and clarify the theory by discarding unnecessary properties of concrete mathematical objects that confuse the situation because they are irrelevant.

We proceed to list the assumptions used to define an *abstract vector space* where the word "abstract" is used to distinguish this from the vector spaces of row and column vectors considered so far. We shall call the entities in an abstract vector space *vectors*, regardless of the fact that they may be quite different from the row or column vectors introduced earlier. Similarly we shall use the word *scalars* for the entities that can multiply vectors, although they may be different from the numbers we have used earlier. No attempt is made to set down a minimum number of assumptions. It is easier to see the implications of the assumptions if we allow a certain amount of redundancy, at the expense of mathematical elegance.

We now consider specific detail. We assume that we have a set of elements called *scalars*, denoted by Greek letters $\alpha, \beta, \gamma, \ldots$ that form a *field* F, by which we mean that they satisfy the following conditions:

To every pair of scalars α, β there corresponds a scalar $\alpha + \beta$ called the *sum* of α and β such that:

(a) Addition is commutative and associative,

$$\alpha + \beta = \beta + \alpha, \qquad \alpha + (\beta + \gamma) = (\alpha + \beta) + \gamma.$$

(b) There exists a unique element 0 called zero such that $\alpha + 0 = \alpha$ for every α in F.

(c) For every α in F there corresponds a unique scalar $(-\alpha)$ such that $\alpha + (-\alpha) = 0$.

To every pair of scalars α, β there corresponds a scalar $\alpha\beta$ called the *product* of α and β such that:

(a) Multiplication is commutative and associative,

$$\alpha\beta = \beta\alpha, \qquad \alpha(\beta\gamma) = (\alpha\beta)\gamma.$$

(b) There exists a unique nonzero scalar 1 (called one or unity) such that $\alpha 1 = \alpha$ for every α in F.

(c) To each nonzero α in F there corresponds a unique scalar α^{-1} called the inverse of α such that $\alpha\alpha^{-1} = 1$.

(d) Multiplication is distributive with respect to addition.

$$\alpha(\beta + \gamma) = \alpha\beta + \alpha\gamma, \qquad (\beta + \gamma)\alpha = \beta\alpha + \gamma\alpha.$$

In this book, in previous sections, we have been dealing sometimes with the field of real numbers and sometimes with the field of complex numbers. Another example of a field is the set of all rational numbers. An example of a set that is not a field is the set of all positive and negative integers, since the inverse of an integer is not in general an integer.

We can now define what we mean by an abstract vector space.

DEFINITION **14.1.** An *abstract vector space* (or *linear space*) consists of:

(a) A field F of *scalars*.

(b) A set V of entities called *vectors*.

(c) An operation called *vector addition* that associates a *sum* $\mathbf{x} + \mathbf{y}$ with each pair of vectors $\mathbf{x}$, $\mathbf{y}$ in such a way that:

(i) Addition is commutative and associative:

$$\mathbf{x} + \mathbf{y} = \mathbf{y} + \mathbf{x}, \qquad \mathbf{x} + (\mathbf{y} + \mathbf{z}) = (\mathbf{x} + \mathbf{y}) + \mathbf{z}.$$

(ii) There exists in V a unique vector $\mathbf{0}$ called the zero vector such that $\mathbf{x} + \mathbf{0} = \mathbf{x}$ for all $\mathbf{x}$ in V.

(iii) For each vector $\mathbf{x}$ in V there is a unique vector $(-\mathbf{x})$ such that $\mathbf{x} + (-\mathbf{x}) = \mathbf{0}$.

(d) An operation called *multiplication by a scalar* that associates with each scalar α in F and vector $\mathbf{x}$ in V a vector $\alpha\mathbf{x}$ in V called the *product* of α and $\mathbf{x}$ such that:

(i) multiplication by a scalar is associative, and distributive with respect to scalar addition:

$$\alpha(\beta\mathbf{x}) = (\alpha\beta)\mathbf{x}, \qquad (\alpha + \beta)\mathbf{x} = \alpha\mathbf{x} + \beta\mathbf{x}.$$

(ii) Multiplication by a scalar is distributive with respect to vector addition:

$$\alpha(\mathbf{x} + \mathbf{y}) = \alpha\mathbf{x} + \alpha\mathbf{y}.$$

(iii) If 1 is the identity element in F then $1\mathbf{x} = \mathbf{x}$.

The fact that if $\mathbf{x}$ and $\mathbf{y}$ are vectors in a vector space, then $\mathbf{x} + \mathbf{y}$ and $\lambda\mathbf{x}$ are also vectors in the space is known as *closure* with respect to the operators of vector addition and scalar multiplication, respectively.

We now give examples of abstract vector spaces:

(a) Free physical vectors in three-dimensional space. The vectors in the space are specified by giving a direction and a length. By saying that the vectors are "free," we mean that the line-segment defining the vector may start at any point in space. The rule for addition is the usual parallelogram law. The rule for multiplication by a scalar is that the direction of the vector remains unchanged and its length is multiplied by the scalar.

(b) Fixed physical vectors in three-dimensional space, where by "fixed" we mean that the vectors all start from the origin of coordinates. The rules for vector addition and multiplication by a scalar are as in (a) with the additional proviso that the results of these operations are vectors that also start from the origin.

(c) $m \times n$ matrices (in particular, column vectors and row vectors) with the usual rules for addition and multiplication by a scalar. The field can be either the field of real numbers, or the field of complex numbers.

(d) The set of vectors with an infinite number of components $[x_1, x_2, \ldots]$, with the obvious definitions for addition and multiplication by a scalar. (This is not a particularly useful vector space unless restrictions are placed on the behavior of x_i as $i \to \infty$.)

(e) The space of functions $f(x)$, $a \le x \le b$, that are continuous in this range. This is denoted by $C[a, b]$, with the usual rules for addition and multiplication by a scalar. This is a vector space since the sum of two continuous functions is continuous, and a multiple of a continuous function is continuous.

(f) The space of functions that are k times differentiable, and whose kth derivatives are continuous, in $a \le x \le b$, $C^{(k)}[a, b]$.

(g) The space of polynomials $P_n(x) = a_0 + a_1x + \ldots + a_nx^n$, for any n.

(h) The space of polynomials $P_n(x)$, $n \le N$, where N is fixed.

(i) The set of all solutions of a given linear homogeneous differential equation

$$a_0(x)\frac{d^ny}{dx^n} + a_1(x)\frac{d^{n-1}y}{dx^{n-1}} + \ldots + a_n(x)y = 0.$$

(j) The set of all solutions y of an integral equation of the form

$$\int_0^a K(x, t)y(t)\,dt + \lambda y(x) = 0, \qquad 0 \le x \le a,$$

where $K(x, t)$ and λ are given, and $K(x, t)$ is continuous in x, t.

(k) If V and W are any two vector spaces over the same field, with vectors denoted by $\mathbf{v}_i$, $\mathbf{w}_i$, respectively, the *product space* of V and W over the same field is the space of vectors $\mathbf{u} = (\mathbf{v}_i, \mathbf{w}_j)$, where, if a second vector in the product space is $(\mathbf{v}_p, \mathbf{w}_q)$, the laws of addition and scalar multiplication are given by

$$(\mathbf{v}_i, \mathbf{w}_j) + (\mathbf{v}_p, \mathbf{w}_q) = (\mathbf{v}_i + \mathbf{v}_p, \mathbf{w}_j + \mathbf{w}_q), \qquad \lambda(\mathbf{v}_i, \mathbf{w}_j) = (\lambda\mathbf{v}_i, \lambda\mathbf{w}_j).$$

Ex. 14.1. Are the following sets abstract vector spaces, under suitable laws of addition and scalar multiplication (to be stated if the answer is yes)? If not, why not?

(a) Fixed vectors in three-dimensional space with end points in the first quadrant.

(b) Free vectors in a plane except for vectors perpendicular to a given line.

(c) Ratios of polynomials $P_m(x)/Q_n(x)$ for all (finite) m, n.

(d) Ratios of polynomials $P_m(x)/Q_n(x)$ for $m \leq M$, $n \leq N$.

(e) The set of all solutions of the differential equation

$$\frac{dy}{dx} + \alpha y = 1.$$

(f) The set of vectors with an infinite number of components $[x_1, x_2, \ldots]$ with convergent sum of absolute values $|x_1| + |x_2| + \ldots$.

Ex. 14.2. In the examples of abstract vector spaces (a)–(k), define the rules for addition and multiplication by a scalar where these have not been specified in detail. Also, prove that if $\mathbf{x}$, $\mathbf{y}$ are vectors in the space, then $\mathbf{x} + \mathbf{y}$ and $\lambda\mathbf{y}$ are also in the space, where this has not been done in the examples.

14.2 Abstract Spaces and Isomorphism

Many of the theorems that we developed in Chapter 4 for vector spaces of row and column vectors can be generalized to provide corresponding theorems in abstract vector spaces. We shall not list these theorems in detail, since this would, for the most part, simply repeat results in Chapter 4.

Vectors $\mathbf{u}_1, \mathbf{u}_2, \ldots, \mathbf{u}_n$ are said to be *linearly independent* if their *linear combination* $\alpha_1\mathbf{u}_1 + \ldots + \alpha_n\mathbf{u}_n$ is zero only if $\alpha_1 = \ldots = \alpha_n = 0$. Otherwise, they are linearly dependent. The *dimension* of a vector space V, denoted by dim V, is the largest number of linearly independent vectors that exist in V. If this number is finite, we say that we have a *finite-dimensional space;* if no such number exists, the space is said to be *infinite-dimensional.*

Ex. 14.3. State for each of the examples (a)–(k) in Section 14.1 whether the corresponding vector space is finite- or infinite-dimensional.

A subset W of a vector space V is a set such that any vector in W is also in V. A subset W of V is a *subspace* of V if W is itself a vector space under the same linear operations as in V. The dimension of W does not exceed that of V. A vector space is a subspace of itself. Often it is clear, from the definition of W as a subspace of V, that all we need to do, to see if W is a subspace of V, is to check whether, if $\mathbf{u}$ and $\mathbf{v}$ are in W, then $\alpha\mathbf{u} + \beta\mathbf{v}$ is also in W. This was implicitly the situation in Chapter 4, where Definition 4.2 does not mention explicitly the axioms in Section 14.1. In Chapter 4 we deal mostly with vector spaces that are subspaces of V_n, and this is the context of Definition 4.2. For any set of vectors S selected from V, the set W of all linear combinations of these vectors S is also a vector space, and we say that W is *spanned* or *generated* by S. If S consists of k vectors, the dimension of W is at most k. W is k-dimensional if and only if the k vectors in S are linearly independent.

If V is an n-dimensional space with elements $\mathbf{u}_i$, then there exist families of n linearly independent vectors $\mathbf{u}_1, \ldots, \mathbf{u}_n$ such that any vector $\mathbf{u}$ belonging to V can be expanded *uniquely* as a linear combination of $\mathbf{u}_1, \ldots, \mathbf{u}_n$,

$$\mathbf{u} = \sum_{i=1}^{n} \alpha_i \mathbf{u}_i.$$

Such a family consisting of n vectors $\mathbf{u}_i$ that span the space is called a *basis*. Every basis in a finite-dimensional space consists of the same number of vectors. Any independent set of vectors in a given space is part of a basis for the space. In a p-dimensional space, any p linearly independent vectors constitute a basis for the space, and any $p + 1$ vectors are linearly dependent.

A basis in an infinite-dimensional space has, of course, an infinite number of members. We give three examples:

(a) A basis for example (d) in Section 14.1, the set of all vectors with an infinite number of components $[x_1, x_2, \ldots]$, is the set of unit vectors $[1, 0, 0, \ldots]$, $[0, 1, 0, \ldots]$, ... with zeros except for a 1 in the jth place, for $j = 1, 2, \ldots$.

(b) A basis for example (g) in Section 14.1, the set of all polynomials, is the set $1, x, x^2, \ldots$. To prove that these are linearly independent, suppose that

$$\alpha_0 + \alpha_1 x + \ldots + \alpha_p x^p = 0.$$

This is true for all x, so in particular it must be true for $p + 1$ distinct values of x, say $x_0, x_1, x_2, \ldots, x_p$. Then $\mathbf{A}\boldsymbol{\alpha} = \mathbf{0}$ where $\boldsymbol{\alpha} = [\alpha_0, \ldots, \alpha_p]^T$ and $\mathbf{A}$ is the Vandermonde matrix with x_{i-1}^{j-1} as its (i, j)th element. Since $\mathbf{A}$ is known to be nonsingular (Ex. 7.10), $\boldsymbol{\alpha} = \mathbf{0}$ and the functions $1, x, x^2, \ldots$ are linearly independent.

(c) A basis for example (e) in Section 14.1, the set of all functions $f(x)$, defined in $0 \leq x \leq 1$, and continuous in this range, is

$$\sin \pi x, \quad \sin 2\pi x, \quad \sin 3\pi x, \quad \ldots.$$

The reason for this is that, first of all, any function in $C[a, b]$ can be expanded as a series of such functions [this is the standard Fourier sine series of $f(x)$]. In the second place, the functions are linearly independent since, if

$$\alpha_1 \sin \pi x + \alpha_2 \sin 2\pi x + \ldots + \alpha_n \sin n\pi x = 0,$$

and we multiply by $\sin m\pi t$ and integrate with respect to t from 0 to 1, we obtain $\alpha_m = 0$, $m = 1, \ldots, n$. This is true no matter how large n is, and the space cannot be finite-dimensional.

There is a fundamental distinction between finite- and infinite-dimensional spaces. We have to be careful to remember that theorems that are true for finite-dimensional spaces are not necessarily true when the basis of a space contains an infinite number of elements. (We need only remember the convergence difficulties that arise for infinite series, which simply do not arise in connection with finite series, to see that infinite-dimensional spaces are likely to present difficulties that are nonexistent in the finite-dimensional case.)

We show that an abstract vector space with a basis consisting of n vectors does not differ essentially from any other n-dimensional space. This means that the space of $n \times 1$ column vectors, V_n, that we have considered previously, is a typical finite-dimensional vector space. All finite-dimensional abstract vector spaces are essentially the same as V_n. We proceed to make these ideas more precise.

DEFINITION 14.2. Suppose the V' and V'' are two abstract vector spaces. A correspondence between vectors $\mathbf{x}'$, $\mathbf{x}''$ in V', V'', respectively is called *one-to-one* if:

(a) To each vector $\mathbf{x}'$ in V' there corresponds one and only one vector in V''.
(b) To each vector $\mathbf{x}''$ in V'' there corresponds one and only one vector in V'.

DEFINITION 14.3. Two abstract vector spaces are called *isomorphic* if we can establish a one-to-one correspondence between the vectors in V', V'' that preserves linear relations, i.e., if $\mathbf{x}''$, $\mathbf{y}''$ in V'' correspond to $\mathbf{x}'$, $\mathbf{y}'$ in V', respectively, then $\alpha\mathbf{x}'' + \beta\mathbf{y}''$ corresponds to $\alpha\mathbf{x}' + \beta\mathbf{y}'$.

THEOREM 14.1. *Every n-dimensional abstract vector space is isomorphic to V_n.*

Proof: By "n-dimensional space" we mean a space possessing a basis with precisely n elements. Suppose that $\mathbf{x}_1, \ldots, \mathbf{x}_n$ is a basis in the abstract vector space we are considering. Each vector $\mathbf{x}$ in this space can be written in the form $p_1\mathbf{x}_1 + \ldots + p_n\mathbf{x}_n$, where the scalars $p_1, \ldots, p_n$ are uniquely determined by $\mathbf{x}$. Consider the one-to-one correspondence

$$\mathbf{x} \leftrightarrow \begin{bmatrix} p_1 \\ \cdot \\ \cdot \\ \cdot \\ p_n \end{bmatrix} = \mathbf{p},$$

between the abstract vector space and V_n. If $\mathbf{y} = q_1\mathbf{x}_1 + \ldots + q_n\mathbf{x}_n$, then

$$\alpha\mathbf{x} + \beta\mathbf{y} \leftrightarrow \begin{bmatrix} \alpha p_1 + \beta q_1 \\ \cdot \\ \cdot \\ \cdot \\ \alpha p_n + \beta q_n \end{bmatrix} = \alpha\mathbf{p} + \beta\mathbf{q}.$$

This establishes the desired isomorphism.

The reader may wonder why, if all vector spaces are isomorphic to V_n, we should bother to study any vector space other than V_n. One fundamental reason is that arguments involving vector spaces are often easier if carried out in a completely abstract way, without reference to a system that has a "natural" basis, like V_n. Another reason is that the abstract theory gives us much deeper and clearer understanding of the properties of vector spaces, and a much more powerful tool for further developments, especially when the vector space is no longer finite-dimensional.

Ex. 14.4. Prove that Theorems 4.2, 4.3 are true when the vectors belong to an abstract vector space. Prove that Theorems 4.4–4.7 and 4.9 are true when the vectors belong to an n-dimensional abstract space. (Consideration of the infinite-dimensional case would lead us outside the scope of this book.)

Ex. 14.5. Show that if V and W are isomorphic and $\mathbf{v}_1, \ldots, \mathbf{v}_n$ is a basis in V, then if $\mathbf{w}_i$ in W corresponds to $\mathbf{v}_i$ in V, $i = 1, \ldots, n$, the set $\mathbf{w}_1, \ldots, \mathbf{w}_n$ constitutes a basis in W. (This proves incidentally that isomorphic finite-dimensional spaces have the same dimension.)

Ex. 14.6. Establish explicitly one-to-one correspondences between the spaces (h) and (i) in Section 14.1, and V_k, for suitable k.

14.3 Linear Transformations

In Section 4.8 the problem of solving the linear system $\mathbf{Ax} = \mathbf{b}$ was considered from a vector space point of view. If $\mathbf{A}$, $\mathbf{x}$ are $m \times n$ and $n \times 1$, respectively, then we regard $\mathbf{x}$ as a vector in n-dimensional space, and the relation $\mathbf{y} = \mathbf{Ax}$ transforms $\mathbf{x}$ into an $m \times 1$ vector in an m-dimensional space. In the abstract vector spaces introduced in Section 14.1, we are dealing with entities that are not necessarily column vectors. An essential step in the development of the theory of abstract vector spaces is to introduce a generalization of the relation $\mathbf{y} = \mathbf{Ax}$ for matrices, so as to deal with situations in which an *abstract* vector $\mathbf{x}$ is transformed into another *abstract* vector $\mathbf{y}$ by a transformation which has properties directly analogous to those of the simple matrix relation $\mathbf{y} = \mathbf{Ax}$.

DEFINITION **14.4.** A *linear transformation* or *linear operator A* on an (abstract) vector space V is a correspondence that assigns to every (abstract) vector $\mathbf{x}$ in V an (abstract) vector $A\mathbf{x}$ in such a way that

$$A(\alpha\mathbf{x} + \beta\mathbf{z}) = \alpha A\mathbf{x} + \beta A\mathbf{z} \tag{14.1}$$

for any scalars α, β and any vectors $\mathbf{x}$, $\mathbf{z}$ in V.

We shall use the words "transformation" and "operator" interchangeably. The word transformation is closer to the geometrical picture in which the equation $\mathbf{y} = A\mathbf{x}$ is interpreted in terms of "transforming" a vector $\mathbf{x}$ into a vector $\mathbf{y}$.

(The word *mapping* is also used in this connection.) On the other hand, we can equally think of A as "operating" on $\mathbf{x}$ to produce $\mathbf{y}$, as in differentiation or integration, for example.

Note that the symbol A for a linear transformation or operator is not the same as the symbol $\mathbf{A}$ for a matrix. The abstract idea of a linear transformation does not involve matrices, and in the general theory of linear transformations or operators it is not necessary to mention matrices, except as a special tool, as in Section 14.5.

We consider some examples. The idea of a linear operator on an abstract vector space covers a wide variety of situations.

(a) If $\mathbf{x}$ is a vector in an abstract vector space, then the transformation A such that $A\mathbf{x} = \gamma\mathbf{x}$, where γ is a scalar, is linear. However, the transformation A such that $A\mathbf{x} = \gamma\mathbf{x} + \mathbf{x}_0$, where $\mathbf{x}_0$ is a fixed vector, independent of $\mathbf{x}$, is *not* linear, for

$$A(\alpha\mathbf{x} + \beta\mathbf{y}) = \gamma(\alpha\mathbf{x} + \beta\mathbf{y}) + \mathbf{x}_0,$$

whereas

$$\alpha A\mathbf{x} + \beta A\mathbf{y} = \alpha(\gamma\mathbf{x} + \mathbf{x}_0) + \beta(\gamma\mathbf{y} + \mathbf{x}_0),$$

and these are not in general the same.

(b) If V is the vector space of $n \times 1$ column vectors, then $A\mathbf{x} = (\mathbf{b}, \mathbf{x})$, where $\mathbf{b}$ is a fixed vector in V, is linear, since

$$A(\alpha\mathbf{x} + \beta\mathbf{y}) = (\mathbf{b}, \alpha\mathbf{x} + \beta\mathbf{y}) = \alpha(\mathbf{b}, \mathbf{x}) + \beta(\mathbf{b}, \mathbf{y}) = \alpha A\mathbf{x} + \beta A\mathbf{y}.$$

However, $A\mathbf{x} = (\mathbf{x}, \mathbf{b})$ is *not* linear, since then

$$A(\alpha\mathbf{x} + \beta\mathbf{y}) = (\alpha\mathbf{x} + \beta\mathbf{y}, \mathbf{b}) = \bar{\alpha}(\mathbf{x}, \mathbf{b}) + \bar{\beta}(\mathbf{y}, \mathbf{b}) = \bar{\alpha}A\mathbf{x} + \bar{\beta}A\mathbf{y}.$$

Also, $A\mathbf{x} = (\mathbf{x}, \mathbf{x})$ is *not* linear since

$$A(\alpha\mathbf{x} + \beta\mathbf{y}) = (\alpha\mathbf{x} + \beta\mathbf{y}, \alpha\mathbf{x} + \beta\mathbf{y}) \neq \alpha A\mathbf{x} + \beta A\mathbf{y}.$$

(c) If V is the vector space of $n \times 1$ column vectors, then $A\mathbf{x} = \mathbf{A}\mathbf{x}$, where $\mathbf{A}$ is any $m \times n$ matrix, is linear.

(d) If V is the space of continuous functions of a variable t in $a \leq t \leq b$, so that $\mathbf{x} = x(t)$, a scalar function of t, then $A\mathbf{x} = f(t)x(t)$, where $f(t)$ is a fixed function independent of $\mathbf{x}$, is linear.

(e) If V is the same space as in (d), then

$$A\mathbf{x} = x(t) + \int_a^b K(t, s)x(s)\, ds$$

is linear if $K(t, s)$ is linear in t and s.

(f) If V is the same space as in (d), then integration is linear,

$$A\mathbf{x} = \int_0^t x(s)\, ds.$$

(g) If V is the space of differentiable functions of t, then differentiation is linear,

$$A\mathbf{x} = \frac{dx(t)}{dt}.$$

Similarly, if V is the space of twice-differentiable functions of t, then

$$A\mathbf{x} = \frac{d}{dx}\, p(t)\, \frac{dx(t)}{dt} - q(t)\, x(t)$$

is a linear transformation.

Note that in each case we have been careful to specify the class of functions on which the transformation acts. Also, the class of functions that appears as a result of a transformation may not be the same as the class from which we started. Thus for differentiation in (g), the result of differentiating $x(t)$ may not itself be differentiable. It is useful to introduce terminology to describe this situation. We first require a preliminary theorem which follows immediately from the definition of a vector space.

THEOREM **14.2.** *Consider a linear transformation A on a vector space V.*

(i) *The set of vectors $\mathbf{y} = A\mathbf{x}$, where $\mathbf{x}$ is any vector in V, is a vector space.*

(ii) *The set of vectors $\mathbf{x}$ in V such that $A\mathbf{x} = \mathbf{0}$ form a subspace.*

Proof: We define a set of vectors W by saying that any member $\mathbf{y}$ of W is produced from a vector $\mathbf{x}$, that lies in a vector space V, by means of a linear transformation A. Suppose that a vector $\mathbf{w}$ also lies in W, so that $\mathbf{w} = A\mathbf{z}$, where $\mathbf{z}$ lies in V. From the definition of A,

$$A(\alpha\mathbf{x} + \beta\mathbf{z}) = \alpha A\mathbf{x} + \beta A\mathbf{z} = \alpha\mathbf{y} + \beta\mathbf{w},$$

i.e., $\alpha\mathbf{y} + \beta\mathbf{w}$ is produced by A from a vector $\alpha\mathbf{x} + \beta\mathbf{z}$ that, by definition of a vector space, lies in V. Hence, the set of vectors W forms a vector space. This proves (i). Let U be the set of vectors $\mathbf{x}$ defined by $A\mathbf{x} = \mathbf{0}$, where $\mathbf{x}$ is a vector in V. Let $\mathbf{z}$ be a second vector in U. Then, by definition of a linear transformation,

$$A(\alpha\mathbf{x} + \beta\mathbf{z}) = \alpha A\mathbf{x} + \beta A\mathbf{z} = \mathbf{0},$$

so that $\alpha\mathbf{x} + \beta\mathbf{z}$ lies in U. Hence, U is a vector space.

As a result of this theorem, we can extend Definition 14.4 in the following way.

DEFINITION **14.5.** The vector space consisting of all vectors $\mathbf{y} = A\mathbf{x}$ where A is a linear transformation and $\mathbf{x}$ lies in a vector space V is known as the *range* (or *image space*) of A. The vector space V is known as the *domain* of A. The space of vectors $\mathbf{x}$ such that $A\mathbf{x} = \mathbf{0}$ is the *null space* (or *kernel*) of A. If, when $\mathbf{x}$ lies in

V, the resulting vector $\mathbf{y} = A\mathbf{x}$ lies in a vector space W, we say that we are dealing with a linear transformation *on a vector space V to a vector space W*. We write $A: V \rightarrow W$.

Note that, according to this definition, the range is a subspace of W but it need not coincide with W.

It is often helpful to think of a linear transformation pictorially as in Figure 14.1. A linear transformation goes in one direction, from V to W. We say nothing about going from W back to V.

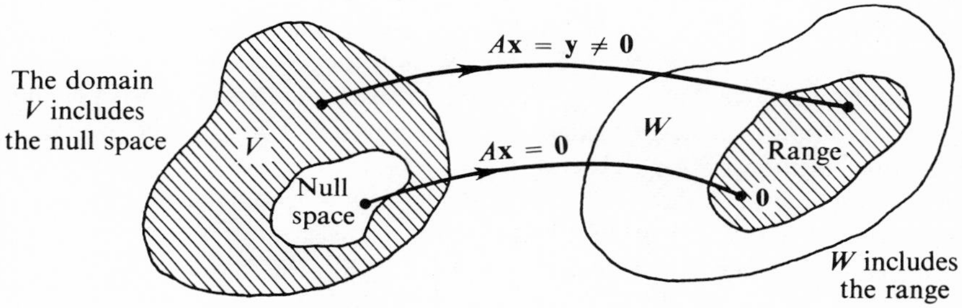

Figure 14.1 Pictorial representation of a linear transformation.

In order to illustrate the importance of careful specification of the domain of a linear transformation, we extend example (c) given at the beginning of this section in which $A\mathbf{x}$ was the vector $\mathbf{Ax}$, where $\mathbf{A}$ is any $m \times n$ matrix, and the domain of A is the space of all $n \times 1$ column vectors. Instead of defining the domain in this way, we can restrict $\mathbf{x}$ to lie in a p-dimensional subspace of the whole space of $n \times 1$ column vectors. The precise specification of the domain will be important if we wish to consider the equation $A\mathbf{x} = \mathbf{b}$. That is, given $\mathbf{b}$, what values of $\mathbf{x}$ are transformed into $\mathbf{b}$ by the linear transformation A? Even though the vector $\mathbf{y} = A\mathbf{x}$ is obtained by forming $\mathbf{Ax}$ where $\mathbf{A}$ is an $m \times n$ matrix, the equation $A\mathbf{x} = \mathbf{b}$ must be carefully distinguished from the matrix equation $\mathbf{Ax} = \mathbf{b}$. In order to solve $A\mathbf{x} = \mathbf{b}$ we can first solve $\mathbf{Ax} = \mathbf{b}$ and then pick out, from all possible $\mathbf{x}$ satisfying this equation, those $\mathbf{x}$ that lie in the domain V of the operator A. As a specific example, suppose that the transformation A is defined by $\mathbf{y} = \mathbf{Ax}$, where $\mathbf{x}$ is a 2×1 vector whose second element is zero (this specifies the domain of A) and

$$\mathbf{A} = \begin{bmatrix} 1 & 1 \\ -1 & 1 \end{bmatrix}. \tag{14.2}$$

Since the domain of A consists of all vectors of the form $x_1 = k$, $x_2 = 0$, the range of A consists of all vectors of the form

$$\mathbf{Ax} = \begin{bmatrix} k \\ -k \end{bmatrix}.$$

What this means is that it will be possible to solve the equation $A\mathbf{x} = \mathbf{b}$ if and only if $b_2 = -b_1$. In this case $A\mathbf{x} = \mathbf{b}$ has a unique solution $x_1 = b_1$, $x_2 = 0$. Otherwise $A\mathbf{x} = \mathbf{b}$ has no solution. This should be contrasted with the situation where the domain of A is the set of all 2×1 column vectors. Then $A\mathbf{x} = \mathbf{b}$ always has a unique solution. As a second example, if the domain of A is again given by vectors with second element zero, but

$$\mathbf{A} = \begin{bmatrix} 1 & -1 \\ -2 & 2 \end{bmatrix}, \qquad \mathbf{b} = \begin{bmatrix} 2 \\ -4 \end{bmatrix}, \tag{14.3}$$

then the general solution of $\mathbf{Ax} = \mathbf{b}$ is given by $x_1 = k$, $x_2 = k - 2$. The equation $A\mathbf{x} = \mathbf{b}$, where now $\mathbf{x}$ must have its second element zero, has, therefore, the unique solution $x_1 = 2$, $x_2 = 0$. Another way of seeing this is to recognize that any vector $x_1 = k$, $x_2 = 0$ is transformed into $\mathbf{Ax}$ with elements k, $-2k$. Comparison of this result with $\mathbf{b}$ shows that $k = 2$ and we recover the unique solution of $A\mathbf{x} = \mathbf{b}$.

We conclude this section by considering some geometrical examples of linear transformations. In two dimensions, a transformation $\mathbf{y} = A\mathbf{x}$ involves a point (x_1, x_2) which is moved to a point (y_1, y_2) in the plane.

(a) Consider

$$y_1 = x_1, \qquad y_2 = 4x_2.$$

The x_1-coordinate of the point is unchanged so that it moves parallel to the x_2-axis in such a way that the x_2-coordinate is multiplied by 4. This is a simple example of a *magnification*. In the general n-dimensional case, if a vector $\mathbf{x}$ is represented by

$$\mathbf{x} = \alpha_1\mathbf{u}_1 + \ldots + \alpha_n\mathbf{u}_n$$

relative to a basis $\mathbf{u}_1, \ldots, \mathbf{u}_n$ in the n-dimensional space, we have

$$\mathbf{y} = k_1\alpha_1\mathbf{u}_1 + \ldots + k_n\alpha_n\mathbf{u}_n,$$

where the k_i are constants. Algebraically, we have $\mathbf{y} = \mathbf{Dx}$ where $\mathbf{D}$ is a diagonal matrix.

(b) Consider

$$y_1 = x_1, \qquad y_2 = -x_2.$$

The point (x_1, x_2) is transformed (or mapped) into its *reflection* in the x_1-axis. The matrix of the transformation, $\mathbf{y} = \mathbf{Cx}$, is given by

$$\mathbf{C} = \begin{bmatrix} 1 & 0 \\ 0 & -1 \end{bmatrix}.$$

In the general n-dimensional case, the matrix $\mathbf{C}$ will be a unit matrix, except that one of the diagonal elements will be -1.

(c) Consider

$$y_1 = x_1 + x_2, \qquad y_2 = x_2.$$

The point (x_1, x_2) is mapped into $(x_1 + x_2, x_2)$, so that points are shifted parallel to the x_1-axis by an amount x_2. Points that lie on a straight line through the origin before the transformation lie on a straight line through the origin after the transformation. The reader will readily verify that circles become ellipses. A transformation of the type described here is known as a *shear*.

(d) Consider the transformation which rotates every vector in the plane from the origin to a point (x_1, x_2) through an angle θ. It is easy to see that this is a linear transformation since the result of rotating $\alpha\mathbf{x} + \beta\mathbf{y}$ through θ is the same as the result of rotating $\mathbf{x}$ and $\mathbf{y}$ through θ, multiplying the results by α and β, respectively, and adding. Algebraically, if r is the distance from the origin to (x_1, x_2) and α is the angle that this vector makes with the x_1-axis, we have $x_1 = r \cos \alpha$, $x_2 = r \sin \alpha$, $y_1 = r \cos (\alpha + \theta)$, $y_2 = r \sin (\alpha + \theta)$, so that

$$\begin{bmatrix} y_1 \\ y_2 \end{bmatrix} = \begin{bmatrix} \cos\theta & -\sin\theta \\ \sin\theta & \cos\theta \end{bmatrix} \begin{bmatrix} x_1 \\ x_2 \end{bmatrix}.$$

The linearity of the transformation follows from this representation, independent of the previous argument.

(e) Consider

$$y_1 = x_1, \qquad y_2 = 0.$$

The point (x_1, x_2) is mapped into its *projection* $(x_1, 0)$ on the x_1-axis. In the previous examples we could start from any transformed vector (y_1, y_2) and recover uniquely the original vector (x_1, x_2). This is not possible in the present example, and the transformation is said to be singular. A generalization to n-dimensional space is given by a transformation which starts with a general $n \times 1$ column vector and transforms it into a p-dimensional subspace, where $p < n$. An example is given by $\mathbf{y} = \mathbf{D}\mathbf{x}$, where $\mathbf{D}$ is a diagonal matrix with at least one zero element on its diagonal.

This concludes our discussion of examples of linear transformations or operators.

Ex. 14.7. Which of the following transformations are linear? Justify your answers.

(a) $A\mathbf{x} = (\mathbf{a}, \mathbf{x})\mathbf{a}$; $\mathbf{a}$, $\mathbf{x}$ in V_n, $\mathbf{a}$ fixed.

(b) $A\mathbf{x} = (\mathbf{a}, \mathbf{x})\mathbf{x}$; $\mathbf{a}$, $\mathbf{x}$ in V_n, $\mathbf{a}$ fixed.

(c) $A\mathbf{x}(t) = x(t + 1)$; $x(t)$ a polynomial in t of degree $\leq n$.

(d) $A\mathbf{x}(t) = tx'(0) = t(dx/dt)_{t=0}$; $x(t)$ a differentiable function of t.

Ex. 14.8. Are the following statements true or false? Justify your answers.

(a) If A is a linear transformation on V to W, and $A\mathbf{u}_1, \ldots, A\mathbf{u}_p$ are linearly independent, then so are $\mathbf{u}_1, \ldots, \mathbf{u}_p$.

(b) If A is a linear transformation on V to W, and $\mathbf{u}_1, \ldots, \mathbf{u}_p$ are linearly independent, then so are $A\mathbf{u}_1, \ldots, A\mathbf{u}_p$.

14.4 The Algebra of Linear Transformations

We now develop some aspects of the algebra of linear transformations. It is necessary to define various operations involving more than one linear transformation.

DEFINITION **14.6.** Two linear transformations A, B on V to W are said to be *equal*, $A = B$, if $A\mathbf{x} = B\mathbf{x}$ for every $\mathbf{x}$ in V. The *sum* $A + B$ is defined by

$$(A + B)\mathbf{x} = A\mathbf{x} + B\mathbf{x},$$

where $\mathbf{x}$ is any element in V. The transformation αA where α is a scalar is defined by

$$(\alpha A)\mathbf{x} = \alpha(A\mathbf{x}).$$

The *product* AB of two linear transformations A on V to W and B on U to V is defined by

$$(AB)\mathbf{x} = A(B\mathbf{x})$$

where $\mathbf{x}$ is any element of U.

THEOREM **14.3.** *The transformations $A + B$, αA, and AB are linear.*

Proof: The proofs of these results are easy but necessary. We give only the proof that AB is linear:

$$\begin{aligned}(AB)(\alpha\mathbf{x} + \beta\mathbf{z}) &= A[B(\alpha\mathbf{x} + \beta\mathbf{z})] \\ &= A(\alpha B\mathbf{x} + \beta B\mathbf{z}) \\ &= \alpha A(B\mathbf{x}) + \beta A(B\mathbf{z}) \\ &= \alpha(AB)\mathbf{x} + \beta(AB)\mathbf{z}.\end{aligned}$$

Hence, AB is linear.

DEFINITION **14.7.** The *zero* transformation on a space V to a space W is the transformation 0 such that

$$0\mathbf{x} = \mathbf{0}$$

for all $\mathbf{x}$ in V. The *identity* (or *unit*) *transformation* on V to W is the transformation I such that

$$I\mathbf{x} = \mathbf{x}$$

for all $\mathbf{x}$ in V.

THEOREM **14.4.** *If A, B, C, D are linear transformations, where A, B are on V to W, C is on U to V, and D is on W to X, then*

(i) $(A + B)C = AC + BC$,
(ii) $D(A + B) = DA + DB$,
(iii) $D(AC) = (DA)C$,

(iv) $AI = IA = A$,
(v) $A0 = 0$, $0A = 0$

In the last two cases it is assumed that the identity and zero transformations are defined in connection with the appropriate spaces.

Proof: The proof of these results follows directly from Definitions 14.6, 14.7 and is left to the reader.

It is extremely convenient that the rules for the algebra of linear transformations are the same as the rules for the algebra of matrices. The exceptional situations for matrices are also exceptional for linear transformations, which is not surprising since matrices are a special type of linear transformation. In particular, if A, B are linear transformations on V to W, and on U to V, respectively, then AB is defined but BA is meaningless unless U and W coincide. Even if U and W coincide, it is unusual to have $AB = BA$. In general, $AB \neq BA$. If $AB = 0$, we cannot deduce that either A is 0 or B is 0.

Ex. 14.9. If V is the space of all differentiable functions $\mathbf{x} = x(t)$, and

$$A\mathbf{x} = tx(t), \qquad D\mathbf{x} = \frac{dx(t)}{dt},$$

for any $\mathbf{x}$ in V, prove that

$$DA - AD = I.$$

Ex. 14.10. Prove that for linear transformations A, B for which AB is defined, the null space of AB contains the null space of B, and the range of AB is contained in the range of A.

14.5 Coordinates, Change of Basis, and Linear Transformations

Many theorems in two- or three-dimensional geometry are quite independent of the existence of coordinate axes, but it is often convenient to introduce coordinate axes to prove these theorems. A similar situation exists in connection with vector spaces. For instance, many theorems involving linear transformations are quite independent of the existence of a basis in the space. (Theorems 14.3 and 14.4 in the last section are examples.) Nevertheless, it is often convenient to introduce a basis in a vector space. It will turn out that matrices appear in a natural way, when bases are introduced in abstract vector spaces that themselves may have nothing to do with matrices. From this point of view, matrices are tools for dealing with representations of abstract vector spaces in particular coordinate systems.

The coordinates x_i of a vector $\mathbf{x}$ representing a point in n-dimensional space can also be regarded as the coefficients of the unit vectors $\mathbf{e}_i$ if $\mathbf{x}$ is represented as a sum of multiples of the unit vectors

$$\mathbf{x} = \begin{bmatrix} x_1 \\ \cdot \\ \cdot \\ \cdot \\ x_n \end{bmatrix} = x_1\mathbf{e}_1 + \ldots + x_n\mathbf{e}_n.$$

If we decide to work in terms of another basis $\mathbf{u}_1, \ldots, \mathbf{u}_n$, in terms of which

$$\mathbf{x} = \alpha_1\mathbf{u}_1 + \ldots + \alpha_n\mathbf{u}_n,$$

it is natural to call $\alpha_1, \ldots, \alpha_n$ the *coordinates* of $\mathbf{x}$ relative to the new basis. We have to be careful about the order in the general case. For the unit vectors there is a natural order $\mathbf{e}_1, \ldots, \mathbf{e}_n$. In the general case there may be no natural order. If we refer to $\alpha_1, \ldots, \alpha_n$, in the above example, as the coordinates of $\mathbf{x}$, we must remember the order in which we assume that the basis vectors are arranged.

DEFINITION **14.8.** If a set of basis vectors are arranged in a definite order, we say that we are dealing with an *ordered basis*. If a vector $\mathbf{x}$ is expressed as a linear combination of an ordered basis $\mathbf{u}_1, \ldots, \mathbf{u}_n$, distinguished by a letter N,

$$\mathbf{x} = \alpha_1\mathbf{u}_1 + \ldots + \alpha_n\mathbf{u}_n,$$

the numbers $\alpha_1, \ldots, \alpha_n$ are called the *coordinates* of $\mathbf{x}$ relative to N, and we write

$$[\mathbf{x}]_N = \begin{bmatrix} \alpha_1 \\ \cdot \\ \cdot \\ \cdot \\ \alpha_n \end{bmatrix}. \tag{14.4}$$

Suppose that we change from one basis in an n-dimensional space to another. Specifically, let $\mathbf{u}_1, \ldots, \mathbf{u}_n$ be an ordered basis N, and $\mathbf{v}_1, \ldots, \mathbf{v}_n$ be a second ordered basis Q. By the definition of a basis, each of the $\mathbf{v}_j$ can be expressed as a linear combination of the $\mathbf{u}_i$,

$$\mathbf{v}_j = \sum_{i=1}^{n} p_{ij}\mathbf{u}_i, \qquad j = 1, \ldots, n. \tag{14.5}$$

Consider any vector $\mathbf{x}$ in the space. Suppose that when $\mathbf{x}$ is expressed in terms of the ordered bases we obtain

$$\begin{aligned} \mathbf{x} &= \alpha_1\mathbf{u}_1 + \ldots + \alpha_n\mathbf{u}_n \\ &= \beta_1\mathbf{v}_1 + \ldots + \beta_n\mathbf{v}_n. \end{aligned} \tag{14.6}$$

On substituting for the $\mathbf{v}_i$ in this second equation from (14.5), we obtain

$$\mathbf{x} = \sum_{j=1}^{n} \beta_j \sum_{i=1}^{n} p_{ij}\mathbf{u}_i = \sum_{i=1}^{n} \mathbf{u}_i \sum_{j=1}^{n} p_{ij}\beta_j.$$

Comparing this with (14.6) we see that, since the expression for a vector in terms of basis vectors is unique,

$$\alpha_i = \sum_{j=1}^{n} p_{ij}\beta_j$$

or, in matrix notation,

$$\boldsymbol{\alpha} = \mathbf{P}\boldsymbol{\beta}. \tag{14.7}$$

This gives the following theorem.

THEOREM **14.5.** *Let V be an n-dimensional space and let N, Q be two ordered bases for V. Then there is a unique nonsingular matrix $\mathbf{P}$ of order n such that, for any vector $\mathbf{x}$ in V,*

$$[\mathbf{x}]_N = \mathbf{P}[\mathbf{x}]_Q. \tag{14.8}$$

Proof: Equation (14.8) is simply a restatement of (14.7), using the notation (14.4). The matrix $\mathbf{P}$ is nonsingular since, if the α_i are zero, then $\mathbf{x}$ in (14.6) is zero, which means that the β_i are zero. In terms of (14.7) this means that if $\boldsymbol{\alpha}$ is zero then $\boldsymbol{\beta}$ is zero, so that $\mathbf{P}$ is nonsingular.

We conclude the section by discussing briefly the relation between linear transformations and matrices. Let V and W be n- and m-dimensional spaces with bases

$$\mathbf{u}_1, \ldots, \mathbf{u}_n \quad \text{and} \quad \mathbf{w}_1, \ldots, \mathbf{w}_m,$$

respectively. Suppose that a linear transformation A on V to W transforms the basis vectors $\mathbf{u}_j$ into vectors $\mathbf{z}_j$ in W. We can express the $\mathbf{z}_j$ as linear combinations of the $\mathbf{w}_i$,

$$A\mathbf{u}_j = \mathbf{z}_j = \sum_{i=1}^{m} a_{ij}\mathbf{w}_i, \qquad j = 1, \ldots, n. \tag{14.9}$$

Suppose now that we consider the transform of any vector $\mathbf{v}$ in V. This vector can be expressed as a linear combination of the base vectors, say

$$\mathbf{v} = \sum_{j=1}^{n} x_j\mathbf{v}_j.$$

Then

$$A\mathbf{v} = \sum_{j=1}^{n} x_j A\mathbf{u}_j = \sum_{j=1}^{n} x_j \sum_{i=1}^{n} a_{ij}\mathbf{w}_i = \sum_{i=1}^{n}\left\{\sum_{j=1}^{n} a_{ij}x_j\right\}\mathbf{w}_i.$$

This shows that the coordinates of the transformed vector $A\mathbf{v}$, with respect to the base vectors $\mathbf{w}_i$ in W, are given by $\mathbf{Ax}$ where $\mathbf{x}$ is the $n \times 1$ column vector representing the coordinates of $\mathbf{v}$ in the ordered basis $\mathbf{u}_1, \ldots, \mathbf{u}_n$, and $\mathbf{A}$ is the matrix of the a_{ij} introduced in (14.9), relating the transforms of the $\mathbf{u}_j$ to the $\mathbf{w}_i$. In terms of the notation (14.4), we have proved:

THEOREM **14.6.** *Let V and W be n- and m-dimensional spaces with ordered bases N and M, respectively. Corresponding to a linear* *transformation A on V to W there is an $m \times n$ matrix* **A** *such that, for every vector* **v** *in V*

$$[A\mathbf{v}]_M = \mathbf{A}[\mathbf{v}]_N. \tag{14.10}$$

The matrices corresponding to the sum or product of linear transformations are simply the sum and product of the corresponding matrices.

THEOREM 14.7. *Let V, W, Z be spaces of dimensions m, n, p, with ordered bases N, M, P, respectively. For linear transformations A, B on V to W and C on W to Z, let the corresponding matrices relative to the appropriate bases be* **A**, **B**, **C**, *respectively. Then, for each* **v** *in V,*

$$[(\alpha A + \beta B)\mathbf{v}]_M = (\alpha\mathbf{A} + \beta\mathbf{B})[\mathbf{v}]_N$$
$$[CA\mathbf{v}]_P = \mathbf{CA}[\mathbf{v}]_N. \tag{14.11}$$

Proof: The proof follows immediately from (14.10) and the properties of linear transformations. We prove only the second result. From (14.10),

$$[A\mathbf{v}]_M = \mathbf{A}[\mathbf{v}]_N,$$
$$[C(A\mathbf{v})]_P = \mathbf{C}[A\mathbf{v}]_M = \mathbf{CA}[\mathbf{v}]_N,$$

and, since $C(A\mathbf{v}) = CA\mathbf{v}$, this is (14.11).

In conclusion, we ask what happens to the matrix representing a linear operator if we change from one ordered basis to another. For simplicity, suppose that A is a linear transformation acting on a space V into the same space V. Let two ordered bases N, Q for V be given by

$$\mathbf{u}_1, \ldots, \mathbf{u}_n \quad \text{and} \quad \mathbf{v}_1, \ldots, \mathbf{v}_n.$$

From Theorem 14.5, a nonsingular matrix **P** exists such that, for any **x** in V,

$$[\mathbf{x}]_N = \mathbf{P}[\mathbf{x}]_Q. \tag{14.12}$$

Also, from Theorem 14.6, equation (14.10), remembering that the spaces M and N are now the same,

$$[A\mathbf{x}]_N = \mathbf{A}[\mathbf{x}]_N.$$

On using (14.12) in this equation, we obtain

$$\mathbf{P}[A\mathbf{x}]_Q = \mathbf{AP}[\mathbf{x}]_Q$$

or, since **P** is nonsingular (Theorem 14.5),

$$[A\mathbf{x}]_Q = \mathbf{P}^{-1}\mathbf{AP}[\mathbf{x}]_Q.$$

This gives the following theorem.

THEOREM **14.8.** *If the matrix representations of a linear operator A from a space V to the same space V, relative to ordered bases N, Q in V, are* **A**, **B**, *respectively, then*

$$\mathbf{B} = \mathbf{P}^{-1}\mathbf{A}\mathbf{P}, \tag{14.13}$$

where **P** *is the matrix expressing the ordered basis N in terms of Q.*

Matrices **A**, **B** related by an equation like (14.13) have already turned up in this book in connection with eigenvectors and eigenvalues, where the matrices **A** and **B** were said to be *similar*. Similarity transformations were studied in great detail in Chapter 11. Theorem 14.8 shows that similarity transformations are important when studying linear transformations on an abstract vector space.

Ex. 14.11. Let A be a linear transformation on the space of polynomials of degree less than or equal to 3 defined by

$$A\mathbf{x} = \frac{d}{dt}\{tx(t)\}.$$

What is the matrix of A relative to the basis $\mathbf{u}_i = t^i$, $i = 0, 1, 2, 3$?

Ex. 14.12. Prove that if k vectors in an n-dimensional space are linearly dependent, then the matrix whose columns are the coordinates of these vectors in terms of a basis for the space has a rank less than min $(k, n + 1)$.

14.6 Linear Equations

We are now in a position to consider the problem of solving the linear equation

$$A\mathbf{x} = \mathbf{b}, \tag{14.14}$$

i.e., given a linear transformation A on V to W, and a vector **b** in the range of A, what can we say about **x**? As one might expect, we introduce the idea of an inverse transformation.

DEFINITION **14.9.** If A is a linear transformation on V to W, then B is said to be the *inverse* of A if B is a transformation on W to V such that

$$AB = I_W, \qquad BA = I_V, \tag{14.15}$$

where I_W, I_V are the identity transformations in W and V, respectively. A transformation B satisfying $AB = I_W$ is called a *right-inverse* of A, one satisfying $BA = I_V$ is called a *left-inverse* of A. The transformation A is said to be *nonsingular* if it has a (two-sided) inverse.

We prove the following basic properties of the inverse transformation.

THEOREM **14.9.** (i) *The (two-sided) inverse B of a linear transformation A is a linear transformation.*

(ii) *If B is a left-inverse of A, and C is a right-inverse of A, then $B = C$ and A is nonsingular.*

(iii) *A linear transformation has at most one inverse.*

Proof: Suppose that $A\mathbf{x} = \mathbf{z}$, $A\mathbf{y} = \mathbf{w}$. On multiplying each of these by B, we find that $\mathbf{x} = B\mathbf{z}$, $\mathbf{y} = B\mathbf{w}$. If we define $\mathbf{u} = B(\alpha\mathbf{z} + \beta\mathbf{w})$, then

$$A\mathbf{u} = \alpha\mathbf{z} + \beta\mathbf{w} = \alpha A\mathbf{x} + \beta A\mathbf{y} = A(\alpha\mathbf{x} + \beta\mathbf{y}),$$

where we use the fact that A is linear. On multiplying this result by B, we obtain

$$B(\alpha\mathbf{z} + \beta\mathbf{w}) = \mathbf{u} = \alpha\mathbf{x} + \beta\mathbf{y} = \alpha B\mathbf{z} + \beta B\mathbf{w}.$$

Hence, B is linear. To prove (ii) we note that if $\mathbf{x}$ is any vector in W we have, in succession,

$$B(AC)\mathbf{x} = (BA)C\mathbf{x} \rightarrow BI_W\mathbf{x} = I_VC\mathbf{x} \rightarrow B\mathbf{x} = C\mathbf{x}.$$

Hence B and C transform any vector $\mathbf{x}$ in W into the same vector, and we can write $B = C$. This common transformation satisfies the conditions for an inverse in Definition 14.9 so that A is nonsingular. If D is another left-inverse, then the same proof shows that $D = C$ so that $D = B$ and the inverse of A is unique, if it exists.

Our original definition of a linear transformation involved going from a space V to a space W, and we said nothing about what happens if we try to go in the reverse direction. If A is nonsingular, we can multiply the equation $A\mathbf{x} = \mathbf{y}$ by A^{-1} to obtain $\mathbf{x} = A^{-1}\mathbf{y}$. In terms of the pictorial representation in Figure 14.1, this means that if we start from a point $\mathbf{y}$ in the range of A, then a linear transformation exists which brings us back to a unique point in the domain of A. This implies that if A is to have an inverse, the domain of A can have no null space other than the point $\mathbf{x} = \mathbf{0}$. The reason for this is that otherwise the point $\mathbf{y} = \mathbf{0}$ cannot be transformed back into a unique point in the domain of A, and this is an essential condition for the existence of an inverse of A. Similarly, we must arrange that the domain of A^{-1} is the range of A, since otherwise we cannot expect to be able to transform back any point in the domain of A^{-1} into a point in the domain of A. These considerations are made more precise in the following theorem.

THEOREM **14.10.** *If A is a linear transformation on V to W, then an inverse transformation A^{-1} on W to V exists if and only if*

(i) $A\mathbf{x} = \mathbf{0}$ *implies* $\mathbf{x} = \mathbf{0}$ *and*

(ii) *W is the range of A, i.e., for any $\mathbf{y}$ in W there exists (at least one) $\mathbf{x}$ in V such that $A\mathbf{x} = \mathbf{y}$.*

Proof: By (ii), for any y in W there exists at least one $\mathbf{x}$ in V such that $A\mathbf{x} = \mathbf{y}$. This $\mathbf{x}$ is unique since, if $\mathbf{x}_1$ is such that $A\mathbf{x}_1 = \mathbf{y}$, then $A(\mathbf{x} - \mathbf{x}_1) = \mathbf{0}$ so that, by (i), $\mathbf{x} - \mathbf{x}_1 = \mathbf{0}$, and $\mathbf{x} = \mathbf{x}_1$. We define the transformation A^{-1} by $A^{-1}\mathbf{y} = \mathbf{x}$ for any $\mathbf{y}$ in W, where $\mathbf{x}$ is the element which we have just been considering. We have $A(A^{-1}\mathbf{y}) = A\mathbf{x} = \mathbf{y}$ or $(AA^{-1})\mathbf{y} = \mathbf{y}$ for any $\mathbf{y}$ in W so that $AA^{-1} = I_W$. For all $\mathbf{x}$ in V we have $(A^{-1}A)\mathbf{x} = A^{-1}(A\mathbf{x}) = A^{-1}\mathbf{y} = \mathbf{x}$, so that $A^{-1}A = I_V$. This proves the existence of the inverse transformation if (i) and (ii) are true. Conversely, if an inverse exists and $A\mathbf{x} = \mathbf{0}$, then $A^{-1}A\mathbf{x} = A^{-1}\mathbf{0} = \mathbf{0}$ so that $\mathbf{x} = \mathbf{0}$. Also, the equation $A\mathbf{x} = \mathbf{y}$ is satisfied by $\mathbf{x} = A^{-1}\mathbf{y}$ (verification of this used the property $AA^{-1} = I_W$), so that for every element $\mathbf{y}$ in W there exists an element $\mathbf{x}$ in V such that $A\mathbf{x} = \mathbf{y}$, and W is the range of V. This completes the proof.

Ex. 14.13. Consider the linear transformation A defined by the matrix

$$\mathbf{A} = \begin{bmatrix} 1 & 1 \\ 2 & 2 \end{bmatrix}, \tag{14.16}$$

where the domain V of A is the space of 2×1 vectors with $x_1 = 2x_2$. We have

$$A\mathbf{x} = \begin{bmatrix} 1 & 1 \\ 2 & 2 \end{bmatrix}\begin{bmatrix} 2k \\ k \end{bmatrix} = \begin{bmatrix} 3k \\ 6k \end{bmatrix}.$$

Hence, $A\mathbf{x} = \mathbf{0}$ implies $\mathbf{x} = \mathbf{0}$. The range W of A consists of 2×1 vectors with $x_2 = 2x_1$, and it is easy to see that, if $\mathbf{y}$ is any vector in W, we can find an $\mathbf{x}$ in V such that $A\mathbf{x} = \mathbf{y}$. Hence, Theorem 14.10 tells us that A must have an inverse. To find a 2×2 matrix representing A^{-1}, we determine a, b, c, d such that [see (14.15)]

$$\begin{bmatrix} 1 & 1 \\ 2 & 2 \end{bmatrix}\begin{bmatrix} a & b \\ c & d \end{bmatrix}\begin{bmatrix} p \\ 2p \end{bmatrix} = \begin{bmatrix} p \\ 2p \end{bmatrix}, \qquad \begin{bmatrix} a & b \\ c & d \end{bmatrix}\begin{bmatrix} 1 & 1 \\ 2 & 2 \end{bmatrix}\begin{bmatrix} 2q \\ q \end{bmatrix} = \begin{bmatrix} 2q \\ q \end{bmatrix}.$$

This leads to the following "inverse" of $\mathbf{A}$:

$$\mathbf{B} = \frac{1}{3}\begin{bmatrix} 2 - 6b, & 3b \\ 1 - 6d, & 3d \end{bmatrix} \tag{14.17}$$

for abitrary b, d. Although this matrix representation of A^{-1} contains arbitrary constants, these are not important, since we can check that if $\mathbf{Ax} = \mathbf{y}$ then $\mathbf{By} = \mathbf{x}$, independent of b, d. Check that $\mathbf{AB}$ and $\mathbf{BA}$ lead to matrix representations of I_W and I_V, the identity transformations introduced in Definition 14.9.

In the proof of Theorem 14.10 we nowhere assumed that V and W are finite-dimensional. If we confine our attention to finite-dimensional spaces, we can build up an elegant theory which generalizes the theory of simultaneous linear algebraic equations developed earlier in this book. It would carry us too far afield to do this in any detail, but we give some isolated results. We first state and prove the generalization of the result that only square matrices possess inverses.

THEOREM **14.11.** *If A is a linear transformation on V to W where V is n-dimensional, and if A^{-1} exists on W to V, then W is also n-dimensional.*

Proof: Let $\mathbf{x}_1, \ldots, \mathbf{x}_n$ be a basis in V and consider the corresponding set $A\mathbf{x}_1, \ldots, A\mathbf{x}_n$ in W. If

$$\alpha_1 A\mathbf{x}_1 + \ldots + \alpha_n A\mathbf{x}_n = \mathbf{0},$$

then, on applying A^{-1} to this equation, we see that

$$\alpha_1 \mathbf{x}_1 + \ldots + \alpha_n \mathbf{x}_n = \mathbf{0},$$

which implies that $\alpha_i = 0$, $i = 1, \ldots, n$, so that the $A\mathbf{x}_i$ are linearly independent. Consider any $n + 1$ vectors $\mathbf{y}_i$ in W. If

$$\beta_1 \mathbf{y}_1 + \ldots + \beta_{n+1} \mathbf{y}_{n+1} = \mathbf{0},$$

then

$$\beta_1 A^{-1}\mathbf{y}_1 + \ldots + \beta_{n+1} A^{-1}\mathbf{y}_{n+1} = \mathbf{0}.$$

The vectors $A^{-1}\mathbf{y}_i$ are in V, and any $n + 1$ vectors in V are linearly dependent, so that nonzero β_i exist which satisfy this equation, and the $\mathbf{y}_i$ are linearly dependent. Hence, there are precisely n linearly dependent vectors in W and the dimension of W is n.

In order to generalize our results on linear equations in Section 4.8, we require the following generalization of Theorem 4.17.

THEOREM **14.12.** *If A is a linear transformation on V to W and $\dim N(A)$, $\dim R(A)$, and $\dim V$ denote the dimensions of the null space, range, and domain of A, then*

$$\dim N(A) + \dim R(A) = \dim V.$$

Proof: Suppose first that $\dim V$ is finite. If A transforms every vector into the zero vector, then the theorem is trivial. Otherwise, let $\mathbf{x}_1, \ldots, \mathbf{x}_r$ be a basis for the null space. Vectors $\mathbf{x}_{r+1}, \ldots, \mathbf{x}_n$ can be added in such a way that $\mathbf{x}_1, \ldots, \mathbf{x}_n$ form a basis for V. Let $\mathbf{y}_i = A\mathbf{x}_i$ for $i = r + 1, \ldots, n$. We show that the $\mathbf{y}_i$ form a basis for the range of A. We first show that the $\mathbf{y}_i$ are linearly independent. For, if

$$\alpha_{r+1}\mathbf{y}_{r+1} + \ldots + \alpha_n \mathbf{y}_n = \mathbf{0},$$

this implies

$$A(\alpha_{r+1}\mathbf{x}_{r+1} + \ldots + \alpha_n \mathbf{x}_n) = \mathbf{0}.$$

Hence the vector in parentheses is in the null space of A and can therefore be expressed as a linear combination of $\mathbf{x}_1, \ldots, \mathbf{x}_r$, i.e.,

$$\alpha_{r+1}\mathbf{x}_{r+1} + \ldots + \alpha_n \mathbf{x}_n = a_1 \mathbf{x}_1 + \ldots + a_r \mathbf{x}_r.$$

However, $\mathbf{x}_1, \ldots, \mathbf{x}_n$ are linearly independent so that all the coefficients in this equation are zero. Hence, $\mathbf{y}_{r+1}, \ldots, \mathbf{y}_n$ are linearly independent. We next show that $\mathbf{y}_{r+1}, \ldots, \mathbf{y}_n$ span the range of A. Consider an arbitrary $\mathbf{y}$ in the range of A. From the definition of the range we know that there exists an $\mathbf{x}$ in V such that $A\mathbf{x} = \mathbf{y}$. We express $\mathbf{x}$ in terms of the basis $\mathbf{x}_1, \ldots, \mathbf{x}_n$ for V, obtaining, say,

$$\mathbf{x} = \beta_1\mathbf{x}_1 + \ldots + \beta_n\mathbf{x}_n.$$

Hence,

$$\mathbf{y} = A\mathbf{x} = \beta_{r+1}\mathbf{y}_{r+1} + \ldots + \beta_n\mathbf{y}_n,$$

so that $\mathbf{y}_{r+1}, \ldots, \mathbf{y}_n$ span the range of A. Hence, $\mathbf{y}_{r+1}, \ldots, \mathbf{y}_n$ form a basis for the range of A, so that $\dim R(A) = n - r$. The result in the theorem follows immediately. It is of interest that the theorem can also be proved by a similar argument when V is infinite-dimensional. We have to show that the null space and range cannot both be finite-dimensional. Assuming the contrary, suppose that $\mathbf{x}_1, \ldots, \mathbf{x}_r$ is a basis for the null space, and $\mathbf{x}_1, \ldots, \mathbf{x}_m$ is a linearly independent set in the domain of A, where $m - r$ is greater than the dimension of the range of A. Then $A\mathbf{x}_{r+1}, \ldots, A\mathbf{x}_m$ are a linearly dependent set in the range of A, and nonzero constants c_i exist such that

$$c_{r+1}A\mathbf{x}_{r+1} + \ldots + c_mA\mathbf{x}_m = \mathbf{0},$$

that is,

$$A(c_{r+1}\mathbf{x}_{r+1} + \ldots + c_m\mathbf{x}_m) = \mathbf{0}.$$

The vector in brackets therefore belongs to the null space of A so that it can be written as a linear combination of $\mathbf{x}_1, \ldots, \mathbf{x}_r$. The linear independence of $\mathbf{x}_1, \ldots, \mathbf{x}_m$ then indicates that all the c_i are zero, by the argument used in the finite-dimensional case. This gives a contradiction. This completes the proof.

We recall that in the proof of this theorem the null space of A is assumed to have a basis $\mathbf{x}_1, \ldots, \mathbf{x}_r$, and the domain of A has a basis $\mathbf{x}_1, \ldots, \mathbf{x}_n$. The subspace spanned by $\mathbf{x}_{r+1}, \ldots, \mathbf{x}_n$ is called the *complement* of the null space. The theorem then says that the dimensions of the range and the complement of the null space are the same. This can be represented diagrammatically as in Figure 14.2. Note that the complement of a null space is not unique. Thus if

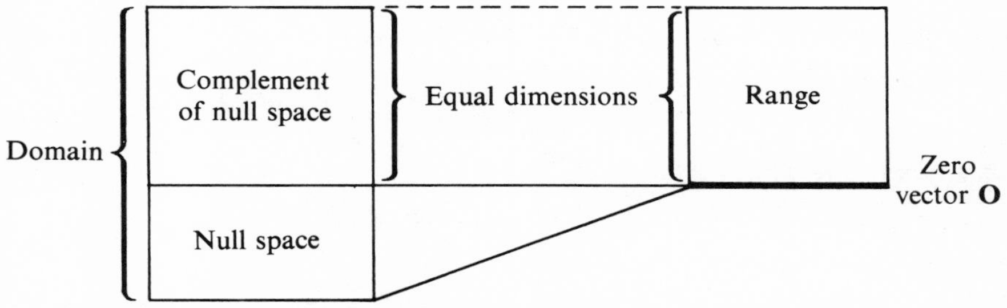

Figure 14.2 Diagrammatic representation of a linear transformation.

we are working with the space of 3×1 column vectors and the null space is spanned by two vectors $\mathbf{x}_1, \mathbf{x}_2$, then a complement of the null space is given by multiples of any vector that is linearly independent of $\mathbf{x}_1, \mathbf{x}_2$.

We can now conclude our discussion of the equation $A\mathbf{x} = \mathbf{y}$ by means of the theorem given below. Before stating the theorem precisely, we give a motivation in terms of the diagrammatic representation in Figure 14.2. Since the complement of the null space and the range have the same dimension, we shall construct a linear transformation B on the complement of the null space, which has an inverse, B^{-1}. If we are given a vector $\mathbf{y}$ in the range, we form $B^{-1}\mathbf{y}$ which gives us a vector $\mathbf{x}_0$ in the complement of the null space. We should then expect that the solution of $A\mathbf{x} = \mathbf{y}$ will be given by adding to $\mathbf{x}_0$ any vector in the null space of A. The result is clearly a generalization to abstract vector spaces of Theorem 4.18(iii).

THEOREM **14.13.** *Let A be a linear transformation on a finite-dimensional space V to W and let M be a complement of the null space of A.*

(i) *If B is the transformation on M to the range of A defined by $B\mathbf{x} = A\mathbf{x}$ for $\mathbf{x}$ in M, then B has an inverse.*

(ii) *If B^{-1} is the inverse whose existence is proved in* (i), *then, for each $\mathbf{y}$ in the range of A, the set of all solutions of $A\mathbf{x} = \mathbf{y}$ is given by*

$$\mathbf{x} = B^{-1}\mathbf{y} + \mathbf{z}$$

where $\mathbf{z}$ is any vector in the null space of A.

Proof: Choose a basis $\mathbf{x}_{r+1}, \ldots, \mathbf{x}_n$ for M as in Theorem 14.12, where $A\mathbf{x}_{r+1}, \ldots, A\mathbf{x}_n$ form a basis for the range of A. For each $\mathbf{y}$ in the range of A there is a unique set of scalars α_i such that

$$\mathbf{y} = \alpha_{r+1}A\mathbf{x}_{r+1} + \ldots + \alpha_n A\mathbf{x}_n.$$

We define a transformation C by

$$C\mathbf{y} = \alpha_{r+1}\mathbf{x}_{r+1} + \ldots + \alpha_n\mathbf{x}_n.$$

To show that C is the inverse of B we first examine

$$BC\mathbf{y} = \alpha_{r+1}A\mathbf{x}_{r+1} + \ldots + \alpha_n A\mathbf{x}_n = \mathbf{y},$$

since $B\mathbf{x}_i = A\mathbf{x}_i$, $i = r + 1, \ldots, n$, (the vectors $\mathbf{x}_i$ are in M). This is true for any $\mathbf{y}$ in the range of B so that $BC = I$. Let

$$\mathbf{x} = \beta_{r+1}\mathbf{x}_{r+1} + \ldots + \beta_n\mathbf{x}_n$$

for any $\mathbf{x}$ in M. Then

$$B\mathbf{x} = \beta_{r+1}A\mathbf{x}_{r+1} + \ldots + \beta_n A\mathbf{x}_n.$$

By definition of C this means that

$$C(B\mathbf{x}) = \beta_{r+1}\mathbf{x}_{r+1} + \ldots + \beta_n\mathbf{x}_n = \mathbf{x}$$

so that $(CB)\mathbf{x} = \mathbf{x}$ for any $\mathbf{x}$ in M, and therefore $CB = I$. Hence, C is the inverse of B. To prove (ii), we note first that the vector $\mathbf{x}_0 = B^{-1}\mathbf{y}$ certainly satisfies $A\mathbf{x} = \mathbf{y}$. Hence,

$$A(\mathbf{x} - \mathbf{x}_0) = \mathbf{y} - \mathbf{y} = \mathbf{0},$$

so that, if $\mathbf{x}$ is a solution, then $\mathbf{x} - \mathbf{x}_0$ is in the null space of A. Conversely, if $\mathbf{x} - \mathbf{x}_0$ is in the null space of A,

$$A\mathbf{x} = A\{(\mathbf{x} - \mathbf{x}_0) + \mathbf{x}_0\} = A(\mathbf{x} - \mathbf{x}_0) + A\mathbf{x}_0 = \mathbf{y}$$

and $\mathbf{x}$ is a solution of $A\mathbf{x} = \mathbf{y}$. This completes the proof.

Ex. 14.14. Go through this section in detail and identify each result with a more specific result proved previously in this book. (Most of these are in Chapter 4.) The transformation involved is $A\mathbf{x} = \mathbf{A}\mathbf{x}$, where $\mathbf{A}$ is an $m \times n$ matrix, the domain V is V_n, the range W is V_m. [Note, however, that even when the transformations are represented by matrices, the analysis in this section is more general than that considered earlier. Thus, in Ex. 14.13, the theory in Chapter 4 would have simply stated that the matrix in (14.16) is singular.]

14.7 Inner Product Spaces

We have already met inner products in Chapter 9, Section 9.3, where a quantity $(\mathbf{u}, \mathbf{v})$ associated with two $n \times 1$ vectors $\mathbf{u}$, $\mathbf{v}$ was defined by an explicit formula (9.32), and certain properties of $(\mathbf{u}, \mathbf{v})$ were then deduced in Theorem 9.5. If the reader reviews the way in which the quantity $(\mathbf{u}, \mathbf{v})$ is used in Chapter 9, he will realize that it is the properties in Theorem 9.5 that are important, not the explicit form of $(\mathbf{u}, \mathbf{v})$. In the more general setting of abstract vector spaces, we define an inner product in terms of the desired properties, without worrying about the explicit representation.

DEFINITION **14.10.** An inner product in an abstract vector space V is a number associated with any pair of elements $\mathbf{u}$, $\mathbf{v}$ in V, denoted by $(\mathbf{u}, \mathbf{v})$ with the following properties:

(a) *Linearity in the second element*: $(\mathbf{u}, \alpha\mathbf{v} + \beta\mathbf{w}) = \alpha(\mathbf{u}, \mathbf{v}) + \beta(\mathbf{u}, \mathbf{w})$.
(b) *Hermitian symmetry:* $(\mathbf{u}, \mathbf{v}) = \overline{(\mathbf{v}, \mathbf{u})}$.
(c) *Positive-definiteness:* $(\mathbf{u}, \mathbf{u}) > 0$ if $\mathbf{u} \neq \mathbf{0}$.

These properties imply (Ex. 14.15):

(a′) $(\alpha\mathbf{u} + \beta\mathbf{w}, \mathbf{v}) = \bar{\alpha}(\mathbf{u}, \mathbf{v}) + \bar{\beta}(\mathbf{w}, \mathbf{v})$.
(b′) $(\mathbf{u}, \mathbf{u})$ is real. $(\mathbf{u}, \mathbf{u}) = 0$ if and only if $\mathbf{u} = \mathbf{0}$.

An *inner product space* is an abstract vector space with an inner product. We restrict our attention to the case where the scalars are either real or complex numbers. If the scalars are real and $(\mathbf{u}, \mathbf{v}) = (\mathbf{v}, \mathbf{u})$, we are dealing with a *real inner product space*; otherwise, we have a complex inner product space. The number

$$(\mathbf{u}, \mathbf{u})^{1/2} = \|\mathbf{u}\|$$

is called the *norm* or *length* of $\mathbf{u}$ in the inner product space.

We consider some examples of inner product spaces.

(a) We have already met one inner product of two $n \times 1$ column vectors $\mathbf{u} = [u_i]$, $\mathbf{v} = [v_i]$:

$$\begin{aligned}(\mathbf{u}, \mathbf{v}) &= \bar{u}_1 v_1 + \bar{u}_2 v_2 + \ldots + \bar{u}_n v_n,\\ \|\mathbf{u}\|^2 &= |u_1|^2 + |u_2|^2 + \ldots + |u_n|^2.\end{aligned} \tag{14.18}$$

(b) From the results on positive-definite quadratic forms in Section 12.3 we can deduce that, if $\mathbf{A}$ is a positive-definite (hermitian) matrix, the expression

$$[\mathbf{u}, \mathbf{v}] = (\mathbf{u}, \mathbf{A}\mathbf{v}), \tag{14.19}$$

where $\mathbf{u}$, $\mathbf{v}$ and the inner product on the right are defined as in (a), defines an inner product $[\mathbf{u}, \mathbf{v}]$.

(c) Let V be the vector space of all continuous real-valued functions on the unit interval $0 \le t \le 1$. Then

$$(\mathbf{u}, \mathbf{v}) = \int_0^1 u(t)v(t)w(t)\, dt \tag{14.20}$$

is an inner product, where $w(t)$ is a given positive function in $0 \le t \le 1$. Also,

$$\|\mathbf{u}\|^2 = \int_0^1 u^2(t)w(t)\, dt.$$

(d) Let V be the set of all real sequences $\mathbf{x} = (x_1, x_2, \ldots)$ with an infinite number of elements, with the property

$$\sum_{i=1}^{\infty} x_i^2 \quad \text{finite.} \tag{14.21}$$

We define $\alpha\mathbf{x} = (\alpha x_1, \alpha x_2, \ldots)$ and, if $\mathbf{y}$ is a second entity in the set, we define

$$\mathbf{x} + \mathbf{y} = (x_1 + y_1, x_2 + y_2, \ldots),$$

$$(\mathbf{x}, \mathbf{y}) = \sum_{i=1}^{\infty} x_i y_i. \tag{14.22}$$

We have, of course, to prove that the series defining $(\mathbf{x}, \mathbf{y})$ converges. This is easy since

$$|2x_i y_i| \le x_i^2 + y_i^2.$$

It should also be noted that it is not obvious that $\mathbf{x} + \mathbf{y}$ is defined for every $\mathbf{x}$, $\mathbf{y}$ in V. We have to prove that the sequence defined by $\mathbf{x} + \mathbf{y}$ is such that

$$\sum_{i=1}^{\infty} (x_i + y_i)^2$$

is finite. This is true since $(x_i + y_i)^2 \leq 2x_i^2 + 2y_i^2$.

These examples illustrate two points, in particular:

(a) A wide variety of mathematical entities are included under the term "inner product" in the context of abstract vector spaces.

(b) Even when working with a specific vector space, it is still possible to choose an inner product in many different ways. Thus, in (14.19) any positive-definite $\mathbf{A}$ is suitable, and in (14.20) any positive $w(t)$. In any piece of work we must of course choose the appropriate inner product that is suitable for the problem in hand.

It is important to verify that the norm $\|\mathbf{u}\| = (\mathbf{u}, \mathbf{u})^{1/2}$ introduced in Definition 14.10 has the properties required of a norm in Definition 13.1.

THEOREM **14.14.** *In an inner product space, the norm $\|\mathbf{u}\|$ of a vector $\mathbf{u}$ has the following properties:*

(i) $\|k\mathbf{u}\| = |k|\,\|\mathbf{u}\|$.

(ii) $\|\mathbf{u}\| > 0$ *unless* $\mathbf{u} = \mathbf{0}$; $\|\mathbf{u}\| = 0$ *implies* $\mathbf{u} = \mathbf{0}$.

(iii) $|(\mathbf{u}, \mathbf{v})| \leq \|\mathbf{u}\|\,\|\mathbf{v}\|$ (*Schwarz's inequality*).

(iv) $\|\mathbf{u} + \mathbf{v}\| \leq \|\mathbf{u}\| + \|\mathbf{v}\|$ (*the triangle inequality*).

Proof: Parts (i), (ii) follow directly from Definition 14.10. Parts (iii) and (iv) can be proved by exactly the same method used for Theorem 13.1.

If we apply the Schwarz inequality to the inner product (14.18), we obtain

$$\left|\sum_{i=1}^{n} u_i v_i\right| \leq \left\{\sum_{i=1}^{n} |u_i|^2\right\}^{1/2} \left\{\sum_{i=1}^{n} |v_i|^2\right\}^{1/2}. \tag{14.23}$$

Similarly, the inner product

$$(\mathbf{u}, \mathbf{v}) = \int_0^1 \bar{u}(t)v(t)\,dt$$

gives

$$\left|\int_0^1 u(t)v(t)\,dt\right| \leq \left\{\int_0^1 |u(t)|^2\,dt\right\}^{1/2} \left\{\int_0^1 |v(t)|^2\,dt\right\}^{1/2}. \tag{14.24}$$

Note that although we are working in complex vector spaces, it is not necessary to insert a bar on u_i or $u(t)$ in (14.23) and (14.24). This is a trivial remark.

We conclude this section by defining what we mean by the angle between two vectors in an abstract vector space.

DEFINITION **14.11.** The angle θ between two vectors $\mathbf{u}$, $\mathbf{v}$ in an abstract vector space is defined by

$$\cos\theta = \frac{(\mathbf{u}, \mathbf{v})}{\|\mathbf{u}\|\,\|\mathbf{v}\|}. \tag{14.25}$$

If we are working in a real vector space, the Schwarz inequality ensures that $-1 \le \cos\theta \le 1$, which is a good thing, since it might be expected that a satisfactory definition of angle should yield real angles between real vectors.

Ex. 14.15. Prove that properties (a), (c) of Definition 14.10 imply that $(\mathbf{u}, \mathbf{u}) = 0$ if and only if $\mathbf{u} = \mathbf{0}$.

Ex. 14.16. Prove that if $\|\mathbf{u}\|$ is a norm derived from an inner product $(\mathbf{u}, \mathbf{v})$, then the inner product can be expressed in terms of the norm by

$$(\mathbf{u}, \mathbf{v}) = \tfrac{1}{4}\{\|\mathbf{u} + \mathbf{v}\|^2 - \|\mathbf{u} - \mathbf{v}\|^2 - i\|\mathbf{u} + i\mathbf{v}\|^2 + i\|\mathbf{u} - i\mathbf{v}\|^2\}.$$

In a real vector space

$$(\mathbf{u}, \mathbf{v}) = \tfrac{1}{4}\{\|\mathbf{u} + \mathbf{v}\|^2 - \|\mathbf{u} - \mathbf{v}\|^2\}.$$

Ex. 14.17. Prove the following extension of the triangle inequality:

$$\left\|\sum_{j=1}^{m} c_j\mathbf{x}_j\right\| \le \sum_{j=1}^{m} |c_j|\,\|\mathbf{x}_j\|.$$

Ex. 14.18. Prove that in the space of real 2×1 column vectors the following expression defines an inner product if and only if $\alpha > 0$, $\alpha\gamma - \beta^2 > 0$:

$$(\mathbf{u}, \mathbf{v}) = \alpha u_1 v_1 + \beta(u_1 v_2 + u_2 v_1) + \gamma u_2 v_2.$$

14.8 Orthogonality

The use of rectangular or orthogonal coordinates for the description of three-dimensional space is simple, useful, and efficient. Analogous coordinate systems can be set up in an abstract vector space by introducing the idea of orthogonality. Two vectors are said to be orthogonal if the angle between them is 90°, i.e., from Definition 14.11, if their inner product is zero.

DEFINITION **14.12.** Let $\mathbf{u}$, $\mathbf{v}$ be two vectors in an abstract vector space V. We say that $\mathbf{u}$ and $\mathbf{v}$ are *orthogonal* if $(\mathbf{u}, \mathbf{v}) = 0$. If we have a set of vectors $\mathbf{u}_1, \mathbf{u}_2, \ldots$ in V, we say that we have an *orthogonal set* if any two distinct vectors in the set are orthogonal. An *orthonormal set* is an orthogonal set, with the additional property that $\|\mathbf{u}\| = 1$ for every vector $\mathbf{u}$ in the set.

For an orthonormal set we have

$$(\mathbf{u}_r, \mathbf{u}_s) = \delta_{rs},$$

where δ_{rs} is the *Kronecker delta*, which is unity if $r = s$ and zero if $r \neq s$.

We have already met these ideas in Chapter 9. The main difference is that we are now talking about any abstract vector space instead of the space of $n \times 1$ column vectors. As an example of a type that we have not met before, consider

$$\mathbf{u}_r = 2^{1/2} \sin r\pi t, \qquad 0 \leq t \leq 1, \qquad r = 1, 2, 3, \ldots, \tag{14.26}$$

the inner product being that defined in (14.20) with $w(t) = 1$. We have

$$(\mathbf{u}_r, \mathbf{u}_s) = 2\int_0^1 \sin r\pi t \sin s\pi t \, dt = \int_0^1 \{\cos (r - s)\pi t - \cos (r + s)\pi t\} \, dt.$$

It is left to the reader to show that this is unity if $r = s$ and zero if $r \neq s$, so that the $\mathbf{u}_r$ form an orthonormal set. Note that the set contains an infinite number of vectors.

We now give a theorem which generalizes results proved in Chapter 9 for $n \times 1$ column vectors (Theorems 9.13, 9.14).

THEOREM **14.15.** *Suppose that the vectors* $\mathbf{u}_1, \mathbf{u}_2, \ldots, \mathbf{u}_m$ *constitute an orthonormal set in a vector space* V. *Then*

(i) *The vectors in such a set are linearly independent.*

(ii) *The number of vectors,* m, *is less than or equal to the dimension of* V.

(iii) *If a vector* $\mathbf{u}$ *can be expressed as a linear combination of the vectors in the set, then*

$$\mathbf{u} = \sum_{j=1}^{n} (\mathbf{u}_j, \mathbf{u})\mathbf{u}_j. \tag{14.27}$$

Proof: Suppose that, for any vector $\mathbf{v}$, we write

$$\mathbf{v} = \alpha_1\mathbf{u}_1 + \alpha_2\mathbf{u}_2 + \ldots + \alpha_m\mathbf{u}_m. \tag{14.28}$$

On taking the inner product with $\mathbf{u}_j$,

$$(\mathbf{u}_j, \mathbf{v}) = \left(\mathbf{u}_j, \sum_{i=1}^{n} \alpha_i\mathbf{u}_i\right) = \sum_{i=1}^{n} \alpha_i(\mathbf{u}_j, \mathbf{u}_i) = \alpha_j(\mathbf{u}_j, \mathbf{u}_j) = \alpha_j. \tag{14.29}$$

If we choose $\mathbf{v} = \mathbf{0}$, this gives $\alpha_j = 0$ for all j, which shows that the vectors in the set are linearly independent. We know that if the dimension of the space V is k, then any $k + 1$ vectors in the space must be linearly dependent. Hence, from (i), the orthonormal set cannot contain more than k vectors, which proves (ii). On taking $\mathbf{v} = \mathbf{u}$ in (14.28), (14.29) and combining these equations, we obtain (14.27), which proves (iii).

The maximum number of mutually orthogonal vectors in a space is what we should intuitively think of as the geometric dimension of the space, by analogy with the three mutually perpendicular axes in three-dimensional space. The result (ii) in the above theorem says that this geometric dimension is not less than the dimension defined algebraically as the number of vectors in a basis. We can show that the geometric and algebraic dimensions are identical, as we should expect. To prove this we make use of a direct generalization of the Gram-Schmidt orthogonalization procedure considered in Theorem 10.4.

THEOREM **14.16.** (i) (*Gram-Schmidt orthogonalization*). *Given a set of s linearly independent vectors* $\mathbf{u}_1, \ldots, \mathbf{u}_s$ *belonging to an inner product space, we can construct an orthonormal set* $\mathbf{x}_1, \ldots, \mathbf{x}_s$, *where the* $\mathbf{x}_i$ *are linear combinations of the* $\mathbf{u}_i$, $i = 1$ *to s.*

(ii) *Every n-dimensional inner product space has an orthonormal basis.*

Proof: The proof of part (i) follows word for word that for Theorem 10.4, using the more general definitions of inner product and orthogonality introduced in this chapter. Part (ii) follows immediately from part (i). Every n-dimensional space has a basis consisting of n linearly independent vectors. By Gram-Schmidt orthogonalization we can construct an orthonormal set of n vectors from the vectors in the basis. By Theorem 14.15(i) the vectors in the orthonormal set are linearly independent, so that the orthonormal set is also a basis for the space.

It is often useful to consider pairs of subspaces U, W such that any vector in U is orthogonal to any vector in W.

DEFINITION **14.13.** Let V be an inner product space and let U, W be subspaces of V. A vector $\mathbf{u}$ in U is said to be *orthogonal to* W if it is orthogonal to every vector in W. We write $\mathbf{u} \perp W$. If every element of U is orthogonal to W, we write $U \perp W$. The *orthogonal complement* of U is the set $U^{\perp}$ of all vectors in V which are orthogonal to every vector in U.

THEOREM **14.17.** *Let V be an inner product space and U an n-dimensional subspace of V.*

(i) *Each vector* $\mathbf{v}$ *in V can be uniquely decomposed into the sum* $\mathbf{v} = \mathbf{v}_1 + \mathbf{v}_2$ *of a vector* $\mathbf{v}_1$ *in U and a vector* $\mathbf{v}_2$ *orthogonal to U.*

(ii) *If* $\mathbf{x}_1, \ldots, \mathbf{x}_n$ *is an orthonormal basis for U, then, for any vector* $\mathbf{v}$ *in V, we have Bessel's inequality,*

$$\sum_{i=1}^{n} |(\mathbf{v}, \mathbf{x}_i)|^2 \leq \|\mathbf{v}\|^2. \tag{14.30}$$

Proof: We first prove that the decomposition in (i) is unique, if it exists. Suppose that

$$\mathbf{v} = \mathbf{v}_1 + \mathbf{v}_2 = \mathbf{u}_1 + \mathbf{u}_2, \tag{14.31}$$

where $\mathbf{v}_1$, $\mathbf{u}_1$ are in U, and $\mathbf{v}_2$, $\mathbf{u}_2$ are orthogonal to U, i.e., to $\mathbf{v}_1$, $\mathbf{u}_1$, so that

$$(\mathbf{v}_1 - \mathbf{u}_1, \mathbf{v}_2 - \mathbf{u}_2) = 0. \tag{14.32}$$

From (14.31), $\mathbf{v}_2 - \mathbf{u}_2 = \mathbf{v}_1 - \mathbf{u}_1$, so that (14.32) implies

$$(\mathbf{v}_1 - \mathbf{u}_1, \mathbf{v}_1 - \mathbf{u}_1) = 0.$$

Hence, $\mathbf{v}_1 = \mathbf{u}_1$ and (14.31) then implies $\mathbf{v}_2 = \mathbf{u}_2$. To prove that the decomposition exists, suppose that $\mathbf{x}_1, \ldots, \mathbf{x}_n$ is an orthonormal basis for U and set

$$\begin{aligned} \mathbf{v}_1 &= \sum_{i=1}^{n} (\mathbf{v}, \mathbf{x}_i)\mathbf{x}_i, \\ \mathbf{v}_2 &= \mathbf{v} - \mathbf{v}_1. \end{aligned} \tag{14.33}$$

The vector $\mathbf{v}_1$ is obviously in U. Also

$$(\mathbf{v}_2, \mathbf{x}_j) = (\mathbf{v}, \mathbf{x}_j) - (\mathbf{v}_1, \mathbf{x}_j) = 0, \qquad j = 1, \ldots, n,$$

so that $\mathbf{v}_2$ is orthogonal to $\mathbf{x}_1, \ldots, \mathbf{x}_n$, i.e., to any linear combination of $\mathbf{x}_1, \ldots, \mathbf{x}_n$, and therefore to any vector in U. This completes the proof of part (i). To prove (14.30), we have

$$\|\mathbf{v}\|^2 = (\mathbf{v}_1 + \mathbf{v}_2, \mathbf{v}_1 + \mathbf{v}_2) = (\mathbf{v}_1, \mathbf{v}_1) + (\mathbf{v}_2, \mathbf{v}_2) \geq (\mathbf{v}_1, \mathbf{v}_1) = \sum_{i=1}^{n} |(\mathbf{v}, \mathbf{x}_i)|^2,$$

which is the required result. Note that in this theorem we have *not* assumed that V is a finite-dimensional space.

DEFINITION 14.14. The vector $\mathbf{v}_1$ in Theorem 14.17, a formula for which is given in (14.33), is known as the *orthogonal projection* of $\mathbf{v}$ on U.

THEOREM 14.18. *Let V be an inner product space and U a finite-dimensional subspace of V.*

(i) *If $\mathbf{v}$ is any vector in V and $\mathbf{v}_1$ is its orthogonal projection on U, then, for any vector $\mathbf{u}$ in U,*

$$\|\mathbf{v} - \mathbf{v}_1\| \leq \|\mathbf{v} - \mathbf{u}\| \tag{14.34}$$

with equality only if $\mathbf{u} = \mathbf{v}_1$.

(ii) *If $\mathbf{x}_1, \ldots, \mathbf{x}_n$ is an orthonormal basis for U and $\mathbf{v}$ is any vector in V,*

$$\left\| \mathbf{v} - \sum_{i=1}^{n} (\mathbf{v}, \mathbf{x}_i)\mathbf{x}_i \right\| \leq \left\| \mathbf{v} - \sum_{i=1}^{n} c_i\mathbf{x}_i \right\|, \tag{14.35}$$

where the c_i are any constants. Equality holds only if $c_i = (\mathbf{v}, \mathbf{x}_i)$, $i = 1, \ldots, n$.

Proof: If we set $\mathbf{v}_2 = \mathbf{v} - \mathbf{v}_1$ as in (14.33), we have

$$\begin{aligned} \|\mathbf{v} - \mathbf{u}\|^2 = (\mathbf{v} - \mathbf{u}, \mathbf{v} - \mathbf{u}) &= (\mathbf{v}_1 + \mathbf{v}_2 - \mathbf{u}, \mathbf{v}_1 + \mathbf{v}_2 - \mathbf{u}) \\ &= (\mathbf{v}_1 - \mathbf{u}, \mathbf{v}_1 - \mathbf{u}) + (\mathbf{v}_2, \mathbf{v}_2), \end{aligned} \tag{14.36}$$

where we have used the fact that $\mathbf{v}_2$ is orthogonal to $\mathbf{v}_1$ and $\mathbf{u}$. Also,

$$(\mathbf{v}_2, \mathbf{v}_2) = (\mathbf{v} - \mathbf{v}_1, \mathbf{v} - \mathbf{v}_1) = \|\mathbf{v} - \mathbf{v}_1\|^2.$$

This equation and (14.36) imply (14.34). There is equality only if we have $(\mathbf{v}_1 - \mathbf{u}, \mathbf{v}_1 - \mathbf{u}) = 0$, i.e., $\mathbf{v}_1 = \mathbf{u}$. Part (ii) follows directly from part (i), in view of (14.33).

Part (i) has the interesting geometrical interpretation that the "distance" between $\mathbf{v}$ and $\mathbf{v}_1$ is less than the distance between $\mathbf{v}$ and any other vector in U. Part (ii) states that if we wish to minimize the "difference" (in the sense of the norm) between $\mathbf{v}$ and a linear combination of an orthonormal set, the constant multipliers should be chosen to be simply the Fourier coefficients $(\mathbf{v}, \mathbf{x}_i)$.

The next step would be to introduce the idea of an adjoint operator, and then discuss the spectral theorem for self-adjoint operators. However, this would take us too far afield, and we finish at this point, in the middle of a tantalizing glimpse of the elegant theory of abstract finite-dimensional spaces.

Ex. 14.19. If $\mathbf{x}$ and $\mathbf{y}$ are given vectors, the constant α that minimizes $\|\mathbf{x} - \alpha\mathbf{y}\|$ is $\alpha = (\mathbf{x}, \mathbf{y})/\|\mathbf{y}\|^2$. This value of α makes $\mathbf{x} - \alpha\mathbf{y}$ perpendicular to $\mathbf{y}$. Interpret these results geometrically.

Ex. 14.20. Show that in any inner product space:

(a) $(\mathbf{x}, \mathbf{y}) = 0$ implies $\|\mathbf{x}\|^2 + \|\mathbf{y}\|^2 = \|\mathbf{x} + \mathbf{y}\|^2$,

(b) $\|\mathbf{x} + \mathbf{y}\|^2 = \|\mathbf{x}\|^2 + \|\mathbf{y}\|^2$ implies $(\mathbf{x}, \mathbf{y}) = 0$.

Why are these called Pythagorean theorems?

Ex. 14.21. Apply the Gram-Schmidt procedure to the functions $1, x, x^2, x^3$ to obtain an orthogonal set of polynomials, with inner product

$$(\mathbf{f}, \mathbf{g}) = \int_{-1}^{+1} f(t)g(t)\,dt.$$

Miscellaneous Exercises 14

Ex. 14.22. Prove that the polynomials

$$p_i(x) = \sum_{j=0}^{n} a_{ij}x^j, \qquad i = 1, \ldots, m$$

are linearly dependent if and only if the rank of $\mathbf{A} = [a_{ij}]$ is less than m.

Ex. 14.23. Are the following statements true or false? Justify your answers.

(a) The functions $1, \cos^2 x, \cos 2x$ are linearly dependent.

(b) The functions $\sin x, \cos x, \sin 2x$ are linearly dependent.

(c) If two nonzero vectors are linearly dependent, they are proportional to each other.

(d) If the zero vector is included in a set of vectors, the set is always linearly dependent.

(e) If $\mathbf{u}_1, \ldots, \mathbf{u}_n$ are n linearly independent vectors in an n-dimensional space, then any vector in the space can be expressed as a linear combination of the $\mathbf{u}_i$.

Ex. 14.24. Under what conditions are the following statements true? Justify your answers.

(a) The functions $t^p, t^q, \ldots, t^s$ are linearly independent.

(b) The polynomials $(t - a)(t - b)$, $(t - b)(t - c)$, $(t - c)(t - a)$ form a basis for the space of polynomials of degree less than or equal to 2.

Ex. 14.25. Consider the set W consisting of all positive real numbers $p, q, \ldots$ with rules that "the sum of p and q" is pq, and "α times p" is p^α. Prove that this set constitutes a vector space. What is the zero vector in the space? What is the dimension k of the space? Specify a basis for the space.

Ex. 14.26. If V is the space of all functions continuous in $-1 \le t \le 1$, which of the following sets are subspaces of V?

(a) All polynomials of degree 3.

(b) All polynomials of degree less than 3.

(c) All continuous functions with $|f(t)| \le 1$, $-1 \le t \le 1$.

(d) All odd functions continuous in $-1 \le t \le 1, f(t) = f(-t)$.

(e) All functions continuous in $-1 \le t \le 1$ with $f(-1) = -f(1)$.

(f) All functions differentiable in $-1 \le t \le 1$.

(g) All functions continuous in $-1 \le t \le 1$ with $|f(t)| \le 0$.

(h) All functions continuous in $-1 \le t \le 1$ with $|f(t)| > 0$.

(i) All functions that are integrable in $-1 \le t \le 1$.

Ex. 14.27. Are the following statements true or false? Justify your answers.

(a) If a basis $\mathbf{u}_1, \ldots, \mathbf{u}_n$ is given in an n-dimensional space V, and S is a subspace of V, then a basis for S can always be chosen from the $\mathbf{u}_i$.

(b) If S is a subpsace of a finite-dimensional space V and it has the same dimension as V, then S is identical with V.

Ex. 14.28. If an n-dimensional space contains two subspaces S and T of dimensions s and t which have only the zero vector in common, show that $s + t \le n$.

Ex. 14.29. A linear transformation that transforms a vector in an m-dimensional space into a number in its scalar field is known as a *linear functional*. State, with reasons, whether the following are linear functionals.

(a) $A\mathbf{x} = x_1$, where $\mathbf{x}$ is a vector in V_n with first element x_1.

(b) $A\mathbf{x} = \int_0^1 x(t)e^{-t}\,dt$, where $x(t)$ is in the space of functions integrable in $0 \le t \le 1$.

(c) $A\mathbf{x} = \int_0^1 |x(t)|\,dt$, where $x(t)$ is in the space of real functions integrable in $0 \le x \le 1$.

(d) $A\mathbf{x} = x(1)$ where $x(t)$ is in the space of functions continuous in $0 \leq t \leq 2$.

(e) $A\mathbf{x} = (\mathbf{a}, \mathbf{x})\mathbf{a}$, where $\mathbf{a}$, $\mathbf{x}$ are in V_n, and $\mathbf{a}$ is a fixed vector.

Ex. 14.30. If A is a linear transformation on V to W, show that any subspace of V is transformed by A into a subspace of W. Show conversely that if T is a subspace of W, then the set of all vectors in V transformed into vectors in T by A is a subspace of V.

Ex. 14.31. When A is a linear transformation on V to W and the range of A is the whole of W, we say that A is on V *onto* W. Prove that if A is one-one and onto, the inverse A^{-1} exists and it is a linear transformation on W to V. If V is the space of polynomials $f(t)$ and $D\mathbf{x} = df/dt$, $A\mathbf{x} = tf(t)$, prove that A is one-one but not onto, and D is onto but not one-one.

Ex. 14.32. If A is a linear transformation on V to V and for some basis $\mathbf{u}_1, \ldots, \mathbf{u}_n$ of V the vectors $A\mathbf{u}_1, \ldots, A\mathbf{u}_n$ also form a basis for V, prove that A has an inverse.

Ex. 14.33. Let $\mathbf{u}_1, \ldots, \mathbf{u}_n$ be a basis in V and let $\mathbf{w}_1, \ldots, \mathbf{w}_n$ be *any* vectors in W. Show that the correspondence $\mathbf{u}_i \to \mathbf{w}_i$, $i = 1, \ldots, n$ can be used to define a linear transformation on V to W.

Ex. 14.34. Let N, N' be two ordered bases of an n-dimensional space V, and let M, M' be two ordered bases of an m-dimensional space W. Consider a linear transformation A from V to W. Suppose that $\mathbf{A}$, $\mathbf{A}'$ are the matrices of the transformation relative to N, M and N', M', respectively, and that $\mathbf{P}$, $\mathbf{Q}$ are the matrices for the change of basis from N to N' and M to M'. Prove that $\mathbf{A}' = \mathbf{QAP}^{-1}$.

Ex. 14.35. Suppose that $\mathbf{v}$, $\mathbf{w}$ are elements of vector spaces V, W, respectively, which are subspaces of a common larger space. Prove that the sum of all vectors $\mathbf{v} + \mathbf{w}$ defines a vector space. This vector space is denoted by $V + W$, the *sum* of V and W. Show that the set of all vectors common to two vector spaces forms a vector space. This space is denoted by $V \cap W$, the *intersection* of V and W. If dim V denotes the dimension of V, etc., show that

$$\dim V + \dim W = \dim (V + W) + \dim V \cap W.$$

As an example, suppose that V, W have bases

$$\begin{bmatrix} 1 \\ 0 \\ -3 \\ -2 \end{bmatrix}, \quad \begin{bmatrix} 0 \\ 2 \\ 2 \\ -3 \end{bmatrix} \quad \text{and} \quad \begin{bmatrix} 2 \\ 3 \\ 0 \\ 1 \end{bmatrix}, \quad \begin{bmatrix} 2 \\ 1 \\ 3 \\ -1 \end{bmatrix}, \quad \begin{bmatrix} 3 \\ 2 \\ 4 \\ -3 \end{bmatrix}.$$

Find a basis for $V \cap W$, and check the above relation between dimensions.

Ex. 14.36. If $U = V + W$, where V and W are subspaces of the vector space U, and V, W have only the null vector in common (i.e., $V \cap W = 0$), then we write $U = V \oplus W$ and say that U is the *direct sum* of V and W. Show that every vector $\mathbf{u}$ in U can be expressed uniquely in the form $\mathbf{u} = \mathbf{v} + \mathbf{w}$, where $\mathbf{v}$

is in V and $\mathbf{w}$ is in W. Conversely, show that if every vector $\mathbf{u}$ in U can be expressed uniquely in the form $\mathbf{v} + \mathbf{w}$, where $\mathbf{v}$, $\mathbf{w}$ are in vector spaces V, W, then U must be the direct sum of V and W. Interpret the decomposition $U = V \oplus W$ geometrically when U is a three-dimensional space and V is a two-dimensional subspace. Show that W can be any line not lying in V. This shows, incidentally, that if $U = V \oplus W$, where V is fixed, then W is *not unique*. If U is V_3 and V has a basis

$$\begin{bmatrix} 2 \\ -1 \\ 4 \end{bmatrix}, \quad \begin{bmatrix} 1 \\ 2 \\ -3 \end{bmatrix},$$

find two subspaces W such that $U = V \oplus W$.

Ex. 14.37. If V and W are vector spaces, the set of all vectors in either V or W is known as the *union* of V and W, written $V \cup W$. Show that $V \cup W$ is *not* a vector space.

Ex. 14.38. A transformation L of an n-dimensional space U into itself is called a *projection* if there exist spaces V and W with $U = V \oplus W$ such that $L\mathbf{x} = \mathbf{x}$ for all $\mathbf{x}$ in V and $L\mathbf{x} = \mathbf{0}$ for all $\mathbf{x}$ in W. Show that (a) L is a linear transformation, (b) a linear transformation is a projection if and only if $L^2 = L$, and (c) the orthogonal projection defined in Definition 14.14 is a projection in this more general sense.

Ex. 14.39. If $\mathbf{x}$ is an element in an inner product space V and $(\mathbf{x}, \mathbf{u}) = 0$ for all $\mathbf{u}$ in V, show that $\mathbf{x} = \mathbf{0}$.

Ex. 14.40. If $(\mathbf{u}, \mathbf{v})$ and $[\mathbf{u}, \mathbf{v}]$ are inner products in an inner product space, show that $(\mathbf{u}, \mathbf{v}) + [\mathbf{u}, \mathbf{v}]$ is also an inner product.

Ex. 14.41. Show that in an inner product space:

(a) $2\|\mathbf{x}\|^2 + 2\|\mathbf{y}\|^2 = \|\mathbf{x} + \mathbf{y}\|^2 + \|\mathbf{x} - \mathbf{y}\|^2$.

(b) $\|\mathbf{x} + \mathbf{y}\| \, \|\mathbf{x} - \mathbf{y}\| < \|\mathbf{x}\|^2 + \|\mathbf{y}\|^2$.

Interpret these results in terms of the geometry of parallelograms.

Ex. 14.42. The *distance* $d(\mathbf{v}, \mathbf{u})$ between two elements (or "points") of a vector space is defined to be a real number with the properties:

(a) $d(\mathbf{u}, \mathbf{v}) = d(\mathbf{v}, \mathbf{u})$.

(b) $d(\mathbf{u}, \mathbf{w}) \leq d(\mathbf{u}, \mathbf{v}) + d(\mathbf{v}, \mathbf{w})$, where $\mathbf{u}$, $\mathbf{v}$, $\mathbf{w}$ are any three elements of the space. This is the *triangle inequality*.

(c) $d(\mathbf{u}, \mathbf{v}) > 0$ if $\mathbf{u} \neq \mathbf{v}$; $d(\mathbf{u}, \mathbf{u}) = 0$.

A vector space with a distance function is called a *metric space*. Show that an inner product space is a metric space. (*Hint:* Show that the distance axioms are satisfied for $d(\mathbf{u}, \mathbf{v}) = \|\mathbf{u} - \mathbf{v}\|$.)

Hints and Answers to Selected Exercises

Chapter 1

Ex. 1.1. When brackets are used, operations inside brackets are performed *first.*

Ex. 1.6. $a_{3j} = 4a_{1j}$. Third row of **AB** is $\Sigma\, a_{3j}b_{jk} = 4\, \Sigma\, a_{1j}b_{jk}$.

Ex. 1.7. Since equation is true for *all* b_1, b_2, choose (*a*) $b_1 = 1$, $b_2 = 0$. (b) $b_1 = 0$, $b_2 = 1$.

Ex. 1.12. See Ex. 1.10.

Ex. 1.21.
$$\frac{1}{12}\begin{bmatrix} -7 & -6 & 5 \\ 2 & 0 & 2 \\ 1 & -6 & 1 \end{bmatrix}$$

Ex. 1.22. $\dfrac{1}{2}\begin{bmatrix} 1+\alpha & 1-5\alpha & 2\alpha \\ -1+\beta & 1-5\beta & 2\beta \end{bmatrix}$, any α, β.

Ex. 1.36. Use induction.

Ex. 1.37. Only null matrices. (Consider diagonal elements of $\mathbf{A}^T\mathbf{A}$.)

Ex. 1.40. Use the fact that **A** must commute with

$$\begin{bmatrix} 1 & 0 \\ 0 & 0 \end{bmatrix}, \quad \begin{bmatrix} 0 & 1 \\ 0 & 0 \end{bmatrix}, \quad \begin{bmatrix} 0 & 0 \\ 1 & 0 \end{bmatrix}, \quad \begin{bmatrix} 0 & 0 \\ 0 & 1 \end{bmatrix}.$$

Ex. 1.42. "Proof" assumes that **HA** has a left-inverse.

Ex. 1.43. (a) Let $\mathbf{A}^{-1} = \mathbf{B}$. Then $\mathbf{AB} = \mathbf{BA} = \mathbf{I}$, so that $\mathbf{B}^T\mathbf{A}^T = \mathbf{A}^T\mathbf{B}^T = \mathbf{I}$. Hence $\mathbf{B}^T = (\mathbf{A}^T)^{-1}$ which is the required result.

Ex. 1.45. $(\mathbf{I} + \mathbf{K})^T = \mathbf{I} - \mathbf{K}$; $(\mathbf{I} - \mathbf{K})(\mathbf{I} + \mathbf{K}) = (\mathbf{I} + \mathbf{K})(\mathbf{I} - \mathbf{K})$.

Ex. 1.46. Equations $\mathbf{A}\mathbf{x}_i = \mathbf{e}_i$ will be contradictory.

Ex. 1.49. (b) $\begin{bmatrix} \cos\theta & \sin\theta \\ -\sin\theta & \cos\theta \end{bmatrix}$ or $\begin{bmatrix} \cos\theta & \sin\theta \\ \sin\theta & -\cos\theta \end{bmatrix}$.

Ex. 1.57. Proof of (d) follows directly from (c).

Chapter 2

Ex. 2.3. See references quoted in Ex. 2.27.

Ex. 2.6. $\begin{bmatrix} 0.39 \\ 0.19 \\ 0.42 \end{bmatrix}, \begin{bmatrix} 0.381 \\ 0.183 \\ 0.436 \end{bmatrix}, \frac{1}{6}\begin{bmatrix} 2 \\ 1 \\ 3 \end{bmatrix}$.

Chapter 3

Ex. 3.4. When Gauss-Jordan is applied to $[\mathbf{A}, \mathbf{e}_i]$ we obtain $[\mathbf{I}, \mathbf{x}_i]$.

Ex. 3.8. The row-echelon form of the augmented matrix is

$$\begin{bmatrix} 1 & -1 & 0 & 0 & 4 \\ 0 & 0 & 1 & 1 & -3 \\ 0 & 0 & 0 & 0 & 0 \end{bmatrix}.$$

Ex. 3.9. x_1; x_2 or x_3; any two of x_4, x_5, x_6, x_7 except x_5 and x_6.

Ex. 3.10. (a) 0. (b) ∞. (c) 1.

Ex. 3.14. (a) ∞. (b) ∞. (c) 0. (d) ∞. (e) 0. (f) 1.

Ex. 3.16. If the rank were less than m, the last row of the row-echelon form of $[\mathbf{A}, \mathbf{I}]$ would be zero. From Theorem 3.4 this means that a linear combination of the rows of the unit matrix would be zero which is impossible.

Ex. 3.22. $\alpha = 5$.

Ex. 3.26. Examine the question of whether the equations $\mathbf{A}\mathbf{x}_i = \mathbf{e}_i$ possess solutions by reducing the matrix $[\mathbf{A}, \mathbf{I}]$ to row-echelon form. Note Ex. 3.16.

Ex. 3.27. See hint for Ex. 3.26. (Before the existence of inverses can be discussed completely we need certain properties of rank discussed in Section 5.2. See Section 5.3.)

Ex. 3.28. $\mathbf{B} = \mathbf{C} + \mathbf{x}\boldsymbol{\alpha}^T$ where $\mathbf{x} = [-3 \quad 0 \quad 1]^T$ and $\boldsymbol{\alpha}$ is an arbitrary 3×1 vector.

Ex. 3.29. $\mathbf{b} = [b_1, b_2, b_1 + b_2]^T$.

Ex. 3.30. Contradictory for $k = -4$. For $k = 0$, solution is $x_1 = 3 - 3\alpha$, $x_2 = 1$, $x_3 = \alpha$, any α.

Ex. 3.31. Row-echelcn form of $\mathbf{A}$ must be the unit matrix.

Chapter 4

Ex. 4.6. $1 - \beta + \alpha\beta \neq 0$.

Ex. 4.9. $[x\ y\ z] = \frac{1}{4}(x + y + z)[1\quad 2\quad 1] + \frac{1}{2}(x - z)[1\quad 0\quad -1] + \frac{1}{4}(x - y + z)$ $[1\quad -2\quad 1]$.

Ex. 4.10. The second. (This can be seen immediately from Ex. 4.1.)

Ex. 4.16. (i) $\mathbf{A} = [0\quad 1\quad 0\quad 0]$. (ii) $\mathbf{A} = [1\quad -1\quad 1]$, $\mathbf{b} = [1]$,

(iii)

$$\mathbf{A} = \begin{bmatrix} 1 & -1 & 0 \\ 0 & 1 & -1 \\ 1 & 1 & 1 \end{bmatrix}.$$

Ex. 4.18. (a) Yes. (b) Yes. (c) No. (d) No. (e) Yes. (f) No. (g) No. (h) Yes.

Ex. 4.22. $[1\quad 1\quad 1\quad 0]^T$, $[0\quad 0\quad 0\quad 1]^T$.

Ex. 4.23 (a) Yes. (b) No.

Ex. 4.24. $k = 1, 3$, or 4.

Ex. 4.28. Yes. Show that row-echelon forms of *transposes* are identical.

Ex. 4.29. If any vector can be omitted, it must be linearly dependent on the others.

Ex. 4.31. Columns of V span space and this implies $\mathbf{U} = \mathbf{VP}$. Similarly $\mathbf{V} = \mathbf{UQ}$. Hence $\mathbf{U} = \mathbf{UQP}$, $\mathbf{V} = \mathbf{VPQ}$. Deduce $\mathbf{QP} = \mathbf{PQ} = \mathbf{I}$ from independence of vectors in basis, so that $\mathbf{P}$ is nonsingular.

Ex. 4.32. $2n - 1$.

Ex. 4.34. $\mathbf{x} = \mathbf{x}_0 + \mathbf{x}_1$ where $\mathbf{x}_0 = [7\quad 0\quad -5\quad 0\quad 0]^T$ and $\mathbf{x}_1$ is given in (4.35).

Ex. 4.37. The first three vectors.

Ex. 4.38. Add any unit vector.

Ex. 4.39. Add $[0\quad 0\quad 0\quad 1]^T$.

Ex. 4.40. Use method in Section 4.6.

Ex. 4.41. $\dim \mathbf{A} = 3$. Columns 1, 2, 4.

Ex. 4.42. (b) or (c).

Ex. 4.43. If $\mathbf{AB} = \mathbf{C}$, then $\mathbf{x} = \mathbf{C}\boldsymbol{\beta}$ where $\boldsymbol{\beta} = \mathbf{B}^{-1}\boldsymbol{\alpha}$.

Ex. 4.46. Basis $[2\quad -7\quad 1]^T$.

Ex. 4.47. Let the columns of the $n \times p$ matrix $\mathbf{U}$ be a basis for the null space of $\mathbf{Ax} = \mathbf{0}$, so that the rank of $\mathbf{U}$ is p. The equations $\mathbf{U}^T\mathbf{x} = \mathbf{0}$ have $n - p$ independent solutions. These, transposed, are the rows of one possible $\mathbf{A}$ (why?). For the given example, one answer is $x_1 = x_3 = x_5$, $x_2 = x_4$.

Ex. 4.48. The first two are, the third is not. (Reduce to row-echelon form the 4×6 matrix whose first three columns are the spanning vectors. Alternatively, use the method in Section 4.6 to show that $[1\ \ 0\ \ 0\ \ \frac{1}{2}]$, $[0\ \ 1\ \ 0\ \ 0]$, $[0\ \ 0\ \ 1\ \ \frac{1}{2}]$ is a basis in standard form, and check whether the vectors in question are multiples of these.)

Ex. 4.49. *Hint:* The row echelon form of $[\mathbf{u}_1\ \ \mathbf{u}_2\ \ \mathbf{u}_3\ \ \mathbf{v}_1\ \ \mathbf{v}_2\ \ \mathbf{x}] = [\mathbf{U}, \mathbf{V}, \mathbf{x}]$ is

$$\begin{bmatrix} 1 & 0 & 0 & 1 & \frac{1}{2} & 1 & \frac{1}{2}x_2 \\ 0 & 1 & 0 & -1 & \frac{1}{2} & 2 & \frac{1}{6}(6x_1 - 5x_2 + 4x_4) \\ 0 & 0 & 1 & 0 & \frac{1}{2} & -1 & \frac{1}{6}(x_2 - 2x_4) \\ 0 & 0 & 0 & 0 & 0 & 0 & x_3 - 2x_1 \end{bmatrix} = \begin{bmatrix} \mathbf{I} & \mathbf{K} & \boldsymbol{\alpha} \\ \mathbf{0} & \mathbf{0} & \alpha_4 \end{bmatrix}.$$

Ex. 4.50. Show that the last three vectors in each of the expressions for $\mathbf{x}$ span the same space (see Ex. 4.27), and the difference of the first vectors belongs to this space.

Chapter 5

Ex. 5.2. 2.

Ex. 5.6. If $\mathbf{AB} = \mathbf{C}$, $\mathbf{C}$ nonsingular, then $\mathbf{A}(\mathbf{BC}^{-1}) = \mathbf{I}$, and $\mathbf{A}$ has a right-inverse. But $\mathbf{A}$ is square.

Ex. 5.8. Use Exs. 5.5, 5.7.

Ex. 5.10. Any column of $\mathbf{A} + \mathbf{B}$ is a sum of multiples of the columns of $[\mathbf{A}\ \ \mathbf{B}]$.

Ex. 5.11. Let $\mathbf{AB}$ have rank k. The equations $\mathbf{ABx} = \mathbf{0}$ have $p - k$ linearly independent solutions. Try to find these by first solving $\mathbf{Ay} = \mathbf{0}$, which gives $n - r$ independent solutions, say $\mathbf{y}_i$. Then find solutions of $\mathbf{Bx} = \mathbf{y}_i$, if any. This gives at most $(n - r) + (p - s)$ independent solutions, which must be less than or equal to $p - k$.

Ex. 5.13. Note that $\mathbf{P}^2 = \mathbf{Q}^2 = \mathbf{I}$.

Ex. 5.14. Let $\mathbf{A}_1^+$, $\mathbf{A}_2^+$ be two generalized inverses of $\mathbf{A}$.

$$\mathbf{AA}_2^+ = \mathbf{AA}_1^+\mathbf{AA}_2^+ = (\mathbf{AA}_1^+\mathbf{AA}_2^+)^T = (\mathbf{AA}_2^+)^T(\mathbf{AA}_1^+)^T = \mathbf{AA}_2^+\mathbf{AA}_1^+ = \mathbf{AA}_1^+.$$

$$\mathbf{A}_1^+ = (\mathbf{A}_1^+\mathbf{A})\mathbf{A}_1^+ = (\mathbf{A}_2^+\mathbf{A})\mathbf{A}_1^+ = \mathbf{A}_2^+(\mathbf{AA}_1^+) = \mathbf{A}_2^+(\mathbf{AA}_2^+) = \mathbf{A}_2^+.$$

Ex. 5.19. Consider $\mathbf{H} = \mathbf{A} + \boldsymbol{\beta}\mathbf{e}_j^T$ and $\mathbf{H} = \mathbf{A} + \mathbf{e}_i\boldsymbol{\gamma}^T$.

Ex. 5.20.

$$(\mathbf{PXP}^T)^{-1} = \frac{1}{12}\begin{bmatrix} 7 & 5 & 6 \\ 5 & 7 & 6 \\ 6 & 6 & 12 \end{bmatrix}, \qquad (\mathbf{QZQ}^T)^{-1} = \frac{1}{27}\begin{bmatrix} 18 & 6 & 3 \\ 6 & 10 & 2 \\ 3 & 2 & 4 \end{bmatrix}.$$

In the notation of (5.31), $\mathbf{D}^{-1} + \mathbf{CA}^{-1}\mathbf{B} = [\frac{8}{3}]$, and $\mathbf{A}^{-1}\mathbf{B}(\mathbf{D}^{-1} + \mathbf{CA}^{-1}\mathbf{B})^{-1}\mathbf{CA}^{-1} = \frac{1}{864}\mathbf{uu}^T$ where $\mathbf{u} = [9, 9, 18, -12, -4, -2]$.

Ex. 5.25. See Ex. 5.8.

Ex. 5.29. Use last sentence in Ex. 5.13.

Ex. 5.30. $\mathbf{A} = \mathbf{u}\mathbf{v}^T$, $c = \mathbf{v}^T\mathbf{u}$.

Ex. 5.31. Use Theorem 5.15.

Ex. 5.35. See hint for Ex. 1.40.

Ex. 5.36. Last part: consider $\mathbf{A}^{-1}\mathbf{A}$.

Ex. 5.39. If $\mathbf{A}$ is $m \times n$, rank of $\mathbf{A}$ must be n.

Ex. 5.40. Write $\mathbf{U} = \mathbf{XA}$ and consider ranks (Theorems 5.14, 5.15).

Ex. 5.43. Compare results of reducing to row-echelon form the matrices $[\mathbf{A}, \mathbf{b}]$ and $\begin{bmatrix} \mathbf{A}^T & \mathbf{0} \\ \mathbf{b}^T & 1 \end{bmatrix}$.

Ex. 5.45. Deduce from (5.14) that

$$[\mathbf{I} + \mathbf{P}^T\mathbf{P}]\mathbf{A}_{11}(\mathbf{x}_1 + \mathbf{Q}\mathbf{x}_2) = \mathbf{b}_1 + \mathbf{P}^T\mathbf{b}_2.$$

Ex. 5.47. (c) Apply Theorem 5.15 to $\mathbf{A}^C\mathbf{A} = (\mathbf{A}^C)\mathbf{A}$ and $\mathbf{A} = \mathbf{A}(\mathbf{A}^C\mathbf{A})$. Let $\mathbf{B} = \mathbf{I} - \mathbf{A}^C\mathbf{A}$ be of rank p. From Ex. 5.10 applied to $\mathbf{I} = \mathbf{A}^C\mathbf{A} + \mathbf{B}$ deduce $p \geq n - k$. From $\mathbf{AB} = \mathbf{0}$ deduce $p \leq n - k$. (d) $\mathbf{A}\mathbf{A}^C\mathbf{A}\mathbf{x} = \mathbf{A}\mathbf{x}$. Hence $\mathbf{A}\mathbf{A}^C\mathbf{b} = \mathbf{b}$, or $\mathbf{x} = \mathbf{A}^C\mathbf{b}$. (e) If $\mathbf{a}_j$ is the jth column of $\mathbf{A}$, $\mathbf{A}\mathbf{x}_j = \mathbf{a}_j$ is consistent, and $\mathbf{x}_j = \mathbf{B}\mathbf{a}_j$. Hence $\mathbf{A}\mathbf{B}\mathbf{a}_j = \mathbf{a}_j$, or $\mathbf{ABA} = \mathbf{A}$.

Chapter 6

Ex. 6.10. Replace $\mathbf{Ax} = \mathbf{b}$ by $\mathbf{Ax} \leq \mathbf{b}$, $-\mathbf{Ax} \leq -\mathbf{b}$. Problem is then in form (6.79) if we replace $\mathbf{A}$, $\mathbf{x}$, $\mathbf{b}$ in (6.79) by

$$\begin{bmatrix} \mathbf{A} \\ -\mathbf{A} \end{bmatrix}, \quad \begin{bmatrix} \mathbf{x}_1 \\ \mathbf{x}_2 \end{bmatrix}, \quad \begin{bmatrix} \mathbf{b} \\ -\mathbf{b} \end{bmatrix}.$$

Chapter 7

Ex. 7.9. Expand by last row or column.

Ex. 7.10. Multiply each column by x_1 and subtract from the next column on the right, starting at the right-hand end. Deduce $V_n = (x_n - x_1) \ldots (x_2 - x_1)V_{n-1}$ and use induction.

Ex. 7.11. Subtract last column from each of remaining columns, remove common factors from rows and columns. Subtract resulting last row from each of remaining rows. Use induction. Choose $\alpha_i = i - \gamma$, $\beta_j = j$.

Ex. 7.13. Last part. Insert minus sign.

Exs. 7.15 and 7.16. $\det \mathbf{A}^T = \det \mathbf{A}$.

Ex. 7.21.

$$\begin{bmatrix} \mathbf{A} & \mathbf{0} \\ \mathbf{0} & \mathbf{I} \end{bmatrix} \begin{bmatrix} \mathbf{I} & \mathbf{0} \\ \mathbf{C} & \mathbf{D} \end{bmatrix} = \begin{bmatrix} \mathbf{A} & \mathbf{0} \\ \mathbf{C} & \mathbf{D} \end{bmatrix}.$$

Ex. 7.24.

$$\begin{bmatrix} A & 0 \\ C & D \end{bmatrix}\begin{bmatrix} A^{-1} & 0 \\ 0 & D^{-1} \end{bmatrix}\begin{bmatrix} A & B \\ -C & D \end{bmatrix} = \begin{bmatrix} A & B \\ 0 & D + CA^{-1}B \end{bmatrix},$$

$$\begin{bmatrix} A & B \\ -C & D \end{bmatrix}\begin{bmatrix} A^{-1} & 0 \\ 0 & D^{-1} \end{bmatrix}\begin{bmatrix} A & 0 \\ C & D \end{bmatrix} = \begin{bmatrix} A + BD^{-1}C & B \\ 0 & D \end{bmatrix}.$$

Ex. 7.25. Choose $\mathbf{A} = \mathbf{I}_m$, $\mathbf{D} = \mathbf{I}_1$, $\mathbf{B} = \mathbf{u}$, $\mathbf{C} = \mathbf{v}^T$ in Ex. 7.24.

Ex. 7.25. To see the value of (sgn), interchange rows so that $a_{\sigma(1),1}, \ldots, a_{\sigma(n),n}$ lie along principal diagonal.

Chapter 8

Ex. 8.4. From symmetry simply replace 2 by 1 and 1 by 2 in subscripts of a_{ij}, b_i, x_j in (8.30). p, q become $1 + p, q(1 + p)/p$.

Ex. 8.16. If we interchange first and second rows and columns we obtain matrix of type that has been used as an example throughout this chapter (e.g., Ex. 8.14).

Ex. 8.17. If n is large enough, $2^{n-1} + \delta$ will round to 2^{n-1}, i.e., computer will give the same answer for the two sets of equations, whereas actual answers can be significantly different.

Ex. 8.18. Use (c) unless faced with ill-conditioning, in which case I would probably use (f) if the iteration converges, otherwise (d), and finally (e) or (g). There is little advantage in (a) or (b). Note that this does not answer the question of what is the "best" method for least-squares work since special methods are convenient for special purposes. For statistical work see the article by Efroymson in Vol. I of [59]. Exercise: Show that (e) is convenient if auxiliary equations $\mathbf{Bx} = \mathbf{d}$ have to be satisfied.

Ex. 8.21. Computer gives $\varepsilon x_i = \beta$ for inconsistent equations, $\varepsilon x_i = \delta$ for consistent equations, for some i, where ε, δ are comparable with each other and much smaller than β.

Ex. 8.22. Choose the $\mathbf{x}_0$ that minimizes $\mathbf{x}^T\mathbf{x}$ over all α_i (Section 5.6). Arrange that $[\mathbf{x}_1, \ldots, \mathbf{x}_p]$ is in column echelon form.

Ex. 8.23. Small changes in the coefficients produce small changes in the solution in the unique form of Ex. 8.22. Extend checks for system with unique solution. One way of checking the rank of an $m \times n$ matrix $\mathbf{A}$ is to examine the condition of $\mathbf{Ax} = \mathbf{0}$ for various assumed numerical ranks.

Ex. 8.24. Main point is to clarify what is meant by "poor" and "reasonable".

Chapter 9

Ex. 9.1. Eigenvalues 1, 4 and $-1, 0, 2$.

Ex. 9.4. $\mathbf{x}_i = [1 \ \sqrt{2} \ 1]^T$, $[1 \ 0 \ -1]^T$, $[1 \ -\sqrt{2} \ 1]^T$, $\lambda_i = 2 - \sqrt{2}, 2, 2 + \sqrt{2}$.

Ex. 9.5. $[1 \quad -2 \quad 0]^T$, $[0 \quad 3 \quad 1]^T$, $[2 \quad 1 \quad -1]^T$, $\lambda_3 = 6$.

Ex. 9.8. If $\mathbf{x}$ is eigenvector corresponding to λ, $f(\mathbf{A})\mathbf{x} = f(\lambda)\mathbf{x}$.

Ex. 9.9. Complex zeros of real polynomial occur in conjugate pairs. Real polynomial of odd degree always has a real zero.

Ex. 9.11. For last part see Exs. 9.6 and 9.7(e).

Ex. 9.13. All eigenvalues of hermitian matrix are real.

Ex. 9.20. Eigenvalues $e^{\pm i\theta}$ and $e^{\pm\theta}$ respectively.

Ex. 9.21.

$$\begin{bmatrix} 1 & 1 & 1 \\ 2 & -1 & 0 \\ -1 & 3 & 2 \end{bmatrix}\begin{bmatrix} 2 & 0 & 0 \\ 0 & 1 & 0 \\ 0 & 0 & -1 \end{bmatrix}\begin{bmatrix} 2 & -1 & -1 \\ 4 & -3 & -2 \\ -5 & 4 & 3 \end{bmatrix} = \begin{bmatrix} 13 & -9 & -7 \\ 4 & -1 & -2 \\ 18 & -15 & -10 \end{bmatrix}.$$

Ex. 9.22. $(\mathbf{Au}_i, \mathbf{Au}_j) = (\mathbf{u}_i, \mathbf{A}^T\mathbf{Au}_j) = (\mathbf{u}_i, \mathbf{u}_j)$.

Ex. 9.25. In terms of the eigenvectors $\mathbf{x}_i$ (see answer to Ex. 9.4):

$$4\begin{bmatrix} 1 \\ 1 \\ 1 \end{bmatrix} = (2 + \sqrt{2})\mathbf{x}_1 + (2 - \sqrt{2})\mathbf{x}_3; \qquad 4\begin{bmatrix} 1 \\ 0 \\ 0 \end{bmatrix} = \mathbf{x}_1 + 2\mathbf{x}_2 + \mathbf{x}_3.$$

Rate of convergence in first case is determined by λ_3/λ_1. In second case, the largest element in the iterates will eventually be the second one, and the second element of $\mathbf{x}_2$ is zero.

Ex. 9.26. $|\lambda_1| \geq |\lambda_2| > \lambda_3 \geq \ldots$, and $\mathbf{u}_0$ contains components of the eigenvectors corresponding to λ_1 and λ_2.

Ex. 9.30. $\lambda_i = k + 2\cos\{i\pi/(n+1)\}$.

Ex. 9.32. det $\mathbf{A}$ is product of eigenvalues and product of complex conjugate numbers is positive.

Ex. 9.34. Since $\mathbf{ABx} = \lambda\mathbf{x}$, $\lambda \neq 0$, $\mathbf{x} \neq \mathbf{0}$ then $\mathbf{Bx} \neq \mathbf{0}$ and $\mathbf{BA}(\mathbf{Bx}) = \lambda(\mathbf{Bx})$. Let $\mathbf{AB}$ and $\mathbf{BA}$ have r, s independent eigenvectors corresponding to $\lambda \neq 0$. Since $\mathbf{A}\Sigma\alpha_i\mathbf{Bx}_i = \lambda\Sigma\alpha_i\mathbf{x}_i$ the $\mathbf{Bx}_i$ are linearly independent if the $\mathbf{x}_i$ are, and $s \geq r$. Interchange roles of $\mathbf{A}$ and $\mathbf{B}$ and deduce $r = s$. $\mathbf{AB}$ and $\mathbf{BA}$ have orders m, n and the same numbers of eigenvectors corresponding to nonzero eigenvalues.

Ex. 9.35. The ranks of $\mathbf{A} - \lambda\mathbf{I}$ and $\mathbf{A}^T - \lambda\mathbf{I}$ are the same.

Ex. 9.36. Consider coefficient of λ^r in the expansion of det $(\mathbf{A} - \lambda\mathbf{I})$.

Ex. 9.37. If there are p independent eigenvectors, rank of $\mathbf{A} - \lambda_1\mathbf{I}$ is $n - p$ and sum of all $(n - p + 1)$-rowed principal minors is zero. From Ex. 9.36 the coefficient of λ_1^{p-1} in the characteristic polynomial is zero and multiplicity of λ_1 is at least p. (Another proof is given in Theorem 11.6.) Example is an upper triangular matrix with zero diagonal elements.

Ex. 9.40. See Ex. 9.37.

Ex. 9.52. $\omega_1 = 0$ corresponds to a translation.

Ex. 9.53.
$$\det\begin{vmatrix} -\lambda\mathbf{I} & \mathbf{I} \\ \mathbf{Q} & -\lambda\mathbf{I} \end{vmatrix} = \det\begin{vmatrix} -\lambda\mathbf{I} & \mathbf{I} \\ \mathbf{Q} - \lambda^2\mathbf{I} & \mathbf{0} \end{vmatrix} = \det|\mathbf{Q} - \lambda^2\mathbf{I}|.$$

Chapter 10

Ex. 10.4. (i) $\|\mathbf{x} + \mathbf{y}\|^2 = \|\mathbf{x}\|^2 + 2\,\mathrm{Re}\,(\mathbf{x}, \mathbf{y}) + \|\mathbf{y}\|^2$. Replace $\mathbf{x}$, $\mathbf{y}$ by $\mathbf{Px}$, $\mathbf{Py}$ and deduce $\mathrm{Re}\,(\mathbf{Px}, \mathbf{Py}) = \mathrm{Re}\,(\mathbf{x}, \mathbf{y})$. Repeat with $i\mathbf{y}$ in place of $\mathbf{y}$. (ii) If $\mathbf{P}$ unitary, $(\mathbf{Px}, \mathbf{Px}) = (\mathbf{x}, \mathbf{P}^H\mathbf{Px}) = (\mathbf{x}, \mathbf{x})$. For the converse, use part (i) with $\mathbf{x} = \mathbf{e}_i$, $\mathbf{y} = \mathbf{e}_j$, unit vectors.

Ex. 10.7. Use Gram-Schmidt on any basis.

Ex. 10.8. Hermitian transpose of $\mathbf{P}^H\mathbf{AP} = \mathbf{D}$ gives $\mathbf{P}^H\mathbf{A}^H\mathbf{P} = \mathbf{D}^H = \overline{\mathbf{D}}$.

Ex. 10.9. $\mathbf{AP} = \mathbf{PD}$, $\mathbf{P}$ nonsingular.

Ex. 10.14. Second part. If $\mathbf{u} = [u_i]$, $\mathbf{v} = [v_i]$ and $u_1 = |u_1|e^{i\alpha}$, we can transform an arbitrary $\mathbf{u}$ into a $\mathbf{v}$ with $v_1 = \|\mathbf{u}\|e^{i\alpha}$, $v_i = 0$ $(i > 1)$.

Ex. 10.20.
$$u_1 = \sqrt{12}, \quad \mathbf{U} = \frac{1}{\sqrt{2}}\begin{bmatrix} 1 & 1 \\ -1 & 1 \end{bmatrix}, \quad \mathbf{V} = \frac{1}{\sqrt{6}}\begin{bmatrix} 1 & \sqrt{3} & \sqrt{2} \\ -1 & \sqrt{3} & \sqrt{2} \\ 2 & 0 & \sqrt{2} \end{bmatrix}.$$

Ex. 10.21. Use Theorems 5.17–5.20 and (10.65).

Ex. 10.22. If $\mathbf{x}$ is one type of singular vector, $\mathbf{Ax}$ is another, which is not convenient for dealing with $(\mathbf{A} - \lambda\mathbf{I})\mathbf{x}$.

Ex. 10.23. $\mathbf{AP} = k\mathbf{P}$, $\mathbf{A} = k\mathbf{PP}^H = k\mathbf{I}$.

Ex. 10.24. $\mathbf{P}^H\mathbf{P} = \mathbf{I}$ so that $\mathbf{P}^H$ is left-inverse. $\mathbf{P}$ is square. Hence $\mathbf{P}^H$ must be right-inverse, and $\mathbf{PP}^H = \mathbf{I}$ which gives first half.

Ex. 10.27. Follows directly from fact that normal matrices can be diagonalized.

Ex. 10.28. Deduce $(\mathbf{x}, \mathbf{A}^H\mathbf{Ay}) = (\mathbf{x}, \mathbf{AA}^H\mathbf{y})$ for all $\mathbf{x}$, $\mathbf{y}$ (compare Ex. 10.4).

Ex. 10.30. (a) 'If' – $\mathbf{A} = \mathbf{PDP}^H$ which is hermitian if $\mathbf{D}$ is real. (b) 'If' – $\mathbf{A}^H\mathbf{A} = \mathbf{P}\overline{\mathbf{D}}\mathbf{DP}^H = \mathbf{I}$. Similarly $\mathbf{AA}^H = \mathbf{I}$.

Ex. 10.31. Theorem 10.8.

Ex. 10.32. (a) Let basis for subspace be $[\mathbf{u}_1, \ldots, \mathbf{u}_p] = \mathbf{U}$. $\mathbf{AU} = \mathbf{UM}$ where $\mathbf{M}$ is $p \times p$. $\mathbf{M}$ has at least one eigenvector, $\mathbf{Mz} = \lambda\mathbf{z}$. Then $\mathbf{A}(\mathbf{Uz}) = \mathbf{UMz} = \lambda(\mathbf{Uz})$. (b) 'Prove dim $W \geq 1$'. The $\mathbf{x}_i$ cannot span V_n. Let $\mathbf{z}$ be vector linearly independent of $\mathbf{z}$. Use Gram-Schmidt to derive vector in W. Use induction to complete the proof.

Ex. 10.33. $\mathbf{A}^r = \mathbf{PU}^r\mathbf{P}^H$. 'Only if' is easy. 'If' – Let $\mathbf{V}$ be any matrix such that $v_{ii} = \alpha$, $v_{ij} = \beta$ $(i \neq j)$, $|u_{ii}| \leq \alpha < 1$, $|v_{ij}| < \beta$. Set $\mathbf{V} = \alpha\mathbf{I} + \beta\mathbf{J}$. $\mathbf{J}^n = \mathbf{0}$ and $\mathbf{V}^r \to \mathbf{0}$ as $r \to \infty$, whatever the value of β.

Ex. 10.34. Induction on (10.41).

Ex. 10.35. $\mathbf{A}^T\mathbf{A} = \mathbf{A}^T\mathbf{b} \rightarrow \mathbf{U}^T\mathbf{Q}^T\mathbf{Q}\mathbf{U}\mathbf{x} = \mathbf{U}^T\mathbf{Q}^T\mathbf{b}$, $\mathbf{U}$ nonsingular.

Ex. 10.39. Deduce from proof of Theorem 10.6. Last part not true since $\mathbf{P}^T\mathbf{A}\mathbf{P}$ real but complex eigenvalues must appear on diagonal of triangle.

Ex. 10.40. The first formula is simply $\mathbf{A} = \mathbf{P}\mathbf{\Lambda}\mathbf{P}^H$. To express $\mathbf{I}$ in terms if the $\mathbf{E}_i$, expand columns of $\mathbf{I}$ in terms of the $\mathbf{x}_i$. (Multiplication of result by $\mathbf{A}$ gives first formula.)

Ex. 10.42. If $\mathbf{A} = \mathbf{P}\mathbf{D}\mathbf{P}^H$ and $\mathbf{AB} = \mathbf{BA}$ deduce $\mathbf{DR} = \mathbf{RD}$ where $\mathbf{R} = \mathbf{P}^H\mathbf{B}\mathbf{P}$. Hence $\mathbf{R}$ is hermitian and block diagonal where blocks correspond to repeated eigenvalues of $\mathbf{A}$. If $\mathbf{R} = \mathbf{Q}\mathbf{D}_1\mathbf{Q}^H$ then $\mathbf{B} = \mathbf{P}\mathbf{Q}\mathbf{D}_1(\mathbf{P}\mathbf{Q})^H$, $\mathbf{Q}\mathbf{D}\mathbf{Q}^H = \mathbf{Q}$, $\mathbf{A} = \mathbf{P}\mathbf{Q}\mathbf{D}(\mathbf{P}\mathbf{Q})^H$ and columns of $\mathbf{PQ}$ are common eigenvectors. Consider 2×2 example $\mathbf{A} = \mathbf{I}$, $\mathbf{B}$ with distinct eigenvalues.

Chapter 11

Ex. 11.17. If the characteristic polynomial of $\mathbf{A}$ is $p(\lambda)$ then $p(\mathbf{A}) = \mathbf{P}\mathbf{D}\mathbf{P}^{-1}$ where $\mathbf{D}$ is a diagonal matrix with diagonal elements $p(\lambda_i)$, i.e., $\mathbf{D}$ is null.

Ex. 11.18. "If" – if $\mathbf{E}$ is a matrix obtained by interchanging columns i and j of the unit matrix, $\mathbf{E}^{-1} = \mathbf{E}$, and $\mathbf{E}^{-1}\mathbf{D}\mathbf{E}$ is $\mathbf{D}$ with ith and jth diagonal elements interchanged. "Only if" – similar matrices have the same characteristic equation.

Ex. 11.19. "If" – $\mathbf{P}^{-1}\mathbf{A}\mathbf{P} = \mathbf{Q}^{-1}\mathbf{B}\mathbf{Q} = \mathbf{\Lambda}$.

Ex. 11.20. "If" – prove that there are n independent eigenvectors. "Only if" – use $\mathbf{AP} = \mathbf{P}\mathbf{\Lambda}$.

Ex. 11.21. "If" – Jordan canonical form is upper triangular with zeros on diagonal. "Only if" – Theorem 11.10.

Ex. 11.23. 5.

Ex. 11.24. Separate real and imaginary parts in $\mathbf{A}(\mathbf{x} + i\mathbf{y}) = (\alpha + i\beta)(\mathbf{x} + i\mathbf{y})$. Prove that $[\mathbf{x}, \mathbf{y}]$ is nonsingular. This is the required $\mathbf{T}$.

Ex. 11.25. $\mathbf{A}^r = \mathbf{P}\mathbf{J}^r\mathbf{P}^{-1}$ where $\mathbf{J}$ is the Jordan canonical form.

Ex. 11.31. From $\mathbf{AB} = \mathbf{BA}$ deduce $(\mathbf{P}^{-1}\mathbf{A}\mathbf{P})\,\mathbf{\Lambda} = \mathbf{\Lambda}\,(\mathbf{P}^{-1}\mathbf{A}\mathbf{P})$. Partition this result.

Ex. 11.33. Generalize the permutation matrix $\mathbf{B}$ of Ex. 11.32 in an obvious way.

Chapter 12

Ex. 12.4. (a) Hyperbola. (b) Two straight lines. (c) Ellipse. (d) Ellipse centered at $x = 1, y = -1$. (e) Parabola (see Ex. 12.3).

Ex. 12.10. (a) $(\mathbf{A} - \lambda\mathbf{B})\mathbf{x} = \mathbf{0}$ has nonzero solution and $\lambda = (\mathbf{x}, \mathbf{A}\mathbf{x})/(\mathbf{x}, \mathbf{B}\mathbf{x})$.

Ex. 12.11. $(\mathbf{x}, \mathbf{Ax}) - (\alpha + i\beta)(\mathbf{x}, \mathbf{Bx}) = 0$, where α, $(\mathbf{x}, \mathbf{Ax})$, and $(\mathbf{x}, \mathbf{Bx})$ are real.

Ex. 12.12. (a) follows directly from $\partial Q/\partial\alpha_{ij} = 0$. For (b) note that either $\mathbf{r}_j = \mathbf{0}$ for some $j < n$, or, from (a), $\mathbf{r}_n$ is orthogonal to n mutually orthogonal vectors $\mathbf{r}_0, \ldots, \mathbf{r}_{n-1}$.

Ex. 12.18. Solve $(\mathbf{A} - \rho\mathbf{B})\boldsymbol{\alpha} = \mathbf{0}$, where $\mathbf{A} = [(\mathbf{z}_i, \mathbf{Az}_j)]$, $\mathbf{B} = [(\mathbf{z}_i, \mathbf{z}_j)]$.

Ex. 12.20. If neither $\mathbf{A}$ nor $\mathbf{B}$ is positive definite, we cannot obtain any inequalities relating ρ and the eigenvalues. If $\mathbf{A}$ is positive definite, $\mathbf{B}$ indefinite, and λ_1, λ_{-1} are the positive and negative eigenvalues of smallest modulus, then $\lambda_1 \le \rho$ or $\rho \le \lambda_{-1}$.

Ex. 12.27. $(\mathbf{x}, \mathbf{Ax}) = (\mathbf{y}, \mathbf{A}^{-1}\mathbf{y})$, $\mathbf{y} = \mathbf{Ax}$.

Ex. 12.28. $(\mathbf{x}, \mathbf{B}^H\mathbf{ABx}) = (\mathbf{z}, \mathbf{Az})$, $\mathbf{z} = \mathbf{Bx}$. If rank $\mathbf{B} < n$, there exists a nonzero $\mathbf{x}$ with $\mathbf{Bx} = \mathbf{0}$.

Ex. 12.30. $\alpha + \beta\lambda + \gamma\lambda^2 = 0$, where $\alpha = (\mathbf{x}, \mathbf{Ax})$, $\beta = (\mathbf{x}, \mathbf{Bx})$, $\gamma = (\mathbf{x}, \mathbf{Cx})$, and $(\mathbf{A} + \mathbf{B}\lambda + \mathbf{C}\lambda^2)\mathbf{x} = \mathbf{0}$, $\mathbf{x} \ne \mathbf{0}$.

Ex. 12.31. "Only if" – $\mathbf{A}$ is not positive definite, so must have zero eigenvalue.

Ex. 12.33. Use (7.49) with $\mathbf{L} = \mathbf{CD}^{1/2}$ (elements of $\mathbf{D}$ are real and positive).

Ex. 12.34. Use Ex. 12.33. Let $\mathbf{A}^{-1} = \mathbf{M}^H\mathbf{M}$, $\mathbf{A} = \mathbf{M}^{-1}(\mathbf{M}^H)^{-1}$. Then $\mathbf{I} - \mathbf{MBM}^H = \mathbf{MCM}^H$, and the eigenvalues of $\mathbf{MBM}^H$ are such that $0 < \lambda_i \le 1$. Hence det $\mathbf{MBM}^H \le 1$ from which (b) follows. Eigenvalues of $(\mathbf{MBM}^H)^{-1}$ are ≥ 1 so that $(\mathbf{MBM}^H)^{-1} - \mathbf{I}$, and hence $\mathbf{B}^{-1} - \mathbf{A}^{-1}$, is positive semidefinite. (Alternatively, use Theorem 12.7.)

Ex. 12.35. $\mathbf{B}$ is nonsingular. See Ex. 12.10(a).

Ex. 12.36. $3y_1^2 + 6y_2^2 + 9y_3^2$; $2x_1^2 + 5x_2^2$; $5x_1^2 - x_2^2 - x_3^2$.

Ex. 12.37.

$$\begin{bmatrix} \mathbf{I} & \mathbf{0} \\ -\boldsymbol{\alpha}^H\mathbf{A}_1^{-1} & 1 \end{bmatrix} \begin{bmatrix} \mathbf{A}_1 & \boldsymbol{\alpha} \\ \boldsymbol{\alpha}^H & a_{nn} \end{bmatrix} = \begin{bmatrix} \mathbf{A}_1 & \boldsymbol{\alpha} \\ \mathbf{0} & a_{nn} - \boldsymbol{\alpha}^H\mathbf{A}_1^{-1}\boldsymbol{\alpha} \end{bmatrix}.$$

Hence det $\mathbf{A} = (a_{nn} - \boldsymbol{\alpha}^H\mathbf{A}_1^{-1}\boldsymbol{\alpha})$ det $\mathbf{A}_1$. Since $\mathbf{A}_1^{-1}$ is positive definite, the first formula follows by induction. Apply to $\mathbf{BB}^H$. Equality is attained if $\mathbf{B}$ is unitary.

Exs. 12.38 and 12.39. Use solution (11.76) of (11.68).

Ex. 12.41. (a) $(\mathbf{A} - \lambda\mathbf{I})\mathbf{x} = \mathbf{0}$ implies $(\mathbf{A}^2 - \lambda\mathbf{A})\mathbf{x} = \mathbf{0}$ or $(1 - \lambda)\mathbf{Ax} = \mathbf{0}$. Hence $\lambda = 1$ or $\mathbf{Ax} = \mathbf{0}$ which implies $\lambda = 0$. (b) If $\mathbf{A}$ is nonsingular, $\mathbf{A}^2 = \mathbf{A}$ implies $\mathbf{A} = \mathbf{I}$. (d) Trace equals sum of eigenvalues.

Ex. 12.43. First part, use $\mathbf{P}^H\mathbf{AP} = \boldsymbol{\Lambda}$. Suppose $\mathbf{S}^H\mathbf{AS} = \mathbf{D}_1$, $\mathbf{R}^H\mathbf{AR} = \mathbf{D}_2$, with $\mathbf{D}_1$ as given, $\mathbf{D}_2$ similar except that diagonal blocks are $\mathbf{I}_p$, $-\mathbf{I}_q$, $\mathbf{0}$. From rank invariance deduce $r + s = p + q$. Switch to quadratic form and prove that a nonsingular $\mathbf{Q}$ exists, with $\mathbf{z} = \mathbf{Qy}$, such that

$$y_1^2 + \ldots + y_r^2 - y_{r+1}^2 - \ldots - y_{r+s}^2 = z_1^2 + \ldots + z_p^2 - z_{p+1}^2 - \ldots - z_{p+q}^2.$$

If $p < r$, show that we can find nonzero $\mathbf{y}$, $\mathbf{z}$ such that $y_i = 0$ ($i = r + 1$ to $r + s$), $z_i = 0$ ($i = 1$ to p), which gives a contradiction. Deduce $p = r$.

Ex. 12.45. Use law of inertia, Ex. 12.43.

Ex. 12.46. $\mathbf{A} = \mathbf{P}^H \mathbf{\Lambda} \mathbf{P}$, $\mathbf{B} = \mathbf{P}^H \mathbf{\Lambda}^{1/2} \mathbf{P}$. To prove uniqueness, if $\mathbf{B}$ is hermitian and $\mathbf{B}^2 = \mathbf{A}$ this means $\mathbf{B} = \mathbf{Q}^H \mathbf{D} \mathbf{Q}$, $\mathbf{B}^2 = \mathbf{Q}^H \mathbf{D}^2 \mathbf{Q}$ and diagonal elements must be the eigenvalues of $\mathbf{A}$ in some (unimportant) order.

Ex. 12.47. (a) Use formula (11.15) for exp $\mathbf{A}$. (b) Prove $\mathbf{A}^H\mathbf{A} = \mathbf{M}^2$, $\mathbf{A}\mathbf{A}^H = \mathbf{N}^2$, so that $\mathbf{M}$, $\mathbf{N}$ are the unique square roots (Ex. 12.46). Use theory of singular values, $\mathbf{A} = \mathbf{P}\mathbf{D}\mathbf{Q}^H$, unitary $\mathbf{P}$, $\mathbf{Q}$. Find $\mathbf{M} = \mathbf{Q}\mathbf{D}\mathbf{Q}^H$, $\mathbf{N} = \mathbf{P}\mathbf{D}\mathbf{P}^H$. If $\mathbf{A}$ nonsingular, prove $\mathbf{U} = \mathbf{V} = \mathbf{P}\mathbf{Q}^H$. If $\mathbf{A}$ singular, $\mathbf{A} = \mathbf{U}\mathbf{M}$ gives $\mathbf{P}\mathbf{D} = \mathbf{U}\mathbf{Q}\mathbf{D}$ and can still construct (nonunique) $\mathbf{U}$.

Ex. 12.52. $\lambda_1 + \lambda_2 + \lambda_3 = a_{11} + a_{22} + a_{33}$. $\mathbf{P}^{-1} = \mathbf{P}^H$ gives identities between elements.

Ex. 12.55. Consider projections on the x_j-axes of unit vectors along the x_i'-axes. Prove also $\mathbf{x} = \mathbf{L}^T\mathbf{x}'$ so that $\mathbf{x} = \mathbf{L}^T\mathbf{L}\mathbf{x}$, $\mathbf{x}' = \mathbf{L}\mathbf{L}^T\mathbf{x}'$, for any $\mathbf{x}$, $\mathbf{x}'$. Hence $\mathbf{L}$ orthogonal.

Ex. 12.56. Note answer to Ex. 12.52.

Chapter 13

Ex. 13.3. $\|\mathbf{A}\|_2^2 = \rho(\mathbf{A}^H\mathbf{A}) \le \|\mathbf{A}^H\mathbf{A}\|_\infty$. Remember that $\|\mathbf{A}^H\|_\infty = \|\mathbf{A}\|_1$.

Ex. 13.7. In Theorem 13.6 take $\mathbf{I} + \mathbf{S}$ to be the matrix obtained by dividing each row of $\mathbf{A}$ by its diagonal element, and use the ∞ norm.

Ex. 13.15. (a) If $\mathbf{z}$ is another eigenvector, $\mathbf{C}(\mathbf{x}_0 + k\mathbf{z}) = \mu(\mathbf{x}_0 + k\mathbf{z})$. Hence $\mathbf{x}_0 + k\mathbf{z} > \mathbf{0}$. But if $\mathbf{x}_0$, $\mathbf{z}$ lin. indep., k can be chosen so that $\mathbf{x}_0 + k\mathbf{z}$ has a zero element. (b) Suppose $\mathbf{x}$, $\mathbf{y}$ are two positive eigenvectors of $\mathbf{C}$, $\mathbf{C}^T$, corresponding to eigenvalues ξ, η. Since $\xi(\mathbf{x}, \mathbf{y}) = (\mathbf{C}\mathbf{x}, \mathbf{y}) = (\mathbf{x}, \mathbf{C}^T\mathbf{y}) = \eta(\mathbf{x}, \mathbf{y})$, hence $\xi = \eta$ and all positive eigenvectors must correspond to same eigenvalue. Then (b) follows from (a).

Ex. 13.16. If $\beta\mathbf{z} = \mathbf{C}\mathbf{z}$ then $|\beta|\,\mathbf{z}_+ \le \mathbf{C}\mathbf{z}_+$.

Ex. 13.19. $|0.5 - \lambda_2| \le 7 \cdot 10^{-9}$, $|0.1 - \lambda_3| \le 4 \cdot 10^{-9}$.

Ex. 13.30. Prove that $\mathbf{x} - \mathbf{x}_{i+1} = (\mathbf{L}\mathbf{U})^{-1}\mathbf{E}(\mathbf{x} - \mathbf{x}_i)$.

Ex. 13.37. Only the first $20 - r + 1$ components of $\mathbf{x}_r$ are nonzero and the last r components of $\mathbf{y}_r$.

Ex. 13.38. $(z - x)^2 f''(z) + \varepsilon g(z) \approx 0$.

Ex. 13.39. $\mathbf{v}^T\mathbf{A}^{-1}\mathbf{u} = \|\mathbf{A}^{-1}\|$, $(\mathbf{A} + \Delta\mathbf{A})\mathbf{A}^{-1}\mathbf{u} = \mathbf{0}$, so $\mathbf{A} + \Delta\mathbf{A}$ is singular. This choice of $\Delta\mathbf{A}$ gives equality in (13.108).

Ex. 13.45. For (ii) use (i) and for (iv) use (iii). For (v), (vi) use Theorem 13.10 and Ex. 13.15. For (vii) let $\mathbf{P}^{-1}\mathbf{A}\mathbf{P} = \mathbf{J}$, the Jordan form of $\mathbf{A}$. Then $\mathbf{A}^r = \mathbf{P}\mathbf{J}^r\mathbf{P}^{-1}$. First column of $\mathbf{P}$ is $\mathbf{z}$ (see (vi)) and first row of $\mathbf{P}^{-1}$ is $\mathbf{e}^T$. Largest eigenvalue of $\mathbf{J}$ is 1.

Chapter 14

Ex. 14.1. (a) No. (b) No. (c) Yes. (d) No. (e) No. (f) Yes.

Ex. 14.3. (a), (b), (c), (h), (i) are finite-dimensional; (j) may or may not be; (k) is if V and W are.

Ex. 14.7. (a), (c), (d).

Ex. 14.8. (a) True. (b) False.

Ex. 14.21. $1, x, \frac{1}{2}(3x^2 - 1), \frac{1}{2}(5x^3 - 3x)$.

Ex. 14.23. (a) Yes. (b) No. (c) Yes. (d) Yes. (e) Yes.

Ex. 14.24. (a), (c), (d), (e) True. (b) False.

Ex. 14.25. Zero vector is 1, $k = 1$, and basis is any number $a \neq 1$.

Ex. 14.26. (b), (d), (e), (f), (g).

Ex. 14.27. (a) False. (b) True.

Ex. 14.29. (a) Yes. (b) Yes. (c) No. (d) Yes. (e) Yes.

Ex. 14.35. Find the row-echelon form of the 4×5 matrix whose columns are the basis vectors.

Notes and References

Chapter 1

Nearly all textbooks on linear algebra contain an account of matrix algebra. However the applied scientist may find the clearest exposition, for his purposes, in textbooks on engineering mathematics, for example:

F. B. Hildebrand, *Methods of Applied Mathematics*, 2nd ed., Prentice-Hall (1965).
E. Kreysig, *Advanced Engineering Mathematics*, Wiley (1962).
I. S. Sokolnikoff and R. M. Redheffer, *Mathematics of Physics and Modern Engineering*, McGraw-Hill (1958).
C. R. Wylie, *Advanced Engineering Mathematics*, McGraw-Hill (1960).

Chapter 2

This chapter is intended as background material for the student, and little classroom time need be spent on it. The example in Section 2.2 is probably the most illuminating. As emphasized in Section 2.3, the "matrix + computer" approach is revolutionizing our method of attack on problems in the applied sciences—both in practice and in the textbooks.

The material in Sections 2.2, 2.3 (which has also appeared in [91], pp. 206–212), is taken from:

Ben Noble, *Matrix Calculations and Applications*, The Mathematics Research Center, U.S. Army, University of Wisconsin, Madison, Wis. (mimeo)(1964).

For references on mechanical structures see Ex. 2.16, and on electrical networks see Ex. 2.19. As mentioned in Ex. 2.14, Table 2.1 gives only a small part of a much larger picture, but we had to stop somewhere.

The least-squares procedure in Section 2.4 is covered in many books on regression analysis and the statistical design of experiments (see Ex. 2.27). The star problem was described to the author by Dr. H. Eichhorn during a visit of several members of the Army Map Service to the Mathematics Research Center, U.S. Army, University of Wisconsin. This material appears also in [91], Section 10.6, where an extension to the case of several overlapping plates is given.

The Markov chain example in Section 2.5 was suggested by Chapter 11 in:

R. I. Levin and C. A. Kirkpatrick, *Quantitative Approaches to Management*, McGraw-Hill (1965).

Chapter 3

This chapter is deliberately long-winded to help the beginner. The student should read it in detail, but lecturers may prefer to summarize essentials and move on to Chapter 4 as quickly as possible.

The basic tools are elementary row operations and the row-echelon form. It is not necessary to spend much time proving the uniqueness of the row-echelon form since the proof is not particularly illuminating, and students are usually willing to accept the result as intuitively reasonable. A strong argument in its favor is that otherwise we would really be in trouble when solving linear systems!

The important result reiterated throughout this chapter is that the number of solutions of the system of linear equations $\mathbf{Ax} = \mathbf{b}$ is given by one of the three important numbers 0, 1, ∞.

Historically mathematics has proceeded from the particular to the general. Around 1900, Fredholm spotted that a similar result holds for a certain type of integral equation. Later it was noted that it holds for quite general linear operators. The result that certain kinds of linear equations have 0, 1, or ∞ solutions is known as the *Fredholm alternative*.

Chapter 4

This chapter is fundamental. It is necessary to spend considerable time on it if students are meeting vector spaces for the first time. The chapter will have succeeded if students are persuaded that the idea of a vector space is really quite simple.

The dimensional analysis example at the end of Section 4.8 (from equation (4.36) on) was brought to the author's attention by J. Mahoney, Department of Chemical Engineering, West Virginia University. It also appears in [91], pp. 235–237.

Chapter 5

The time spent on this chapter will vary according to taste. At least one should prove that row rank is equal to column rank, and review the various equivalent definitions of rank.

The application of rank to chemical reactions given in Section 5.4 has also appeared in [91], pp. 240–244, and this account is based on:

R. Aris and R. H. S. Mah, *The Independence of Chemical Reactions*, Ind. Eng. Chem. Fundamentals, **2**, 90–94 (1963).

A comprehensive review of generalized inverses is given by:

T. N. E. Greville, "Generalized inverses of finite matrices," to be published in the *SIAM Review* (1969).

Kron's "method of tearing" is expounded in [88], where he refers to it as "diakoptics." The method is basically simple, although most accounts seem to be obscure. A brief account is given in Braae [36], Chapter 11.

Chapter 6

The most important thing the teacher should realize here is the *flexibility* of the material in this chapter. The sections are almost independent. They can be taught in various orders, in greater or lesser detail, and at various levels of sophistication. The main reason for expounding the theory in terms of elementary row operations in Sections 6.3, 6.4, is that this is a logical sequel to the material in Chapters 3, 4.

References on linear programming are [68], [69], [70], [72], [75], [80], [98].

Chapter 7

Variants of the method of triangular decomposition (Section 7.7) are discussed in books on numerical analysis, for instance [54].

Chapter 8

This chapter of course owes a great deal to the work of Wilkinson, summarized in his books [61], [62]. An elementary treatment of the problem of solving simultaneous linear equations is given in Forsythe and Moler [53].

After various efforts at writing this chapter it was decided that insight and clarity were much improved when the introduction of norms was postponed to

Chapter 13, and backward error analysis simply sketched in Ex. 8.25. The main place where the results of the backward error analysis are used is in the argument in the paragraph preceding Definition 13.4.

Chapter 9

This is designed as an introductory chapter, to prepare the way for Chapters 10–12. However the chapter is self-contained, and Sections 9.1–9.5, supplemented by selected sections from later chapters, will suffice for an introductory course.

Chapter 10

The chapters on unitary and similarity transformations have been separated because it is convenient to develop the two theories along different lines. The main service the lecturer can provide the student is probably to clarify the overall picture (Figures 10.2, 11.1), and emphasize the simplicity of the properties of hermitian (as a special case of normal) matrices, and the structure of the Jordan canonical form (where difficulties arise only if the matrix is defective).

A geometrical interpretation of singular values and vectors is given in Forsythe and Moler [53].

Chapter 11

The Jordan canonical form can be derived using ideas pitched at various levels of abstraction. The more abstract the treatment, the more elegant the argument can be. We have deliberately avoided direct sums and invariant subspaces, perhaps at the expense of elegance. One of the most important statements in this chapter is the one preceding Ex. 11.13, namely that the practical importance of the theorems is that they tell us what we are looking for. Once this is known, if we wish to reduce a given matrix to Jordan form, we operate directly on the original matrix, ignoring the methods used in the proofs of the theorems.

Once the Jordan canonical form has been understood, the applications to systems of differential equations in Section 11.7 can be covered very quickly. For further material see the references in Ex. 11.28. The temptation to include some of this material was resisted because this book is already too long, and it is a book on linear algebra, not differential equations.

Chapter 12

For further material on the subject matter of this chapter see Bellman [34]. Ex. 12.6 is based on part of an article by G. E. P. Box in:

> *The Design and Analysis of Industrial Experiments* (O. L. Davies, ed.) Oliver and Boyd (1956).

Chapter 13

Historically Schwarz, in 1885, discovered only a special case of the inequality that bears his name, and other special cases were discovered previously by Cauchy in 1821 and by Bunyakovsky in 1859. In the Russian literature the result is known as the Bunyakovsky inequality, and there is as much justification for this as for our use of the name Schwarz.

The references to the books of Wilkinson and Forsythe-Moler quoted in Chapter 8 are relevant to this chapter. Also Householder [55] and Isaacson-Keller [57]. The reader will find the following articles illuminating:

G. E. Forsythe, "Today's computational methods of linear algebra," *SIAM Review*, **9,** 489–515.
W. Kahan, "Numerical linear algebra," *Can. Math. Bull.*, **9** (1966), 757–801.

We have deliberately developed the theory in a very specific way in terms of the 1-, 2-, and ∞-norms. It is possible to develop the theory at various levels of abstraction. (Compare our inequalities (13.7) with the general inequalities in Isaacson-Keller [57], Theorem 2, p. 7; also our assumption in Theorem 13.3, verified in specific cases in Theorem 13.4, that a vector $\mathbf{z}$ exists, with the existence proof in Isaacson-Keller [57], p. 8.)

The main references available on the treatment of the scaling problem, Section 13.5, are rather abstract:

F. L. Bauer, "Optimally scaled matrices," *Num. Math.*, **5** (1963), 73–83.
P. Businger, *Matrix Scaling*, Ph.D. Thesis, University of Texas (1967).

Chapter 14

It is a pity to place abstract vector spaces and linear transformations right at the end of the book, but these are not needed earlier because of the way the theory has been developed. However many lecturers may prefer to introduce the concepts in this chapter much earlier.

Bibliography

Mathematical textbooks.

[1] A. C. Aitken, *Determinants and Matrices*, Oliver and Boyd, Interscience (1956).

[2] F. Ayres, *Matrices*, Schaum outlines (1962).

[3] G. Birkhoff and S. MacLane, *A Survey of Modern Algebra*, Macmillan (1953).

[4] C. G. Cullen, *Matrices and Linear Transformations*, Addison-Wesley (1966).

[5] C. W. Curtis, *Linear Algebra*, Allyn & Bacon (1963).

[6] P. J. Davis, *The Mathematics of Matrices*, Blaisdell (1965).

[7] D. T. Finkbeiner, *Introduction to Matrices and Linear Transformations*, W. H. Freeman (1960).

[8] L. E. Fuller, *Basic Matrix Theory*, Prentice-Hall (1961).

[9] F. R. Gantmacher, *Theory of Matrices*, Vols. I, II, Chelsea (1959).

[10] I. M. Gel'fand, *Lectures on Linear Algebra*, Interscience (1961).

[11] P. R. Halmos, *Finite-Dimensional Vector Spaces*, Van Nostrand (1958).

[12] K. Hoffman and R. Kunze, *Linear Algebra*, Prentice-Hall (1961).

[13] F. E. Hohn, *Elementary Matrix Algebra*, Macmillan (1957).

[14] N. Jacobson, *Lectures in Abstract Algebra*, Vol. II, Van Nostrand (1953).

[15] S. Lang, *Linear Algebra*, Addison-Wesley (1966).

[16] C. C. MacDuffee, *Vectors and Matrices* (Carus Monograph No. 7), Mathematical Association of America, Open Court (1943).

[17] M. Marcus and H. Minc, *Introduction to Linear Algebra*, Macmillan (1965).

[18] ———, *A Survey of Matrix Theory and Matrix Inequalities*, Allyn & Bacon (1964).

[19] L. Mirsky, *Introduction to Linear Algebra*, Oxford (1955).

[20] T. Muir, *Determinants*, Dover (1960).

[21] J. R. Munkres, *Elementary Linear Algebra*, Addison-Wesley (1964).

[22] D. C. Murdoch, *Linear Algebra for Undergraduates*, Wiley (1957).

[23] E. D. Nering, *Linear Algebra and Matrix Theory*, Wiley (1963).

[24] L. J. Paige and J. D. Swift, *Elements of Linear Algebra*, Blaisdell (1965).

[25] S. Perlis, *Theory of Matrices*, Addison-Wesley (1952).

[26] H. Schneider and G. P. Barker, *Matrices and Linear Algebra*, Holt, Rinehart & Winston (1968).

[27] V. I. Smirnov, *Linear Algebra and Group Theory*, McGraw-Hill (1961).

[28] R. R. Stoll, *Linear Algebra and Matrix Theory*, McGraw-Hill (1952).

[29] F. M. Stewart, *Introduction to Linear Algebra*, Van Nostrand (1963).

[30] R. M. Thrall and L. Tornheim, *Vector Spaces and Matrices*, Wiley (1957).

[31] H. W. Turnbull and A. C. Aitken, *An Introduction to the Theory of Canonical Matrices*, Dover (1961).

[32] N. V. Yefimov, *Quadratic Forms and Matrices*, Academic (1964).

Textbooks with more of an applied flavor than those quoted above.

[33] N. R. Amundsen, *Mathematical Methods in Chemical Engineering, Matrices and Their Applications*, Prentice-Hall (1966).

[34] R. E. Bellman, *Introduction to Matrix Algebra*, McGraw-Hill (1960).

[35] W. G. Bickley and R. S. H. G. Thompson, *Matrices, Their Meaning and Manipulation*, Van Nostrand (1964).

[36] R. Braae, *Matrix Algebra for Electrical Engineers*, Addison-Wesley (1963).

[37] J. N. Franklin, *Matrix Theory*, Prentice-Hall (1968).

[38] R. A. Frazer, W. J. Duncan, and A. R. Collar, *Elementary Matrices and Some Applications to Dynamics and Differential Equations*, Cambridge Univ. Press (1938).

[39] G. Hadley, *Linear Algebra*, Addison-Wesley (1961).

[40] G. G. Hall, *Matrices and Tensors*, Macmillan and Pergamon (1963).

[41] J. Heading, *Matrix Theory for Physicists*, Wiley (1960).

[42] J. B. Johnston, G. B. Price, and F. S. Van Vleck, *Linear Equations and Matrices*, Addison-Wesley (1966).

[43] S. Karlin, *Mathematical Methods and Theory in Games, Programming, and Economics*, Vols. I, II, Addison-Wesley (1959).

[44] J. G. Kemeny, J. L. Snell, and G. L. Thompson, *Introduction to Finite Mathematics*, Prentice-Hall (1957).

[45] M. C. Pease, *Methods of Matrix Algebra*, Academic Press (1965).

[46] L. A. Pipes, *Matrix Methods in Engineering*, Prentice-Hall (1963).

[47] S. R. Searle, *Matrix Algebra for the Biological Sciences (Including Applications in Statistics)*, Wiley (1966).

[48] A. v. Weiss, *Matrix Analysis for Electrical Engineers*, Van Nostrand (1964).

[49] R. Zurmuhl, *Matrizen und ihre technischen Anwendungen*, 3rd Ed., Springer (1961).

Numerical Methods.

[50] E. Bodewig, *Matrix Calculus*, 2nd Ed., North-Holland (1959).

[51] V. N. Faddeeva, *Computational Methods of Linear Algebra*, Dover (1959).

[52] D. K. Faddeev and V. N. Faddeeva, *Computational Methods of Linear Algebra*, W. H. Freeman and Co. (1963).

[53] G. E. Forsythe and C. B. Moler, *Computer Solution of Linear Algebraic Systems*, Prentice-Hall (1967).

[54] L. Fox, *An Introduction to Numerical Linear Algebra*, Oxford (1957).

[55] A. S. Householder, *Principles of Numerical Analysis*, McGraw-Hill (1953).

[56] ———, *The Theory of Matrices in Numerical Analysis*, Blaisdell (1964).

[57] E. Isaacson and H. B. Keller, *Analysis of Numerical Methods*, Wiley (1966).

[58] *Modern Computing Methods*, 2nd Ed., H.M. Stationery Office, London (1961).

[59] A. Ralston and H. S. Wilf, Eds., *Mathematical Methods for Digital Computers*, Vol. II, Wiley (1967).

[60] R. S. Varga, *Matrix Iterative Analysis*, Prentice-Hall (1962).

[61] J. H. Wilkinson, *Rounding Errors in Algebraic Processes*, Prentice-Hall (1963).

[62] ———, *The Algebraic Eigenvalue Problem*, Oxford (1965).

Books containing applications of linear algebra and matrices. (See also books quoted in exercises at the end of Chapter 2.)

[63] R. G. D. Allen, *Mathematical Economics*, St. Martin's Press (1957).

[64] H. H. Argyris, *Energy Theorems and Structural Analysis*, Butterworth (1960).

[65] S. F. Borg, *Matrix-Tensor Methods in Continuum Mechanics*, Van Nostrand (1963).

[66] W. Brouwer, *Matrix Methods in Optical Instrument Design*, W. A. Benjamin (1964).

[67] H. B. Chenery and P. B. Clark, *Interindustry Economics*, Wiley (1959).

[68] G. B. Dantzig, *Linear Programming and Extensions*, Princeton Univ. Press (1963).

[69] R. Dorfman, P. A. Samuelson, and R. M. Solow, *Linear Programming and Economic Analysis*, McGraw-Hill (1958).

[70] D. Gale, *The Theory of Linear Economic Models*, McGraw-Hill (1960).

[71] F. R. Gantmacher and M. G. Krein, *Oszillationsmatrizen, Oszillationskerne und kleine Schwingungen mechanischer Systeme*, Akademic-Verlag, Berlin (1960).

[72] S. I. Gass, *Linear Programming*, McGraw-Hill (1964).

[73] J. J. Gennaro, *Computer Methods in Solid Mechanics*, Macmillan (1965).

[74] W. J. Gibbs, *Tensors in Electrical Machine Theory*, Chapman and Hall (1952).

[75] A. M. Glicksman, *An Introduction to Linear Programming and the Theory of Games*, Wiley (1963).

[76] A. Goldberger, *Econometric Theory*, Wiley (1964).

[77] H. Goldstein, *Classical Mechanics*, Addison-Wesley (1950).

[78] F. A. Graybill, *An Introduction to Linear Statistical Models*, Vol. I, McGraw-Hill (1961).

[79] E. A. Guillemin, *The Mathematics of Circuit Analysis*, Wiley (1949).

[80] G. Hadley, *Linear Programming*, Addison-Wesley (1962).

[81] B. Higman, *Applied Group-Theoretic and Matrix Methods*, Oxford (1955).

[82] W. C. Hurty and M. F. Rubinstein, *Dynamics of Structures*, Prentice-Hall (1964).

[83] J. Johnston, *Econometric Methods*, McGraw-Hill (1963).

[84] J. G. Kemeny and J. L. Snell, *Finite Markov Chains*, Van Nostrand (1960).

[85] ———, *Mathematical Models in the Social Sciences*, Ginn (1962).

[86] G. Kron, *Tensor Analysis of Networks*, Wiley (1939).

[87] ———, *Tensors for Circuits*, Dover (1959).

[88] ———, *Diakoptics*, Macdonald (1963).

[89] P. Lancaster, *Lambda-Matrices and Vibrating Systems*, Pergamon (1966).

[90] P. LeCorbeiller, *Matrix Analysis of Electrical Networks*, Harvard Univ. Press (1950).

[91] B. Noble, *Applications of Undergraduate Mathematics in Engineering*, Mathematical Association of America, Macmillan (1967).

[92] H. M. Nodelman and F. W. Smith, *Mathematics for Electronics*, McGraw-Hill (1956).

[93] J. F. Nye, *Physical Properties of Crystals: Their Representation by Tensors and Matrices*, Oxford (1957).

[94] E. C. Pestel and F. A. Leckie, *Matrix Methods in Elastomechanics*, McGraw-Hill (1963).

[95] C. R. Rao, *Advanced Statistical Methods in Biometric Research*, Wiley (1952).

[96] J. Robinson, *Structural Matrix Analysis for the Engineer*, Wiley (1966).

[97] J. T. Schwartz, *Lectures on the Mathematical Method in Analytical Economics*, Gordon and Breach (1961).

[98] S. Vajda, *An Introduction to Linear Programming and the Theory of Games*, Methuen and Wiley (1960).

[99] E. B. Wilson, J. C. Decius, and P. Gross, *Molecular Vibrations*, McGraw-Hill (1955).

[100] L. A. Zadeh and C. A. DeSoer, *Linear System Theory*, McGraw-Hill (1963).

Notation

u, x, boldface small letters refer to vectors (column and row matrices)

A, P, boldface capital letters refer to matrices other than vectors

$k, \alpha,$ italic Roman and Greek small letters denote scalars

$V, A,$ italic capital letters denote vector spaces or linear transformations

$\mathbf{A} = [a_{ij}]$, matrix, 1

$\bar{\mathbf{A}} = [\bar{a}_{ij}]$, complex conjugate of **A,** 11

$\mathbf{A}^{\mathrm{T}} = [a_{ji}]$, transpose of **A,** 9

$\mathbf{A}^{\mathrm{H}} = [\bar{a}_{ji}]$, hermitian transpose of **A,** 11, 286

$\mathbf{A}^{-1} = [\alpha_{ij}]$, inverse of **A,** 13, 15

$\mathbf{A}_{+} = [|a_{ij}|]$, 438

$\mathbf{A}_{+}^{-1} = [|\alpha_{ij}|]$, (note that this is *not* the inverse of $\mathbf{A}_{+}$), 438

$\mathbf{A}^{+}$, generalized inverse, 144

$a_{ij}^{(r)}, m_{ir}, b_{i}^{(r)}$, notation introduced in Gauss elimination, 213

A_{ij}, cofactor of a_{ij}, 200

$\mathbf{e}_i$, unit column vector, 20

$\mathbf{e}$, column vector all of whose elements are unity, 458

$\mathbf{E}_{pq}, \mathbf{E}_p(c), \mathbf{E}_{pq}(c)$, elementary matrices, 87

$\mathbf{I}_m$, $m \times m$ unit matrix, 12

L, **U**, lower and upper triangular matrices, 216

M_{ij}, $M_{ip,qj}$, minors, 200, 202

p, q, constants introduced in connection with the condition of a 2×2 system, 251

$\vec{u}$, geometrical vector, 96

V_n, space of $n \times 1$ column vectors, 117

α_{ij}, (i, j)th element of inverse, 15

δ_{rs}, Kronecker delta, 487

λ, eigenvalue, or parameter in $(\mathbf{A} - \lambda\mathbf{I})\mathbf{x} = \mathbf{b}$

λ_i, $\mathbf{x}_i$, $i = 1, \ldots, n$, eigenvalues and corresponding eigenvectors of matrix, 279

$\mathbf{\Lambda}$, diagonal matrix whose ith diagonal element is λ_i, 292

$\rho(\mathbf{x})$, spectral radius, 303, Rayleigh quotient, 407

Adj **A**, adjoint, 210

B-orthogonal, 398

Det **A**, determinant, 200

Dim **A**, dimension of column space of **A**, 111

Dim V, dimension of vector space V, 463

Fl(z), floating point representation of z, 247

Inf and Sup, 440, 428

$[\mathbf{x}]_N$, ordered basis, 474

$(\mathbf{u}, \mathbf{v})$, inner product, 285 (In Chapter 6 the notation $\mathbf{u}^T\mathbf{v}$ is used, since this is customary in linear programming)

$(\mathbf{x}, \mathbf{A}\mathbf{x})$, quadratic form, 386

$||\mathbf{x}||$, $||\mathbf{x}||_1$, $||\mathbf{x}||_2$, $||\mathbf{x}||_\infty$, vector norms, 425

$||\mathbf{A}||$, matrix norm, 427

$||\mathbf{A}||_1$, $||\mathbf{A}||_2$, $||\mathbf{A}||_\infty$, 429

$M(\mathbf{A}) = ||\mathbf{A}||\ ||\mathbf{A}^{-1}||$, 434

$K(\mathbf{A})$, minimum condition number, 436

$N(\mathbf{A})$, null space of **A**, 119

$>, \geq, <, \leq$, applied to matrices, 156

Index

S

T

U

V

W